Tectonics and Geochemistry of the Northeastern Caribbean

Edited by

Edward G. Lidiak
Department of Geology and Planetary Science
University of Pittsburgh
Pittsburgh, Pennsylvania 15260

and

David K. Larue
Chevron Petroleum Technology Company
P.O. Box 446
La Habra, California 90633-0446

1998

Published by The Geological Society of America, Inc.
3300 Penrose Place, P.O. Box 9140, Boulder, Colorado 80301

Printed in U.S.A.

GSA Books Science Editor Abhijit Basu

Library of Congress Cataloging-in-Publication Data

Tectonics and geochemistry of the northeastern Caribbean / edited by
Edward G. Lidiak and David K. Larue.
p. cm. -- (Special paper ; 322)
Includes bibliographical references and index.
ISBN 0-8137-2322-1
1. Geology--Puerto Rico. 2. Geochemistry--Puerto Rico.
3. Geology, Structural--Caribbean Area. I. Lidiak, Edward G.
II. Larue, D. K. III. Series: Special papers (Geological Society of America) ; 322.
QE225.T43 1998
557.295--dc21 97-51386
CIP

Cover: Puerto Rico and the neighboring islands of Culebra and Vieques viewed from orbit by Gemini V in 1966, at the height of the U.S. Geological Survey Puerto Rico Mapping Project. Main topographic features: Cordillera Central, west-trending mountains in south-central Puerto Rico; Sierra de Cayey, southeast Puerto Rico; Sierra de Luquillo, northeast Puerto Rico. Photograph by NASA.

10 9 8 7 6 5 4 3 2 1

Contents

Preface

INTRODUCTION

The Caribbean is a complex region that has attracted a variety of geologic, geochemical, and geophysical research over the past 50 years and more. The importance of the region stems from its geographic location among major marine and terrestrial provinces and from its development during and after the disruption of Pangea by plate interactions of the Farallon (proto-Caribbean), North American, and South American plates. As a result of these interactions, the present Caribbean lithospheric plate (Fig. 1) consists mainly of anomalously thick oceanic crust that is bounded by oceanic crust of normal thickness and by two major continental regions. The Caribbean thus provides an excellent opportunity to study the tectonic interaction among various types of oceanic and continental lithospheric plates and the temporal evolution of island arc and related systems.

The focus of this volume is the northeastern Caribbean, with primary emphasis on Puerto Rico and immediately adjacent areas. The island of Puerto Rico, in the eastern Greater Antilles, is located along the northern boundary of the Caribbean plate, where it juxtaposes against the North American plate (Fig. 1). According to current views, the present Caribbean plate originated as a part of the Jurassic Farallon plate in the eastern Pacific basin (Burke, 1988; Donnelly, 1989). The initial development of the Caribbean plate is poorly understood, but it is reasonably clear that, during the Early Cretaceous, convergent plate motion resulted in the subduction of oceanic crust and initiation of island arc magmatism (Pindell and Dewey, 1982; Mattson, 1984; Burke, 1988; Donnelly, 1989). Island arc development continued throughout the Cretaceous. By Aptian-Albian time, orogenic movements resulted in the obduction of serpentinized peridotite onto the early Antillean arc and in a possible reversal in arc polarity (Draper et al., 1996). This event was followed by renewed subduction and the arrival of an oceanic plateau (Caribbean oceanic plateau of Burke). The original magmatic centers (islands) of the developing Caribbean arc were gradually concentrated along the northern boundary of the plate margin by left-lateral transcurrent faulting and eventually became isolated from the subduction zone. The details of the tectonic development and configuration of these magmatic centers remain topics of active research activity.

Most of the magmatism in the Greater Antilles occurred during Cretaceous time. However, volcanism in the eastern Greater Antilles continued into the Eocene and extended into the Oligocene in the northern Virgin Islands (Cox et al., 1977; Pindell and Barrett, 1990). Termination of volcanism in late Eocene time is poorly understood, but may have been related to the collision of the western (Cuba) part of the Greater Antilles arc with the Bahamas Bank (Pindell and Barrett, 1990), subduction of the Bahamas Bank beneath the Puerto Rican part of the arc (Erikson et al., 1990), or subduction of buoyant oceanic crust (Larue et al., 1991). This event was followed in the Puerto Rican region by deposition of Oligocene to Recent carbonate sediments and sediments derived from weathering of the emerged island arc massif (Sieglie and Moussa, 1984). Continued tectonism from the middle Miocene to the Recent in Puerto Rico and the Virgin Islands is associated with easterly transtensional motion of the Caribbean plate relative to North America (Jordan, 1975; DeMets et al., 1990) and 25° counterclockwise rotation of the Puerto Rico and Virgin Islands platform (Reid et al., 1991). Surrounding this composite arc terrane are zones of complex tectonic activity, including the Puerto Rico and Muertos Trenches (and associated subbasins), where oceanic plates are being underthrust and extensional basins are separating the Puerto Rico–northern Virgin Islands arc terrane from adjacent arc terranes in Hispaniola and the northern Lesser Antilles.

SCOPE

The chapters in this volume are organized informally into two sections. Following an introductory chapter by Jolly and coworkers on tectonic setting and stratigraphic correlations of the volcanic strata in Puerto Rico, five chapters deal with geochemical aspects of these and related igneous rocks. The second chapter, by Schellekens, summarizes the geochemical characteristics of the entire volcanic sequence and provides a framework on which other chapters in the volume can be referred. Schellekens's chapter is followed by a detailed geochemical evaluation of the volcanic rocks of eastern Puerto Rico (Jolly and coworkers), a chapter on the characteristics of batholith emplacement in the northeastern Caribbean (Smith and coworkers), an isotopic study of the Cretaceous and Tertiary igneous rocks of Puerto Rico (Frost and coworkers), and a chapter on the geochemistry of the igneous rocks on St. Croix (Lidiak and Jolly). The second group of three chapters deals primarily with the tectonics and stratigraphy of Tertiary and younger sedimentary rocks on Puerto Rico and adjacent areas. Larue and coworkers present new information on a Tertiary basin along the north coast of Puerto Rico, and Montgomery provides stratigraphic and sedimentologic data on the exposed Paleogene rocks of this basin. The volume concludes with a chapter on an interpretation of seismic profiles in the Puerto Rico Trench by Larue and Ryan.

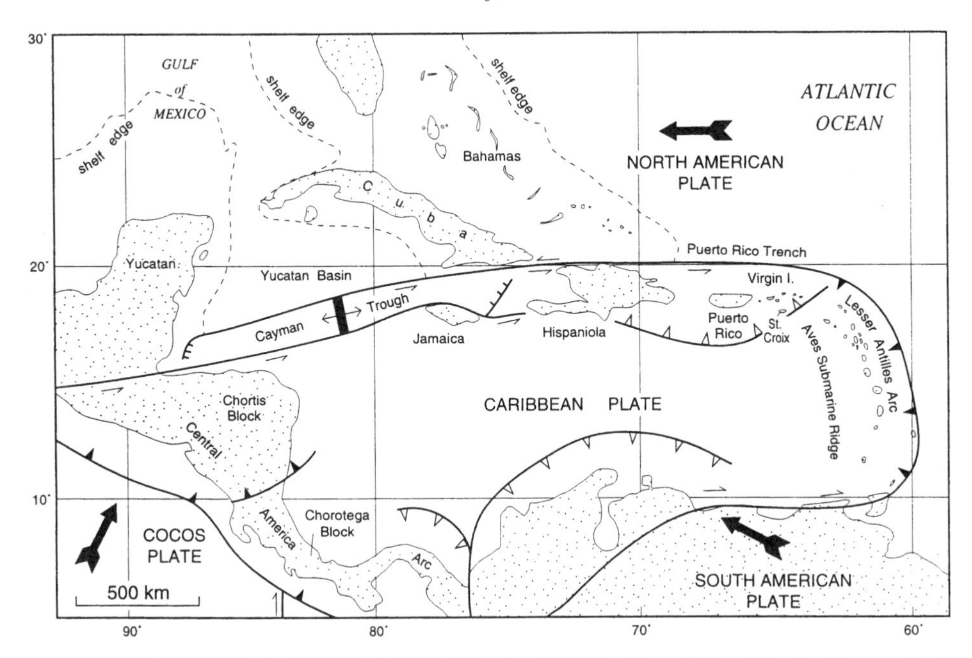

Figure 1. Main structural elements of the modern Caribbean region. Adapted from Jordan (1975), Case and Holcombe (1980), and Mann et al. (1991).

ACKNOWLEDGMENTS

We thank the following colleagues for volunteering their time and energy in reviewing the papers presented in this volume: Gerald E. Adams, Thomas H. Anderson, Hans G. Ave Lallemant, Reginald P. Briggs, Jon Davidson, Jack Donahue, Thomas W. Donnelly, Grenville Draper, Mark S. Drummond, N. Terrance Edgar, Mark D. Feigenson, Luis A. Gonzales, Troy Holcombe, James Joyce, John F. Lewis, Paul Mann, Glen S. Mattioli, Peter H. Mattson, Arthur E. Nelson, James Pindell, Edward Robinson, James A. Walker, and five anonymous reviewers. The editors and contributors also thank Abhijit Basu, GSA Books Science Editor, for his editorial expertise and constructive suggestions that significantly improved the contents of this volume.

Edward G. Lidiak, Pittsburgh, Pennsylvania
David K. Larue, La Habra, California

REFERENCES CITED

Burke, K., 1988, Tectonic evolution of the Caribbean: Annual Reviews of Earth and Planetary Sciences, v. 16, p. 201–230.

Case, J. E., and Holcombe, T. L., 1980, Geologic-tectonic map of the Caribbean region: U.S. Geological Survey Miscellaneous Investigation Series, I–1100, scale 1:2,500,000.

Cox, D. P., Marvin, R. F., M'Gonigle, J. W., McIntyre, D. H., and Rogers, C. L., 1977, Potassium-argon geochronology of some metamorphic, igneous, and hydrothermal events in Puerto Rico and the Virgin Islands: U.S. Geological Survey, Journal of Research, v. 5, p. 689–703.

DeMets, C., Gordon, R. G., Argus, D. F., and Stein, S., 1990, Current plate motions: Geophysical Journal International, v. 101, p. 425–478.

Donnelly, T. W., 1989, Geologic history of the Caribbean and Central America, *in* Bally, A. W., and Palmer, A. R., eds., The Geology of North America—An overview: Boulder, Colorado, Geological Society of America, The Geology of North America, v. A, p. 299–321.

Draper, G., Gutierrez, G., and Lewis, J. F., 1996, Thrust emplacement of the Hispaniola peridotite belt: Orogenic expression of mid-Cretaceous arc polarity reversal?: Geology, v. 24, p. 1143–1146.

Erikson, J. P., Pindell, J. L., and Larue, D. K., 1990, Mid-Eocene—Early Oligocene sinistral transcurrent faulting in Puerto Rico associated with formation of the northern Caribbean plate boundary: Journal of Geology, v. 98, p. 365–384.

Jordan, T. H., 1975, The present-day motions of the Caribbean plate: Journal of Geophysical Research, v. 80, p. 4433–4439.

Larue, D. K., Joyce, J., and Ryan, H. F., 1991, Neotectonics of the Puerto Rico Trench: Extensional tectonism and forearc subsidence, *in* Larue, D. K., and Draper, G., eds., Transactions, 12th Caribbean Geological Conference: Coral Gables, Florida, Miami Geological Society, p. 231–247.

Mann, P., Draper, G., and Lewis, J. F., 1991, An overview of the geologic and tectonic development of Hispaniola, *in* Mann, P., Draper, G., and Lewis, J. F., eds., Geologic and tectonic development of the North American–Caribbean plate boundary in Hispaniola: Boulder, Colorado, Geological Society of America Special Paper 262, p. 1–28.

Mattson, P. H., 1984, Caribbean structural breaks and plate movements, *in* Bonini, W. E., Hargraves, R. B., and Shagam, R., eds., The Caribbean–South American plate boundary and regional tectonics: Geological Society of America Memoir 162, p. 131–152.

Pindell, J. L., and Barrett, S. F., 1990, Geological evolution of the Caribbean region: a plate tectonic perspective, *in* Dengo, G., and Case, J. E., eds., The Caribbean region: Boulder, Colorado, Geological Society of America, The Geology of North America, v. H, p. 405–432.

Pindell, J. L., and Dewey, J. F., 1982, Permo-Triassic reconstruction of western Pangea and the evolution of the Gulf of Mexico/Caribbean region: Tectonics, v. 1, p. 179–212.

Reid, J. A., Plumley, P. W., and Schellekens, J. H., 1991, Paleomagnetic evidence for late Miocene counterclockwise rotation of north coast carbonate sequence, Puerto Rico: Geophysical Research Letters, v. 18, p. 565–568.

Sieglie, G. A., and Moussa, M. T., 1984, Late Oligocene–Pliocene transgressive-regressive cycles of sedimentation in northwestern Puerto Rico, *in* Schlee, J. S., ed., Interregional unconformities and hydrocarbon accumulation: American Association of Petroleum Geologists Memoir 36, p. 89–96.

Geological Society of America
Special Paper 322
1998

Volcanism, tectonics, and stratigraphic correlations in Puerto Rico

Wayne T. Jolly
Department of Earth Sciences, Brock University, St. Catherines, Ontario L2S 3A1, Canada
Edward G. Lidiak
Department of Geology and Planetary Science, University of Pittsburgh, Pittsburgh, Pennsylvania 15260
Johannes H. Schellekens and Hernan Santos
Department of Geology, University of Puerto Rico, Mayagüez, Puerto Rico 00681-5000

ABSTRACT

Island arc volcanic strata in Puerto Rico, ranging in age from Lower Cretaceous (Aptian) to Eocene and dating from about 120 to 45 Ma, represent one of the longest oceanic arc sequences preserved in the world. Detailed and systematic mapping by the U.S. Geological Survey published between 1959 and 1986 reveal that, although post-volcanic sedimentary platform deposits consisting of limestone and other detrital materials ring the island and cover extensive parts of the arc platform, representative strata of the entire sequence are exposed. The island is subdivided into three volcanic provinces all containing strata without correlative units elsewhere; they are (1) a northeastern volcanic province, separated from the central province by the Cerro Mula Fault, a left-lateral strike-slip fault of mid-Santonian age with displacement of at least 50 km; (2) a central volcanic province, dominated by volcanic debris accumulated during sequential development of five east-west–oriented volcanic belts, and (3) a western volcanic province, with a northwest-southeast–trending boundary of uncertain origin, containing remnants of two sequential island arc volcanic belts of Campanian-Maastrichtian and Eocene age.

Additionally, in the southwestern corner of the island, the Sierra Bermeja Complex consists of a tectonic melange of partly serpentinized ultramafic rocks representing the lithospheric upper mantle originally composed of spinel-bearing peridotites, including lherzolite, harzburgite, and dunite. The melange incorporates rafts, blocks, and boulder-sized clasts of (1) Lower Jurassic to Upper Cretaceous pelagic sediments (Mariquita Chert), including radiolarian chert of Pacific provenance and later siliceous volcanogenic strata, representing pre–island arc oceanic deposits; and (2) altered mid-ocean ridge basalt (MORB)-like basalts (Cajul Basalt) and amphibolites (Las Palmas amphibolite melange) of probable Lower Jurassic age, representing pre–island arc oceanic crust. Serpentinized peridotite bodies, containing amphibolite, altered MORB-like basalt, and chert, protruded the arc platform in a cold state at several places in the western province. The largest of these, the Monte del Estado Peridotite, was emplaced during the Maastrichtian, through crustal extension associated with left-lateral strike-slip faulting along the Cordillera fault.

Volcanic strata preserved in the central province are subdivided into five major volcanic phases on the basis of stratigraphic and geochemical relations. Basalts evolved progressively from early primitive island arc tholeiites in phase I, to calc-alkaline basalts in phase II, and finally to incompatible element-enriched shoshonite

Jolly, W. T., Lidiak, E. G., Schellekens, J. H., and Santos, H., 1998, Volcanism, tectonics, and stratigraphic correlations in Puerto Rico, *in* Lidiak, E. G., and Larue, D. K., eds., Tectonics and Geochemistry of the Northeastern Caribbean: Boulder, Colorado, Geological Society of America Special Paper 322.

basalts in phase III. Correlative strata in the northeast province display a more restricted compositional range from early island arc tholeiites during phase I to calc-alkaline basalts in phases II and III. Volcanic strata of dominantly calc-alkaline affinities from phases IV and V in both the northeastern and central provinces are chemically identical. It is inferred the two blocks were tectonically juxtaposed by strike-slip movement along the Cerro Mula fault, the principal strand of the Northern Puerto Rico Fault Zone (NPRFZ), during mid-Santonian time. Tectonic activity corresponds temporally with development of the East Pacific Rise and a change in spreading vectors for the Pacific basin from northeast to a more easterly orientation.

In the western volcanic province, island arc strata date from about 85 Ma (mid-Santonian), and the basement is inferred to have been transported into the active volcanic zone of the island arc simultaneously with left-lateral displacement along the Cerro Mula fault. A further left-lateral strike-slip dislocation near the end of volcanism in the upper Eocene brought the province to its present position during deflection and rotation of the island around the eastern terminus of the Bahama Platform; movement took place along the Southern Puerto Rico Fault Zone (SPRFZ). Volcanic phases IV and V are represented in the west by a sequential pair of subparallel island arc belts of Campanian-Maastrichtian and late Paleocene–Eocene age, accompanied by extensive flanking sedimentary basins. A hiatus between phases IV and V, representing both a period of erosion and a nonvolcanic interval, persisted across the entire island from uppermost Maastrichtian through the lower Paleocene.

No consensus has developed regarding the polarity and tectonic history of subduction during generation of the Greater Antilles Arc. Structural fabric data from central Hispaniola suggest a reversal from east- to west-dipping subduction occurred early in arc history during the mid-Cretaceous (Aptian to Albian time), and it has been suggested that initial subduction was from the west until arrival of a buoyant oceanic basalt plateau, the Caribbean Cretaceous Basalt Province (CCBP), that developed in the Pacific basin at about 88 Ma, forcing a reversal in polarity of subduction between 105 and 55 Ma. Alternatively, the early arc might have formed along the margin of the CCBP and advanced eastward locked with the plateau accompanied by west-dipping subduction of the proto-Caribbean (Atlantic) plate throughout arc history.

INTRODUCTION

Stratigraphic relations in modern intraoceanic island arcs, particularly during early stages of arc evolution, are normally submarine or obscured by voluminous extrusive strata produced by the developing arc, and are, therefore, largely inaccessible to investigation. In contrast, in the deeply dissected Eastern Greater Antilles Arc, the island of Puerto Rico exposes an almost continuous succession of island arc volcanic strata from inception to termination, ranging in age from Albian in the Lower Cretaceous (about 120 Ma) to upper Eocene (40 Ma) (Donnelly et al., 1990). Additionally, representative rocks from the lithospheric upper mantle and pre-arc oceanic crust are exposed beneath the eroded volcanic strata in the western part of the island. Moreover, stratigraphic and paleogeographic relations within the island arc platform are well constrained by almost three decades of systematic, detailed investigation by the U.S. Geological Survey during the Puerto Rico mapping project (1959 to 1986). These detailed maps and stratigraphic studies, in conjunction with more recent regional paleoecologic, sedimentologic, structural, and geochemical data, clearly make Puerto Rico the best known ancient island arc complex in the world. Thus, the island provides a unique opportunity to document in detail developmental patterns in a major island arc system. The primary objective of this survey is to present island-wide compilations of arc geology and stratigraphic correlations (Figs. 1 and 2; Table 1) from which the sequential history of development of the arc platform can be established. Ancillary objectives include review of the temporal and stratigraphic distribution of volcanic strata within each volcanic province, development of paleogeographic reconstructions of the island arc as it evolved through time, and investigation of the origin of major tectonic features of the arc platform.

GEOLOGIC SETTING

Sources of Puerto Rican geologic data

Systematic study of Puerto Rican geology was first undertaken by the New York Academy of Sciences Scientific Survey (see historical sketch of Donnelly, 1998), which produced preliminary geologic maps and established the stratigraphic and volcanic framework of the island, particularly in the northeastern (Berkey,

1915, 1919; Meyerhoff, 1933; Meyerhoff and Smith, 1931; Semmes, 1919) and western regions (Hubbard, 1920, 1923; Mitchell, 1922). Intensive modern investigation began with the Princeton University ultramafic study program in South America and Puerto Rico under the direction of H. H. Hess. Major projects of this period included mapping and stratigraphic investigations in the Sabana Grande (Slodowski, 1956), Mayagüez (Mattson, 1960), and Ponce (Pessagno, 1960, 1962) regions; the Barranquitas area (Otalora, 1961); Culebra, Vieques, and the northern Virgin Islands (Donnelly, 1966); and the Coamo area (Glover, 1971). Also included was extensive investigation of a drill core through serpentinite in western Puerto Rico (Hess and Otalora, 1964; Mattson, 1964). A second wave of graduate thesis and dissertation projects, organized by T. W. Donnelly, included investigation of the Sierra Bermeja region (Almy, 1969), and of northcentral (Lidiak, 1965) and southcentral (Jolly, 1970; 1971) Puerto Rico. Shortly following initiation of the Princeton project, the U.S. Geological Survey, in association with the Economic Development Association of the Commonwealth of Puerto Rico, began preparation of geologic quadrangle sheets, scale 1:20,000 published between 1959 and 1986, eventually covering the entire island (exclusive of Sabana Grande, Guánica and Rincón quadrangles) (Fig. 3).

In recent years, geologic investigations have been extended by members and coworkers from the Geology Department, University of Puerto Rico at Mayagüez (Joyce, 1986; Joyce et al., 1987a,b; Erikson et al., 1990, 1991; Joyce, 1991; Larue et al., 1991a,b; Schellekens et al., 1991; Larue, 1994), and numerous additional thesis and dissertation studies (Tzeng, 1976; Barabas, 1982; Joyce, 1985; Curet, 1976, 1986; Kazcor, 1987; Sampayo, 1992; Santos, 1990; Schellekens, 1993; Weiland, 1988). The work included multidisciplinary investigation (Larue, 1991) of Eocene strata recovered from a drill core at Toa Baja on the north shore sedimentary platform (Erikson et al., 1991; Frost and Schellekens, 1991; Montgomery et al., 1991; Reid et al., 1991).

Tectonic subdivision

Puerto Rico exhibits an unusually thick crust, reaching a maximum in the northeast of about 30 km (Boynton et al., 1979). Donnelly et al. (1990) suggested much of this represents underplating by arc-related plutonic bodies, rather than accumulations of material produced through volcanism. The volcanic core of the island has traditionally been subdivided into three geographic volcanic provinces (Fig. 1) separated by major fault zones (Briggs and Akers, 1965; Glover, 1971; Mattson, 1979; Joyce, 1985; Joyce et al., 1987b; Schellekens et al., 1991; Larue et al., 1991a,b, Schellekens, 1993, and Larue, 1994, who further subdivided the western region into several domains). The central and northeastern provinces are bounded by the Cerro Mula fault, forming the major strand of the Northern Puerto Rico Fault Zone (NPRFZ) of Glover (1971). This fault, trending east-southeast across the northeastern corner of the island, is approximately 50 km in length, and because no units are common to both sides, this distance represents the minimum displacement (Pease, 1968a-c). Convex-northward curvature and orientation of offshoots (Fig. 1) suggest left-lateral displacement (Pease, 1968a-c). The boundary between the central and western volcanic provinces is formed by the complex and poorly understood Southern Puerto Rico Fault Zone (SPRFZ) (Glover, 1971; Glover and Mattson, 1973). While there is general agreement that a major tectonic feature separates the two provinces, the origin of the boundary is so controversial that even its location is a matter of considerable debate (Briggs and Akers, 1965; Mattson, 1967; Glover, 1971; Glover and Mattson, 1973; Krushensky, 1978; Krushensky and Curet, 1984; Joyce, 1985; Erikson et al. 1990, 1991; Larue et al., 1991a,b; Schellekens, 1993; Larue, 1994). The boundary selected for use in Figure 1 subdivides the two provinces along a line separating Cariblanco-Coamo-Jacaguas strata on the east from the Anón Formation and equivalents on the west, such that the only unit appearing on both sides is the late-stage Guayo conglomerate.

Character and subdivision of volcanic strata

Puerto Rican volcanic strata, depicted according to lithologic type on the accompanying correlation chart (Fig. 2), consist primarily of marine lava and lava breccia, volcanic breccia, and subaerial pyroclastic deposits of Cretaceous and Lower Tertiary age. The Puerto Rican stratigraphic succession is unusual compared with many island arcs in that not all stages of oceanic island arc development, in the classification of Larue et al. (1991b), are represented. The characteristic early phase, consisting entirely of deep submarine volcanic rocks dominated by lava, lava breccia, and volcanic breccia, is largely absent, and instead all strata display evidence (oxidized volcanic breccia and lava, widespread epiclastic sandstone and alluvial or deltaic fan deposits, abundant tuffaceous deposits of pyroclastic or laharic origin, and localized unconformities) of subaerial volcanism on an elevated ocean floor.

The complex sequence of interfingering volcanic facies in Puerto Rico was complicated by intense strike-slip faulting (Briggs and Akers, 1965; Pease, 1968c; Glover, 1971; Seiders, 1971c; Erikson et al., 1990, 1991). Because of this deformation, correlation of stratigraphic units across fault boundaries is not always possible, and a proliferation of stratigraphic names resulted (Fig. 2) during early years (1959–1965) of the U.S. Geological Survey mapping project. At that time many units, such as Formations A, B, and C of the Río Majada Group, were designated with alphabetic notations. In subsequent periods (1966–1976), stratigraphic units were correlated across wide zones even when intervening exposures were absent. Examples include extension of the Robles Formation (Pease and Briggs, 1960) to the margin of the San Lorenzo batholith in the Caguas quadrangle (Rogers, 1979) (Figs. 1 and 3) and to the west side of the Utuado stock in the Adjuntas quadrangles (Mattson, 1967, 1968a), and extension of the Palma Escrita Formation from the Maricao area into the Central la Plata quadrangle (McIntyre, 1974). During the final years of the project (1977–1986), Krushensky (1978) and Krushensky and Curet (1984) abandoned

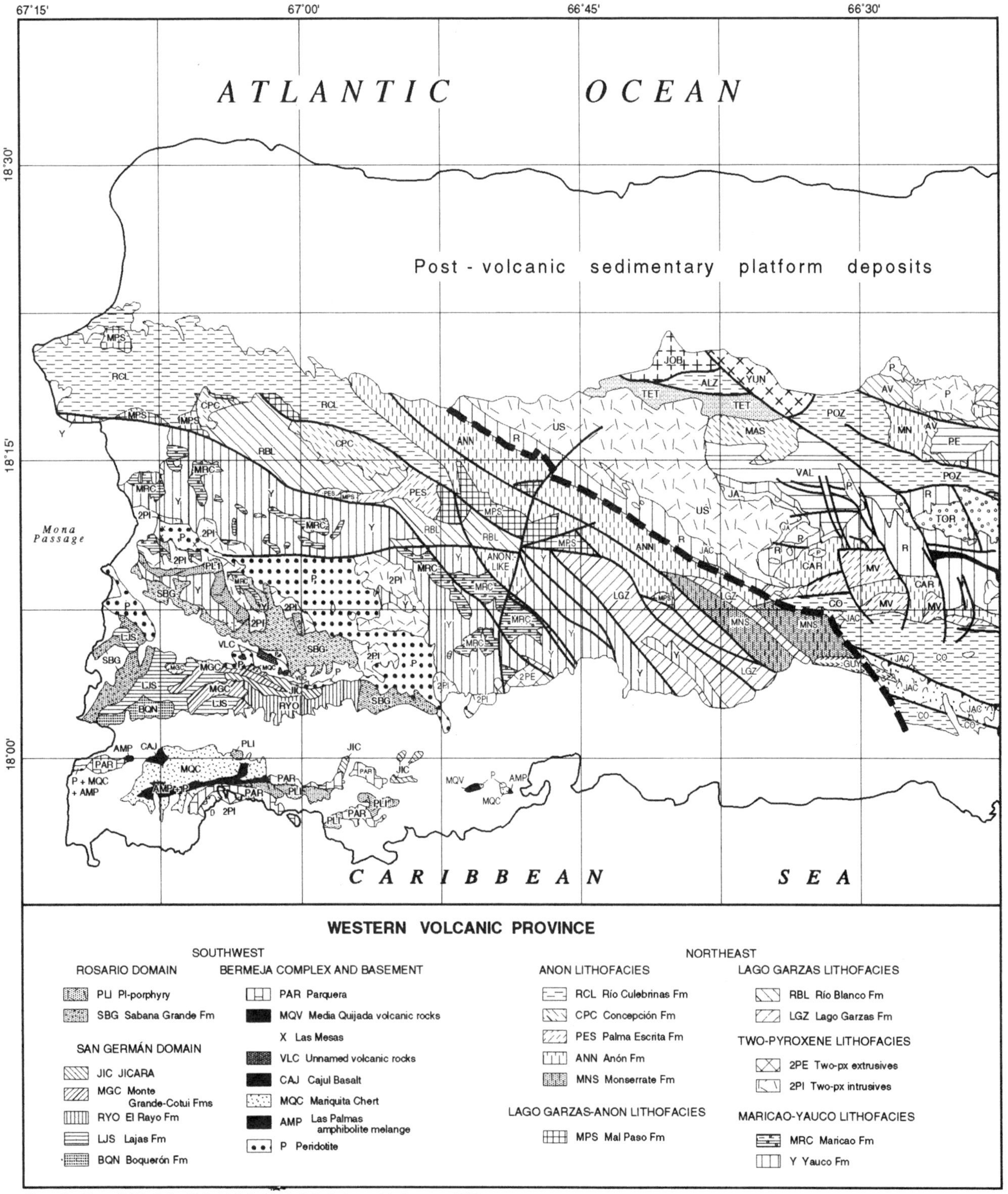

Figure 1 (on this and facing page). Distribution of volcanic strata in Puerto Rico. Symbols assigned to units are used to identify given features in text and all figures; see text and Table 1 for sources.

STRATA IN PUERTO RICO

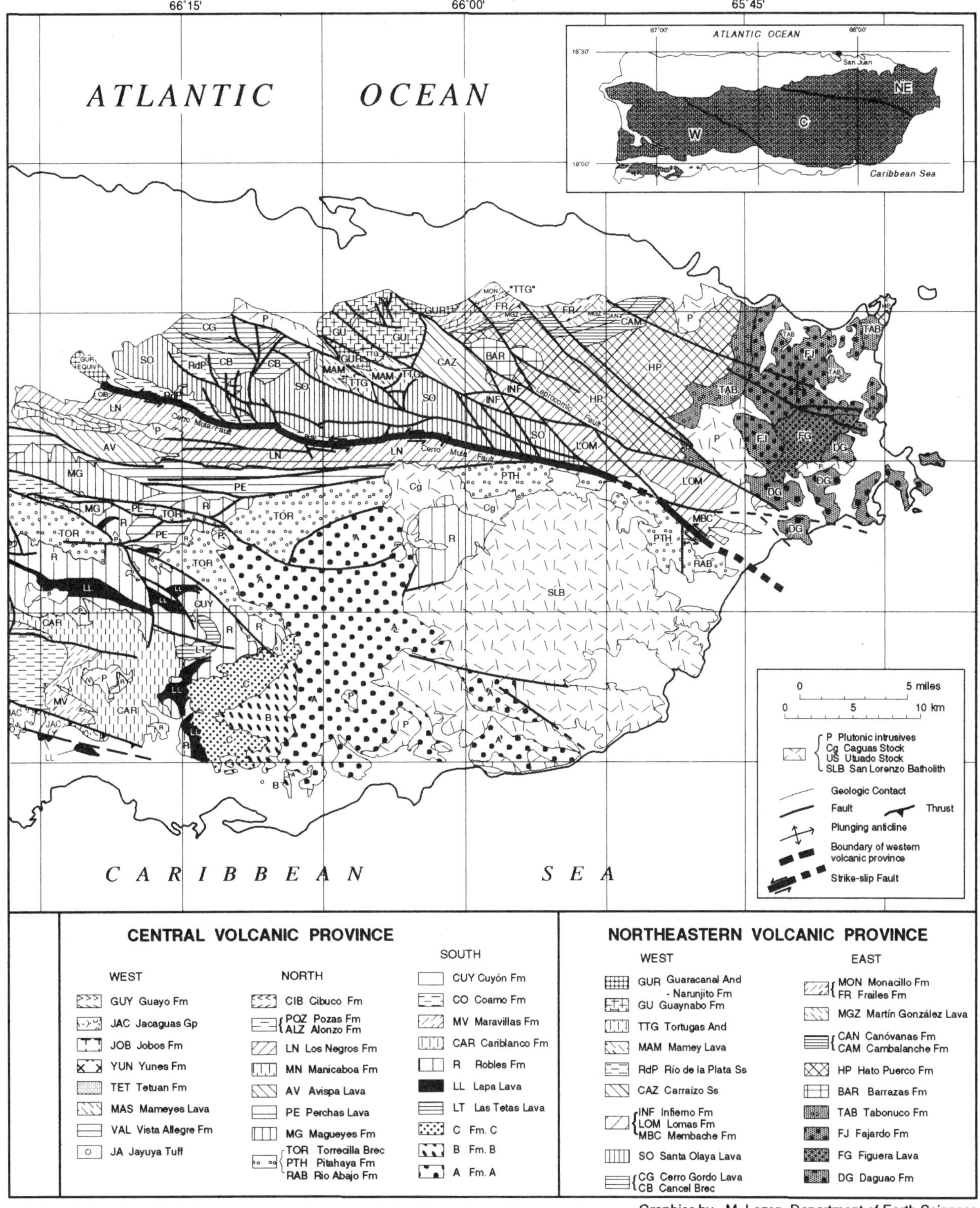

Graphics by M. Lozon, Department of Earth Sciences
Brock University

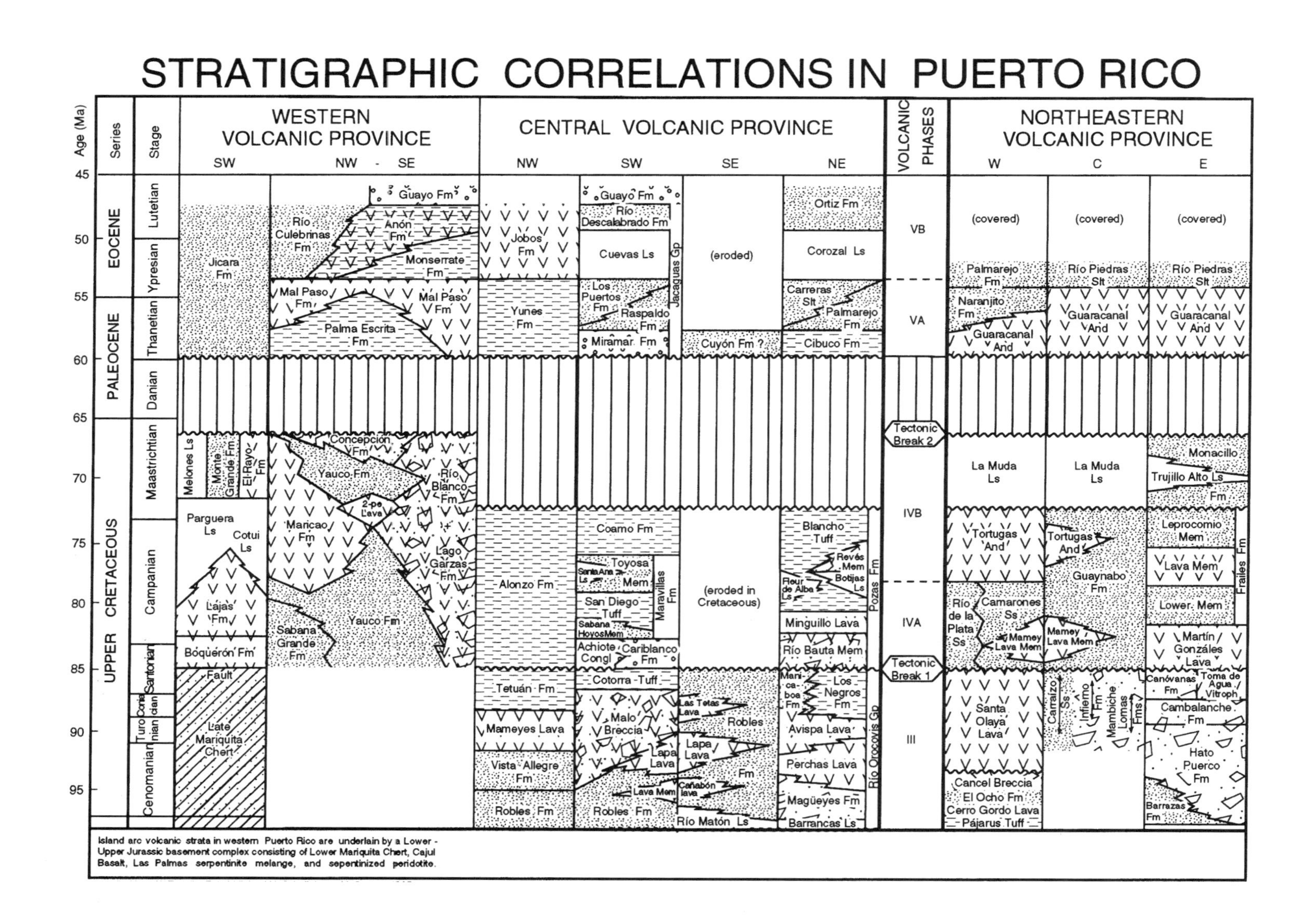
STRATIGRAPHIC CORRELATIONS IN PUERTO RICO
Age (Ma)
45
50
55
60
65
70
75
80
85
90
95
Series
Stage
EOCENE
PALEOCENE
UPPER CRETACEOUS
Lutetian
Ypresian
Thanetian
Danian
Maastrichtian
Campanian
Santonian
Coniacian
Turonian
Cenomanian
WESTERN VOLCANIC PROVINCE
SW
NW - SE
CENTRAL VOLCANIC PROVINCE
NW
SW
SE
NE
VOLCANIC PHASES
NORTHEASTERN VOLCANIC PROVINCE
W
C
E
Jicara Fm
Melones Ls
Monte Grande Fm
El Rayo Fm
Parguera Ls
Cotui Ls
Lajas Fm
Boquerón Fm
Fault
Late Mariquita Chert
Guayo Fm
Río Culebrinas Fm
Anón Fm
Monserrate Fm
Mal Paso Fm
Palma Escrita Fm
Concepción Fm
Yauco Fm
2-pe Lava
Río Blanco Fm
Maricao Fm
Lago Garzas Fm
Sabana Grande Fm
Jobos Fm
Yunes Fm
Alonzo Fm
Tetuán Fm
Mameyes Lava
Vista Allegre Fm
Robles Fm
Guayo Fm
Río Descalabrado Fm
Cuevas Ls
Jacaguas Gp
Los Puertos Fm
Raspaldo Fm
Miramar Fm
Coamo Fm
Santa Ana Ls
Toyosa Mem
San Diego Tuff
Sabana Hoyos Mem
Maravillas Fm
Achiote Congl
Cariblanco Fm
Cotorra Tuff
Malo Breccia
Lapa Lava
Lava Mem
Robles Fm
(eroded)
Cuyón Fm ?
(eroded in Cretaceous)
Las Tetas Lava
Robles Fm
Lapa Lava
Cañabón lava
Río Matón Ls
Ortiz Fm
Corozal Ls
Carreras Slt
Palmarejo Fm
Cibuco Fm
Blancho Tuff
Revés Mem
Botijas Ls
Fleur de Alba Ls
Pozas Fm
Minguillo Lava
Río Bauta Mem
Manicaboa Fm
Los Negros Fm
Avispa Lava
Perchas Lava
Magüeyes Fm
Barrancas Ls
Río Orocovis Gp
VB
VA
Tectonic Break 2
IVB
IVA
Tectonic Break 1
III
(covered)
(covered)
(covered)
Palmarejo Fm
Naranjito Fm
Guaracanal And
La Muda Ls
Tortugas And
Río de la Plata Ss
Camarones Ss
Mamey Lava Mem
Santa Olaya Lava
Cancel Breccia
El Ocho Fm
Cerro Gordo Lava
Pájarus Tuff
Río Piedras Slt
Guaracanal And
La Muda Ls
Tortugas And
Guaynabo Fm
Mamey Lava Mem
Carraizo Ss
Infierno Fm
Mambiche Lomas Fms
Río Piedras Slt
Guaracanal And
Monacillo
Trujillo Alto Ls
Fm
Leprocomio Mem
Lava Mem
Lower Mem
Frailes Fm
Martín Gonzáles Lava
Canóvanas Fm
Toma de Agua Vitroph
Cambalanche Fm
Hato Puerco Fm
Barrazas Fm
Island arc volcanic strata in western Puerto Rico are underlain by a Lower - Upper Jurassic basement complex consisting of Lower Mariquita Chert, Cajul Basalt, Las Palmas serpentinite melange, and sepentinized peridotite.

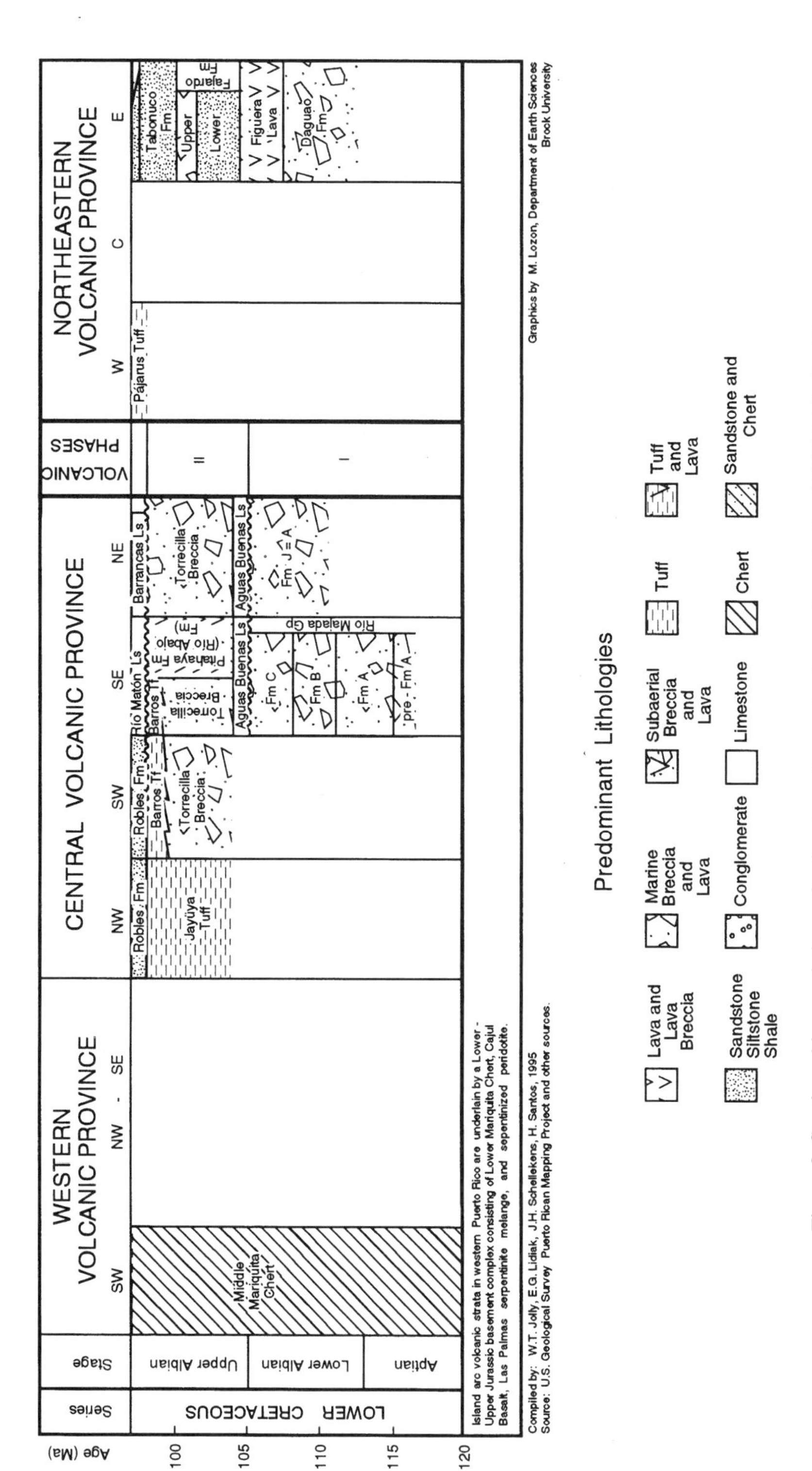

Figure 2. Stratigraphic correlations of volcanic rocks ranging in age from Aptian (120 Ma) in the Mesozoic to mid-Eocene (50 Ma) in Puerto Rico; see Table 1 for sources.

TABLE 1. SOURCES OF STRATIGRAPHIC CORRELATIONS*

Unit	Stage	Notes	Reference
	NORTHEASTERN VOLCANIC PROVINCE		
Volcanic phase V			
1. Palmerejo Formation	Middle Eocene		Berryhill, 1965; Montgomery, 1995
2. Río Piedras Slt	U. Paleocene–L. Eocene		Pease, 1968c
3. Narajanito Formation	U. Paleocene–L. Eocene		Pease, 1968c
4. Guaracanal Andesite	U. Paleocene		Pease, 1968c
Volcanic phase IV			
5. La Muda Ls	Maastrichtian		Berkey, 1915, 1919; Meyerhoff and Smith, 1931; Pease, 1968c
6. Monacillo Formation	Maastrichtian	1	Kaye, 1959; **Pease, 1968c**
7. Trujillo Alto Ls	Maastrichtian	1	Kaye, 1959; Pease 1968c
8. Tortugas Andesite	Campanian–Maastrichtian	2	Kaye, 1959; Pease, 1968c
9. Guaynabo Formation	Campanian–Maastrichtian		Meyerhoff and Smith, 1931; Kaye, 1959; **Pease, 1968c**
10. Frailes Formation	Campanian		Kaye, 1959; **Pease, 1968c**
11. Leprocomio Member	Campanian		Pease, 1968c
12. Río de la Plata Ss	Santonian–Campanian	2	Lidiak, 1965; **Pease, 1968c**
13. Camarones Ss	Santonian–Campanian	2	Pease, 1968c
14. Mamey Lava Member	Santonian–Campanian	2	Pease, 1968c
15. Martín Gonzáles Lava	Santonian–Campanian	2	Pease, 1968c; Seiders, 1971c
Volcanic phase III			
16. Santa Olaya Lava	Cenomanian–Santonian		Lidiak, 1965; Pease, 1968c
17. Celada Formation	Cenomanian–Santonian	3	Seiders, 1971c
18. Carraízo Brec	?	4	Pease, 1968c
19. Infierno Formation	Cenomanian–Santonian		Seiders, 1971c
20. Lomas Formation	Cenomanian		Seiders, 1971c
21. Mambiche Formation	Cenomanian–Santonian		M'Gonigle, 1978
22. Canóvanas Formation	Turonian–Santonian		Seiders, 1971c
23. Toma de Agua Vit	Turonian–Santonian		Seiders, 1971c
24. Cambalanche Formation	Turonian–Santonian		Seiders, 1971c
25. Hato Puerco Formation	Cenomanian		Meyerhoff and Smith, 1931; **Seiders, 1971c**
26. Barrazas Formation	Cenomanian		Seiders, 1971c
Volcanic phase II			
27. Cancel Brec	U. Albian	2	Pease, 1968c
28. El Ocho Formation	U. Albian	2	Pease, 1968c
29. Cerro Gordo Lava	U. Albian	2	Lidiak, 1965; Pease, 1968c; Jolly et al., 1995
30 Pájarus Tuff	U. Albian	2	Pease, 1968c
31.Tabonuco Formation	U. Albian		Seiders, 1971c
32. Fajardo Formation	U. Albian		Berkey, 1915; Meyerhoff and Smith, 1931; **Briggs, 1973**; Weiland, 1988
Volcanic phase I			
33. Figuera Lava	L. Albian		Meyerhoff and Smith, 1931; Briggs, 1973; Briggs and Aguilar-Cortés, 1980; **Weiland, 1988**
34. Daguao Formation	Aptian–L. Albian		M'Gonigle, 1977; Briggs and Aguilar-Cortés, 1980; Weiland, 1988
	CENTRAL VOLCANIC PROVINCE		
Volcanic phase V			
35. Jobos Formation	M. Eocene		Nelson and Monroe, 1967
36. Yunes Formation	U. Paleocene–L. Eocene		Nelson and Monroe, 1967
37. Guayo Formation	Eocene		Pessagno, 1960; Glover, 1971; **Krushensky and Monroe, 1975**

TABLE 1. SOURCES OF STRATIGRAPHIC CORRELATIONS* (continued - page 2)

Unit	State	Notes	Reference
	CENTRAL VOLCANIC PROVINCE (continued)		
Volcanic phase V			
38. Jacaguas Group	U. Paleocene–Eocene	5	Glover and Mattson, 1967
39. Río Descalabrado Fm	L. Eocene		Glover and Mattson, 1967
40. Cuevas Ls	L. Eocene	5	Glover, 1961b, 1971; **Glover and Mattson, 1967**; Krushensky, 1978
41. Los Puertos Formation	U. Paleocene-M. Eocene		Glover and Mattson, 1967
42. Raspaldo Formation	U. Paleocene–L. Eocene		Glover and Mattson, 1967
43. Miramar Formation	U. Paleocene	5	Pessagno, 1969; **Glover and Mattson, 1967**
44. Cuyón Formation	U. Paleocene (?)		Glover, 1967, 1971
45. Ortiz Formation	U. Paleocene–Eocene		Berryhill, 1965; **Montgomery, 1995**
46. Corozal Ls	U. Paleocene		Berryhill, 1965; **Montgomery, 1995**
47. Carreras Slt	U. Paleocene		Berryhill, 1965
48. Cibuco Formation	U. Paleocene		Berryhill, 1965
Volcanic phase IV			
49. Alonzo Formation	Campanian		Nelson and Monroe, 1957
50. Coamo Formation	U. Campanian		Glover, 1961b, 1971
51. Maravillas Formation	Campanian		Mattson, 1967; Glover, 1961b, 1971
52. Toyosa Member	Campanian		Briggs, 1969; **Glover, 1971**
53. Santa Anna Ls	Campanian		Glover, 1961b, 1971
54. San Diego Tuff	Campanian		Glover, 1961b, 1971
55. Sabanas Hoyos Member	Campanian		Glover, 1961b, 1971
56. Achiote Cong	L. Campanian		Mattson, 1967, 1968b
57. Cariblanco Formation	L. Campanian		Glover, 1961b, 1971
58. La Guaba Lava Member	L. Campanian		Glover, 1961b, 1971
59. Pozas Formation	Santonian– L. Maastrichtian		Berryhill, 1965; Nelson 1966; **Briggs, 1969**
60. Blanco Tuff Member	Campanian		Berryhill, 1965
61. Revés Member	Santonian–L. Campanian		Briggs, 1969
62. Fleur de Alba Ls	Campanian		Nelson and Monroe, 1966; Briggs, 1969
63. Botijas Ls	Campanian		Briggs, 1969
64. Minguillo Lava Member	Campanian		Berryhill, 1965
65. Río Bauta Member	Campanian– L. Maastrichtian		Berryhill, 1965
Volcanic phase III			
66. Tetuán Formation	Cenomanian– Santonian		Nelson and Monroe, 1967
67. Mameyes Lava	Cenomanian– Santonian		Nelson and Monroe, 1967
68. Vista Allegre Formation	Cenomanian		Nelson and Monroe, 1967; **Mattson, 1967**
69. Cotorra Tuff	Cenomanian– Santonian		Briggs, 1967
70. Malo Brec	Cenomanian– Santonian		Briggs, 1967
71. Robles Formation	Cenomanian– Santonian		Pease and Briggs, 1960
72. Lapa Lava Member	Cenomanian		Berryhill and Glover, 1960; **Jolly, 1970, 1971**
73. Cañabon Lava Member	Cenomanian		Briggs and Gelabert, 1962
74. Las Tetas Lava Member	Cenomanian		Berryhill and Glover, 1960
75. Río Matón Ls	U. Albian–Cenomanian		Berryhill and Glover, 1960; **Kazcor and Rogers, 1990**
76. Río Orocovis Group	Cenomanian–Santonian		Berryhill, 1965; Nelson, 1966a
77. Manicaboa Formation	Turonian–Santonian		Berryhill, 1965
78. Los Negros Formation	Turonian–Santonian		Berryhill, 1965; Nelson, 1967b
79. Avispa Lava	U. Cenomanian		Lidiak, 1965; Berryhill, 1965

TABLE 1. SOURCES OF STRATIGRAPHIC CORRELATIONS* (continued - page 3)

Unit	State	Notes	Reference
	CENTRAL VOLCANIC PROVINCE (continued)		
Volcanic phase III			
80. Perchas Lava	Cenomanian		Lidiak, 1965; Berryhill, 1965
81. Magüeyes Formation	L. Cenomanian		Berryhill, 1965
82. Barrancas Ls	L. Cenomanian		Briggs, 1969
Volcanic phase II			
83. Jayüya Tuff	Albian		Mattson, 1967, 1968b
84. Barros Tuff	U. Albian		Briggs, 1969
85. Torrecilla Brec	U. Albian		Briggs and Gelabert, 1962; **Briggs, 1969**
86. Petahaya Formation	U. Albian		M'Gonigle, 1977
87. Río Abajo Formation	U. Albian	6	M'Gonigle, 1977
88. Aguas Buenas Ls	U. Albian	7	Glover, 1971; **Kazcor and Rogers, 1990**
Volcanic phase I			
89. Río Majada Group	Aptian–L. Albian		Jolly et al., 1995
90. Formation C	L. Albian		Berryhill and Glover, 1960
91. Formation B	L. Albian		Berryhill and Glover, 1960
92. Formation A	Aptian–L. Albian		Berryhill and Glover, 1960; Glover, 1971
	WESTERN VOLCANIC PROVINCE		
Volcanic phase V			
93. Jicara Formation	U. Paleocene–Eocene		Slodowski, 1956; Mattson and Pessagno, 1971; Mattson et al., 1972
94. Río Culebrinas Fm	Eocene		Hubbard, 1923; Mattson, 1960, 1967; Tobisch, 1968
95. Anón Formation	Eocene		Pessagno, 1960; **Mattson, 1968a**
96. Milagros Formation	L. Eocene		Nelson and Tobisch, 1967; Tobisch, 1968; McIntyre, 1971
97. Matilde Formation	L. Eocene		Nelson and Tobisch, 1967; Tobisch, 1969; McIntyre, 1971
98. Monserrate Formation	U. Paleocene–M. Eocene		Pessagno, 1960; Mattson, 1968a
99. Mal Paso Formation	U. Paleocene–L. Eocene		McIntyre, 1970
100. Palma Escrita Fm	U. Paleocene–L. Eocene		McIntyre, 1970
Volcanic phase IV			
101. Concepcíon Formation	U. Maastrichtian		McIntyre et al., 1970; McIntyre, 1970
102. Río Blanco Formation	Santonian–Maastrichtian		Hubbard, 1923; McIntyre, 1970
103. Lago Garzas Formation	Santonian–Maastrichtian		Mattson, 1968b; Krushensky and Monroe, 1978
104. Pastillo Member	Santonian–Maastrichtan		Mattson, 1968b
105. Santas Pascuas M	Santonian–Maastrichtian		Mattson, 1968b
106. Yauco Formation	Santonian–Maastrichtian	8	Mattson, 1960, 1967; McIntyre, 1970; **Krushensky and Monroe, 1978**; Larue et al., 1991a
107. Maricao Formation	Santonian–Campanian	8	Mattson, 1960, 1967; **McIntyre, 1970;** Krushensky and Monroe, 1978; Curet, 1986
108. Sabana Grande Fm	Santonian–Campanian	8, 9	Slodowski, 1956; Volckmann, 1984; Santos, 1995
109. El Rayo Formation	Maastrichtian		Volckmann, 1984; Santos, 1995
110. Monte Grande Fm	U. Campanian	9	Sampayo, 1993; Santos, 1995
111. Melones Ls	U. Campanian		Mattson, 1960; Volckmann, 1984; Santos, 1990
112. Parguera Ls	M. Campanian		Mattson, 1960; Almy, 1969; Volckmann, 1984; Santos, 1990
113. Cotui Ls	M. Campanian		Volckmann, 1984; Santos, 1995
114. Lajas Formation	L. Campanian		Volckmann, 1984c
115. Boquerón Basalt	Santonian–Campanian	9	Volckmann, 1984c; Schellekens et al., 1991
116. Las Mesas Grnst (melange)	Santonian-Maastrichtian	10	Mattson, 1960; **Schellekens et al., 1991**

TABLE 1. SOURCES OF STRATIGRAPHIC CORRELATIONS* (continued - page 4)

Unit	State	Notes	Reference
	WESTERN VOLCANIC PROVINCE (continued)		
Pre-island arc strata			
117. Mariquita Chert (melange)	L. Juirassic–Santonian		Mattson, 1960, 1973; Volckmann, 1984d; **Montgomery et al., 1994a**
118. Cajul Basalt (melange)	L. Jurassic?	11	Mattson, 1960, 1973; Volckmann, 1984d; Joyce, 1986; Joyce et al., 1987a; **Schellenkens et al., 1991**
119. Las Palmas Amph (melange)	L. Jurassic?	12	Mattson, 1960, 1973; Tobisch, 1968; Volckmann, 1984d; Joyce et al., 1987b; **Schellekens et al., 1991**

*References to original definitions of a given unit are listed first followed by additional references listed in chronological order. Bold face references presenting currently accepted redefinitions of a given unit; U = Upper; L = Lower. Numbered notes in the table refer to the following comments:

1. The Trujillo Alto Limestone and associated Monacillo Formation (Pease, 1968c), both lateral equivalents of the La Muda Limestone, were deposited on or near the northern shelf slope, and therefore possibly extend into the Lower Paleocene. Elsewhere, the La Muda Limestone is unconformably overlain by Upper Paleocene limestone lenses forming the base of the Guaracanal Andesite (Pease, 1968c).

2. The Río de la Plata and Camarones Sandstone were considered by Pease (1968c) to be comformable with the underlying Santa Olaya Lava because lenses of Santa Olava–like lava were identified within Camarones Sandstone. Analyses of the associated Mamey Lava Member and the lenses (Jolly et al., this volume) reveal the flows to be geochemically similar to other volcanic phase IV basalts. Therefore, a Santonian–Lower Campanian age is assigned to these units, and they are inferred to be unconformable with the Santa Olaya Lava of Crenomian age. The presence of cruciform plagioclase phenocrysts in basal flows of the Cerro Gordo Lava were compared to textures in the Lapa Lava of the central tectonic block and led Pease (1968c) to attribute the unit and associated unfossiliferous sediments (Pájarus Tuff, El Ocho Formation, and Cancel Breccia) to the Cenomanian. However, Cerro Gordo lavas carry an unusual orthopyroxene-rich phenocryst assemblage and a trace element geochemistry similar (Jolly et al., this volume) to flows in the Fajardo Formation (Weiland, 1988), and is here considered to be Upper Albian (Volcanic phase II) in age.

3. The name Celada Formation of Seiders (1971c) was applied to lavas in the southwest Gurabo quadrangles (Figs, 1, 3) prior to exposure of identical unweathered Santa Olaya Lava in the adjacent Aguas Bunas quadrangle during construction of Highway 52, thereby demonstrating the two units are correlative.

4. The age of the unfossiliferous Carraízo Sandstone is unknown, and because it is contained wholly within a fault-bounded block, stratigraphic correlations are uncertain. Pease (1968c) suggested the Carraízo represents a lateral equivalent of the Guaynabo Formation, but Seiders (1971a, c) reported the unit is interlayered with upper Hato Puerco–like strata in the Gurabo quadrangle (Figs, 1, 3), with which it is correlated in Figure 2.

5. Glover and Mattson (1967) considered the Cuevas Limestone and Miramar Formation members of their Eocene Jacaguas Group, whereas Krushensky (1978) proposed these units represent Cretaceous-age material that became involved in southward gravity slides during Tertiary time; the Miramar conglomerate was viewed by Krushensky as the fault breccia (mylonite) formed beneath the sliding block.

6. The Río Abajo Formation of M'Gonigle (1977) was considered a possible correlative of the Río Majada Group. However, compositions reported by Jolly et al. (this volume) reveal the rocks to be similar to the Pitahaya Formation (M'Gonigle, 1977), with which the strata are correlated in this compliation.

7. The Aguas Buenas and Río Matón Limestones contain fauna of similar age and type, but stratigraphic relations (Briggs, 1969) demonstrate the former underlies the Torrecilla Breccia, which in turn is overlain by the Río Matón Lower Cenomanian (Kazcor and Rogers, 1990).

8. The Yauco and Sabana Grande Formations have traditionally been regarded as Turonian to Maastrichtian (Krushensky and Monroe, 1979; Volckmann, 1984d; Larue et al., 1991b). However, no fauna restricted in range to the Turonian-Coniacian are reported, and ranges of all observed taxa extend through the Santonian-Campanian (see summary of Krushensky and Monroe, 1978b). Therefore, these units are inferred in this compilation to be restricted to the Santonian-Maastrichtian (Fig. 2). Earlier strata in the region have been included in the Mariquita Chert (Volckmann, 1984c).

9. Recent investigations by Santos (1995) have confirmed that sandstone in the western part of the San Germain Domain (Figs. 1, 6A), attributed by Sampayo (1992) to the Monte Grande Formation, underlies the Boquerón Basalt and is lithologically and temporally similar to the Sabana Grande Formation, with which it is included in Figure 1. The overlying Cotui Limestone, in part equivalent to the Parguera Limestone in the Sierra Bermeja complex, is not present in the western San Germain Domain due to the topographic high generated by earlier strata. Santos (1995) reported the succeeding Campanian "Upper" Yauco Formation of Volckmann (1984d) in the San German Domain (Fig. 6A) grades toward the west from deep water shale and sandstone to near-shore volcanic breccia and sandstone of the Monte Grande Formation, and finally to an unnamed platform limestone. These strata all contribute to formation of the Lajas-Cotui shelf (Fig. 8B).

10. New data from the Las Mesas Greenstones of Schellekens et al. (1991) exposed in quarries east of Mayagüez (Figs. 1, 6A), included together with amphibolite as blocks in the Monte del Estado Peridotite belt, reveal the lavas to be geochemically identical (Fig. 7C-D) to MORB basalts. Other blocks in this belt exposed near the terminus of H105, consist of lava similar to Campanian types in western Puerto Rico (Schellekens, this volume), with which they are tentatively correlated.

11. Cajul Basalt (Mattson, 1960) in the central part of the Sierra Bermeja complex and at the type section along Arroyo Cajul (Fig. 6B) exhibits MORB-like Sr, Nd, and Pb isotope ratios (our unpublished data) and depleted normalized REE patterns (Fig. 7B), and is inferred to be similar in age to the oldest Mariquita Chert (Lower Jurassic). Larger masses of lava concentrated in fault blocks on the northern and southern borders of the complex (Fig. 6B), correlated with the Cajul Basalt by Mattson (1960), exhibit enriched REE patterns (Fig. 7D), similar to Campanian volcanic rocks in the San German Domain (Fig. 6A).

12. Amphibolites similar to the Las Palmas amphibolite melange (Fig. 6B) in the Sierra Bermeja complex (Mattson, 1960) also occur (Figs. 1, 6A-B) associated with serpentinized peridotite at Media Quijada (Krushensky and Monroe, 1978b), Punta Melones (Volckmann, 1968c; Schellekens et al., 1991), and east of Mayagüez (Curet, 1986).

use of formations altogether in the Puerto Rican Cordillera in favor of lithofacies based on phenocryst assemblages (i.e., the orthopyroxene-augite–bearing lithofacies [Río Loco Formation of Slodowski, 1956]; the augite-bearing Maricao-Yauco lithofacies; the plagioclase-augite–bearing Lago-Garzas lithofacies; and the hornblende-plagioclase–bearing Anón lithofacies). In this classification mixed units of widely different ages and stratigraphic relations (Upper Maastrichtian Concepcíon Formation; upper Paleocene to lower Eocene Palma Escrita and Mal Paso Formations) (Fig. 1) were grouped into single entities.

Stratigraphic relations within the arc platform

Massive strato-volcanic accumulations of pillow lava and lava breccia, generated near volcanic vent areas, represented permanent additions to the developing arc crust, and normally persisted as prominent topographic features, such as platforms, banks, or shoals commonly supporting shallow platform reefs during quiescent intervals (cf. Río Matón and Aguas Buenas Limestones [Kazcor and Rogers, 1990] of the central province) (Figs. 1 and 2). As a result, an extensive arc platform gradually developed along the active volcanic zone as volcanism progressed. Puerto Rican volcanic provinces of each stratigraphic interval consist of a principal linear belt of volcanic centers, analogous to volcanic fronts in modern island arcs, and more isolated volcanism on the margins of the platform, where intra-arc sedimentary and volcanic basins commonly developed (Dolan et al., 1991). Due to the permanence of relict volcanic piles, the present two-dimensional erosional surface through the arc exposes most volcanic belts comprising the platform, except where extensive erosion removed uppermost strata (central province, where most post-Cenomanian strata were removed during Cenozoic time) (see Figs 1 and 2), or where volcanic centers developed sequentially atop or in near proximity to one another (northeastern province).

Within thick volcanic piles, lava and lava breccia interfinger with crudely bedded volcanic breccia and well-stratified tuffaceous and epiclastic, sandstone-dominated sedimentary rocks. Fragmental rocks tend to become progressively more common upward in the stratigraphic sequence and laterally away from volcanic centers (Pease, 1968c; Berryhill, 1961; Larue et al., 1991b), but lavas and volcanoclastic units are intertongued over long distances, and zones of alternating facies commonly characterize transitions from one unit to another. Consequently, contacts between mappable lithologic units are indefinite across appreciable intervals of section, even though the total character of each mappable unit is quite distinctive. Marine strata display little or no angular discordance between units, but in areas of massive lava and lava breccia accumulation, tuff breccia and other volcanoclastic deposits and limestone units occur as thin discontinuous lenses between which contacts are locally discordant (Joyce, 1985). Nonmarine deposits of volcanic materials occur at several stratigraphic intervals, and are marked by the presence of reddish to purplish-gray volcanic breccia and shallow mudstone and conglomerate deposits; lenses of limestone are commonly stratigraphically associated with such materials.

Metamorphism of volcanic strata

Postdepositional burial metamorphism of the zeolite and prehnite-pumpellyite facies has transformed much of the original mineralogy of groundmasses of Puerto Rican strata (Otalora, 1964; Jolly, 1971; Cho, 1991), but augite and partly albitized plagioclase phenocrysts and relict textures are preserved in most specimens. Stratigraphic reconstructions and mineralogic compositions indicate metamorphism occurred at shallow levels, normally less than about 1.5 to 3 km. Lidiak (1991) reported hornblende compositions in Puerto Rican plutons are consistent with elevated geothermal gradients (>35° to 45° C/km) during intrusion. Low-temperature–high P_t blueschist-grade metamorphic assemblages are unknown in Puerto Rico, but are represented in trench related strata generated along the north shore of Hispaniola during collision with the Bahama Banks (Joyce, 1991).

NORTHEASTERN VOLCANIC PROVINCE

Structural relations

Stratigraphic reconstructions in northeastern Puerto Rico (Figs. 1 and 2) are difficult, because this tectonic block has itself been deformed by folding and large-scale strike-slip faulting into three separate domains. The oldest rocks on the east are separated from other parts of the province by the Leprocomio Fault (Fig. 1), exhibiting right-lateral movement of about 7 km (Seiders, 1971a-c). Within the eastern domain, attitudes are dominated by westerly dips (Briggs and Aguilar-Cortés, 1980), such that strata grow progressively younger toward the northwest. The central zone is highly tectonized and composed of independent fault-bounded blocks with highly variable attitudes, while in the western part of the province and along the Cerro Mula fault, strata display consistent easterly to southeasterly dips (Pease, 1968a-c), and face toward the east-southeast. Considered as a whole, the province is essentially formed of a twisted synclinorium over 50 km in width with extensive deformation across the axial zone.

The Cerro Mula fault was originally considered Maastrichtian in age or even later (Pease, 1968c), but geochemical data (Jolly et al., Chapter 3, this volume) reveal that compositions of volcanic rocks in the two adjacent volcanic provinces, which were markedly different before mid-Santonian time, afterward became identical. This suggests strike-slip faulting that brought the central and northeastern volcanic provinces into juxtaposition occurred at that time (designated tectonic break 1 in Fig. 2). Basalts of the Mamey, Tortugas, and Río de la Plata lavas and breccia of the Guaynabo Formation (Kaye, 1959; Pease, 1968b,c), considered by Pease (1968a-c) to have been erupted during final stages of Santa Olaya volcanism, are here grouped into a separate volcanic phase postdating strike-slip movement on the Cerro Mula fault (Fig. 1; Table 1). Ages of other major strike-slip faults in the area

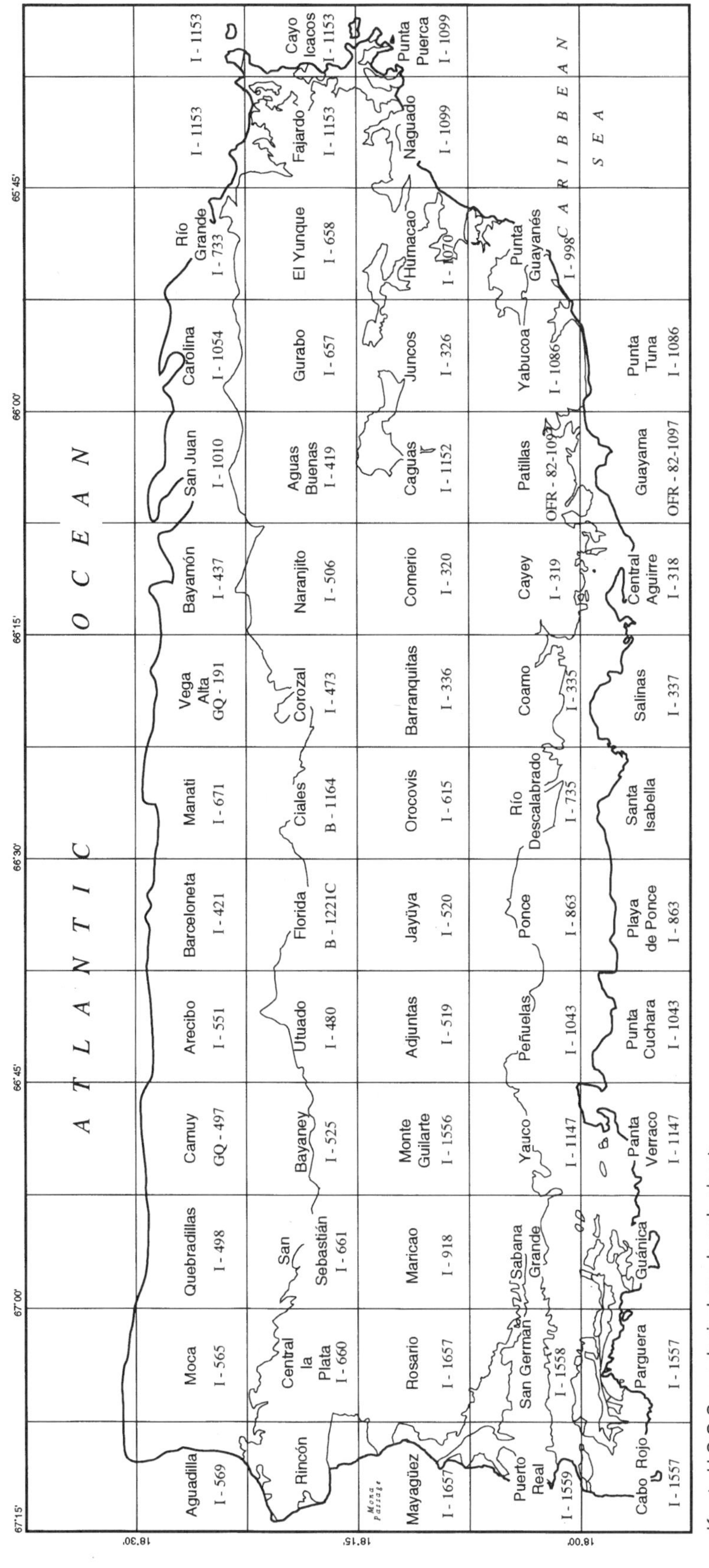

Figure 3. Key to geologic quadrangles in Puerto Rico. Relevant U.S. Geological Survey geologic quadrangle sheets, published at a scale of 1:20,000, are listed in the references.

are less certain, but the Campanian Martín Gonzáles Basalt (an equivalent of the Mamey Lava) (Seiders, 1971a-c) and Monacillo Formation, and the Upper Paleocene Guaracanal Andesite are all cut by the Leprocomio fault, indicating some deformation was of Tertiary age. It is apparent from these relations that strike-slip faulting took place during a prolonged period extending at least from mid-Santonian to Eocene time.

Distribution of volcanic strata

Although correlations across major faults are difficult or even impossible, principal strato-volcanic accumulations in the northeastern volcanic province, dominated by the Daguao-Figuera-Fajardo complex (Lower Albian to Lower Cenomanian) (Briggs, 1973; Briggs and Aguilar-Cortés, 1980; M'Gonigle, 1977, 1978; Weiland, 1988) and the overlying Santa Olaya Lavas (Lower Cenomanian to mid-Santonian) (Monroe and Pease, 1962; Lidiak, 1965; Pease, 1968a-c) are concentrated along the bounding Cerro Mula fault (Jolly et al., Chapter 3, this volume). A few kilometers to the northeast, strata grade to finer grained, commonly carbonate-bearing epiclastic volcanic materials, including deltaic deposits of the Upper Albian Fajardo Formation (Briggs, 1973; Briggs and Aguilar-Cortés, 1980) and mixed volcanic breccia and sandstone of the Cenomanian Hato Puerco Formation (Seiders, 1971c; Monroe, 1977; Monroe and Pease, 1962). The central part of the northeast tectonic block contains several fault-bounded blocks of Carraízo Sandstone and the Lomas, Infierno, and Mambiche Formations (Pease, 1968c; Seiders, 1971a-c; M'Gonigle, 1978), consisting predominantly of volcanic breccia and sandstone. In the present compilation these strata are all considered temporally equivalent, dating from Upper Cenomanian to mid-Santonian (Fig. 2), although nonfossiliferous Carraízo Sandstone was considered by Pease (1968b) to be correlative with the Guaynabo Formation and therefore may be slightly younger.

Pre-Santonian unconformities in the northeastern volcanic province are restricted to the elevated part of the arc platform along the northern border of the Cerro Mula fault, and are absent on the northern flank of the pile, where thicknesses of units are significantly decreased. An extensive erosional interval, designated as the second tectonic break in Figure 2, occurred during Maastrichtian and lower Paleocene time. The early part of this period was characterized by deposition of the La Muda–Trujillo Alto Limestones in northeastern Puerto Rico, and by intrusion of the Utuado and Caguas stocks and the San Lorenzo batholith (Weaver, 1958; Donnelly et al., 1990) in the central province (Fig. 1). Donnelly et al. (1990) suggested intrusion corresponded with a period of extensive erosion in the central part of the island during the Maastrichtian when plutonic activity replaced volcanism. Smith and Schellekens (this volume) considered intrusion to correspond temporally with a decrease in degree of melting in the arc source resulting from a reversal in polarity of the subduction zone. The lower Paleocene part of the interval was characterized by an island-wide unconformity reflecting both a depositional and volcanic hiatus (Berryhill, 1965; Mattson, 1967, 1968a,b; Pease, 1968c; Glover, 1971; Glover and Mattson, 1967, 1973; McIntyre, 1974; Volckmann, 1984a-d; Santos, 1995; see Krushensky [1978] for alternative views in north-central Puerto Rico).

CENTRAL VOLCANIC PROVINCE

Structural relations

The most extensive volcanic province occupies the central part of the island (Fig. 1), confined to an area between two large intermediate to felsic intrusive plutons of Maastrichtian age, the San Lorenzo batholith (Broedel, 1961; Glover, 1982; M'Gonigle, 1978; Rogers et al., 1979) in the east and the Utuado stock (Mattson, 1967, 1968a,b; Nelson, 1966a,b, 1967b; Weaver, 1958) in the west. Between these two bodies strata are broadly warped by the east-trending Puerto Rico Anticlinorium. The structural style of both the northern and southern boundaries of the tectonic block are characterized by plumose, convex-northward, northwest-southeast–trending strike-slip faults (Berryhill et al., 1960; Briggs and Pease, 1960; Pease, 1968c; Mattson, 1979) deflected around the plutons (Fig. 1). Hence, it is inferred these highly resistant masses largely sheltered the province from further tectonic disintegration following emplacement in the Maastrichtian. Several east-west strike-slip faults along the northern boundary of the province, subparallel with the Cerro Mula fault, probably have significant horizontal displacement of several kilometers (Berryhill et al., 1960). The faults are approximately parallel to the major volcanic axis and had minimal effect on transverse (north-south) variations in lithologic facies.

Distribution of volcanic strata

The principal volcanic accumulations in the fortuitously preserved central volcanic province, representing remnants of volcano-stratigraphic complexes, are concentrated along five east-west volcanic belts, that migrated northward with time and behaved as positive topographic features during subsequent volcanic episodes (Jolly et al., Chapter 3, this volume; see also Donnelly and Rogers, 1980; Donnelly et al., 1990): (I) Aptian through mid-Albian island arc tholeiitic basalt volcanic piles, composed of vent facies in the Cayey quadrangle (Formations A, B, and C of Berryhill and Glover, 1960) and a north marginal facies in the Comerio quadrangle (Fig. 3) (Pease and Briggs, 1960), are concentrated along the southeastern margin of the province; (II) Upper Albian accumulations of the calc-alkaline Torrecilla-Pitahaya basalt breccia (Briggs, 1969) occur in a continuous belt across the center of the island; (III) Cenomanian to mid-Santonian shoshonitic basalts and andesites, including Perchas and Avispa Lavas of the Río Orocovis Group (Lidiak, 1965; Berryhill, 1965; Nelson, 1966a,b, 1967a), together with Tetuán and Mameyes Lavas (Nelson and Monroe, 1966) farther west, are all aligned along a belt located south of and approximately parallel to the northern boundary of the province; (IV)

Campanian calc-alkaline accumulations, containing the Alonzo (Nelson and Monroe, 1966) and Pozas Formations (Berryhill, 1965; Nelson, 1966a; see also Briggs and Gelabert, 1962), are located along the northern border and within a graben extending southward into the area dominated by Cenomanian volcanic strata; and (V) extensive Tertiary calc-alkaline pyroclastic deposits of near-vent coarse dacitic volcanic breccia, and lava of the Jobos and lapilli tuff of Yunes Formations (Nelson and Monroe, 1966; Nelson and Tobisch, 1967), largely covered by postvolcanic sedimentary platform deposits, are present in a restricted zone forming the northernmost volcanic strata exposed in the central province, and in several isolated occurrences in the San Juan area (Guaracanal Formation) (Pease, 1968a; Pease and Monroe, 1977). Studies of Eocene basins of northern Puerto Rico (Montgomery, this volume) and of Eocene volcanic strata intersected by a drill core from Toa Baja, west of San Juan (Larue, 1991; Frost and Schellekens, 1991; Montgomery et al., 1991) suggest additional Eocene strata are buried beneath postvolcanic Oligocene platform carbonate deposits (Larue et al., this volume). The five volcanic phases in the central volcanic province are extended using recognized stratigraphic correlations into adjacent provinces as outlined in Table 1 and Figure 2.

Paleogeographic reconstructions

The major volcano-stratigraphic complexes, oriented subparallel to the long axis of the island, are composed of great accumulations of volcanic materials, with thicknesses ranging from over 6 km in the Río Majada Group (Berryhill and Glover, 1960), up to 3 km in the Torrecilla-Pitahaya belt (Briggs, 1967), 6 km in the Río Orocovis Group (Lidiak, 1965), and about 5 km in the Pozas Formation (Berryhill. 1965). Strata associated with volcanic centers evolved from predominantly submarine breccia and lava (volcanic phase I), through epiclastic sandstone-dominated turbidite assemblages (phases II and III), to mixtures of subaerial volcanic and epiclastic breccia and lahars, and to tuff-dominated pyroclastic flows and related assemblages (phases IV and V). Because volcanic belts behaved as positive topographic features during long periods following deposition, they effectively restricted configuration of subsequent sedimentary basins until they were buried and became graded by younger deposits.

Within individual volcanic belts, strata grade northward and southward of the central axis from coarse, lava–lava breccia–volcanic breccia dominated near-vent assemblages to turbiditic epiclastic or tuffaceous sediments on the flanks. In many belts, vent areas or volcanic centers may be distinguished on the basis of lithologic criteria, or approximated from sedimentologic patterns. In the Cayey quadrangle (Berryhill and Glover, 1960), for example, within Formations A, B, and C of the Río Majada Group, internal structure of the earliest volcanic belt, measuring about 12 km in width, is clearly exposed (Fig. 4). Lava and lava lenses, concentrated in a central zone of both Formations A and B, pinch out toward the north and south, giving way to massive volcanic breccia. Within Formation A, on the far flanks of the pile, thicknesses decrease, and sandstone lenses, representing fine-grained debris generated by submarine volcanic processes, are commonly interlayered with finer grained volcanic breccia.

Regional relations between strata of the five volcanic phases are illustrated schematically in Figure 4B, which is a restored reconstruction of the arc platform, eliminating effects of postvolcanic structural deformation, syn-volcanic isostatic downwarp, and upper Cenozoic erosion. Thicknesses of units reflect generalized variations of measured values in the preserved volcanic succession. Volcanic products of major accumulations from phases I, II, and III are dominated by lava and lava breccia, while later phases IV and V consist primarily of tuff and subordinate volcanic breccia and lava. Strata of phases III to V grade laterally (southward) to sandstone-dominated clastic wedge deposits.

Volcanic phase I (Aptian–Lower Albian, about 120 to 105 Ma). Initial volcanic strata of eruptive phase I in the central volcanic province, here grouped for convenience into the Río Majada Group (Jolly et al., Chapter 3, this volume), form a volcanic accumulation with a total maximum thickness of over 6 km (Berryhill and Glover, 1960; Glover, 1982). The rocks are intruded on the east by the San Lorenzo batholith, which tilted the exposed lava pile about 25° toward the west (Fig. 4), and metamorphosed and hydrothermally altered much of the rocks in its immediate vicinity (Glover, 1982). Exposed vent areas, marked by the presence of extensive augite-plagioclase phyric lava flows and lava breccia, are located about 10 km north of the Caribbean coast (Figs. 4A and 5A) of succeeding volcanic phases II and III become considerably thinner or pinch out altogether in the area of the Río Majada Group (Berryhill and Glover, 1960; Pease and Briggs, 1960; Glover, 1971), indicating the volcanic pile formed a paleogeographic ridge that, though gradually reduced in magnitude by erosion and burial, remained a positive topographic feature throughout the Cretaceous (Fig. 5B-D). Additional accumulations of correlative material toward the west form a basement high of considerable magnitude beneath Upper Cretaceous strata (Glover, 1971). Upper parts of the augite-plagioclase phyric Río Majada Group are reddish to purple in color, reflecting deposition in subaerial conditions. This is consistent with the presence of several local unconformities, used by Berryhill and Glover (1960) to subdivide the pile into Formations A, B, and C.

Volcanic phase II (Upper Albian, 105 to about 97 Ma). Volcanic strata of the second eruptive phase occur unconformably along the northern flank of the linear topographic feature produced by the Río Majada Group and its equivalents (Río Majada platform in Fig. 5B). These rocks were preceded by deposition of a localized reefoidal limestone unit, the Aguas Buenas Limestone, largely restricted to the platform provided by the earlier Río Majada Group (Pease and Briggs, 1960; Kazcor and Rogers, 1990). Phase II strata, including the Torrecilla Breccia (Briggs, 1969) and the Pitahaya Formation (M'Gonigle. 1977, 1978), consist of a maximum of about 2.5 km of augite-plagioclase–bearing marine and subaerial lava flows in the east and volcanic breccia grading upward from marine to subaerial in origin in the west. The rocks are exposed in a broad east-west belt extending 50 km across the central part of the island (Fig. 1), from the Utuado stock to the east coast. A series of plagioclase-rich lava flows (Río Abajo Lava), exposed within a fault block east of the San Lorenzo batholith (M'Gonigle, 1977, 1978), display geochemistry similar to Pitahaya lava flows, and are included within volcanic phase II (Jolly et al., Chapter 3, this volume).

Volcanic phase III (Cenomanian–Lower Santonian, 97 to 85 Ma). Phase II volcanic strata were unconformably succeeded by development of a short-lived carbonate reef on the existing platforms (identified in Fig. 5C as the Torrecilla banks and Río Majada platform). The major carbonate unit, the Río Maton Limestone Member of the Robles Formation, contains a fauna of similar type and age (Albian) as the earlier Aguas Buenas Limestone, but Briggs (1969) and Kazcor and Rogers (1990) demonstrated the two carbonates are separated by the Torrecilla Breccia. Hence, they assigned the Aguas Buenas to the mid-Albian and the Río Maton to the Upper Albian or lowermost Cenomanian, and suggested little time was available for erosion in the region between volcanic episodes, since subsequent Robles strata contain Cenomanian fauna (Briggs and Gelabert, 1962; Briggs, 1969).

Prior to phase III volcanism the region underwent rapid subsidence, perhaps due to initiation of a new and vigorous period of subduction (Kazcor and Rogers, 1990). Absence of detritus in subsequent strata led Glover (1971) to conclude the previous Río Majada and Torrecilla-Pitahaya volcanic belts both became submerged at this time in western parts of the region (Fig. 5C). Accompanying this subsidence, a third series of aligned volcanic accumulations developed some 5 km north of the phase II volcanic belt. The new volcanic centers produced voluminous augite-plagioclase–rich extrusives dominated by the Perchas and Avispa Lavas of the Río Orocovis Group in the east (Fig. 1), and the Tetuán-Mameyes lava sequence in the west (Fig. 1), with maximum thicknesses of about 5 to 6 km. Numerous limestone lenses developed on the Avispa platform during final stages of volcanism (Nelson, 1967a).

Related turbiditic sandstone and siltstone clastic wedge deposits of the Robles Formation (Berryhill et al., 1960; Briggs and Gelabert, 1962; Briggs, 1971) were simultaneously deposited in the basin south of the main volcanic chain, particularly within the trough between older volcanic strata of phases I and II (identified as the Robles basin in Fig. 5C). Basalt concentrations within the Robles basin include submarine Lapa and Las Tetas Lavas in the east (Berryhill and Glover, 1960; Pease and Briggs, 1960; Briggs and Gelabert, 1962), subaerial Malo Breccia and Cotorra Tuff (Briggs, 1967, 1971; these units, restricted to the Orocovis quadrangle [Fig. 3], are included within the Robles Formation in Fig. 1), and marine basalt of the Vista Allegre Sandstone in the west. Along its northern margin, Robles strata unconformably onlap a prominent topographic feature (Torrecilla banks, Fig. 5C) formed by earlier Torrecilla Breccia (Briggs, 1967). Graded conglomerates at the base of the Robles Formation in the vicinity of the Torrecilla belt in the Barranquitas quadrangle (Fig. 3) were interpreted by Briggs (1967) as evidence of alluvial deposits encircling a subaerial island during lower Robles deposition. Southernmost Robles strata thin to less than 25% of maximum thickness of the formation (about 2.5 km in the Robles basin), due to the presence of topographic irregularities inherited from earlier volcanic belts within the basin (Río Majada platform) (Fig. 5C).

The distribution of phase III volcanic rocks, consisting of an aligned northern belt of vent-related volcanic strata and a southerly basin with more randomly distributed volcanic centers, is analogous to geographic distribution in modern island arcs (cf. Central America, Carr et al., 1990; New Britain, Woodhead and Johnson, 1993) with their extensive volcanic front assemblages and more dispersed behind the arc basalt concentrations. Such a comparison is consistent with subduction along a south-dipping Benioff zone, relative to the current orientation of Puerto Rico. In this analogy the Río Orocovis Group represents deposits generated along the principal axis of volcanism while the Robles Formation represents lateral, intraplate basin clastic wedge (Jolly et al., Chapter 3, this volume). Geochemical evidence is inconsistent with a true back arc environment (Jolly et al., Chapter 3, this volume), characterized in modern arcs by upward mantle counterflow and associated low-degree pressure-release melting within the wedge (see, for example, Carr et al., 1990).

Volcanic phase IV (Mid-Santonian–Maastrichtian, 85 to about 75 Ma). Following transcurrent faulting along the Cerro Mula fault, and a brief period of erosion, the central and northeastern blocks were juxtaposed and thereafter share paleogeograpic development. Phase IV volcanic strata in the two provinces, much of which were removed by Cenozoic erosion, are concentrated along a zone a few kilometers north of the chain of phase III vol-

Figure 4. Stratigraphic relations within the interior of the Puerto Rican arc platform. A, Detail of volcanic accumulations comprising the Río Majada Group in the Cayey quadrangle (Fig. 3) modified from Berryhill and Glover (1960). Lava flows pinch out north and south of the central lava-dominated zone, grading to volcanic breccia, and, on the distant flanks of the volcanic pile, tongues of carbonate-bearing sandstone. B, Schematic cross section of the central volcanic province; location of the section is indicated by NW-SE line in the inset. Stratigraphic units are identified as in Figure 1. The section illustrates thicknesses of major volcanic accumulations, lateral stratigraphic relations within the arc platform, and predominant lithologic types. Effects of isostatic downwarp, structural deformation, and erosion are not shown. The approximate position of the present erosional surface along the line of section is included; eroded units are exposed elsewhere. Strata from deep within the arc platform were broadly upwarped in Maastrichtian time by the Puerto Rico anticlinorium in the central part of the cordillera. Uplift was accompanied by intrusion of the San Lorenzo batholith and Utuado stock (Fig. 1). Eocene volcanic phase V, generated following these tectonic events, was deposited on a deeply dissected platform with an erosional surface similar to the present level and the stratigraphic position of these units is diagrammatic. Phase IV and V strata were largely eroded during the upper Cenozoic; remnants are preserved within graben in the northwest (phases IV and V), and as thrust sheets in the southwest (phase V) (Fig. 1). Stratigraphic relations and tectonic development of Tertiary volcanic basins along the north coast, mostly buried by postvolcanic sedimentary platform deposits, are discussed by Montgomery and Larue et al. (this volume).

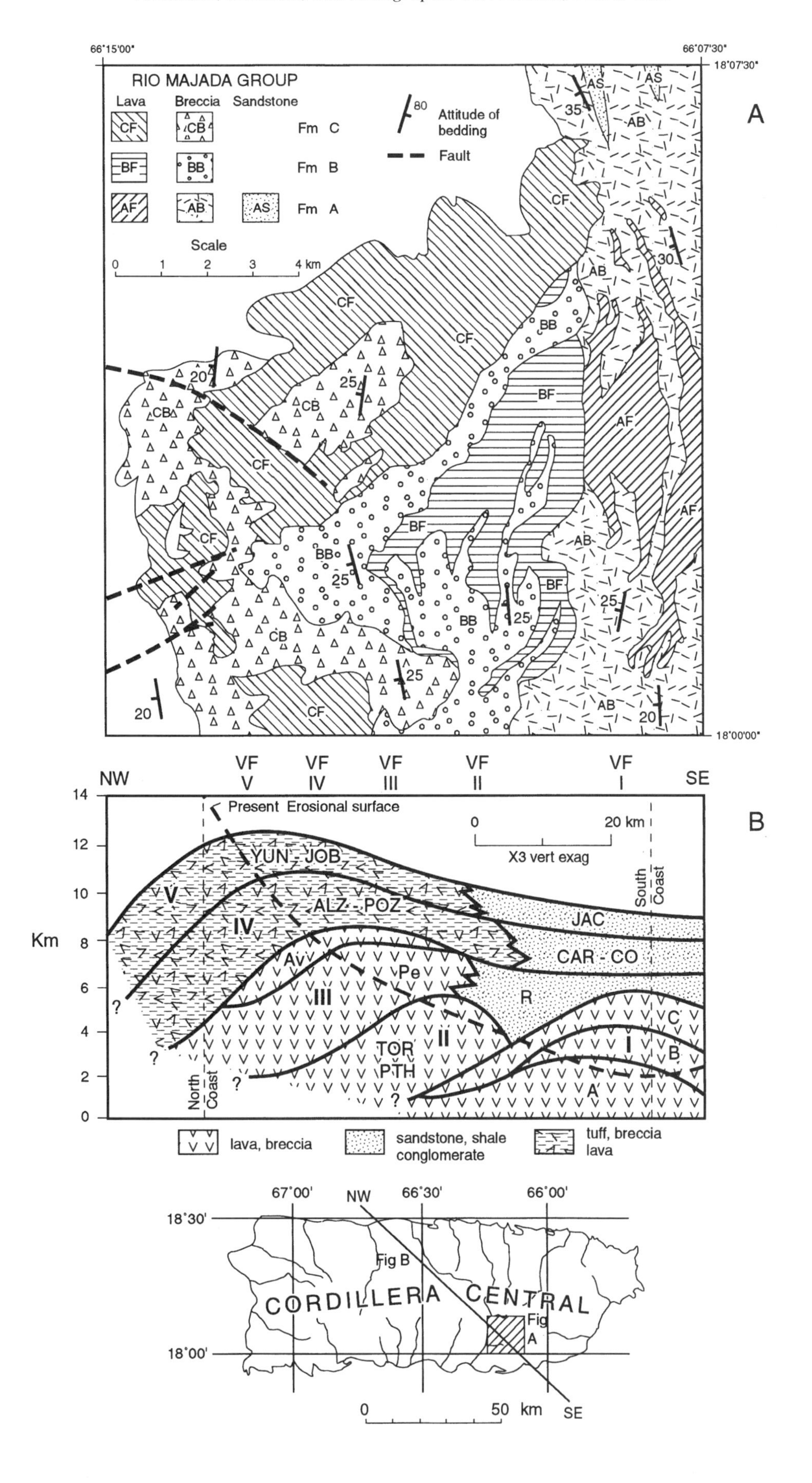
66°15'00"
66°07'30"
18°07'30"
18°00'00"
A
RIO MAJADA GROUP
Lava
Breccia
Sandstone
CF
CB
Fm C
BF
BB
Fm B
AF
AB
AS
Fm A
Attitude of bedding
Fault
Scale
0 1 2 3 4 km
B
NW
SE
VF V
VF IV
VF III
VF II
VF I
Present Erosional surface
0 20 km
X3 vert exag
South Coast
North Coast
YUN - JOB
ALZ - POZ
JAC
CAR - CO
Av
Pe
R
TOR
PTH
Km
lava, breccia
sandstone, shale conglomerate
tuff, breccia lava
67°00'
66°30'
66°00'
18°30'
18°00'
Fig B
CORDILLERA CENTRAL
Fig A
0 50 km

canic centers (VF in Fig. 5D). Preserved plagioclase-augite–rich Campanian strata is confined within graben and downthrown blocks, or concentrated along major fault zones, including, in the northeastern volcanic province, the Cerro Mula fault (Fig. 1). As a result of the elevated topography of the platform throughout this phase of volcanism, the volcanic pile was dominated by pyroclastic deposits, including extensive welded tuff, and epiclastic sediments deposited as alluvial and deltaic fanglomerates, which form high proportions of the Pozas (Berryhill, 1965) and Cariblanco (Glover, 1971) Formations. Correlative volcanic accumulations (Río de la Plata, Mamey, Tortugas, and Martín Gonzáles lavas) in the northeast exhibit identical compositions to those in the central part of the island, leading Jolly et al. (Chapter 3, this volume) to suggest the two provinces were juxtaposed during mid-Santonian time. Predominantly marine strata on the flanks of volcanic piles in the northeast suggest submergence of the older Santa Olaya platform (Fig. 5D), but the localized oxidized Tortugas Andesite is viewed as partly subaerial (Pease, 1968).

South of the aligned chain of phase IV volcanic centers, stratigraphically overlying the earlier Robles Formation, deposition of alluvial and deltaic sandstone and conglomerate together with scattered, short-lived volcanic concentrations, continued with development of the Cariblanco, Maravillas, and Coamo Formations (Glover, 1961a,b, 1971; Briggs, 1971; Lidiak, 1972). Deposition farther west was dominated by the Achiote Conglomerate (Mattson, 1967, 1968b; Briggs, 1971; Glover, 1971), which may reflect in part tectonism in central Puerto Rico contemporaneous with mid-Santonian strike-slip faulting along the Cerro Mula fault. Achiote strata pinch out along an east-west trend (Glover, 1971), parallel to the band of Pozas alluvial fans (Fig. 5D).

Volcanic phase IV was terminated in central Puerto by a prolonged period of erosion. During the earliest part of the erosional interval, extending throughout Maastrichtian time, platform carbonates and shelf sediments continued to develop in the northeast on the flank of the arc platform, while Río Blanco–Lago Garzas volcanism continued unabated in the western province. This interval corresponds with intrusion of major plutonic bodies (Utuado Stock, Caguas Stock, San Lorenzo Batholith) (Fig. 1) within the thickened arc crust (see

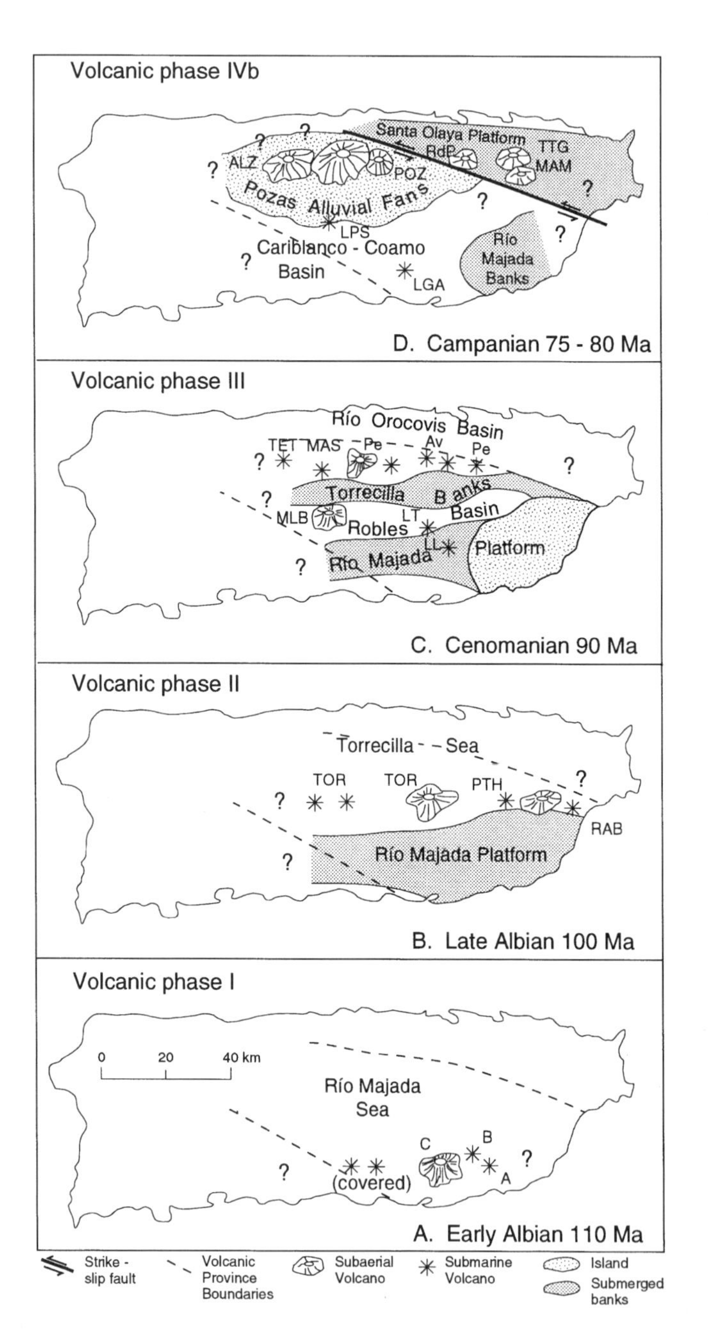

Figure 5. Paleogeographic evolution of the central volcanic province. A, Lower Albian, 110 Ma (volcanic phase I); mostly marine (Formations A and B) and subaerial (upper Formations B and C) Río Majada stratovolcanic accumulations, inferred to represent the principal axis of volcanism, form an east-west belt parallel to the south coast. Covered strata were inferred by Glover (1971) from onlap relations and thinning of overlying Cenomanian strata. B, Upper Albian, 100 Ma (volcanic phase II); subaerial to partly subaerial Torrecilla and Pitahaya volcano-stratigraphic complexes form a second parallel, onlapping belt 15 km north of the submerged Río Majada platform. TOR, Torrecilla Breccia; PTH, Pitahaya Formation; RAB, Río Abajo Formation. C, Cenomanian, 90 Ma (volcanic phase III); marine to subaerial Río Orocovis volcano-stratigraphic complexes are aligned along the north flank of the partly subaerial Torrecilla banks, while Robles basin, containing tuffaceous sandstone and scattered lava concentrations, forms between the partly buried Río Majada platform and the Torrecilla rise (modified from Glover, 1971). TET, Tetuán Formation; MAS, Mameyes Lava; MLB, Malo Breccia–Cotorra Tuff; Pe, Perchas Lava; Av, Avispa Lava; LL, Lapa Lava; LT, Las Tetas Lava. D, Campanian, 75 to 80 Ma (volcanic phases IVa and b); Pozas and Alonzo Formations, dominated by pyroclastic and epiclastic alluvial fans and lahars, form a belt superimposed on earlier Río Orocovis belt. Left-lateral movement on the Cerro Mula fault has brought the northeastern tectonic block into position, and the phase IV belt continues into this terrane on the old Santa Olaya platform. The Cariblanco basin, with an east-west shoreline, buries the older platforms (modified from Glover, 1971). ALZ, Alonzo Formation; POZ, Pozas Formation; RdP, Río de la Plata Sandstone; TTG, Tortugas Andesite; MAM, Mamey Lava; LPS, Los Panes Stock (Glover, 1971); LGA, La Guaba Lava Member (Glover, 1971) of Cariblanco Formation.

summary of Smith et al., this volume), perhaps interrupting flow of magma to the surface (Donnelly et al., 1990). The second part of the period, extending through the lower Paleocene, corresponds to an island wide hiatus, identified in Figure 2 as the second tectonic break.

Volcanic phase V (upper Paleocene to Eocene, 75 to 40 Ma). The most extensive exposed volcanic products of Tertiary phase V include intermediate hornblende-bearing lava breccia of the Jobos Formation and associated tuff of the Yunes Formation, together with lava breccia and volcanic breccia of the Guaracanal Andesite. In the San Juan Area, the sequence begins with a thin limestone, unconformably overlying the earlier La Muda Limestone, that grades upward abruptly to volcanic breccia of the Guaracanal Andesite. These lavas, and other Tertiary volcanic strata, are preserved in fault blocks along the northern margin of the province. They form a belt slightly north of and parallel to the phase IV volcanic zone. Elsewhere extensive strata of this stratigraphic level are buried beneath younger platform sediments of Oligocene or later age (Larue, 1991, 1994, this volume; Frost and Schellekens, 1991; Montgomery et al., 1991, this volume). Tertiary deposits in the south form the predominantly tuffaceous Upper Paleocene to Eocene Jacaguas Group (Glover and Mattson, 1967, 1973; Mattson, 1967, 1968a,b), the basal unit of which is the Miramar conglomerate. Carbonate deposits within this sedimentary package (Cuevas Limestone) were dated to the early Eocene (Glover and Mattson, 1967) (see Fig. 2), similar to foraminiferal ages reported for the Corozal Limestone of the north coast (Montgomery, this volume). Contorted ribbon-like fragments from the Jacaguas Group are exposed at many places along the boundary (Mattson, 1967, 1968a,b; Glover and Mattson, 1973; Glover, 1982), and are used in Figure 1 to separate the central and western volcanic provinces. Late Cretaceous and Eocene erosion removed Maastrichtian to Eocene strata in the southeastern part of the province, except a small remnant of upper Paleocene tuff (Cuyón Formation; Glover, 1967) in the Cayey quadrangle.

WESTERN VOLCANIC PROVINCE

Western Puerto Rico is subdivided into three principal components from southwest to northeast (Fig. 6A) as follows: (1) a pre-arc complex of ultramafic rocks and associated pelagic sediment (Mariquita Chert) and altered MORB-like basalt (Cajul Basalt and Las Palmas amphibolite melange) in the southwest; (2) two isolated domains (Rosario and San German Domains) of Campanian volcanic and sedimentary strata (Sabana Grande, Boquerón, Lajas, Cotui Limestone, El Rayo, and Monte Grande Formations) engulfed by serpentinized peridotite in the central part of the province; (3) Campanian to Eocene subaerial, predominantly pyroclastic accumulations (Río Blanco–Lago Garzas and Anón Formations) together with flanking deltaic fan deposits (Yauco [Curet, 1986; Larue et al., 1991a] and Río Culebrinas [Tobisch, 1968] Formations). These three components form subparallel northwest-southeast–trending belts parallel to the boundary with the central volcanic province. Hence the trend intersects volcanic belts of the central province at an angle of about 30° (Fig. 1).

Pre-arc complex

Distribution of lithologic types. The pre-arc complex in Puerto Rico, consisting of materials generated prior to deposition of subduction-related island arc volcanic rocks, incorporates three rock types that, in modern suites, are most commonly associated with ocean basins. These include (1) partly recrystallized radiolarian chert ranging in age from Lower Jurassic to Upper Cretaceous, representing pelagic sediments of the pre-arc oceanic crust (Krushensky and Monroe, 1978a,b; Schellekens et al., 1991; Montgomery et al., 1994a,b); (2) spinel-peridotite, most of which is partly to completely serpentinized, representing lithospheric upper mantle (Mattson, 1964, 1979; Hess and Otalora, 1964; Frey, 1988, p. 173-174); (3) amphibolite and altered basalt of uncertain age, with depleted normalized light rare earth element (LREE) distributions similar to modern N-MORB, representing altered Mesozoic mid-ocean ridge basalts of pre-arc oceanic crust (Mattson, 1960; Volckmann, 1984a-d; Schellekens et al., 1991). The entire pre-arc complex is a melange (Joyce, 1986; Joyce et al., 1987a) composed of blocks, ranging in size from pebble clasts to kilometer-long rafts of altered basalt and chert, incorporated chaotically within highly sheared serpentinite (Mattson, 1960, 1973; Tobisch, 1968). Characteristically, individual blocks are lozenge shaped with rounded or beveled edges normally oriented parallel to foliation in the surrounding serpentinite. There are no metamorphic aureoles along contacts of the various rock types (Volckmann, 1984a-d).

Pelagic chert. The Mariquita Chert (Mattson, 1973; Volckmann, 1984d; Schellekens et al., 1991; Montgomery et al., 1994a,b) of the Sierra Bermeja complex (Fig. 6B) consists predominantly of recrystallized radiolarian chert of predominantly Upper Jurassic age, but material with Lower Jurassic assemblages is also reported. Red-ribbon chert was attributed to a spreading oceanic ridge environment, but other lithologic types are pelagic in nature (Montgomery et al., 1994b). Ages of chert from the Sierra Bermeja range from Lower Jurassic (about 195 Ma), Upper Jurassic (165 to 145 Ma), to Lower Cretaceous (130 to 113 Ma). Radiolarian assemblages are all of Pacific provenance (Montgomery et al., 1994a,b). Similar material is exposed farther west near El Combate beach at Punta Melones, where Campanian ages were reported (Schellekens et al., 1991). Additional siliceous sandstone and chert of shallow benthonic to neritic origin in the San German Domain (Fig. 6A) and at Media Quijada, were attributed to the Cenomanian and Turonian, respectively (Volckmann, 1984d; Montgomery et al., 1994b).

Serpentinized peridotite. Ultramafic rocks, with depleted rare earth patterns typical of upper mantle peridotite (Fig. 7A), occur in three interconnecting belts in southwestern Puerto Rico, surrounding tectonic domains of Campanian-Maastrichtian island arc volcanic strata (Fig. 7A). Detailed investigation by members of the

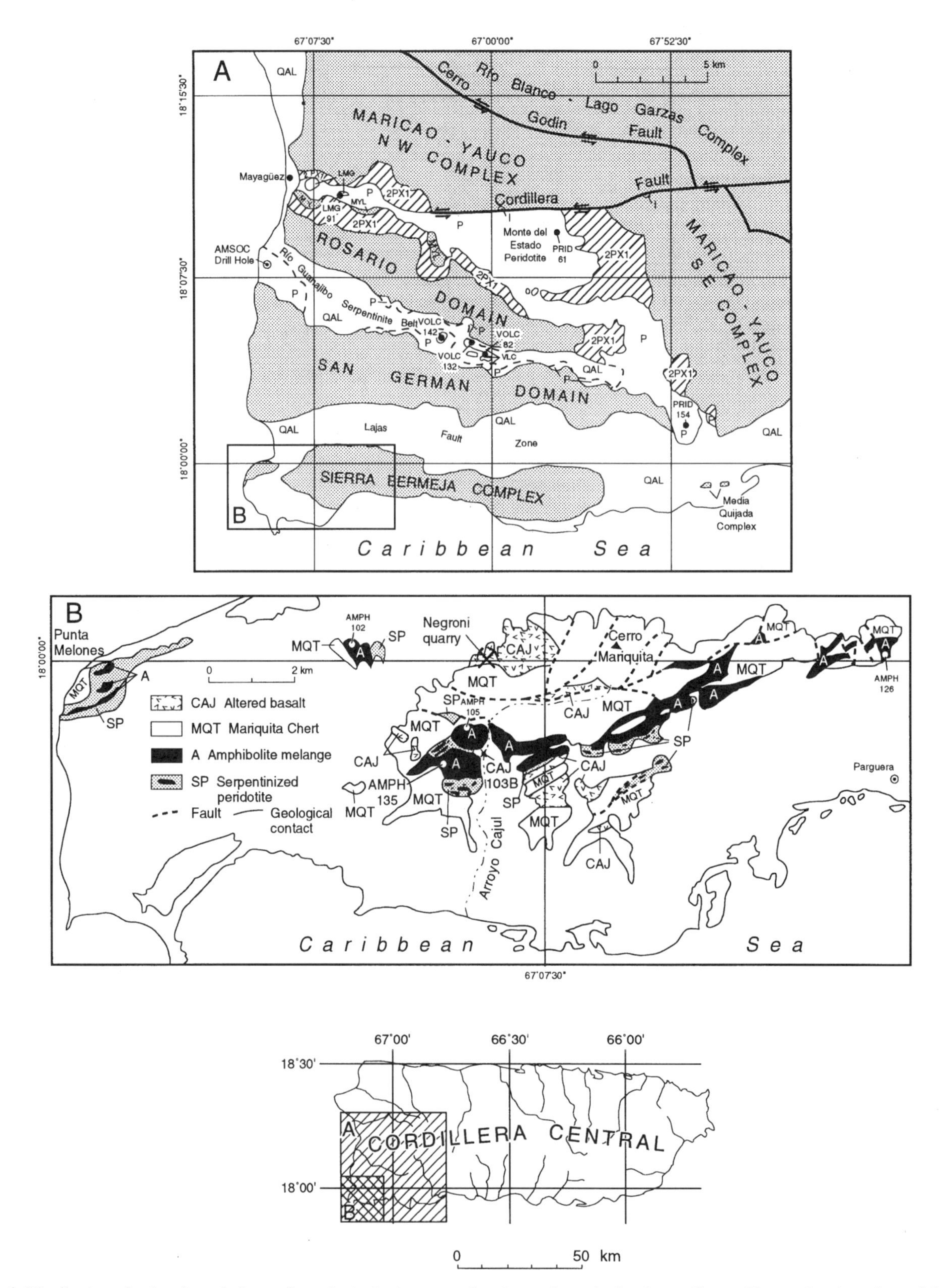

Figure 6. Distribution of volcanic and ultramafic rocks in the western volcanic province. A, Southwest Puerto Rico: volcanic rocks and the Sierra Bermeja complex are shaded; 2PXI, two-pyroxene intrusive basalts (Río Loco Formation of Slodowski, 1956) are stippled; LMG, Las Mesas Greenstone and amphibolite blocks in serpentinite; VLC, blocks of unnamed volcanic rocks in serpentinite; P, serpentinized peridotite; QAL, Quaternary alluvium; I, location of pluton bisected by the Cordillera Fault (McIntyre, 1975). B, Sierra Bermeja region and Arroyo Cajul, modified from Volckmann (1984a-d), illustrating exposures of serpentinized spinel peridotite melange containing numerous blocks of amphibolite (SP), Mariquita Chert (MQT), Las Palmas amphibolite melange (A), and altered Cajul Basalt (CAJ). Location of buried pre-Oligocene (pre–Juana Diáz) post–mid-Eocene (post-Jicara) Lajas Fault Zone is from Almy (1969). Sample numbers indicate location of analyzed altered basalts from the Sierra Bermeja complex illustrated in Figure 6B.

U.S. Geological Survey and others has led to the interpretation that the belts formed through crustal extension produced by diapiric protrusion of cold upper mantle lithosphere into the overlying island arc complex (Krushensky and Monroe, 1978b; Volckmann, 1984a-c; Curet, 1986; Joyce et al., 1987a,b; Schellekens et al., 1991). The peridotites are highly sheared and extensively serpentinized, and in many areas, especially where belts are narrow, rafts and blocks of younger rock types are included.

The term Sierra Bermeja Complex, originally applied by Mattson (1960) to all three ultramafic belts in western Puerto Rico, is here used only in association with the discontinuous belt exposed in the east-west–oriented range of the same name along the southwestern coast (Fig. 6). The most extensive ultramafic concentration is the southeasterly trending northern belt (identified as Monte del Estado Peridotite in Figs. 6 and 8B), which reaches a maximum width over 5 km in the vicinity of Monte del Estado. This body, highly resistant to weathering and erosion, contains abundant fresh spinel-bearing lherzolite and harzburgite peridotite in central parts of the mass. A narrow and highly serpentinized central belt (Río Guanajibo Serpentinite Belt) (Fig.

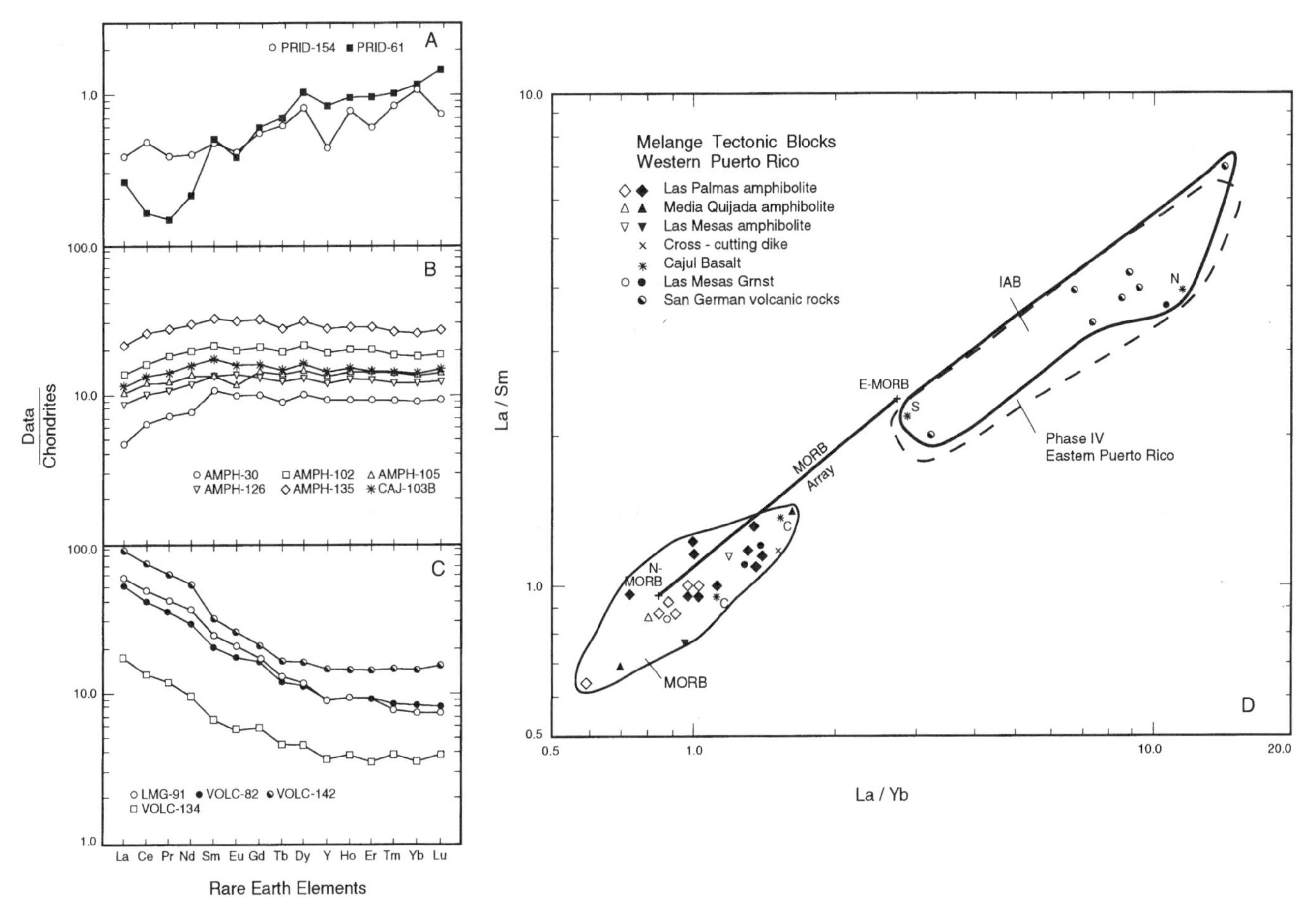

Figure 7. A-C, Chondrite-normalized (factors of Sun and McDonough, 1989) rare earth element (REE) patterns of some rocks from the western volcanic province; ICP-MS analyses performed by S. Jackson at the Memorial University of Newfoundland; see Jolly et al. (Chapter 3, this volume) for analytic methods and errors. A, Spinel peridotite from Monte del Estado Peridotite: PRID-154, lherzolite; PRID-61, dunitic harzburgite. B, MORB-like amphibolites and altered basalts: AMPH-30, Media Quijada amphibolite; AMPH-102, 126, and 135, Las Palmas Amphibolite; AMPH-105, actinolite-bearing dike cross-cutting amphibolite in Arroyo Cajul (Fig. 6B); CAJ-103B, MORB-like Cajul Basalt from type section (denoted by symbol * in Fig. 7B) in Arroyo Cajul; sample localities are given in Figure 6. C, Arc basalts from blocks included in serpentinite at Las Mesas (near Mayagüez, LMG) and San German (VLC); see Fig. 7B for locations of the blocks. The rocks display high REE slopes unlike early lavas from the northeastern and central volcanic provinces, but closely resemble materials from volcanic phase IV (lavas of the Boquerón–Lajas–Maguayo–Monte Grande–El Rayo complex in the west). D, La/Sm and La/Yb ratios of tectonic blocks in melanges from western Puerto Rico, illustrating the two basalt types present, including both MORB-like and arc-like basalts. MORB data from Sun and McDonough (1989). Filled symbols, new data; empty symbols, data from Schellekens et al. (1991). Locations of analyzed Cajul Basalt from the Sierra Bermeja complex as follows: *N, arc-like basalt from the Negroni quarry on the northern border of the complex (Fig. 8B); *S, arc-like basalt from the southern margin of the complex; *C, MORB-like basalt from the central part of the complex near Arroyo Cajul; other sample localities given in Fig. 6A,B.

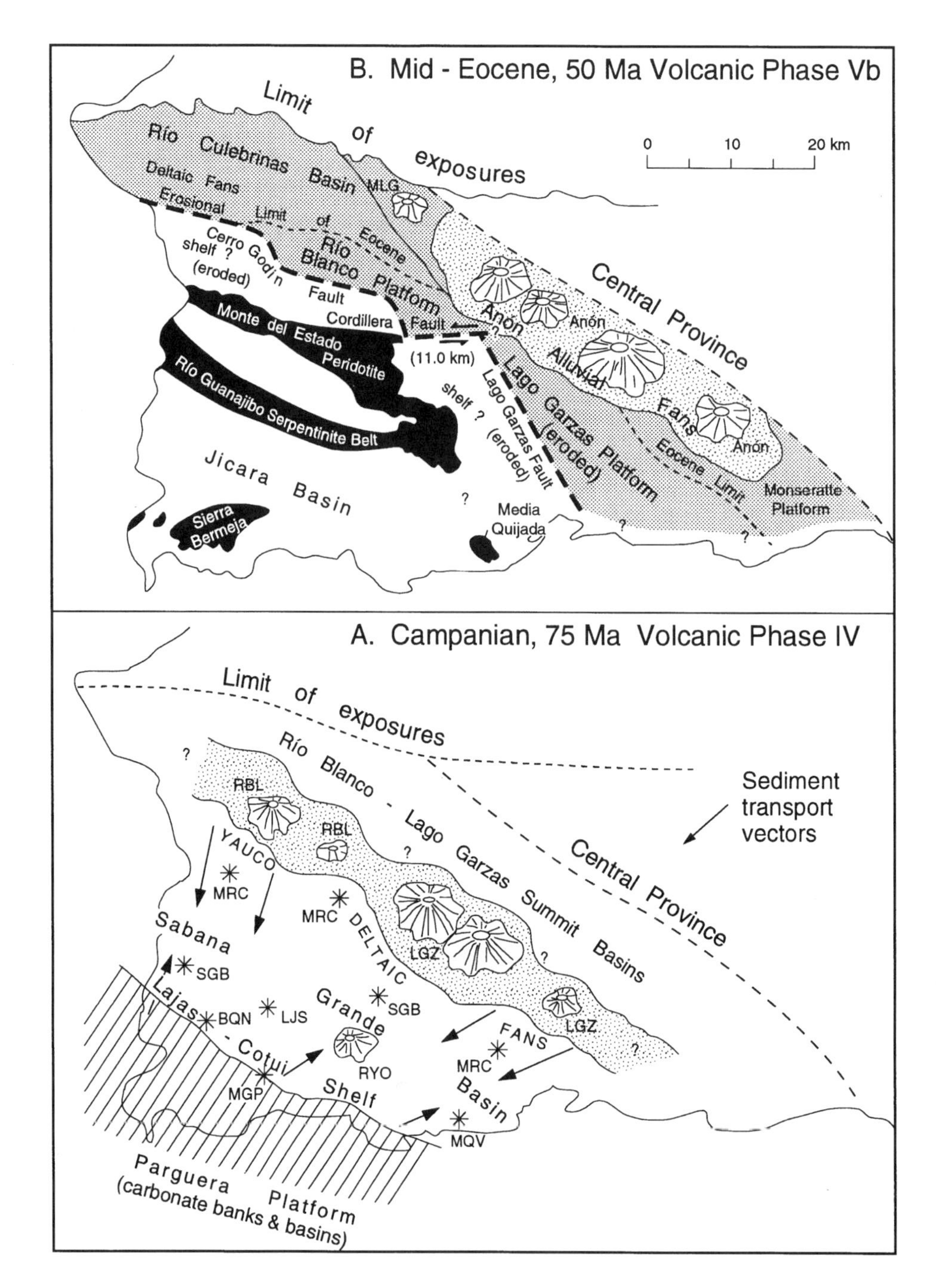

Figure 8. Paleogeographic evolution of the western volcanic province. A, Campanian, 75 Ma (volcanic phase IV); subaerial Río Blanco–Lago Garzas strato-volcanic accumulations of the principal axis of volcanism are aligned diagonally across the province, flanked on the south by deltaic fans of the Yauco Formation, and the Sabana Grande basin, with scattered volcanic accumulations (modified from Larue et al., 1991a). In the southwest corner, the Parguera platform and associated Lajas shelf form a complex topographic feature. Shelf volcanism gave rise to a second, Cotui platform in the Maastrichtian (Santos, 1995). BQN, Boquerón Basalt; MGP, Maguayo Porphyry (Schellekens et al., 1991); LJS, Lajas Formation; RYO, El Rayo Formation; MQV, Media Quijada volcanic rocks (Krushensky and Monroe, 1978b); SBG, Sabana Grande Formation; MRC, Maricao Basalt; RBL, Río Blanco Formation; LGZ, Lago Garzas Formation. Arrows represent sediment transport vectors from Larue et al. (1991a). B, Mid-Eocene, 50 Ma (volcanic phase V); subaerial Anón volcano-stratigraphic complexes are aligned along the border of the central province, parallel to and apparently onlapping the earlier Río Blanco–Lago Garzas belt. Deltaic fans and other shelf deposits are preserved in the northern Río Culebrinas Formation, but have been eroded(?) from Río Blanco–Lago Garzas platforms and the adjoining shelfs. The platform obstructed Anón volcanic debris from entering the Jicara basin, in which deep sea shale predominates. Ultramafic bodies and the Cordillera, Cerro Godin, and Lago Garzas Faults, of Upper Maastrichtian age, are shown for comparison; map symbols in Figure 5.

6A), trending east-southeast along the Río Guanajibo Valley, intersects the northern belt on the border between the Sabana Grande and Yauco quadrangles (Fig. 3). The belt was cored to a depth of 305 m by the Earth Sciences Division of the National Academy of Sciences (AMSOC project, Mattson, 1964; see Fig. 6A). Representative samples from the core were subsequently analyzed by Frey (1988). Although highly serpentinized, original modal mineralogy can be determined from preserved crystal habits, and Hess and Otalora (1964) reported lherzolite ($ol_{67}opx_{19.5}cpx_{10.5}sp_3$), harzburgite ($ol_{75}opx_{15}cpx_7sp_3$), and dunite ($ol_{95}opx_2sp_3$) peridotite were all present.

Altered MORB-like oceanic basalt. In the discontinuous east-west–trending Sierra Bermeja Range (Fig. 6B), in more localized exposures at Media Quijada (Fig. 6A), and in several quarries east of the Mayagüez (Mattson, 1960; Schellekens et al., 1991) areas, a matrix of highly sheared serpentinite engulfs huge tectonic blocks up to a kilometer in length (Mattson, 1960, 1973; Mattson et al., 1973; Mattson and Pessagno, 1979; McIntyre, 1975; Wadge et al., 1983; Joyce, 1986; Joyce et al., 1987a,b; Schellekens et al., 1991). Most consist of MORB-like amphibolite and altered basalt of oceanic ridge affinity (Fig. 7B,D) and pelagic chert, but blocks of island arc volcanic rocks and associated subvolcanic intrusives (Fig. 7C,D), and of Upper Cretaceous limestone, are also present (Mattson, 1973; Krushensky and Monroe, 1977).

In the central part of the Sierra Bermeja Complex, the Las Palmas amphibolite melange forms two discontinuous, subparallel belts about 10 km in length, trending east-northeastward across the central part of the belt (Fig. 6B). The relatively linear southern boundary of the Las Palmas belt has been interpreted as a fault or low-angle thrust (Mattson, 1960, 1979; Joyce et al., 1987b; Schellekens, 1993). The melange consists of a concentration of amphibolite blocks of strongly foliated hornblende gneiss and foliated to massive hornblende schist, intruded by actinolite-bearing dikes of identical composition (Fig. 7B). K-Ar ages of hornblendes from Las Palmas amphibolites (Mattson, 1964; Tobisch, 1968; Cox et al., 1977) display a wide range from Early (126 ± 3 and 110 ± 3.3 Ma) to Late (86.3 ± 8.6 and 84.9 ± 8.5 Ma) Cretaceous, much younger than ages of associated radiolarian chert. The variations probably reflect multiple periods of metamorphism rather than the actual time of MORB volcanism. Spatially associated altered MORB-like basalt, assigned to the Cajul Basalt (Mattson, 1960; Volckmann, 1984d), occurs as blocks within serpentinite, best exposed in Arroyo Cajul (Fig. 6B). Large rafts of similar amphibolite and MORB-like basalt (Fig. 7D), included in Las Mesas Greenstones (Schellekens et al., 1991), are exposed at Mayagüez (Fig. 6A) within the Monte del Estado Peridotite belt, and at Media Quijada.

Emplacement of pre-arc complex

Mariquita chert and altered MORB-like basalt. Stratigraphic relations between rock types, or even between adjacent boulders, are difficult to reconstruct in the jumble of floating blocks that comprise the serpentinite melange. The diverse temporal and lithologic assemblage of the Mariquita Chert also contains diverse radiolarian fauna primarily of equatorial origin, but apparently also from higher paleolatitudes. Montgomery et al. (1994b) viewed the unit as a collection of fragments derived by accumulation of offscraped strata transported to a subduction zone and subsequently stored as an accretionary complex in the trench zone (see also Joyce et al., 1987a).

Chert is interlayered with MORB-like Cajul Basalt in the central part of the belt, suggesting this suite represents the upper part of the transition zone from oceanic basalt to pelagic sediment within the original oceanic crust. If this interpretation is correct, the Cajul Basalt is similar in age to the oldest chert beds preserved in the belt, that is, Lower Jurassic. Alternatively, these basalts, and similar MORB-like basalts (Las Mesas Greenstones east of Mayagüez), might represent remnants of the Caribbean Cretaceous Basalt Plateau recognized throughout the Caribbean basin (120 to 88 Ma) (Donnelly, 1989, 1994).

MORB-like amphibolite, also concentrated in the central the Sierra Bermeja Complex, is cut by younger actinolite-bearing, MORB-like dikes of upper greenschist paragenesis (Fig. 7B-D, sample AMPH-105), demonstrating that generation of hornblende occurred during the pre-arc oceanic phase. Therefore, amphibolites are inferred to represent the relatively high-temperature sole of the basaltic oceanic crust. The widespread distribution of MORB-like basalt at Las Palmas, Punta Melones, Media Quijada, and Las Mesas suggests these rocks represent the pre-arc basement of the entire western province.

Serpentinized peridotite. Emplacement of peridotite occurred over an extended interval. Conglomerate containing weathered serpentinite clasts occur in upper Mariquita Chert at Media Quijada, in the Oligocene Juana Díaz Formation, and perhaps at the base of the Yauco Formation (Krushensky and Monroe, 1978b), suggesting serpentinite was exposed periodically during at least a 50 m.y. period. The principal Upper Maastrichtian (Krushensky and Monroe, 1978b) protrusion event was associated with movement along the Cordillera fault (Fig. 6A and 8B), where approximately 11 km of displacement was generated (McIntyre, 1975).

Arc-like basalt. Blocks of basalt with incompatible element-enriched island arc signatures (Fig. 7c) (Schellekens et al., 1991) are incorporated in serpentinite, together with MORB-like basalts, at numerous localities (in the western Las Mesas area near Mayagüez, in the San German region, and along the north and south borders of the Sierra Bermeja Complex) (Fig. 7D). The rocks have generally been inferred to be arc materials caught up in the serpentinite protrusion event, and Schellekens et al. (1991), Larue et al. (1991b), Schellekens (1993), and Larue (1994) suggested they represent fragmented remnants of early, pre-Campanian island arcs. However, mantle-normalized rare earth element patterns (Fig. 7C) reveal the basalts to be much more incompatible element-enriched than Albian lavas (this chapter, and Schellekens, 1993) from either the central (Formation A) or northeastern (Daguao Formation) volcanic provinces. Compositions more closely resemble Campanian-Maastrichtian lavas from the Boquerón, Lajas, and El Rayo Formations and the Maguayo Porphyry in southwestern Puerto Rico (cf. Schellekens et al., 1991). It seems likely, therefore, the arc-like basalts are Campanian in age, and were derived from the base of the exposed arc stratigraphic pile. Parguera-Cotui–like limestone blocks occur in serpentinite at many localities, especially at Yauco (Krushensky and Monroe, 1978b), consistent with such an interpretation.

Island arc volcanic strata

Campanian-Maastrichtian volcanism. Campanian-Maastrichtian volcanic strata form a belt trending broadly parallel to the boundary with the central volcanic province (Fig. 1). The belt is about 20 km wide, and is itself composed of two discrete components.

1. The first component is an eastern zone of mostly subaerial, highly amygdaloidal volcanic breccia of the Lago Garzas (Mattson, 1967, 1968a,b; Krushensky and Monroe, 1975, 1978a,b) and Río Blanco (McIntyre, 1971; McIntyre et al., 1970) Formations, representing primary subaerial vent-related facies; these rocks were subsequently grouped by Krushensky and Curet (1984) into the andesitic plagioclase-augite–bearing Lago Garzas lithofacies.

2. The second component is a marine sequence of fine- to coarse-grained, thin-bedded sandstone and shale of the Yauco Formation, representing near-shore deltaic deposits derived by fluvial degradation of vent zone accumulations a few kilometers to the northeast (Curet, 1986; Larue et al., 1991a). Yauco sediments are accompanied by pockets of volcanic breccia and subvolcanic intrusives of Maricao basalt, constituting the augite-rich Maricao lithofacies. Hornblende appears late in the Maastrichtian in this region, as illustrated by the Concepcíon Formation (McIntyre, 1971, 1974; McIntyre et al., 1970), which contains mixtures of the Lago Garzas lithofacies with plagioclase-augite-hornblende–bearing basalt of the Anón lithofacies. Anón-like lavas are also interlayered with the Yauco Formation in the Monte Guillarte quadrangle (Fig. 3; Krushensky and Curet, 1984), where hornblende-bearing Anón-like tuff is mixed with Maricao basalt.

Yauco deltaic sediments and Río Blanco–Lago Garzas breccia are extensively intruded by subvolcanic dikes, sills, and stocks (not shown in Fig. 1), many of which are brecciated feeders. Plutons containing mineralogic assemblages of all recognized lithofacies (Krushensky and Monroe, 1978b) have been reported, including abundant, presumably Tertiary-age hornblende dacite identical to that of the Anón lithofacies. Lithofacies present in the region include two-pyroxene (hypersthene-augite) basalts that occur as intrusives of Campanian-Maastrichtian age concentrated along the margins of the Monte del Estado Peridotite belt (Figs. 1 and 6A) and in the Sierra Bermeja Complex (Fig. 6B), as well as in lava flows mixed with other rock types throughout the sequence. The two-pyroxene intrusive bodies predate peridotite protrusion (McIntyre, 1971; Curet, 1986) and probably represent opportunistic underplating by arc-related magmas along the density contrast generated by the arc crust–upper mantle boundary.

Southwest of the Lago Garzas–Río Blanco and Yauco-Maricao complexes, and surrounded by serpentinized peridotite, are two isolated domains of Campanian rocks containing abundant epiclastic sedimentary deposits and reef limestone units together with several localized eruptive centers (Curet, 1986; Volckmann, 1984a-d). The northern Rosario domain (Fig. 6A) contains material similar to the Yauco-Maricao lithofacies, but Campanian Cotui-like limestone, andesitic sandstone, and related lava and volcanic breccia of the Sabana Grande Formation, together with subvolcanic plagioclase-phyric intrusive bodies (Mattson, 1960; Volckmann, 1984a,b) (see Fig. 1) are also present. The complex southern San German domain (Fig. 6A) contains (Santos, 1995) additional Yauco and Sabana Grande strata and several isolated equivalent volcanic units including the Lower Campanian Boquerón Basalt and the mid-Campanian Lajas Formation and Cotui Limestone. These strata are capped by an unnamed platform limestone in the west, volcanic breccia and sandstone of the Monte Grande Formation in the central part of the domain, and deeper water mudstone of the "Upper" Yauco of Volckman (1984d) in the east (Figs. 2 and 3). The Cretaceous stratigraphic sequence is concluded by the partly subaerial El Rayo volcanic complex of Maastrichtian age. All volcanic rocks in the southern domains carry hornblende-bearing phenocryst assemblages.

Paleogeographic reconstructions. Larue et al. (1991a) suggested the simplest interpretation consistent with geographic and stratigraphic relations in the western province is that the dispersed, relatively thin volcanic strata in the Rosario and San German domains represent lateral counterparts of more the extensive contemporaneous vent-related Lago Garzas–Río Blanco Formations. Between these two geographic provinces, the Yauco Formation, which also contains several volcanic concentrations of eruptive rocks (Maricao Basalt) (Fig. 1), represents near-shore turbidites of both deltaic and fluvial origin (Fig. 8A). This interpretation is reinforced by continuous development of carbonate reefs (Parguera, Melones, and Cotui Limestones) (Almy, 1969; Santos, 1990) on the complex Parguera platforms during most of Campanian and Maastrichtian time. In particular, the Cotui rudistid reef developed on a platform of Lower Campanian Lajas and related volcanogenic materials (Santos, 1990). Larue et al. (1991b) and Larue (1994) suggested the presence of a Campanian (Parguera) carbonate platform complex in the vicinity of the Sierra Bermeja region (Figs. 6A and 8A) is consistent with pre-Campanian block faulting. Krushensky and Monroe (1978b), noting the presence of serpentinite clasts in Cenomanian-Turonian Mariquita Chert at Media Quijada, also suggested periodic pre-arc faulting in the region. Almy et al. (this volume) suggested the western province has undergone extensive left-lateral strike-slip faulting, and that the individual tectonic blocks (domains) originated in more westerly locations. Motion on the strike-slip fault was subparallel to geologic boundaries, minimizing the effect on distribution of lithofacies in the region.

In his paleogeographic model of arc development, Schellekens (1993, this volume) proposed a much more complex model in which the western volcanic province was viewed as a fore-arc basin, deposited on the leading edge of the arc. A change from low to high TiO_2 in lavas within the Yauco Formation was interpreted as evidence of decreasing degree of fusion during Upper Campanian–Lower Maastrichtian rifting associated with a reversal in orientation of the subduction zone from northeast- to southwest-dipping. Thus, it was suggested the original Yauco fore-arc basin was gradually transformed during deposition to a behind-the-arc environment. Smith et al. (this volume) extended the model, and correlated intrusion of the Utuado and San Lorenzo plutons (Fig. 1) with reversal of polarity in Maastrichtian time.

Lower Tertiary (upper Paleocene–Eocene) volcanism

Distribution of volcanic strata. Río Blanco–Lago Garzas volcanism was succeeded in the upper Paleocene by eruption of a thick sheet of highly amygdular, pillowed plagioclase-augite–bearing lava of the Mal Paso Formation, and associated tuffaceous accumulations of the Palma Escrita Formation. The rocks are concentrated along a fault boundary that separates Cenomanian-Maastrichtian and Cenozoic strata (McIntyre, 1975), and are interlayered with hornblende-bearing tuff, resembling the Anón lithofacies (Krushensky and Curet, 1984). In their map of the Monte Guillarte quadrangle (Figs. 1 and 3), Krushensky and Curet (1984) abandoned use of earlier Mal Paso (McIntyre, 1971) and Palma Escrita Formations (McIntyre, 1971, 1974), and instead designated these units as part of a mixed Anón–Lago Garzas lithofacies. For the sake of consistency, the more detailed original terminology is retained in Figure 1, and strata composed principally of oxidized, amygdular lavas are included within the Mal Paso Formation.

The youngest arc volcanic deposits of the western volcanic province form a northwest–southeast oriented belt (Dolan et al., 1991), called the Eocene belt by Erikson et al. (1990, 1991), Schellekens et al. (1991), Larue (1994), and Schellekens (1993), ranging from 5 to 10 km in width. The principal unit in the Eocene Belt is the Anón Formation (Mattson, 1967, 1968a,b), composed primarily of alluvial fans, dacitic tuff, and vent-related concentrations of lava, commonly extensively intruded by subvolcanic feeder stocks and dikes (Nelson and Monroe, 1967a,b; Nelson and Tobisch, 1967, 1968; McIntyre, 1971, 1975; Tobisch and Turner, 1971; Krushensky and Monroe, 1975, 1978a,b; Krushensky and Curet, 1984); these rocks form the Anón lithofacies of Krushensky (1978) and Krushensky and Curet (1984). To simplify the map and correlation chart (Figs. 1 and 2), tuff and volcanic breccia of the localized Matilde and Milagros Formations of Nelson and Tobisch (1968) are included within the Anón Formation, their lateral equivalent.

Anón and earlier Río Blanco–Lago Garzas strata are normally separated by strike-slip faults oriented parallel to depositional trends along the arc, obscuring contact relations. Widespread distribution of subvolcanic intrusives identical to Anón lavas within areas of Campanian strata is taken as evidence that Anón materials form an integral part of the volcanic assemblage of the western volcanic province. Supporting such a view, McIntyre (1974) reported the contact between the Upper Maastrichtian Concepcíon and upper Paleocene Palma Escrita Formations is unconformable not tectonic in nature in the northern Maricao quadrangle. This interpretation, later disputed by Krushensky (1978), is retained in this compilation, because a similar depositional hiatus is reported in other parts of the island (Fig. 2). Several authors (Pindell and Barrett, 1990; Erikson et al., 1990; Pindell, 1994; Pindell et al., 1988) suggested Eocene belt strata represent products of rifting, but trace element data are inconsistent with such an origin, since all volcanic rocks display typical arc-like trace element signatures (Schellekens, 1993, this volume). In addition, sedimentologic evidence of rifting has not been reported (Erikson et al., 1991).

Paleogeographic reconstructions. Mattson (1967, 1968a,b) identified three areas along the Anón belt dominated by hornblende-plagioclase dacite lava flows (in the southeastern Jayüya, the central Adjuntas, and along the border between the Monte Guillarte and Adjuntas quadrangles) (Figs. 1 and 3), illustrated as volcanic centers in Figure 8B. The northern part of the Anón belt contains marine tuff breccia, lapilli tuff breccia, and coarse volcanic breccia of the Milagros Formation (Tobisch and Turner, 1971). Deltaic fan deposits (Río Culebrinas Formation) (Figs. 1 and 2) are extensively preserved in the Rincón and San Sebastían quadrangles (Fig. 3), but equivalent strata have been eroded from other parts of the province (shown as Río Blanco and Lago Garzas platforms and associated shelf in Fig. 8B). During Eocene volcanism, detritus from the Anón Formation and equivalents were apparently obstructed from entering the basin by intervening topographic features produced by the older Lago Garzas–Río Blanco volcanic pile, or eroded during the Cenozoic. Therefore, siliceous deep sea sediments of the Jicara Formation (Mattson et al., 1971, 1973; Volckmann, 1984c; Donnelly et al., 1990) are the only deposits of Tertiary age present in the southwest (Figs. 1, 2, and 8B). Jicara shale unconformably overlies Maastrichtian strata north of Sierra Bermeja (Volckmann, 1984c), indicating the ubiquitous lower Paleocene regression observed throughout Puerto Rico lowered sea level below the elevation of the arc platform, parts of which had never before been exposed to erosion.

Age of initial arc volcanism

All taxa reported from the Yauco and Sabana Grande Formations range into the Campanian and Maastrichtian, and no known fauna restricted to earlier periods are present (Pessagno, 1960, 1962; Krushensky and Monroe, 1978b). Thus, it was concluded above these formations date from Santonian time. The presence of blocks of arc-like volcanic rocks and limestone of Campanian to Maastrichtian age incorporated in serpentinite, together with MORB-like basalts (Fig. 7B,D), is consistent with this interpretation. Moreover, exposures of Cenomanian to Santonian Mariquita Chert in the San German area (Volckmann, 1984d) consist of cherty sandstone of benthonic or neritic origin (Schellekens et al., 1991). The only clear evidence of pre-Santonian arc volcanic activity are the sandy tuffaceous lenses in upper (Cenomanian to Turonian) Mariquita Chert at San German (Figs. 2 and 6B) (Volckmann, 1984d; Schellekens et al., 1991) and cherty sandstone and sandstone-clast conglomerate at Media Quijada (Krushensky and Monroe, 1978b; Schellekens et al., 1991; Montgomery et al., 1994a,b), perhaps representing eruptions from a distant arc source. It is inferred, therefore, the western Puerto Rican basement was transported into the active volcanic zone of the arc later than other volcanic provinces. Volcanism in the western province commenced in the Santonian–Lower Campanian, coincident with initiation of volcanic phase IV and immediately following left-lateral strike-slip faulting associated with the Cerro Mula Fault (Fig. 1) in the central province. It is natural to conclude by inference, therefore, that the western province was first emplaced near the axis of volcanism at this time (about 85 Ma) (Fig. 2), and that the original western extension of volcanic belts in the central volcanic province (Fig. 5) were displaced southeastward into the Caribbean. Subaerial or shallow marine volcanism characterized Campanian volcanic rocks almost from the beginning (Larue et al., 1991a), indicating translation of the block produced a shallower than normal ocean floor.

ORIGIN OF BOUNDARIES BETWEEN VOLCANIC PROVINCES

Boundary of northeastern volcanic province

According to current views, based largely on preserved radiolarian fauna in chert of pre-island arc pelagic sediments (Mattson and Pessagno, 1979; Schellekens et al, 1991; Montgomery et al., 1994a,b), the Caribbean plate originated as a part of the now largely disappeared Farallon plate within the eastern Mesozoic Pacific basin (Burke, 1988; Donnelly, 1989; Donnelly et al., 1990; Pindell and Barrett, 1990; Lebron and Perfit, 1994; Montgomery et al., 1994a,b). The Greater Antilles, including Puerto Rico, Hispaniola, and Jamaica (Burke, 1988), plus perhaps Cuba (Pindell and Barrett, 1990), were gradually marginalized by left-lateral strike-slip faulting generated by friction along the northern boundary of the arc. Due to greater frictional resistance between thick slices of island arc volcanic strata compared with serpentinized upper mantle peridotite, the transcurrent faults became locked when island arc blocks were brought into contact. This process produced extensive en echelon arrangement of slices along the plate boundary that ultimately gave rise to the modern Greater Antilles. The principal strike-slip fault forming the boundary between the northeastern and central volcanic provinces in Puerto Rico (the Cerro Mula fault of mid-Santonian age) (Figs. 1 and 2) represents the initial recognizable left-lateral movement. Donnelly (1989) suggested left-lateral displacement in this zone was initiated when eastward movement of the Pacific Farallon plate shifted from northeastward to a more easterly orientation in association with development of the East Pacific Rise about 85 Ma. This period was marked by several other major tectonic events, however, including termination of the Caribbean Cretaceous Basalt Province (88 Ma) (Donnelly, 1989) in the Pacific basin, and collision between Hispaniola and the Bahama banks (about 90 Ma) (Joyce, 1991).

Boundary of western volcanic province

Tectonic relations between the western and central volcanic provinces (Fig. 9) are obscure, because strata in this zone were highly sheared by intrusion of the Utuado Stock (Fig. 1), extensively metamorphosed by Eocene plutonic bodies (Mattson, 1967, 1968a,b), and deformed by a combination of left-lateral strike-slip faults and east-facing thrusts (Erikson et al., 1990, 1991). Matters are further complicated by disagreement about correlations of strata along the western margin of the Utuado Stock (Fig. 9). Augite-bearing sandstone exposed adjacent to the pluton, which becomes increasingly dominated by augite-bearing volcanic breccia toward the north, was originally mapped as Robles Formation (Mattson, 1968b). Krushensky and Monroe (1975) suggested the strata are dissimilar to typical Robles sandstone, and assigned them to the Anón Formation. Later Krushensky and Curet (1984) noted the absence of hornblende and abundance of augite and attributed the rocks instead to the Maricao basalt. Because typical Robles strata east of the Utuado pluton also grade northward from sandstone to mixed augite-rich basalt and sandstone accumulations of the Vista Allegre Formation, the original Robles designation is tentatively retained in this compilation. Robles strata in the northern part of the belt are intruded by five dacitic stocks similar in appearance to Eocene lavas from the spatially associated Jobos (central province) and Anón (western province) Formations.

Provenance of Eocene belt volcanic strata. A basic problem contributing to uncertainty about the origin of the boundary of the western volcanic province concerns provenance of units in the Eocene belt (Fig. 9) and their stratigraphic and tectonic relations with adjacent strata. Tectonic models fall into three major groups: (1) the central and western volcanic provinces that were formed in place, subsequently covered by Eocene strata, and finally deformed by strike-slip faults and thrusts (Krushensky and Monroe, 1975; Krushensky, 1978; Joyce, 1985; Larue et al., 1991a; Schellekens, 1993); (2) Eocene strata that were deposited along the western boundary of the central province and subsequently deformed by collision with the western block (Erikson et al., 1990, 1991; Pindell and Barrett, 1990); and (3) Anón strata that were deposited along the eastern boundary of the western province and subsequently deformed by collision with the central tectonic block (Glover, 1971).

1. Strata in western and central provinces were deposited in place. Larue et al. (1991a) presented analysis of sedimentary fabrics within Santonian-Maastrichtian rocks on both sides of the boundary. The data revealed sediment transport was dominantly

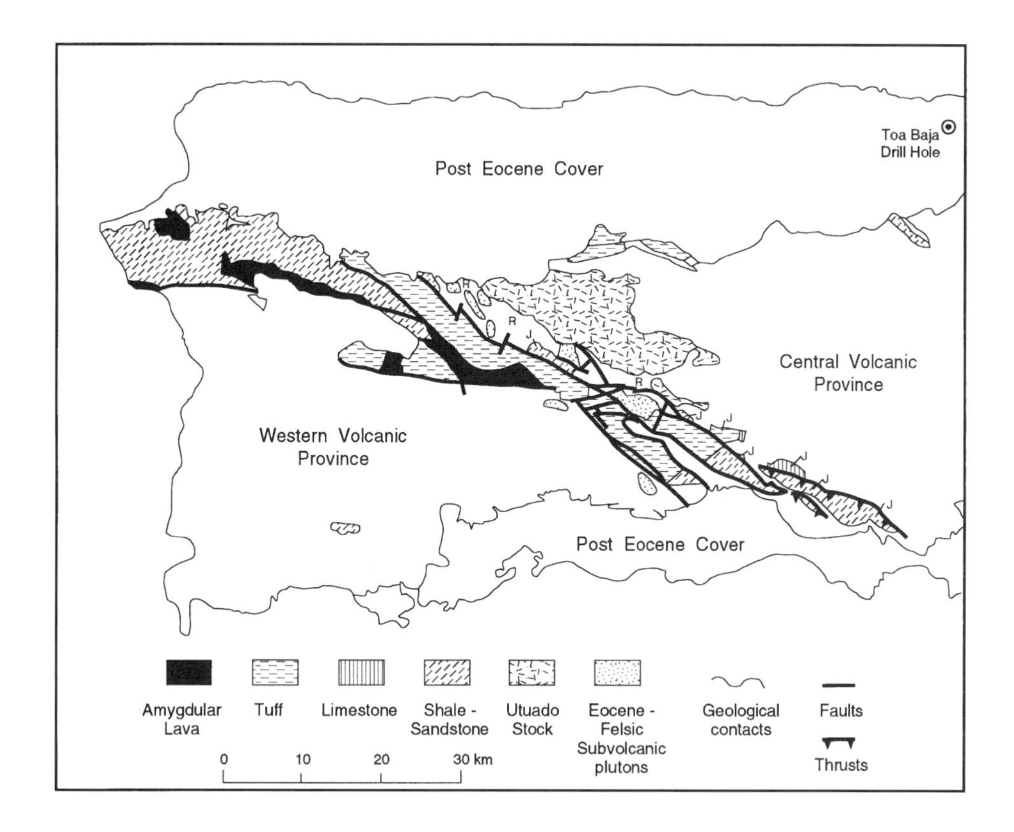

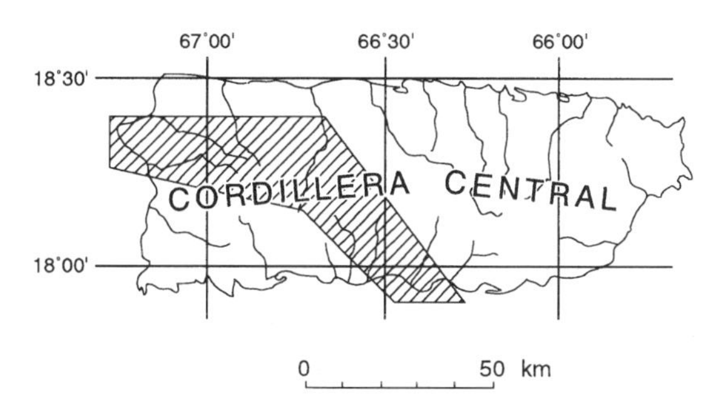

Figure 9. Detail of lithologic and structural features of the Eocene belt, western volcanic province, compiled from USGS quadrangle sheets (Figs. 1 and 3). Location of Toa Baja drill hole (Larue, 1991) is shown on post-Eocene platform; R, Robles Formation; J, Jacaguas Group.

westward in the Lago Garzas Formation, but southeastward in the adjacent Cariblanco Formation (Fig. 8A), consistent with an autochthonous origin of these units on the flanks of a northwest-southeast–trending belt of volcanic summits. A similar but more controversial model proposed by Krushensky and Monroe (1975) and Krushensky (1978) suggested the major phase of deformation produced southward gravity slides in Cretaceous strata. One of the principal difficulties faced by both models is the presence in eastern Puerto Rico of a contemporaneous east-west–trending volcanic belt (Pozas Formation and related units), which intersects the Eocene belt at an angle of about 30°, since intersecting belts are not observed in modern island arc systems generated by a single subduction zone (see, for example, Carr et al., 1990; Woodhead and Johnson, 1993).

2. *Anón and equivalent strata were autochthonous with Cariblanco-Coamo-Jacaguas strata and subsequently deformed by transpressive tectonism generated by collision with allochthonous western block.* Erikson et al. (1990, 1991) presented detailed structural fabric data from the Eocene belt that are consistent with transpressive tectonics trending approximately parallel to the belt. The model developed involved eastward translation of the western tectonic block, inferred to be composed of Lago

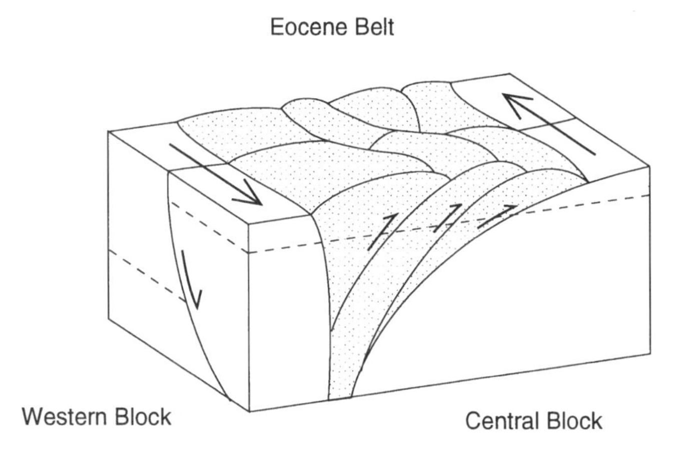

Figure 10. Hypothetical restored transpressive flower structure representing tectonic processes associated with deformation of the Eocene volcanic belt, between the central and western tectonic blocks, modified from Erikson et al. (1990, 1991). Left-lateral transpressive strike-slip faults and a later inferred normal fault have juxtaposed Cretaceous strata of the Puerto Rican Cordillera with thrust-faulted Eocene rocks.

Garzas and equivalent units, and collision with the central block and fringing Eocene belt, producing a flower structure (Fig. 10) dominated by strike-slip faults at deeper levels and by thrusting at shallow levels. This model relegates to a fore-arc setting contemporaneous Late Cretaceous Alonzo-Pozas (volcanic phase IV) and Eocene Jobos-Guaracanal (phase V) strata in the central province, and extensive Eocene volcanic strata buried by post-volcanic platform sediments along the north coast (Larue, 1991, this volume; Montgomery, this volume). Moreover, the presence of abundant, Anón-like subvolcanic intrusive bodies within Lago Garzas–Río Blanco and Yauco-Maricao strata, and the subparallel orientation of the two western volcanic belts is not explained by the model. Erikson et al. (1991) concluded their model was also consistent with allochthonous behavior of the Eocene belt with respect to the central tectonic block.

3. Anón and equivalent strata (western block) were allochthonous with respect to the Jacaguas Group (central block). Glover (1971) considered the contact between the Eocene Jacaguas Group (composed predominantly of fine-grained volcanogenic sediments and limestone) of the central province and adjacent Eocene belt strata (containing vent related lavas, alluvial fans, and pyroclastic water-laid volcanogenic tuff of the Anón and equivalent formations) (Figs. 1 and 2), of the western province to represent a low-angle thrust fault resulting from the western block overriding the central province. The discontinuous, highly contorted ribbon of Jacaguas strata (Figs. 1 and 9) mapped by Mattson (1968a,b) and Glover and Mattson (1973) along the eastern margin of Anón and equivalent strata, was considered by Glover (1971) to represent the remains of Eocene strata that covered the overridden surface. In the Río Descalabrado quadrangle (Figs. 1 and 3), the Jacaguas Group (unit J in Fig. 9) itself became involved in eastward thrusting and moved as sheets across the southwestern corner of the central volcanic province (Glover and Mattson, 1973). This model is consistent with a tectonic transpressive process similar to that of Erikson et al. (1990, 1991).

Summary. Further detailed sedimentologic and structural fabric analysis, of the type presented by Erikson et al. (1990, 1991) in the Ponce region, combined with detailed paleomagnetic studies, are required in the northern sector of the Eocene belt to finally resolve complex relations between the western and central provinces. At present, data are consistent with a transpressive process during final stages of volcanism involving left-lateral strike-slip faulting and a counterclockwise rotation of eastern Puerto Rico (Fig. 11). Such a model is compatible with tectonic (Erikson et al., 1990, 1991) and paleomagnetic studies (Van Fossen et al., 1989; Reid et al., 1991) that characterize motion of the Puerto Rico–Virgin Islands (PR-VI) block from Maastrichtian through Oligocene time (Fig. 11). During that period, the PR-VI block collided with the outer tip of the Bahama Platform, and underwent a counterclockwise rotation of at least 25° (Reid et al., 1991, this volume) to its present orientation.

In the tectonic model presented in Figure 11 (modified from Erikson et al., 1991), volcanic belts of volcanic phases IV and V in the western tectonic block were originally contiguous with those in eastern Puerto Rico (Fig. 11A). Following volcanism during the upper Eocene, the Puerto Rico–Virgin Islands block collided with the Bahama banks (Fig 11B). The western part of the block (western volcanic province) became locked between the Muertos and Peralta faults, and most of the resulting counterclockwise rotation was accomplished by left-lateral strike-slip movement of eastern Puerto Rico (central and northeastern provinces) along the SPRFZ, thereby accounting for intersecting trends displayed by phase IV and V volcanic belts in the western province. Rotation of the entire Puerto Rico–Virgin Islands block continued during the lower Oligocene (Fig. 11C), bringing the islands approximately to their present east-west orientation.

Relations between subsidiary faults in the western provinces

The sinistral nature of major strike-slip faults in the western volcanic province generally supports the model outlined above, but evidence regarding timing of these faults is contradictory. For example, the Cordillera fault, generated by protrusion of the Monte del Estado Peridotite, exhibits about 11 km of displacement (McIntyre, 1975), and offsets the Yauco-Maricao and Río Blanco–Lago Garzas belts and Mal Paso Lavas (Figs. 1 and 6A). It does not transect Eocene Anón and equivalent strata, however, terminating at the western boundary of a block of hornblende-plagioclase bearing Anón-like tuff (the Adjuntas horst of Mattson, 1968b). Thus, the Cordillera Fault either predates deposition of Eocene belt strata (as illustrated in Fig. 8B), or was offset by later strike-slip faulting. In either alternative, the fault is older than strike-slip deformation of the Eocene belt. However, the Cerro Godin Fault, which is itself offset by the Cordillera Fault, cuts much younger upper Eocene Río Culebrinas strata (Figs. 1 and 8B) in the Rincón quadrangle (Fig. 3). Such long-term and complex interrelations suggest left-lateral strike-slip movement along these fault zones occurred over extended periods from Santonian to Eocene time, as observed in the northeastern province. The resulting long-term tectonism explains the absence a detectable relict subduction zone beneath western Puerto Rico, in contrast to the central part of the island, where a south-dipping Benioff zone is clearly preserved (Sykes et al., 1982).

CONSTRAINTS ON POLARITY OF SUBDUCTION

Geophysical data reveal that a well-preserved, south-dipping Benioff zone, representing the final Eocene stage of subduction, is preserved beneath eastern Puerto Rico (Sykes et al., 1982). The question of polarity of earlier subduction cannot be fully resolved by geophysical studies, since diagnostic tectonic elements were eliminated by destructive plate margin processes. Therefore, indirect evidence from combined paleogeographic, stratigraphic, and geochemical data must be utilized to determine properties of earlier subduction zones, as illustrated in the following summary of tectonic models currently in use.

Evidence of early east-dipping subduction

Albian-Cenomanian reversal. In his review of Caribbean tectonics, Mattson (1979) noted that island arc basalts in Hispaniola, the western Cayey quadrangle (see Figs. 1 and 3) in southcentral Puerto Rico, and the Virgin Islands changed from predominantly tholeiitic (primitive island arc [PIA] series of Donnelly [1966] and Donnelly and Rogers [1980]) to calc-alkaline compositions across an unconformity separating Albian from Cenomanian strata (between volcanic phases I and III as defined in this chapter). He suggested a profound shift from south- to north-dipping subduction (in terms of the modern geographic orientations) occurred at this time (about 105 Ma, Fig. 2) (see also Mattson, 1973; Mattson and Pessagno, 1979), due to approach of the Caribbean Cretaceous Basalt Province (CCBP), an extensive contemporaneous basalt plateau, probably centered on the modern Galapagos plume (Duncan and Hargraves, 1984; Donnelly, 1994), that was developing within the Pacific basin. Support for this model was presented in recent structural fabric analysis of eastern Hispaniola (Draper et al., 1996), which suggests northward obduction of peridotite onto early Aptian to Albian age volcanics.

Upper Cenomanian reversal. Pindell and Barrett (1990) conceded the polarity of the earliest arc is uncertain. However, the presence of ultramafic rocks and pelagic chert, which these authors considered an obducted ophiolite complex, along the south side of Puerto Rico led them to adopt the inference of Mattson (1979). Furthermore, since younger plates are normally expected to override less buoyant, older plates, they suggested active eastward subduction of the Pacific (Farallon) plate beneath the younger, hotter proto-Caribbean (Atlantic) plate from 165 to 120 Ma, during the period of spreading between North and South America. This model was also adopted by, among others, Burke (1988), Schellekens et al. (1991), Schellekens (1993), Pindell (1994), Lebron and Perfit (1994), and Montgomery et al. (1994a,b), although timing of reversal from east- to west-dipping subduction became a matter of debate. Pindell and Barrett (1990) and Burke (1988) assigned the change in polarity to the Late Cretaceous (Santonian time, or about 88 Ma, between volcanic phases III and IV in Puerto Rico), to correspond with termination of the CCBP event, while Lebron and Perfit (1994) retained the original mid-Cretaceous interpretation of Mattson (1979). Mont-

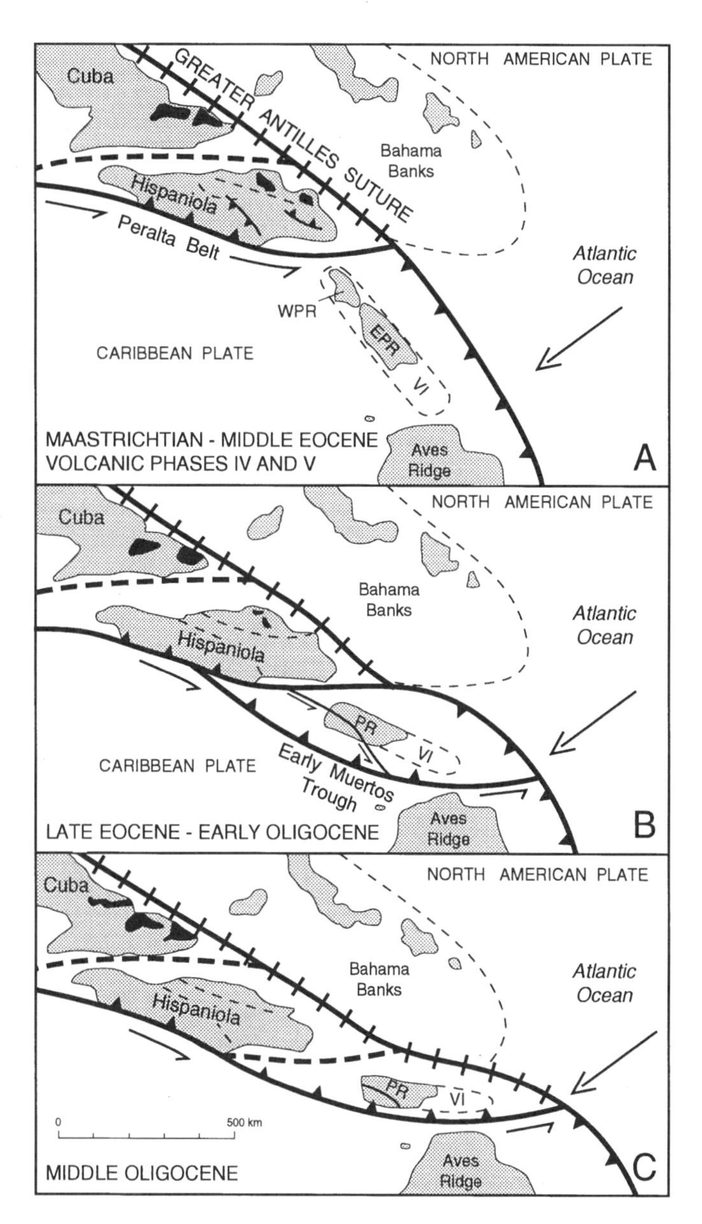

Figure 11. Tectonic evolution of the northeastern Caribbean from Upper Maastrichtian to Oligocene time, modified from Erikson et al. (1991). A, Upper Maastrichtian to middle Eocene, during eruption of Río Blanco–Lago Garzas and Anón lithofacies. B, Late Eocene to early Oligocene, following inferred left-lateral strike-slip rotation of the western block. C, Middle Oligocene, following suturing of Puerto Rico–Virgin Islands block to the Bahama banks and prior to opening of the Cayman Trough.

gomery et al. (1994b) inferred from the diverse lithologic character and radiolarian fauna of Jurassic Mariquita Chert in Puerto Rico that the unit represents an accumulation of Farallon plate fragments derived by offscraping of strata transported from the Pacific basin to an easterly dipping subduction zone and subsequently stored as an accretionary complex in the trench zone. They concluded polarity of subduction reversed during the Late Cretaceous following deposition of the youngest chert (about 90 Ma, late phase III).

Upper Maastrichtian–Lower Paleocene reversal. Schellekens (1993, this volume), Ghosh et al. (1994), Smith and Schellekens (1994), and Smith et al. (this volume) proposed that reversal in polarity of subduction occurred in the Maastrichtian (75 to 55 Ma, during deposition of the Yauco Formation, mid-phase IV), corresponding with an inferred late arrival of the buoyant CCBP at the east-dipping subduction zone. Ghosh et al. (1994) suggested magnetic stripes in the southeastern Caribbean are consistent with plate formation about 135 Ma in association with a triple junction in the Pacific, and subsequent eastward subduction until 75 Ma, when reversal occurred. Eastward movement of the Greater Antilles Arc was accomplished primarily through extensional displacement by the Cayman Trough. Smith et al. (this volume) inferred the change in polarity was preceded by a decrease in the degree of fusion, and correlated Maastrichtian emplacement of the Utuado and San Lorenzo plutons in the central province, and the island-wide upper Paleocene unconformity (Fig. 2), with the reversal.

Evidence of continuous west-dipping subduction

Donnelly (1989, 1994) observed that Jurassic volcanic rocks with arc signatures are unknown in the Caribbean basin outside of continental margins until Aptian-Albian time, and considered the boundary between the proto-Caribbean and Farallon plates essentially passive until initiation of Cretaceous arc volcanism. He further suggested the Caribbean Cretaceous Basalt Province (CCBP) corresponded temporally, and perhaps causally, with the lengthy Cretaceous "magnetic quiet zone" (dating between about 120 and 85 Ma), and that the buoyancy of the Farallon Plate was increased by thickening (Officer et al., 1957; Edgar et al., 1973) and heating associated with the event. Hence, a model was developed in which the proto–Antillean Arc, with a westerly dipping subduction zone, formed fringing the basalt plateau and moved northeastward locked with it throughout the history of the arc (Donnelly et al., 1971; Donnelly, 1989). A similar conclusion was drawn earlier by Glover (1971), who observed that most Upper Cretaceous (volcanic phases III and IV) eruptive centers are aligned along a linear trend, and that smaller, more localized centers were dispersed up to 30 km south of the principle volcanic chain (Fig. 5C). Accordingly, an analogy was drawn between this distribution and modern linear volcanic fronts (VF) with their more scattered behind the arc (BHA) volcanic centers (see, for example, Carr et al., 1990; Woodhead and Johnson, 1993), and it was suggested southward or southwestward subduction of the Atlantic (proto-Caribbean) crust prevailed during that period.

Geographic evidence from volcanic strata in Puerto Rico conflict with models involving an early change from subduction of the Farallon to the proto–Caribbean plate at any time during early stages of arc volcanism. In the first place, no unconformity is observed until mid-Santonian time (about 85 Ma) in the northeastern volcanic province (Fig. 2). In central Puerto Rico, gradual evolution of arc basalt compositions (Schelleckens and Jolly et al., Chapter 3, this volume), and progressive displacement of aligned volcanic centers toward the north (Fig. 5A-D), throughout volcanic phases I, II, and III (Aptian–Lower Albian to Upper Cenomanian) are difficult to reconcile with profound changes in polarity of subduction during the period.

CONCLUSIONS

Puerto Rico, the best known ancient island arc platform in the world, contains a succession of volcanic rocks erupted from the Albian to upper Eocene (120 to about 40 Ma), together with associated sedimentary platform deposits. The island is composed of three volcanic provinces or tectonic blocks (northeastern, central, and western) emplaced by left-lateral strike-slip faulting after mid-Santonian time. Volcanic arc strata in western Puerto Rico were deposited on a pre-arc complex consisting of partly serpentinized spinel peridotite representing subcrustal lithospheric upper mantle; Lower Jurassic basaltic oceanic crust (amphibolite melanges at Las Palmas, Punta Melones, Media Quijada, and Las Mesas; Cajul and Las Mesas altered basalt); and pelagic sediments (Mariquita Chert) from the Pacific Farallon plate.

Arc volcanic strata are subdivided on the basis of exposures in the central province into five volcanic phases: (I) Upper Albian to Lower Albian island arc tholeiitic basalts (dated approximately 120 to 105 Ma); (II) Upper Albian calc-alkaline basaltic volcanic rocks (105 to 97 Ma); (III) Cenomanian to Lower Santonian shoshonites (97 to 85 Ma); (IV) Late Santonian to Maastrichtian calc-alkaline to shoshonitic intermediate volcanic rocks (85 to 70 Ma); and (V) following an island-wide volcanic hiatus, upper Paleocene and Eocene, predominantly felsic, calc-alkaline volcanic rocks (60 to 40–45 Ma). In the central province, each of these phases was characterized by development of linear, east-west–oriented volcanic belts that migrated about 40 km northward as volcanism progressed. Volcanic belts in the western province, which was transported into the volcanic zone of the arc between phases III and IV and therefore contain only Campanian to Eocene volcanic strata, are oriented along southeasterly trends.

The northeastern and central tectonic blocks were juxtaposed during mid-Santonian time, simultaneous with a shift in vectors representing relative motion of the Farallon plate from a northeastern to a more easterly direction. The strike-slip movement also corresponded with termination of basalt eruption associated with Caribbean Cretaceous Basalt Province (CCBP), and with collision of Hispaniola with the Bahama banks. Structural relations between the central and western blocks are obscure, but volcanic belts of identical age in the two blocks intersect along the boundary at an angle of about 30°. Thus, it is inferred that the western block was emplaced by combined sinistral strike-slip faulting, counterclockwise rotation of eastern Puerto Rico, and eastward thrusting during Eocene to Oligocene time. Deformation along this boundary reflects collision of the Puerto Rico–Virgin Islands block with the Bahama banks, and subsequent counterclockwise rotation (Reid et al., 1991) of the block to its present east-west orientation.

Tectonic models of Caribbean basin development are currently in a state of flux, and as a result, the polarity of the subduction zone that produced the Greater Antilles Arc is indeterminate at present. Structural fabric studies in Hispaniola led Draper et al. (1996) to suggest a reversal from east- to west-dipping subduction as early as Aptian-Albian time. Many additional models are based on early east-dipping subduction until arrival at the subduction zone of the Caribbean Cretaceous Basalt Province (CCBP), which had been forming in the Pacific basin. Because such buoyant material resists subduction, these models incorporate a reversal in polarity of subduction to west dipping at some time during arc history. There is disagreement on timing of the inferred reversal, which since 1993 has been correlated with every major stratigraphic and tectonic discontinuity observed in the arc dating between Albian and Eocene time (from about 105 to 55 Ma). The model of Donnelly (1989), which infers the basalt plateau (CCBP) was temporally associated with the Cretaceous magnetic quiet period (120 to 85 Ma), views the incipient arc as forming along the outer fringes of this plateau and advancing eastward above a west-dipping subduction zone throughout arc volcanism. Relative stability of the arc basin and gradual evolution of lava compositions during volcanic phases I, II, III, and IV in Puerto Rico tend to favor the latter model, unless reversal occurred prior to or following deposition of observed strata.

ACKNOWLEDGMENTS

Reviews of the text by Nick Donnelly, Dave Larue, Pete Mattson, and Homer Montgomery, and of the map and correlation compilations by Pete Briggs and Nick Donnelly, together with numerous discussions with Charles Almy, Lynn Glover, James Joyce, John Lewis, Glen Mattiola, Roberto Redondo, and A. L. Smith, are gratefully acknowledged. Suggestions from coeditor Dave Larue regarding format and organization of the manuscript are especially appreciated. Graphics were prepared by Mike Lozon, Department of Earth Sciences, Brock University.

REFERENCES CITED

Almy, C. C., Jr., 1969, Sedimentation and tectonism in the Upper Cretaceous Puerto Rican portion of the Caribbean island arc: Transactions of the Gulf Coast Association of Geological Sciences, v. 19, p. 269–279.

Arkani-Hamed, J., and Jolly, W. T., 1989, Generation of Archean tonalites: Geology, v. 17, p. 307–310.

Barabas, A. H., 1982, Potassium-argon dating of magmatic events and hydrothermal activity associated with porphyry copper mineralization in west central Puerto Rico: Economic Geology, v. 77, p. 109–126.

Berkey, C., 1915, Geological reconnaissance of Porto Rico: New York Academy of Science, v. 26, p. 1–70.

Berkey, C., 1919, Introduction to the geology of Porto Rico: New York Academy of Science, Scientific Survey of Porto Rico and Virgin Islands, v. 1, p. 11–29.

Berryhill, H. L., 1961, Ash-flow deposits, Ciales quadrangle, Puerto Rico, and their significance, *in* Short papers in geologic and hydrologic sciences: U.S. Geological Survey Professional Paper 424–B, p. B224–B226.

Berryhill, H. L., Jr., 1965, Geology of the Ciales quadrangle, Puerto Rico: U.S. Geological Survey Bulletin 1184, 116 p.

Berryhill, H. L., Jr., and Glover, L., 3d, 1960, Geology of the Cayey quadrangle, Puerto Rico: U.S. Geological Survey Miscellaneous Investigations Map I–319, scale 1:20,000.

Berryhill, H. L., Jr., Briggs, R. P., and Glover, L., Jr., 1960, Stratigraphy, sedimentation and structure of Late Cretaceous rocks in eastern Puerto Rico—Preliminary report: American Association of Petroleum Geologists Bulletin, v. 44, p. 137–155.

Boynton, C. H., Westbrook, G. K., and Bott, M. H. P., 1979, A seismic refraction investigation of crustal structure beneath Lesser Antilles island arc: Geophysical Journal, Royal Astronomical Society, v. 58, p. 371–393.

Briggs, R. P., 1967, The Malo Breccia and Cotorra Tuff in the Cretaceous of central Puerto Rico, *in* Cohee, G. V., and others, Changes in stratigraphic nomenclature by the U.S. Geological Survey, 1966: U.S. Geological Survey Bulletin 1254–A, p. A23–A29.

Briggs, R. P., 1969, Changes in stratigraphic nomenclature in the Cretaceous System, east-central Puerto Rico: U.S. Geological Survey Bulletin 1274–O, 31 p.

Briggs, R. P., 1971, Geologic map of the Orocovis quadrangle, Puerto Rico: U.S. Geological Survey Miscellaneous Geologic Investigations Map I–615, scale 1:20,000.

Briggs, R. P., 1973, The Lower Cretaceous Figuera Lava and Fajardo Formation in the stratigraphy of northeastern Puerto Rico: U.S. Geological Survey Bulletin 1372–G, 10 p.

Briggs, R. P., and Aguilar-Cortés, E., 1980, Geologic Map of the Fajardo and Icacos quadrangles, Puerto Rico: U.S. Geological Survey Miscellaneous Geologic Investigations Map I–1153, scale 1:20,000.

Briggs, R. P., and Akers, A., 1965, Hydrogeologic map of Puerto Rico and adjacent islands: U.S. Geological Survey Hydrogeologic Atlas Map HA–197, scale 1:240,000.

Briggs, R. P., and Gelabert, P. A., 1962, Preliminary report of the geology of the Barranquitas quadrangle, Puerto Rico: U.S. Geological Survey Miscellaneous Geologic Investigations Map I–336, scale 1:20,000.

Briggs, R. P., and Pease, M. H., Jr., 1960, Compressional graben and horst structures in east-central Puerto Rico, *in* Short papers in the geological sciences: U.S. Geological Survey Paper 400–B, p. B365–B366, map.

Broedel, C. H., 1961, Preliminary geologic map showing iron and copper prospects in the Juncos quadrangle, Puerto Rico: U.S. Geological Survey Miscellaneous Investigations Map I–326, scale 1:20,000.

Burke, K., 1988, Tectonic evolution of the Caribbean: Annual Reviews of Earth and Planetary Sciences, v. 16, p. 201–230.

Carr, M. J., Feigenson, M. D., and Bennett, E. A., 1990, Incompatible element and isotopic evidence for tectonic control of source mixing and melt extraction along the Central American arc: Contributions to Mineralogy and Petrology, v. 105, p. 369–380.

Cho, M., 1991, Zeolite to prehnite-pumpellyite facies metamorphism in the Toa Baja drill hole: Geophysical Research Letters, v. 18, p. 525–528.

Cox, D. P., Marvin, R. F., M'Gonigle, J. W., McIntyre, D. H., and Rogers, C. L., 1977, Potassium-argon geochronology of some metamorphic, igneous, and hydrothermal events in Puerto Rico and the Virgin Islands: U.S. Geological Survey, Journal of Research, v. 5, p. 689–703.

Curet, A. F., 1976, Geology of the Cretaceous-Tertiary rocks of the southwest quarter of the Monte Guillarte quadrangle, west central Puerto Rico, M.Sc. Thesis, University of Minnesota, Duluth, 121 p.

Curet, A. F., 1986, Geologic map of the Mayagüez and Rosario quadrangles, Puerto Rico: U.S. Geological Survey Miscellaneous Geologic Investigations Map I–1657, scale 1:20,000.

Dolan, J., Mann, P., de Zoeten, R., Heubek, C., and Shiroma, J., 1991, Sedimentologic, stratigraphic, and tectonic synthesis of Eocene-Miocene sedimentary basins, Hispaniola and Puerto Rico, *in* Mann, P., Draper, G., and Lewis, J. F., eds., Geologic and tectonic development of the North America-Caribbean plate boundary in Hispaniola: Geological Society of America Special Paper 262, p. 217–263.

Donnelly, T. W., 1966, The geology of St. Thomas and St. John, U.S. Virgin Islands, *in* Hess, H. H., ed., Caribbean geological investigations: Geological Society of America Memoir 98, p. 85–176.

Donnelly, T. W., 1989, Geologic history of the Caribbean and Central America, *in* Bally, A. W., and Palmer, A. R., eds., Geology of North America—An Overview: Boulder, Colorado, Geological Society of America, The Geology of North America, v. A, p. 299–321.

Donnelly, T. W., 1994, The Caribbean basalt association: a vast igneous province that includes the Nicoya Complex of Costa Rica, *in* Seyfried, H., and Hellman, W., eds., Geology of an evolving arc: the isthmus of southern Nicaragua, Costa Rica, and western Panama: Stuttgart, Germany, Profile (Band 7), Institut fur Geologie und Palaontologie, p. 17–45.

Donnelly, T. W., 1998, The development of geology in Puerto Rico—An historical sketch: New York, New York Academy of Science (in press).

Donnelly, T. W., and Rogers, J. J. W., 1980, Igneous series in island arcs. Bulletin of Volcanology, v. 43–2, p. 347–382.

Donnelly, T. W., Rogers, J. J. W., Pushchair, P., and Armstrong, R. L., 1971, Chemical evolution of igneous rocks of the West Indies: An investigation of Th, U, and K distribution and Pb and Sr isotopic ratios, *in* Donnelly, T. W., ed., Caribbean geologic, tectonic, and petrologic studies: Geological Society of America Memoir 130, p. 181–224.

Donnelly, T. W., and 9 others, 1990, History and tectonic setting of Caribbean magmatism, *in* Dengo, G., and Case, J. E., eds., The Caribbean Region: Boulder, Colorado, Geological Society of America, The Geology of North America, v. H, p. 339–374.

Draper, G., Guitierrez, G., and Lewis, J. F., 1996, Thrust emplacement of the Hispaniola peridotite belt: orogenic expression of the mid-Cretaceous Caribbean arc polarity reversal?: Geology, v. 24, p. 1143–1146.

Duncan, R. A., and Hargraves, R. B., 1984, Plate tectonic evolution of the Caribbean region, *in* Bonini, W. E., Hargraves, R. B., and Shagam, R., eds., The Caribbean–South American plate boundary and regional tectonics: Geological Society of America Memoir 162, p. 81–93.

Edgar, N. T., and others, 1973, Initial reports of the Deep Sea Drilling Project 15: Washington D.C., U.S. Government Printing Office, 1137 p.

Erikson, J. P., Pindell, J. L., and Larue, D. K., 1990, Mid-Eocene–Early Oligocene sinistral transcurrent faulting in Puerto Rico associated with formation of the northern Caribbean plate boundary zone: Journal of Geology, v. 98, p. 365–384.

Erikson, J. P., Pindell, J. L., and Larue, D. K., 1991, Fault zone deformational constraints on Paleogene tectonic evolution in southern Puerto Rico: Geophysical Research Letters, v. 18, p. 569–572.

Frey, F. A., 1988, Rare earth element abundances in upper mantle rocks, *in* Henderson, P., ed., Rare earth geochemistry: Developments in Geochemistry, v. 2, p. 153–203.

Frost, C. D., and Schellekens, J. H., 1991, Rb-Sr and Sm-Nd isotopic characteristic of Eocene volcanic and volcanoclastic rocks from Puerto Rico: Geophysical Research Letters, v. 18, p. 545–548.

Ghosh, N., Hall, S. A., Casey, J. F., and Burke, K., 1994, Magnetic stripes of the Caribbean ocean floor: Formation of the Falleron-Phoenix-Pacific triple junction (abs.): Eos (Transactions, American Geophysical Union), v. 75, p. 594.

Glover, L., 3d, 1961a, Preliminary geologic map of the Salinas quadrangle, Puerto Rico: U.S. Geological Survey Miscellaneous Geologic Investigations Map I–337, scale 1:20,000.

Glover, L., 3d, 1961b, Preliminary report on the geology of the Coamo quadrangle, Puerto Rico: U.S. Geological Survey Miscellaneous Geologic Investigations Map I–335, scale 1:20,000.

Glover, L., 3rd, 1967, Cuyón Formation of east-central Puerto Rico, *in* Cohee, E. V., and others, Changes in stratigraphic nomenclature by the U.S. Geological Survey, 1966: U.S. Geological Survey Bulletin 1254–A, p. A18–A19.

Glover, L., 3d, 1971, Geology of the Coamo area, Puerto Rico, and its relation to the volcanic arc-trench association: U.S. Geological Survey Professional Paper 636, 102 p.

Glover, L., 3d, 1982, Preliminary geologic map of the Patillas and Guayama quadrangles, Puerto Rico: U.S. Geological Survey Open File Report OF–82–1097, scale 1:20,000.

Glover, L., 3d, and Mattson, P. H., 1967, The Jacaguas Group in central Puerto Rico, *in* Cohee, E. V., and others, Changes in stratigraphic nomenclature by the U.S. Geological Survey, 1966: U.S. Geological Survey Bulletin 1254–A, p. A29–A39.

Glover, L., 3d, and Mattson, P. H., 1973, Geologic map of the Río Descalabrado quadrangle, Puerto Rico: U.S. Geological Survey Miscellaneous Geologic Investigations Map I–735, scale 1:20,000.

Hess, H. H., and Otalora, G., 1964, Mineralogical and chemical compositions of the Mayagüez serpentinite cores, *in* Burke, C. A., ed., A study of serpentinite: NAS-NRC Publication 1188, p. 152–168.

Hubbard, B., 1920, The Tertiary formations of Porto Rico: Science, New Series 51, p. 395–396.

Hubbard, B., 1923, The geology of the Lares district, Porto Rico: New York Academy of Science, Scientific Survey of Porto Rico and the Virgin Islands, v. 2, p. 1–115.

Jolly, W. T., 1970, Zeolite and prehnite-pumpellyite facies in south-central Puerto Rico: Contributions to Mineralogy and Petrology, v. 27, p. 204–224.

Jolly, W. T., 1971, Potassium-rich igneous rocks from Puerto Rico: Geological Society of America Bulletin, v. 82, p. 399–408.

Joyce, J., 1985, High pressure-low temperature metamorphism and the tectonic evolution of the Samana Peninsula, Dominican Republic [Ph.D. thesis]: Evanston, Illinois, Northwestern University, 250 p.

Joyce, J., 1986, The tectonic evolution of the northeastern Caribbean plate boundary (Abs): Eos (Transactions, American Geophysical Union), v. 67, p. 1233.

Joyce, J., 1991, Blueschist metamorphism and deformation on the Samana Peninsula: a record of subduction and collision with the Greater Antilles: Geological Society of America Special Paper, 262, p. 47–76.

Joyce, J., McCann, W. R., and Lithgow, C., 1987a, Onland active faulting in the Puerto Rico platelet (abs.): Eos (Transactions, American Geophysical Union), v. 68, p. 1483.

Joyce, J., Smith, A. L., Schellekens, J. H., and Johnson, C. C., 1987b, Tectonic and magmatic processes at convergent margins: Field Guide, 6th Annual Symposium on Caribbean Geology, University of Puerto Rico, Mayagüez, Puerto Rico.

Kaye, C. A., 1959, Geology of the San Juan metropolitan area, Puerto Rico: U.S. Geological Survey Professional Paper 317–A, 48 p.

Kazcor, L, 1987, Petrology of the Mid-Cretaceous Aguas Buenas and Río Matón Limestones in Southeast-Central Puerto Rico [M.Sc. thesis]: Chapel Hill, University of North Carolina, 121 p.

Kazcor, L., and Rogers, J., 1990, The Cretaceous Aguas Buenas and Río Matón Limestones of southern Puerto Rico: Journal of South America Earth Science, v. 3, p. 1–8.

Krushensky, R. D., 1978, Unconformity between Cretaceous and Eocene rocks in central-western Puerto Rico: A concept rejected, *in* McGillavry, H. J., and Beets, D. J., eds.: Geologie en Mijnbouw, v. 57, p. 227–232.

Krushensky, R. D., and Curet, A. F., 1984, Geologic map of the Monte Guillarte quadrangle, Puerto Rico: U.S. Geological Survey Miscellaneous Geologic Investigations Map I–1556, scale 1:20,000.

Krushensky, R. D., and Monroe, W. H., 1975, Geologic map of the Ponce quadrangle, Puerto Rico: U.S. Geological Survey Miscellaneous Geologic Investigations Map I–863, scale 1:20,000.

Krushensky, R. D., and Monroe, W. H., 1978a, Geologic map of the Peñuelas and Punta Cucharra quadrangles, Puerto Rico: U.S. Geological Survey Miscellaneous Geologic Investigations Map I–1042, scale 1:20,000.

Krushensky, R. D., and Monroe, W. H., 1978b, Geologic map of the Yauco and Punta Verraco quadrangles, Puerto Rico: U.S. Geological Survey Miscellaneous Geologic Investigations Map I–1147, scale 1:20,000.

Larue, D. K., 1991, Toa Baja Drilling Project, Puerto Rico: scientific drilling into a non-volcanic island arc massif: Geophysical Research Letters, v. 18, p. 489–492.

Larue, D. K., 1994, Puerto Rico and the Virgin Islands, *in* Donovan, S. K., and Jackson, T. A., eds., Caribbean geology: an introduction: Kingston, Jamaica, University of the West Indies Publishers' Association, p. 151–161.

Larue, D. K., Pierce, P., and Erikson, J., 1991a, Cretaceous intra-arc basin on Puerto Rico: Transactions 2nd Geological Conference, Geological Society of Trinidad and Tobago, p. 184–190.

Larue, D. K., Smith, A. L., and Schellekens, J. H., 1991b, Ocean island arc stratigraphy in the Caribbean region: Sedimentary Geology, v. 74, p. 289–308.

Lebron, M. C., and Perfit, M. R., 1994, Petrochemistry and tectonic significance of Cretaceous island arc rocks, Cordillera Oriental, Dominican Republic: Tectonophysics, v. 229, p. 69–100.

Lidiak, E. G., 1965, Petrology of andesitic, spilitic, and keratophyric flow rock, north central Puerto Rico: Geological Society of America Bulletin, v. 76, p. 57–88.

Lidiak, E. G., 1972, Spatial and temporal variations of potassium in the volcanic rocks of Puerto Rico: 6th Caribbean Geological Conference Transactions, Margarita, Venezuela, p. 203–209.

Lidiak, E. G., 1991, Depth of emplacement of granitoid plutonic rocks in the eastern Greater Antilles island arc: Caribbean Geological Conference Transactions, v. 12, p. 259–267, Miami Geological Society, Miami, Florida.

Mattson, P. H., 1960, Geology of the Mayagüez area, Puerto Rico: Geological Society of America Bulletin, v. 71, p. 319–362.

Mattson, P. H., 1964, Petrography and structure of serpentinite, *in* Burke, C. A., ed., A study of serpentinite: NAS-NRC Publication 1188, p. 7–24.

Mattson, P. H., 1967, Cretaceous and lower Tertiary stratigraphy in west-central Puerto Rico: U.S. Geological Survey Bulletin 1254–B, 35 p.

Mattson, P. H., 1968a, Geologic map of the Adjuntas quadrangle, Puerto Rico: U.S. Geological Survey Miscellaneous Geologic Investigations Map I–519, scale 1:20,000.

Mattson, P. H., 1968b, Geologic map of the Jayüya quadrangle, Puerto Rico: U.S. Geological Survey Miscellaneous Geologic Investigations Map I–520, scale 1:20,000.

Mattson, P. H., 1973, Middle Cretaceous nappe structures in Puerto Rican ophiolites and their relation to tectonic history of the Greater Antilles: Geological Society of America Bulletin, v. 84, p. 21–38.

Mattson, P. H., 1979, Subduction, buoyant braking, flipping, and strike-slip faulting in the northern Caribbean: Journal of Geology, v. 87, p. 293–304.

Mattson, P. H., and Pessagno, E. A., 1971, Caribbean Eocene volcanism and Atlantic Ocean layer A: Science, v. 174, p. 138–139.

Mattson, P. H., and Pessagno, E. A., Jr., 1979, Jurassic and Early Cretaceous radiolarian chert from Puerto Rican ophiolite—tectonic implications: Geology, v. 7, p. 440–444.

Mattson, P. H., Pessagno, E. A., Jr., and Helsley, C. E., 1973, Outcropping Layer A and A″ correlatives in the Greater Antilles, *in* Shagam, R., et al., eds., Studies in earth and space sciences: Geological Society of America Memoir 132, p. 57–66.

McIntyre, D. H., 1971, Geologic map of the Central La Plata quadrangle, Puerto Rico: U.S. Geological Survey Miscellaneous Geologic Investigations Map I–660, scale 1:20,000.

McIntyre, D. H., 1974, Concepcíon and Palma Escrita Formations, western Puerto Rico: U.S. Geological Survey Bulletin 1394–D, p. D1–D9.

McIntyre, D. H., 1975, Geologic map of the Maricao quadrangle, Puerto Rico: U.S. Geological Survey Miscellaneous Geologic Investigations Map I–918, scale 1:20,000.

McIntyre, D. H., Aaron, J. M., and Tobisch, O. T., 1970, Cretaceous and lower Tertiary stratigraphy in northwestern Puerto Rico: U.S. Geological Survey Bulletin 1294–D, 16 p.

Meyerhoff, H. A., 1933, Geology of Puerto Rico: University of Puerto Rico Monograph Series, v. B, no. 1, 306 p.

Meyerhoff, H. A., and Smith, I. F., 1931, The geology of the Fajardo district, Porto Rico: New York Academy of Science Scientific Survey of Porto Rico and Virgin Islands, v. 2, p. 201–360.

M'Gonigle, J. W., 1977, The Rió Abajo, Pitahaya, and Daguao Formations in eastern Puerto Rico: U.S. Geological Survey Bulletin 1435–B, 10 p.

M'Gonigle, J. W., 1978, Geologic map of the Humacao quadrangle, Puerto Rico: U.S. Geological Survey Miscellaneous Geologic Investigations Map I–1070, scale 1:20,000.

Mitchell, G. J., 1922, Geology of the Ponce district, Porto Rico: New York Academy of Science Scientific Survey of Porto Rico and the Virgin Islands, v. 1, p. 229–300.

Monroe, W. H., 1977, Geologic map of the Carolina quadrangle, Puerto Rico: U.S. Geological Survey Miscellaneous Geologic Investigations Map I–1054, scale 1:20,000.

Monroe, W. H., and Pease, M. H., Jr., 1962, Preliminary geologic map of the Bayamón quadrangle, Puerto Rico: U.S. Geological Survey Miscellaneous Geologic Investigations Map I–347, scale 1:20,000.

Montgomery, H., Robinson, E., Saunders, J., and Van den Bold, W., 1991, Paleontology of the Toa Baja #1 well, Puerto Rico: Geophysical Research Letters, v. 18, p. 509–512.

Montgomery, H., Pessagno, E. A., Jr., and Pindell, J. L., 1994a, A 195 Ma terrane in a 165 Ma sea: Pacific origin of the Caribbean plate: GSA Today, v. 4, p. 1–6.

Montgomery, H., Pessagno, E. A., Jr., Lewis, J. F., and Schellekens, J. H., 1994b, Paleogeography of Jurassic fragments in the Caribbean: Tectonics, v. 13, p. 725–732.

Nelson, A. E., 1966a, Cretaceous and Tertiary rocks in the Corozal quadrangle, Puerto Rico: U.S. Geological Survey Bulletin 1244–C, 20 p., scale 1:20,000.

Nelson, A. E., 1966b, Significant changes in volcanism during the Cretaceous in north-central Puerto Rico: U.S. Geological Survey Professional Paper, 550D, p. D172–D177.

Nelson, A. E., 1967a, Geologic map of the Corozal quadrangle, Puerto Rico: U.S. Geological Survey Miscellaneous Geologic Investigations Map I–473, scale 1:20,000.

Nelson, A. E., 1967b, Geologic map of the Utuado quadrangle, Puerto Rico: U.S. Geological Survey Miscellaneous Geologic Investigations Map I–480, scale 1:20,000.

Nelson, A. E., and Monroe, W. H., 1966, Geology of the Florida quadrangle, northern Puerto Rico: U.S. Geological Survey Bulletin 1221–C, 22 p.

Nelson, A. E., and Tobisch, O. T., 1967, The Matilde and Milagros Formations of Early Tertiary age in northwest Puerto Rico: U.S. Geological Survey Bulletin 1254–A, p. A19–A23.

Nelson, A E., and Tobisch, O. T., 1968, Geologic map of the Bayamon quadrangle, Puerto Rico: U.S. Geological Survey Miscellaneous Investigations Map I–525, scale 1:20,000.

Officer, C. B., Ewing, J. I., Edwards, R. S., and Johnson, H, R., 1957, Geophysical investigations in the eastern Caribbean, Venezuelan basin, Antilles island arc, and Puerto Rican outer trench: Geological Society of America Bulletin, v. 68, p. 359–378.

Otalora, G., 1961, Geology of the Barranquitas quadrangle, Central Puerto Rico [Ph.D. thesis]: Princeton, New Jersey, Princeton University, 152 p.

Otalora, G., 1964, Zeolites and related minerals in Cretaceous rocks of east-central Puerto Rico: American Journal of Science, v. 262, p. 726–734.

Pearce, J. A., 1983, Role of sub-continental lithosphere in magma genesis at active continental margins, *in* Hawkesworth, C. J., Norry, M. J., eds., Continental basalts and mantle xenoliths: Cheshire, UK, Shiva Publishing Ltd., p. 230–249.

Pease, M. H., Jr., 1968a, Geologic map of the Aguas Buenas quadrangle, Puerto Rico: U.S. Geological Survey Miscellaneous Geological Investigations Map I–479, scale 1:20,000.

Pease, M. H., Jr., 1968b, Geologic map of the Naranjito quadrangle, Puerto Rico: U.S. Geological Survey Miscellaneous Geologic Investigations Map I–508, scale 1:20,000.

Pease, M. H., Jr., 1968c, Cretaceous and lower Tertiary stratigraphy of the

Naranjito and Aguas Buenas quadrangles and adjacent areas, northern Puerto Rico: U.S. Geological Survey Bulletin 1253, 57 p.

Pease, M. H., Jr., and Briggs, R. P., 1960, Geology of the Comerio quadrangle, Puerto Rico: U.S. Geological Survey Miscellaneous Geologic Investigations Map I–320, scale 1:20,000.

Pessagno, E. A., 1960, Stratigraphy and micropaleontology of the Cretaceous and lower Tertiary of Puerto Rico: Micropaleontology, v. 6, p. 87–110.

Pessagno, E. A., 1962, The Upper Cretaceous stratigraphy and micropaleontology of Puerto Rico: Micropaleontology, v. 8, p. 349–368.

Pindell, J. L., 1994, Evolution of the Gulf of Mexico and the Caribbean, *in* Donovan, S. K., and Jackson, T. A., eds., Caribbean geology: an introduction: Kingston, Jamaica, University of the West Indies Publishers' Association, p. 13–40.

Pindell, J. L., and 6 others, 1988, A plate kinematic framework for models of Caribbean evolution: Tectonophysics, v. 155, p. 121–138.

Pindell, J. L., and Barrett, S. F., 1990, Geological evolution of the Caribbean region: a plate tectonic perspective, *in* Dengo, G., and Case, J. E., eds., The Caribbean Region: Boulder Colorado, Geological Society of America, The Geology of North America, v. H, p. 405–432.

Reid, J. A., Plumley, P. W., and Schellekens, J. H., 1991, Paleomagnetic evidence for Late Miocene counter-clockwise rotation of north-coast carbonate sequence, Puerto Rico: Geophysical Research Letters, v. 18, p. 565–568.

Rogers, C. L., 1979, Geologic map of the Caguas quadrangle, Puerto Rico: U.S. Geological Survey Miscellaneous Investigations Map I–1152, scale 1:20,000.

Rogers, C. L., Cram, C., Pease, M. H., and Tischler, M., 1979, Geologic map of the Yabucoa and Punta Tuna quadrangles, Puerto Rico: U.S. Geological Survey Miscellaneous Investigations Map I–1086, scale 1:20,000.

Sampayo, M. M., 1992, Stratigraphy and sedimentology of the Monte Grande Formation, southwest Puerto Rico [M.Sc. thesis]: Boulder Colorado, The University of Colorado, 97 p.

Santos, H., 1990, The stratigraphy, paleoenvironments, and biofacies of the Upper Cretaceous Cotui Limestone of southwestern Puerto Rico: M.Sc. Thesis, The University of Colorado, Boulder, CO, 107 p.

Schellekens, J. H., 1993, Geochemical evolution of volcanic rocks in Puerto Rico [Ph.D. thesis]: Syracuse, New York, University of Syracuse, 289 p.

Schellekens, J. H., Montgomery, H., Joyce, J., and Smith, A. L., 1991, Late Jurassic to Late Cretaceous development of island arc crust in southwestern Puerto Rico, *in* Larue, D. K., and Draper, G., eds., Transactions of the Caribbean Geological Conference, v. 12, p. 268–281, Miami Geological Society, Miami, Florida.

Seiders, V. M., 1971a, Geologic map of the Gurabo quadrangle, Puerto Rico: U.S. Geological Survey Miscellaneous Geologic Investigations Map I–657, scale 1:20,000.

Seiders, V. M., 1971b, Geologic map of the El Yunque quadrangle, Puerto Rico: U.S. Geological Survey Miscellaneous Geologic Investigations Map I–658, scale 1:20,000.

Seiders, V. M., 1971c, Cretaceous and lower Tertiary stratigraphy of the Gurabo and El Yunque quadrangles, Puerto Rico: U.S. Geological Survey Bulletin 1294–F, 58 p.

Semmes, D. R., 1919, The geology of the San Juan district, Porto Rico: New York Academy of Sciences Scientific Survey of Porto Rico and Virgin Islands, v. 1, p. 33–110.

Slodowski, T. R., 1956, Geology of the Yauco area, Puerto Rico [Ph.D. thesis]: Princeton, New Jersey, Princeton University, 130 p.

Smith, A. L., and Schellekens, J. H., 1994, Batholith emplacement in the northeastern Caribbean: Markers of tectonic change (abs.): Eos (Transactions, American Geophysical Union), v. 75, p. 594.

Sun, S.-S., and McDonough, W. F., 1989, Chemical and isotopic systematics of oceanic basalts: Implications for mantle composition and processes, *in* Saunders, A. D., and Norry, M. J., eds., Magmatism in ocean basins, Geological Society of London Special Publication, v. 42, p. 313–345.

Sykes, L. R., McCann, W. R., and Kafka, A. L., 1982, Motion of the Caribbean Plate during last 7 million years and implications for earlier Cenozoic movements: Journal of Geophysical Research, v. 87, p. 10656–10676.

Tobisch, O. T., 1968, Gneissic amphibolite at Las Palmas, southwestern Puerto Rico, and its significance in the early history of the Greater Antilles island arc: Geological Society of America Bulletin, v. 79, p. 557–574.

Tobisch, O. T., and Turner, M. D., 1971, Geologic map of San Sebastían quadrangle, Puerto Rico: U.S. Geological Survey Miscellaneous Geologic Investigations Map I–661, scale 1:20,000.

Tzeng, S.-Y., 1976, Low-grade metamorphism in east-central Puerto Rico [Ph.D. thesis]: Pittsburgh, Pennsylvania, University of Pittsburgh, 159 p.

Van Fossen, M. C., Channell, J. E. T., and Schellekens, J. H., 1989, Paleomagnetic evidence for Tertiary anticlockwise rotation in southwest Puerto Rico: Geophysical Research Letters, v. 16, p. 819–822.

Volckmann, R. P., 1984a, Upper Cretaceous stratigraphy of southwest Puerto Rico, *in* Stratigraphic Notes 1983: U.S. Geological Survey Bulletin 1537–A, p. A73–A83.

Volckmann, R. P., 1984b, Geologic map of the Cabo Rojo and Parguera quadrangles, southwest Puerto Rico: U.S. Geological Survey Miscellaneous Geologic Investigations Map I–1557, scale 1:20,000.

Volckmann, R. P., 1984c, Geologic map of the San German quadrangle, southwest Puerto Rico: U.S. Geological Survey Miscellaneous Geologic Investigations Map I–1558, scale 1:20,000.

Volckmann, R. P., 1984d, Geologic map of the Puerto Real quadrangle, southwest Puerto Rico: U.S. Geological Survey Miscellaneous Geologic Investigations Map I–1559, scale 1:20,000.

Wadge, G., Draper, G., Lewis, J. F., 1983, Ophiolites of the northern Caribbean: a reappraisal of their roles in the evolution of the Caribbean plate boundary, *in* Gass, I. G., et al., eds., Ophiolites and oceanic boundaries: Geological Society of London Special Publication, v. 13, p. 367–380.

Weaver, J. D., 1958, Utuado pluton, Puerto Rico: Geological Society of America Bulletin, v. 69, p. 1125–1142.

Weiland, T. J., 1988, Petrology of volcanic rocks in lower Cretaceous formations of northeastern Puerto Rico [Ph.D. thesis]: Chapel Hill, North Carolina, University of North Carolina, 205 p.

Woodhead, J. D., and Johnson, R. W., 1993, Isotopic and trace-element profiles across the New Britain island arc, Papua New Guinea: Contributions to Mineralogy and Petrology, v. 113, p. 479–491.

MANUSCRIPT ACCEPTED BY THE SOCIETY JUNE 20, 1997

Printed in U.S.A.

Geological Society of America
Special Paper 322
1998

Geochemical evolution and tectonic history of Puerto Rico

Johannes H. Schellekens
Department of Geology, University of Puerto Rico, Mayagüez, Puerto Rico 00681-5000

ABSTRACT

Puerto Rico, in the Greater Antilles, is a complex arc terrane, with a basement of Jurassic to early Tertiary volcanic, volcaniclastic, and sedimentary rocks intruded by felsic plutonic rocks, which is overlain by Oligocene and younger sedimentary rocks and sediments. Flow rocks of all recognized formations were sampled and analyzed for major, trace, and rare earth elements. Volcano-stratigraphic associations (VSAs) were defined as packets of volcanic and associated sedimentary rocks in which the age of the volcanic rocks was determined based on the fossil ages of the associated rocks.

The basement rocks were divided into the Southwestern, Central, and Northeast Igneous Provinces (SIP, CIP, NIP). Cherts and associated amphibolites of the Bermeja Complex (SIP) are considered to represent Pacific ocean floor fragments. An Early Cretaceous (Aptian-Albian) island arc is represented by greenstones in the Bermeja Complex (SIP), pre-Robles VSAs (CIP), and the Daguao-Figuera VSA (NIP). Magmas have a tholeiitic composition interpreted as generated through partial melting of the mantle wedge enriched by dehydration fluids. Late Cretaceous magmas show possible evidence for the involvement of pelagic oozes and continental material in concordance with the subduction of older oceanic crust and the approach of South America. The Bermeja Complex melange is interpreted as the subduction complex of the Late Cretaceous arc(s) in the CIP, suggesting a northward-dipping subduction.

With the attempted subduction of the buoyant oceanic platform at the end of the Cretaceous, subduction flipped. The chemistry of the volcanic rocks in the SIP confirms reduction in melt generation and a change from a fore-arc basin into a back-arc basin during the Maastrichtian. Magmas show no evidence for the involvement of continentally derived material, but chemical characteristics suggest involvement of pelagic oozes in concordance with the scenario of subduction of old (proto-Caribbean) ocean floor. Early Tertiary magmas show evidence for incorporation of pelagic oozes resulting from subduction of ocean floor close to the Bahamas. This chapter is a contribution to International Geological Correlation Program (IGCP) project 364.

INTRODUCTION

Puerto Rico, the easternmost island in the Greater Antilles, is part of a complex arc terrane with a geologic record of about 195 m.y. The island consists of volcanic, volcaniclastic, and sedimentary rocks of Jurassic to early Tertiary age, which were intruded by felsic plutonic rocks during the Late Cretaceous and early Tertiary, and are unconformably overlain by slightly tilted Oligocene and younger sedimentary rocks and sediments (Briggs and Akers, 1965). Puerto Rico and the northern Virgin Islands are the subaerially exposed parts of the Puerto Rico–Virgin Islands microplate (PRVI) (Byrne et al., 1985) that lies within the seismically active Caribbean–North American plate boundary zone.

Volcano-stratigraphic associations

To unravel the volcanic episodes and tectonic regimes recorded in the Puerto Rican part of the PRVI microplate, a solid

Schellekens, J. H., 1998, Geochemical evolution and tectonic history of Puerto Rico, *in* Lidiak, E. G., and Larue, D. K., eds., Tectonics and Geochemistry of the Northeastern Caribbean: Boulder, Colorado, Geological Society of America Special Paper 322.

stratigraphic basis was needed to place all the events in a chronologic order. Island-wide lithostratigraphic correlation within the basement rocks is difficult, because individual units appear to have limited original lateral extent and the rocks have subsequently been strongly deformed and faulted. To overcome these correlation problems, the central core was divided into a number of igneous provinces (Schellekens, 1991)—namely, a southwestern igneous province (SIP), a central igneous province (CIP), and a northeastern igneous province (NIP)—on the basis of differences in stratigraphy, lithology, petrography, and geochemistry (Fig. 1).

Volcano-stratigraphic associations (VSAs) were defined to place the volcanic rocks in a time frame. A VSA is a packet of volcanic and associated sedimentary rocks (Schellekens, 1991). If no radiometric ages were available for the volcanic rocks, the age of the volcanic rocks was determined as closely as possible on the basis of biostratigraphic ages of the associated sedimentary rocks. Using these VSAs, stratigraphic columns were constructed (Fig. 2). There was one each for the NIP and CIP, and two columns for the SIP, to show more detail. For detailed stratigraphic descriptions, readers are referred to references in Schellekens (1993), Jolly et al. (Chapter 1, this volume), and references in the text.

GEOLOGY AND STRATIGRAPHY

Southwestern igneous province

The Southwestern Igneous Province is different from the remainder of Puerto Rico, both in its tectonic style and its exposures of serpentinite belts. This province does not coincide exactly with the southwestern structural block of previous workers (Garrison et al., 1972; Cox and Briggs, 1973; Cox et al., 1977) because it also includes the northeast-southwest belt of lower Tertiary volcanic and volcaniclastic rocks. The lower Tertiary rocks are included in this province because they are locally not distinguished from the underlying Cretaceous rocks (Krushensky, 1978; Krushensky and Curet, 1984). Cretaceous and lower Tertiary rocks occur together in fault-bounded packets (Krushensky and Monroe, 1975, 1978, 1979), and some lower Tertiary outliers (Jicara Formation) occur west of the fault zone overlying Upper Cretaceous rocks (Volckmann, 1984c). The stratigraphy of the SIP is summarized in two stratigraphic columns (Fig. 2).

The oldest rocks found in Puerto Rico belong to the Bermeja Complex, which consists of serpentinite containing rafts of chert and metabasalt. The Bermeja Complex was first described by Mattson (1960) and is named for the Sierra Bermeja, where the complex is exposed in its greatest variety. Mattson (1960) distinguished four rock types in the complex: serpentinized peridotite, (Mattson, 1960, 1964); spilite, later named the Las Mesas Greenstone (Schellekens et al., 1990); amphibolite, later named the Las Palmas Hornblende Schist and Amphibolite (Mattson, 1973); and silicified volcanic rock and/or chert, later named the Cajul Basalt and the Mariquita Chert (Mattson, 1973). On the basis of radiolarian stratigraphy and radiometric age dating, the Bermeja Complex can be subdivided into a Jurassic (Pliensbachian, and Kimmeridgian-Tithonian) VSA and an Early Cretaceous (Hauterivian-Aptian) VSA (Schellekens et al., 1990; Montgomery et al., 1994a). The radiolarians in the oldest rocks indicate an

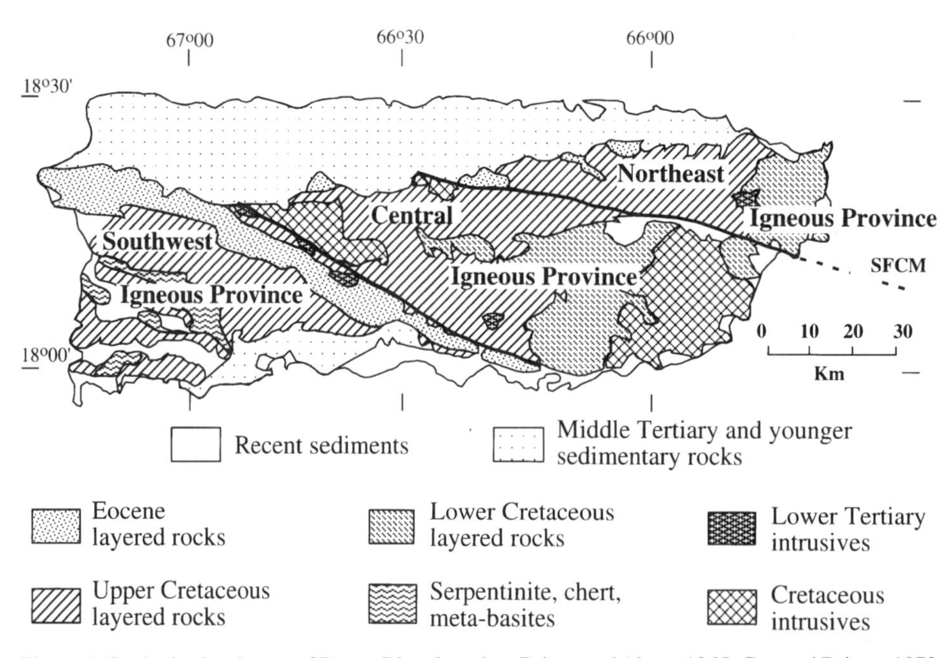

Figure 1. Geologic sketch map of Puerto Rico (based on Briggs and Akers, 1965; Cox and Briggs, 1973; U.S. Geological Survey quadrangle maps).

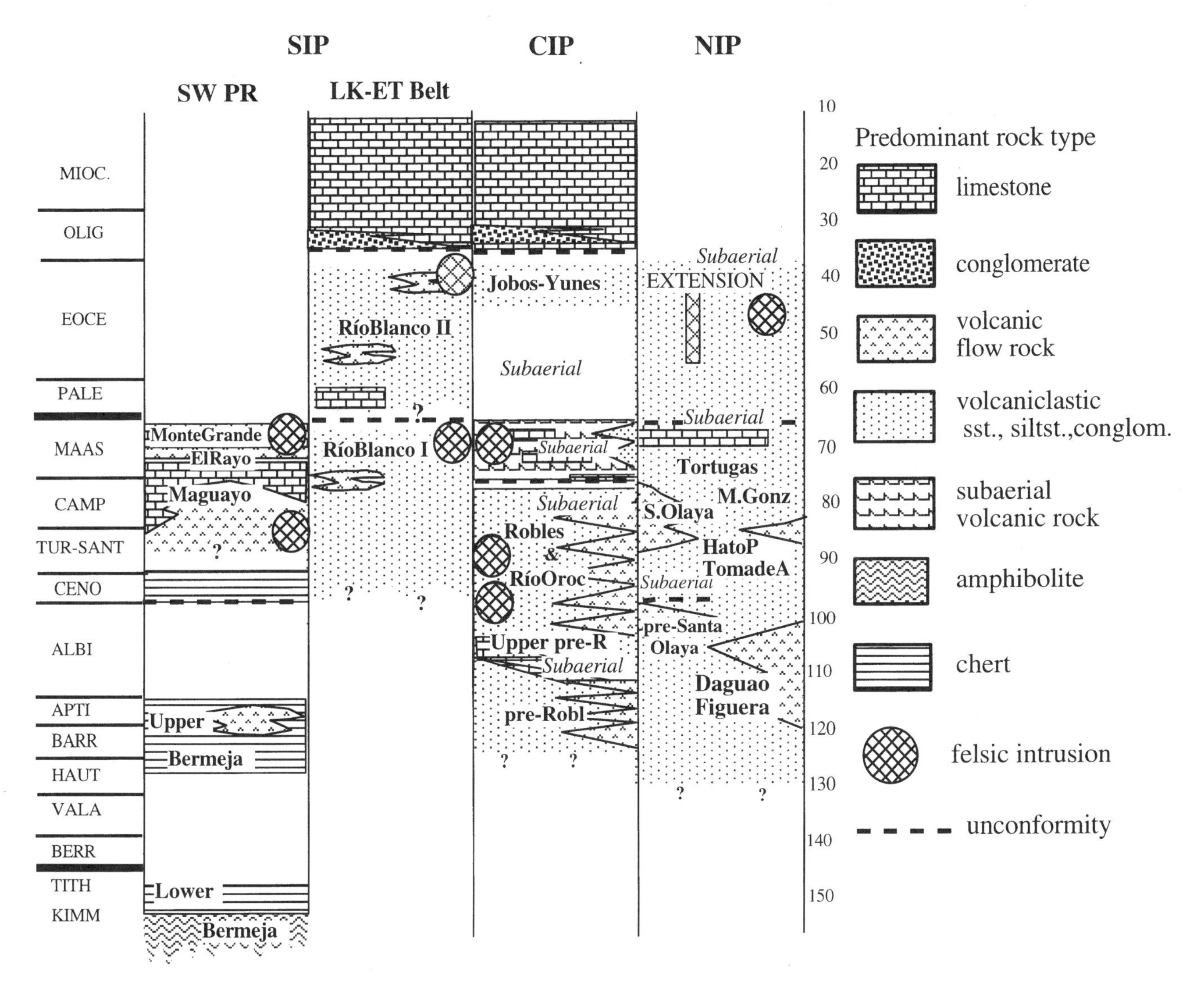

Figure 2. Summary of the occurrence of predominant rock types in Puerto Rico. RioOroc, Río Orocovis; pre-R/pre-Robl, pre-Robles; M.Gonz, Martín Gonzáles; HatoP, Hato Puerco; TomadeA, Toma de Agua; S.Olaya, Santa Olaya.

origin at about 28° to 30° latitude, either north or south, in the Pacific Ocean (Montgomery et al., 1994a). The presence of the Jurassic abyssal cherts suggests that the original ocean floor, on which the radiolarian cherts must have been deposited, could be present as well, and may possibly be represented by the amphibolites in the Bermeja Complex. On the basis of clinopyroxene composition, petrography, metamorphic grade, and radiometric ages, the Las Mesas Greenstone, a microgabbro, and several metabasaltic dikes belonging to the Bermeja Complex were considered to represent Early Cretaceous island arc volcanism (Schellekens et. al., 1990; Schellekens, 1993).

Lying unconformably on the Bermeja Complex in the southern part of the southwestern province is the Maguayo VSA containing basaltic to dacitic volcanic and volcaniclastic rocks overlain by limestones with fossil age dates ranging from Late Santonian to Campanian (H. Santos, personal communication, 1996). The age of the volcanic rocks is inferred to be Santonian-Campanian on the basis of the 85-Ma age of the (probably comagmatic) shallow intrusive Maguayo Porphyry (K-Ar: Cox et al., 1977; Ar-Ar: Schellekens et al., 1990), and the biostratigraphic age of the overlying limestones (Almy, 1965, 1969; Mattson, 1960; Santos, 1990). These limestones are in turn overlain by the Monte Grande–El Rayo VSA, which consists of basaltic to andesitic flow rocks and volcaniclastic rocks, overlain by limestones of middle Maastrichtian age (Fig. 2) (Volckmann, 1984d; Sampayo, 1992).

The remainder of the SIP (Fig. 1) consists of stratified rocks of Late Cretaceous and early Tertiary age that were intruded by mostly shallow stocks (Fig. 2) and are grouped into Río Blanco I and II VSAs. The volcanic rocks of former are of Campanian-Maastrichtian age and consist of flow rocks and pyroclastics (basalt to dacite, and trachyandesite) that are intercalated in the top of a sedimentary sequence (Mattson, 1968a,b; McIntyre et al., 1970; Tobisch and Turner, 1971; McIntyre, 1971, 1974, 1975; Krushensky and Monroe, 1975, 1978, 1979; Krushensky and Curet, 1984; Volckmann, 1984a–d; Curet, 1986) that ranges in age, on the basis of fossil content, from Cenomanian to Maastrichtian (Yauco and Sabana Grande Formations of Volckmann, 1984a).

At the northwestern end of the outcrop belt of the Lower Tertiary Río Blanco II VSA (Fig. 1), predominantly volcanic formations occur intercalated with siltstones, sandstones, and conglomerates derived from the volcanic rocks, as well as some locally occurring limestones (McIntyre, 1971, 1974, 1975; McIntyre et al., 1970; Tobisch and Turner, 1971). In the central part of the belt, the VSA consists of interbedded andesitic to rhyodacitic flow rocks and pyroclastic rocks. Several dacitic intrusions, commonly containing amygdules and trachytic textures, are associated with the flow rocks (Krushensky and Monroe, 1975, 1978). The volcanic rocks interfinger extensively with a number of formations that themselves consist of complexly interfingering members of tuff, volcanic sandstone and conglomerate, various types of limestone, green vitric tuff beds, and white cherts (Mattson, 1967, 1968a,b; Krushensky and Monroe, 1975, 1978). At the southern end of the belt (Fig. 1), Eocene limestone (Krushensky and Monroe, 1975) disconformably overlies intercalated and interfingering beds of volcaniclastic mudstone to conglomerate with minor limestone of lower Paleocene to lower Eocene age, and is itself overlain by dacitic tuffs and mudstones, with minor limestones, and rare conglomerates of middle Eocene age (Glover, 1971; Glover and Mattson, 1967, 1973). Several of the small intrusions sampled, which show flow textures and amygdules, may represent domes.

The stratified rocks of the SIP are intruded by a number of small and mostly shallow intrusives of Late Cretaceous and early Tertiary age (e.g., Volckmann, 1984a–c; Curet, 1986). A number of Eocene stocks (48.2 to 37.9 Ma, K-Ar) (Cox et al., 1977; Barabas, 1982), some of which are mineralized, were intruded along the southern margin of the Utuado Pluton into the lower Tertiary rocks described above.

Central igneous province

The Central Igneous Province (CIP) is here defined as those rocks that occur east of the Late Cretaceous to early Tertiary belt of the southwest province, and west and south of the San Francisco–Cerro Mula fault (Fig. 1). This province is characterized by stratified rocks of Early Cretaceous to Eocene age that were intruded during the Late Cretaceous by a number of felsic plutons, such as the San Lorenzo batholith, and the Utuado, Ciales, and Morovis plutons (M'Gonigle, 1978, 1979; Rogers, 1977, 1979; Rogers et al., 1979; Broedel, 1961; Cox et al., 1977; Weaver, 1958; Smith et al., this volume) (Fig. 2).

The stratigraphy of the CIP (Fig. 2) is divided into a number of VSAs, which usually consist of accumulations of flow rocks, interpreted as proximal volcanic environments, with associated volcanic sandstones and siltstones, representing the contemporaneous distal volcanic environments. Locally occurring limestone lenses provide age constraints.

The Lower pre-Robles VSA, equivalent to the Río Majada Group (Jolly et al., Chapter 1, this volume), which must be Albian or older, includes flows and flow breccias ranging in composition from basalt to andesite. The flow rocks occur as tongues in coarse- to fine-grained volcaniclastic rocks, which also contain a lens of fragmental limestone. The Upper pre-Robles VSA also consists of flows, flow breccias, and volcanic breccias of basaltic to andesitic compositions. Although the environment of deposition of the latter VSA was predominantly subaqueous, it may have been locally subaerial (Briggs, 1969). The occurrence of a major limestone member at the base of, and limestone lenses throughout, the association suggests the existence of a volcanic platform made up of Lower pre-Robles VSA rocks, which was created by a shift of the volcanism to the north.

Overlying the pre-Robles VSAs in the southern part of the CIP is the Robles Formation (Pease and Briggs, 1960; Berryhill and Glover, 1960; Briggs and Gelabert, 1962) and in the northern part the Río Orocovis Group (Nelson, 1967a). The northern and southern sequence are separated by the Damián Arriba fault. Both sequences have comparable lithology and stratigraphy, and Briggs (1971) combined the formations into the Robles–Río Orocovis sequence. This sequence, which ranges in age from Early Cretaceous (Albian) to Late Cretaceous (probably Santonian) (Briggs, 1967, 1969; Sohl and Kollmann, 1985), is here called the Robles-Orocovis VSA. Based on the age of the basal limestones (Sohl and Kollmann, 1985), the lower part of the Robles-Orocovis VSA is contemporaneous with the upper pre-Robles VSA.

The Vista Alegre–Tetuán VSA conformably overlies, and locally is gradational into, the underlying Robles-Orocovis VSA in the north of the CIP. This association consists of proximal volcanic facies (Vista Alegre Formation, Mameyes Formation, Malo Breccia) (Nelson and Monroe, 1966; Nelson, 1967b; Briggs, 1971) and a contemporaneous distal volcanic facies (Tetuán Formation, Mattson, 1967). This association may be partly coeval with the top of the Robles-Orocovis VSA, but represents a more limited time interval, possibly Cenomanian or Santonian to perhaps as young as Campanian (Nelson, 1967a; Nelson and Monroe, 1966; Mattson, 1967; Briggs, 1971) (Fig. 2). Flow rocks only constitute a minor component of the Vista Alegre–Tetuán VSA.

The Cariblanco-Pozas VSA ranges in age from approximately Santonian to Maastrichtian. Toward the south this VSA is made up of interbedded siltstones, sandstones, and conglomerates of Santonian age, together with a distinctive red and purple volcaniclastic conglomerate. The environment of deposition of these rocks is interpreted by R. D. Krushensky (personal communication, 1992) as representing a marine basin facies (Cariblanco Formation) with a coarse channel facies (Achiote Conglomerate) reflecting transport from an oxidized subaerial source. These units are overlain by, and grade into, well-bedded volcanic sandstones, and siltstones, with some subaqueous pyroclastic rocks (Maravillas Formation). The above-mentioned channel facies is correlated with subaerial rocks consisting of an accumulation of pyroclastic materials (including partially welded ash-flow deposits), with some flow rocks, conglomerates, sandstones, and limestones that crop out in the central and north-central part of the island (Nelson and Monroe, 1966; Berryhill, 1961, 1965; Briggs, 1971; Briggs and Gelabert, 1962; Briggs, 1969). The presence in the south of reefs at the Campanian-Maastrichtian boundary overlying the marine basinal facies, and the occurrence in the north of subaerially deposited welded tuffs, suggests the emergence of the island arc.

In the northern part of this province, separated from the Late Cretaceous rocks by a more or less east-west–trending fault, early Tertiary well-bedded volcaniclastic rocks occur (Fig. 1) (Nelson, 1967a; Nelson and Monroe, 1966). Some of the beds are interpreted as submarine pyroclastic flows (Fiske, 1969), possibly from centers toward the south. The CIP is further characterized by the exposure of large intrusive bodies of predominantly granodioritic composition of Late Cretaceous age. The plutonic rocks range from mid-Cretaceous stocks, intruded into the associated volcanic rocks, to Late Cretaceous plutons, without associated volcanism (Smith et al., this volume).

Northeast igneous province

The Northeast Igneous Province (NIP) is characterized by igneous activity from the Early Cretaceous to the early Tertiary (Fig. 2). It is separated from the CIP by the San Francisco–Cerro Mula Fault Zone (Fig. 1). Because there is no direct correlation possible across this fault zone, the total exposed length of the fault zone (35 km) was considered to represent the minimum displacement along the fault (Briggs and Pease, 1968).

The Early Cretaceous is represented by volcanic rocks ranging in composition from basalts to rhyolites. Volcanism continued through the Late Cretaceous and early Tertiary with the extrusion of basaltic and dacitic rocks. The NIP is further characterized by the occurrence of intrusions of both felsic (Cretaceous-Tertiary) and mafic (Tertiary) magmas. The former are present as small plutons, whereas the latter are found as diabase dike swarms.

Only local unconformities can be recognized in the NIP (Fig. 2). The majority of the formations were deposited in a basin and overlie each other conformably, either with gradational or sharp contacts. Formations are distinguished on the basis of differences in grain size, types of components, or composition, which reflect changes of influx of components from nearby volcanic sources. This sequence appears to be continuous (Fig. 2). Locally, toward the west, unconformities are recorded separating packets of layers. The interruptions are probably due to the build-up of a volcanic edifice above the sea level, which was subsequently subjected to erosion and probably contributed to the material deposited in the basin.

The Daguao-Figuera VSA comprises the oldest group of rocks of the continuous sequence. It consists of interbedded volcanic breccia, andesite flow rock, and subordinate volcanic sandstone and tuffs (Briggs, 1973; M'Gonigle, 1977), conformably overlain by volcaniclastic rocks and rare associated flow rocks, locally with more siliceous volcanics, mapped as Figuera, Daguao, and the lowest part of the Fajardo Formations (Briggs, 1973; Briggs and Aguilar-Cortés, 1980; Weiland, 1988). The VSA is gradationally overlain by rocks with Albian fossil ages (Seiders, 1971c), implying that the Daguao-Figuera VSA is Albian or older (Briggs, 1973; M'Gonigle, 1977, 1978, 1979). Compositions for the Daguao-Figuera VSA showed distinct bimodality represented by basalt and rhyolite, with only a few examples of intermediate compositions. This bimodality was considered one of the characteristics of the Primitive Arc basalts of Donnelly and Rogers (1980). This may, however, be an artifact of sampling; because only flows were collected, intermediate compositions have been reported but occur as pyroclastic flows (Fiske, 1969).

The overlying Hato Puerco–Toma de Agua VSA consists predominantly of mudstone and volcanic sandstone of Albian age that is conformably overlain by formations characterized by lithic debris of various grain sizes. Locally also pillowed flow rocks occur (Fig. 2) (Pease, 1968c; Seiders, 1971a–c; Pease and Briggs, 1972; Briggs and Aguilar-Cortés, 1980). The lithic volcanic rocks grade upward into volcanogenic rocks characterized by the presence of pumice and perlite; at the top a vitrophyre occurs (Seiders, 1971c). After a lull during most of the Albian, this latter association represents renewed volcanic activity, starting with formation of basaltic pillows and fragmental rocks, and developing into more explosive (pumiceous) volcanics and the associated vitrophyre. Chemical compositions of the rocks in the Hato Puerco–Toma de Agua VSA range from basalt to andesite. The rocks all contain low-grade metamorphic mineral assemblages (albite + chlorite ± epidote) and the characteristic high Na-content due to sodic metasomatism (spilite and keratophyre).

The Hato Puerco–Toma de Agua VSA is conformably overlain by the Martín González–Tortugas VSA, consisting of a sequence of volcanic sandstones and mudstones with basaltic andesite flows overlain by the massive nonmarine Tortugas Andesite (Kaye, 1959; Pease, 1968c) and finally disconformably overlain by Maastrichtian (Paleocene?) age limestones (Fig. 2) (Pease, 1968a–c). The age of the entire Martín González–Tortugas VSA ranges from Turonian to Campanian; however, the volcanism of the association is restricted to the Santonian-Campanian (Seiders, 1971c; Pease, 1968a). Compositions of the flow rocks in the Martín González–Tortugas VSA range from basalt to andesite.

Contemporaneous with this continuous sequence occur a

number of associations that are separated by unconformities (Fig. 2). The oldest, the pre–Santa Olaya sequence, is a series of tuffs, flow rocks, breccias, and possibly a dome (Cerro Gordo Lava) (Pease, 1968a,c). The rocks are here defined as the pre–Santa Olaya VSA. This VSA is interpreted as representing a proximal volcanic environment, based on the presence of a basaltic andesitic dome, the occurrence of flows near the base of the association, which are followed by andesitic flow rocks and breccias, and ending with subaerial, locally welded tuffs.

The overlying marine sequence consists of the Santa Olaya Formation and its lateral equivalents (Pease, 1968a,c; Seiders, 1971b). They are grouped together as the Santa Olaya VSA. This association represents a proximal marine volcanic environment as suggested by basaltic andesite pillowed flow rocks, together with its contemporaneous distal equivalents. This association is distinctly subaqueous in character, but is capped by the Tortugas Andesite, a subaerial volcanic formation, that is equated with the upper parts of the Martín González–Tortugas VSA (Pease, 1968a; Seiders, 1971c).

Unconformably overlying the Martín González–Tortugas VSA are subaerially deposited sandstone, siltstone, and limestone of probably Maastrichtian age. These rocks are unconformably overlain by lower Tertiary clastic rocks (Kaye, 1959; Pease, 1968a,b; Pease and Monroe, 1977; Seiders, 1971a).

Stratified rocks in the northeast are intruded by dikes and a small stock. The diabase and diabase porphyry dikes and the quartz diorite stock are considered to be early Tertiary in age based on their structural relationship (Seiders, 1971a,b). The age for the stock was confirmed by a K-Ar age of about 46 Ma (Cox et al., 1977; Smith et al., this volume).

Middle Tertiary rocks

Since the beginning of the Oligocene Puerto Rico has been relatively stable. North and south of the Jurassic to Eocene core of the island homoclinal relatively undisturbed sequences of Oligocene to Pliocene sedimentary rocks were deposited. Monroe (1980) discussed and described both the northern and southern middle Tertiary sequences. A recent discussion of ages and environments of the north coast sequence was given by Seiglie and Moussa (1984). Ages and stratigraphic relations of the formations for the rocks in the southern zone are also discussed by Seiglie and Bermúdez (1969), and Moussa and Seiglie (1970, 1975).

GEOCHEMISTRY

Sample collection and analytic methods

For this study, rocks were collected from almost every volcanic formation described on the island. Because the goal was to study the magmatic compositions of the volcanic products, samples had to be collected from those deposits that represent original magmatic compositions. In modern arcs these include lava flows and juvenile clasts in pyroclastic deposits. In ancient arcs, flow rocks are the best representatives of the original magmatic composition. Every formation is represented by a limited number of samples, and although no bias was given to certain rock types, the necessity to sample flow rocks may have lead to the introduction of a false bimodal character. Flow rocks are often best preserved at the low- and high-silica ends of the compositional spectrum. Due to their lower viscosity, volcanic rocks with a lower silica content will have a greater tendency to occur as flows and be present over larger areas. Very siliceous rocks may occur as domes, with considerably smaller areas, however, with excellent preservation. Intermediate to more silicic compositions, which tend to predominate in explosively erupted magmatic products, may be absent or underrepresented due to this sampling method.

Major and trace element analyses were performed by x-ray fluorescence (XRF) spectroscopy at Michigan Technological University, Houghton. Methods for pellet preparation and analytic procedures and corrections were described by Rose et al. (1986). Rare earth elements analysis and analyses for Sc, Cr, Co, Hf, Th, Ta, and Na_2O were carried out by instrumental neutron activation (INAA) at the Massachusetts Institute of Technology, Cambridge. The procedures and methods were described by Ila and Frey (1984). A number of samples were analyzed for major, trace, and rare earth elements by ACTLABS in Ancaster, Ontario. For a discussion of accuracy and precision, see Schellekens (1993).

All analyzed rocks have undergone metamorphism ranging in grade from amphibolite facies through greenschist, and zeolite, to prehnite-pumpellyite facies (e.g., Mattson, 1960; Jolly, 1970b; Cho, 1991; Schellekens, 1993). Characterization of the volcanic rocks is therefore based on immobile elements such as Ti, Zr, Y, and Cr (Pearce and Cann, 1973) and REEs. The latter have also been found to be immobile during metamorphism, hydrothermal alteration, and weathering, unless the processes were obviously severe (Hanson, 1980). The petrography of the analyzed rocks is summarized in Tables 1, 3, and 5, and the chemical analyses are listed in Tables 2, 4, and 6.

Characterization of volcanic rocks

The metabasites of the Bermeja Complex all show slightly depleted chondrite normalized REE patterns, whereas the other rocks in the SIP have chondrite normalized REE patterns, which are usually LREE enriched, typical of calc-alkaline volcanic arcs, rarely with a negative Eu anomaly. On the basis of their major element composition, the rocks of the Upper Cretaceous Río Blanco I VSA can be divided into an alkaline (predominantly mapped as Maricao Formation) and a subalkaline group. The alkaline group is characterized by a high TiO_2 content, which is also reflected in the presence of zoned euhedral titanaugite phenocrysts. In addition to their high total alkali content, the rocks of this group are also characterized by high Sr

TABLE 1. PETROGRAPHY AND LOCATION OF ANALYZED ROCKS OF THE SOUTHWEST IGNEOUS PROVINCE

Number	Rock	Primary Assembly	Secondary Assembly	Location	Puerto Rico Meter Grid		Quadrangle
				UPPER BERMEJA VSA			
Las Mesas Greenstone							
VP2	Metabasalt	Actinolite-green hbl.-plag.(alb.)	Chl-Qtz.	Las Palmas	17,100	78,100	Cabo Rojo
VP117	Basalt	Act.-green hbl-plag.(alb. cpx. relics)		Las Palmas	17,550	78,300	Cabo Rojo
Las Mesas Greenstone							
EC13	Metabasalt	Cpx-plag. (albite)	-Calc.-Qtz-alb	Rt 307 km 7.3	22,860	73,140	Puerto Real
Two-Pyroxene Gabbro							
VP179	Gabbro	Bro.hbl.-cpx-opx-plag. (bytown)	Preh-chl-hgros.	Indiera Fria	36,930	97,180	Maricao
				MAGUAYO VSA			
Boqueron Basalt							
VP110	Trachyandesite	Plag.-cpx	Qtz-malachite	Rt 300 W of rt 103	23,590	76,340	Puerto Real
VP112	Trachyandesite	Plag.(olig)-cpx	Serpentine?	Rt 107	22,200	73,700	Puerto Real
VP113	Basalt. andesite	Plag.(labr)-cpx		Rt 307 km 7.3	22,860	73,140	Puerto Real
VP114	Andesite	Plag.-cpx.	Serp.-seric.-malac.-calc.-Qtz-alb	Rt 307 km 7.3	22,860	73,140	Puerto Real
Basaltic Andesite							
VP119	Basalt. andesite	Opx-cpx-fsp		Rt 305 int. Rt 116	21,000	87,400	San German
VP120	Basalt. andesite	Plag-cpx-cpx		Rt 323 km 1.2	17,940	90,300	Guanica
Laias Formation							
VP106	Trachyandesite	Plag.-oxyhbl.	Calc.-Fe-oxide	Rt 314 km 3.6	26,180	83,200	San German
VP122	Basalt. andesite	Plag.-oxyhbl.	Calc.-Fe-oxide	Rt 316 km 0.7	23,900	84,500	San German
VP124	Trachyandesite	Plag.-oxyhbl	Fe-oxide	N capilla off Rt 314	26,300	83,640	San German
EC15	Trachyandesite			Rt 116 km 0.5	24,300	86,500	San German
Maguayo Porphyry							
VP118	Andesite	Qtz-plag.(olig)-biot. relics	Seric.-chlor.-epid.	S of bo. Maguayo	19,350	83,000	San German
Augite-Hornblende Andesite							
EC11	Andesite	Cpx-oxyhbl		Rt 116 km 18.6	18,000	95,760	Guanica
EC12	Andesite	Cpx-oxyhbl		Rt 116 km 18.6	18,000	95,760	Guanica
				MONTE GRANDE–EL RAYO VSA			
Monte Grande Formation							
VP96	Basaltic andesite	Plag(and)-cpx?-opq	Chl-ep-seric	Bo. Tuna	26,300	82,000	San German
VP132	Andesite	Plag(and)	Calc-Fe ox-seric	Rt 361	31,460	89,420	San German
El Rayo Formation							
VP128	Basalt	Plag(and)-cpx	Seric-ep-calc-chl	Rt 118 km 2.6	25,280	91,450	San German
VP129	Dacite	Plag	Qtz-Fe ox-ep	Quebrada El Rayo/ rt 328	23,600	95,940	Sabana Grande
Dike-Cutting Cotui Limestone							
VP245	Basalt			Bo. Tuna	26,600	82,400	San German
				RIO BLANCO I VSA			
Maricao Formation							
VP10	Basalt	Plag.-cpx	Chlt.-calc.-seric.	Rt 128 km	26,000	107,000	Yauco
VP11	Trachyandesite	Plag-cpx.(augite)	Chlt.-sericite	Rt 128 km 20.7	26,000	107,000	Yauco
Rio Blanco Formation							
VP165	Px basalt	Cpx-plag	Chlorite-sericite	Rt 124 km 1.1	45,860	94,100	Maricao
Concepción Formation							
VP181	Bas. andesite	Cpx-opx?plag(an)	Chlt.-act.-Qt.-carb.	Rt 124 km 2.0	45,860	94,480	Maricao
Lago Garzas Formation							
VP167	Basalt	Cpx-plag(and)	Chlorite-calc.-Qtz.	Rt 129	42,360	114,380	Mt. Guilarte
VP169	Dacite	Plag(olig)	Chlt.-Qtz-actin?	Rt 135 km 70.7	38,320	112,180	Mt. Guilarte
VP173	Basalt	Cpx-plag	Chlt.-act.-sericite	Rt 518 km 2.7	40,225	120,975	Adjuntas
VP174	Basalt	Cpx-camph?-plag(an)	Chit-epidote	Rt 518 km 5.9	33,775	120,700	Adjuntas

TABLE 1. PETROGRAPHY AND LOCATION OF ANALYZED ROCKS OF THE SOUTHWEST IGNEOUS PROVINCE (continued, page 2)

Number	Rock	Primary Assembly	Secondary Assembly	Location	Puerto Rico Meter Grid		Quadrangle
			Rio Blanco I VSA (continued)				
Two-Pyroxene Basalt							
VP126	Bas. andesite	Opx-cpx. plag(and)	Chlrt-serp?-Qtz	Rt 362 km 8.45	31,400	92,200	San German
VP127	Bas. andesite	Cpx-opx-plag(and)	Seric-chlor-serp?	Rt 362 km 9.6	31,800	92,400	San German
VP162	Andesite	Cpx-opx-lag(and)	Chlorite-opaque	Rt 366 km 2.0	35,200	98,260	Maricao
Augite Andesite							
EC4	Bas. andesite	Cpx-hbl-plag(ol?)	Chlorite	Rt 330 km 5.9	35,980	83,980	Rosario
EC5	Basalt	Cpx-plag	Chlrt-sericite	Rt 330 km 5.9	35,980	83,980	Rosario
EC6	Bas andesite	Cpx-opx-plag	Chlt-serpentine?	Rt 330 km 5.9	35,980	83,980	Rosario
VP140	Andesite	Cpx-opx-plag	Calc-chit-Qtz-opq	Duey Alto	....	....	Rosario
Yauco Formation							
EC2	Basalt	Oliv?-cpx-plag.	Chlte/sericite-Qtz.	Rt 346	34,800	82,220	Rosario
EC3	Basalt	Plag-cpx?	Chltr-sericite-opq	Rt 346 km 4.5	35,560	82,980	Rosario
			Rio Blanco II VSA				
Anón Formation							
VP155	Basalt andesite	Hbl.-plag(ab).	Chl-alb-Qtz-calc	Rt 139 km 12.4	30,720	135,520	Ponce
VP157	Andesite	Hbl-plag(oli)	Chl-Qtz-calc	Rt 139 km 14.8	31,580	134,900	Ponce
VP158	Andesite	Plag(and)	Chl-opq-calc	Rt 139 km 16.5	31,520	134,720	Ponce
VP159	Dacite	Cpx-hbl-plag	Chl-Qtz-sercite	Off rt 511, La Mesa	30,650	139,110	Ponce
VP161	Andesite	Hbl?-plag(and)	Chl-opq-calc	Rt 511 km 11.9	33,710	136,930	Jayuya
VP166	Trachyte	Hbl-plag	Calc-opq-chl	Rt 129	44,020	112,500	Mt. Guilarte
VP175	Bsalt. andesite	Cpx-plag(oli)	Chl-zeol?	Rt 10	39,500	120,365	Adjuntas
VP76	Andesite	Cpx-hbl-plag	Chl-ep	Rt 10 km 40.0	40,225	120,975	Adjuntas
Palma Escrita Formation							
EC20	Trachyte			La Tosca	51,880	69,780	Rincon
Mal Paso Formation							
EC7	Basalt	Cpx-plag	Chl-opq-Qtz.-calc--seric.	Rt 416 Ramal km 3	57,400	75,360	Rincon
TKhd							
VP141	Andesite	Cpx-hbl-plag	Chl-opq-alb-Qtz?-act?	Rt 372	27,740	117,000	Yauco
TKha							
VP172	Basalt	Cpx	Chl-calc-alb-act	Rt 128/428	37,220	106,960	Mt. Guilarte
Tad							
VP147	Basalt	Cpx-plag	Chl-calc-alb?	E. of bo. Marueno	25,020	129,900	Peñuelas
Thad							
VP144	Basalt. andesite	Cpx-plag	Calc-sercite	Rt 391	25,800	124,520	Peñuelas
TKqd							
VP100	Granodiorite	Hbl-plag(oli)	Serc.	Rt 318 km 1.9	27,800	85,880	San German
Tip							
EC10	Basalt	Hbl-cpx-plag(oli)	Chl-calc-ep.seric-opq	Rio Grande de A	51,220	87,820	Ctr la Plata

(>500 ppm), and Ba (>500 ppm) contents, and LREE-enriched patterns. All post-Bermeja basaltic rocks of the SIP, whether alkaline or subalkaline, have Cr/Y ratios characteristic of island arc basalts (Pearce, 1982).

The Cr/Y and Ti/Zr ratios of the basalts from CIP are indicative of an island arc environment. The REE patterns from these rocks are flat to slightly enriched in LREE, except those of formation C that are depleted. Overall the patterns are similar to those of island arc tholeiites (Jakes and Gill, 1970). The rocks of the Robles-Orocovis VSA are characterized by a wide range in SiO_2 content (46 to 66%), higher total alkalis and higher Sr, than the pre-Robles. Especially noticeable is the higher K_2O content, which is often accompanied by higher P_2O_5 in the rocks of the Perchas Formation, the Lapa Lava Member, and in some rocks of the Los Negros Formation. Based on the enrichment in K, Rb, Cu, U, and Th, Jolly (1970a, 1971) classified some of these rocks as shoshonites. Basaltic rocks of this VSA have Cr, Y, Ti, and Zr contents characteristic of island arcs. The chondrite normalized REE patterns of all rocks are LREE enriched and thus distinct from the underlying Aptian through Albian pre-Robles VSA.

TABLE 2. CHEMICAL COMPOSITIONS SIP

	Bermeia Complex				Maquayo VSA							
	VP-179 Gabbro	VP-117 Dike	EC-13 Las Mesas Greenstone	VP-2 Dike	VP-113 Boqueron Basalt	VP-122 Lajas Formation	VP-120 Basaltic Andesite	VP-119 Basaltic Andesite	VP-114 Boqueron Basalt	EC-15 Lajas Formation	VP-124 Lajas Formation	VP-110 Boqueron Basalt
SiO_2	48.07	50.27	50.30	51.25	53.80	54.57	54.88	55.00	56.43	56.72	58.74	59.69
TiO_2	1.45	1.36	1.23	1.42	0.89	1.39	1.34	1.17	0.98	0.70	0.90	1.16
Al_2O_3	16.00	13.04	12.80	14.34	16.92	16.76	17.22	17.57	17.83	16.69	16.54	16.91
FeO*	9.67	11.56	11.81	10.64	8.49	9.02	8.16	8.28	6.50	6.82	6.38	4.74
MnO	0.15	0.18	0.20	0.18	0.16	0.32	0.15	0.12	0.15	0.11	0.25	0.31
MgO	8.45	10.20	12.04	8.29	6.66	6.06	4.92	4.09	3.57	5.37	5.45	1.95
CaO	13.47	9.85	7.19	10.27	9.02	7.49	7.90	8.69	6.69	6.27	3.81	8.26
Na_2O	2.47	3.10	4.02	3.05	2.28	3.40	2.85	3.00	4.79	4.30	4.20	5.80
K_2O	0.23	0.36	0.23	0.33	1.38	0.54	2.05	1.56	2.59	2.61	3.32	0.61
BaO	0.02	0.07	0.02	0.09	0.07	0.16	0.13	0.10	0.13	0.13	0.19	0.07
P_2O_5	0.00	0.00	0.15	0.16	0.35	0.29	0.40	0.42	0.35	0.28	0.23	0.48
Total	100.00	100.00	100.00	100.00	100.00	100.00	100.00	100.00	100.00	100.00	100.00	100.00
Hydrous total	*	99.63	95.07	*	95.84	93.01	97.63	101.54	95.76	93.73	94.41	95.13
Cs	....	....	....	....	0.24	....	....	....	....	....	....	....
Sc	42.2	39.2	36.8	39.3	26.4	25.5	26.6	....	....	23.0	....	....
V	326	321	179	294	174	268	253	226	189	114	157	207
Cr	199	201	159	220	232	18	23	51	236	170	20	bd
NI	61	69	60	57	92	13	13	14	57	59	23	8
Cu	78	71	29	70	55	77	50	8	57	<10	26	177
Zn	61	77	84	69	60	74	81	78	86	69	73	72
Rb	<3	3	<5	2	17	4	24	19	33	48	53	1
Sr	364	216	89	180	543	670	448	554	580	498	569	511
Y	24	24	16	22	17	16	19	18	18	16	18	18
Zr	76	87	59	77	171	168	185	166	182	140	149	246
Nb	4	<2	11	3	12	11	19	15	12	14	11	30
Ba	170	627	179	783	591	1,292	1,155	883	1,091	1,075	1,579	584
La	1.89	2.33	2.57	2.77	19.90	21.50	22.40	19.00	14.00	25.00	23.00	37.00
Ce	9.70	8.00	9.30	9.80	43.10	45.00	49.80	68.00	88.00	93.00	110.00	70.00
Nd	7.20	7.10	7.90	7.20	21.40	21.60	23.60	....	....	....	....	....
Sm	2.80	2.77	2.86	2.91	4.13	4.60	5.38	....	....	....	....	....
Eu	1.05	0.98	0.98	1.07	1.20	1.38	1.52	....	....	....	....	....
Tb	0.69	0.70	0.61	0.85	0.46	0.59	0.59	....	....	....	....	....
Yb	2.75	2.76	2.94	2.87	1.68	1.68	2.17	....	....	....	....	....
Lu	0.42	0.41	0.42	0.41	0.26	0.26	0.33	....	....	....	....	....
Hf	1.37	2.07	1.90	2.00	3.49	3.10	4.19	....	....	....	....	....
Th	....	0.10	0.10	0.20	3.40	3.40	3.00	....	....	....	....	....
U	....	....	....	0.00	....	....	....	....	....	....	....	....

Almost all rocks show a slight negative Ce anomaly. Eu anomalies are also present, with the Avispa Formation showing a negative anomaly, and the Perchas Formation and an andesite from the Robles Formation a positive anomaly. Chemically, the rocks of the Vista Alegre–Tetuán VSA resemble some of the rocks of the Robles-Orocovis VSA, with which they are contemporaneous. The high content of total alkalies for the sample of the Vista Alegre Formation classifies this rock as an alkali basalt. The chondrite normalized REE patterns of the Malo Breccia and Mameyes Formation are very similar and show a flat pattern, with positive Nd and Eu anomalies; in contrast, the sample of the Vista Alegre Formation has a LREE enriched pattern and is more depleted in HREE. The flow rocks of the Pozas-Cariblanco VSA are LREE enriched typical of calc-alkaline volcanic rocks.

Basalts are the oldest rocks of the NIP (Figuera-Daguao VSA) and show Cr/Y and Ti/Zr ratios characteristic of island arc basalts (Pearce, 1982). The silicic rocks show similar island arc chemical characteristics. Chondrite normalized REE patterns are all flat, similar to those of island arc tholeiites (Jakes and Gill, 1970). Chondrite normalized REE patterns for the younger rocks in the NIP fall into two groups: flat patterns for basalts, $(La/Lu)_{CN}$ between 1.7 and 2.3, and more enriched patterns for

TABLE 2. CHEMICAL COMPOSITIONS SIP (continued - page 2)

	Maquayuo VSA			Monte Grande–El Rayo VSA				Río Blanco I VSA				
	VP-105 Lajas Fm.	VP-112 Boqueron Basalt	VP-118 Maguayo Porphyry	VP245 Dike thru Cotul Lst	VP-130 El Rayo Fm.	VP-96 Sabana Grande Fm.	VP-129 El Rayo Fm.	VP-153 Lago Garzas Fm.	EC-5 Augite Andesite	VP-165 Río Blanco Fm.	VP-153 Lago Garzas Fm.	EC-5 Augite Andesite
SiO_2	59.73	60.08	62.36	48.27	52.27	54.08	65.90	47.49	47.90	47.96	47.49	47.90
TiO_2	0.82	0.96	0.69	1.01	0.99	1.34	0.68	1.24	1.37	1.44	1.24	1.37
Al_2O_3	16.10	18.12	17.14	14.52	19.36	18.77	15.51	16.95	11.96	14.17	16.95	11.96
FeO*	6.12	4.83	4.51	10.85	5.69	8.77	5.38	10.68	11.64	12.48	10.68	11.64
MnO	0.14	0.19	0.18	0.12	0.27	0.14	0.13	0.20	0.20	0.30	0.20	0.20
MgO	4.55	1.01	4.03	7.40	10.13	3.38	1.40	11.43	13.37	12.51	11.43	13.37
CaO	4.49	7.83	4.26	15.41	6.26	8.86	3.88	7.95	10.72	7.85	7.95	10.72
Na_2O	5.28	4.78	3.86	1.21	4.01	3.13	6.10	1.26	1.89	2.25	1.26	1.89
K_2O	2.40	1.64	2.53	0.46	0.46	1.12	0.58	2.57	0.66	0.77	2.57	0.66
BaO	0.12	0.10	0.15	0.03	0.05	0.07	0.06	0.04	0.04	0.03	0.04	0.04
P_2O_5	0.27	0.46	0.28	0.71	0.50	0.32	0.38	0.20	0.25	0.23	0.20	0.25
Total	100.00	100.00	100.00	100.00	100.00	100.00	100.00	100.00	100.00	100.00	100.00	100.00
Hydrous total	94.44	92.55	95.98	95.41	92.57	96.11	95.77	91.04	99.41	92.66	91.04	99.41
Cs	....	....	....	....	....	....	....	....	....	....	....	....
Sc	...,....	....	....	....	....	22.5	....	....	49.0	18.9	....	49.0
V	142	175	117	201	188	228	87	257	207	299	257	207
Cr	55	21	35	381	5	5	18	42	258	308	42	258
NI	29	3	13	105	16	4	14	51	41	55	51	41
Cu	21	38	28	110	~3,393	19	47	87	266	98	87	266
Zn	68	80	116	58	113	71	50	62	44	72	62	44
Rb	33	27	53	3	1	9	5	45	16	8	45	16
Sr	599	585	489	452	798	543	599	436	319	316	436	319
Y	16	17	17	6	16	18	14	19	13	16	19	13
Zr	161	176	153	83	228	164	202	90	66	71	90	66
Nb	13	10	24	6	8	16	13	2	12	9	2	12
Ba	976	834	1,263	215	405	613	521	326	358	251	326	358
La	27.00	30.00	13.00	5.00	24.00	16.10	21.00	7.00	17.00	5.48	7.00	17.00
Ce	78.00	68.00	91.00	....	45.00	39.20	51.00	33.00	59.00	17.60	33.00	59.00
Nd	....	....	....	....	....	20.70	....	....	....	10.80	....	....
Sm	....	....	....	....	....	4.85	....	....	....	2.93	....	....
Eu	....	....	....	....	....	1.49	....	....	....	0.92	....	....
Tb	....	....	....	....	....	0.69	....	....	....	0.55	....	....
Yb	....	....	....	....	....	2.49	....	....	....	1.85	....	....
Lu	....	....	....	....	....	0.39	....	....	....	0.29	....	....
Hf	....	....	....	....	....	3.46	....	....	....	1.57	....	....
Th	....	....	....	....	....	1.50	....	....	....	0.20	....	....
U	....	....	....	....	....	....	....	....	....	0.00	....	......;

the flows richer in silica with $(La/Lu)_{CN}$ = 5.0 to 6.4; all basaltic rocks, however, have Cr/Y ratios typical of basic rocks erupted in an island arc environment (Pearce, 1982).

GEOCHEMICAL EVOLUTION AND TECTONIC HISTORY

Indicators of geochemical evolution

Major changes in chemistry have occurred within the life span of the active island arcs that make up the Puerto Rico part of the PRVI terrane. Traditionally, volcanic rocks occurring in island arcs were classified as calc-alkalic, tholeiitic, and alkalic (e.g., Gill, 1981); the evolution was thought to occur from an early "tholeiitic" magma followed by a later "calc-alkaline" magma (cf. Ringwood, 1974). Chemical changes occurring in island arc evolution were also discussed by Gill (1981, p. 225), who distinguished, predominantly based on his work in the southwest Pacific, an early stage of "island-arc tholeiite," followed by "calc-alkaline" suites, and as a last volcanic event, the eruption of "shoshonites," which, if present, occurred the farthest from the trench. Based on their work in the Caribbean, Donnelly and Rogers (1980) divided the volcanic rocks originating in island arcs into three categories: a primitive or primitive island arc (PIA)

TABLE 2. CHEMICAL COMPOSITIONS SIP (continued - page 3)

	Río Blanco I VSA											
	VP-165 Río Blanco Fm	VP-11 Maricao Fm	EC-2 Yauco Fm	VP174 Lago Garzas Fm	VP-173 Lago Garzas Fm	EC-3 Yauco Fm	VP-10 Maricao Fm	EC-6 Augite Andesite	EC-4 Augite Andesite	VP-181 Concepción Fm	VP-127 Two-px Basalt	VP-140 Augite Andesite
SiO_2	47.96	48.58	49.63	50.42	51.19	51.55	52.74	53.23	53.67	55.47	55.51	56.50
TiO_2	1.44	1.61	1.01	0.80	0.86	1.61	1.42	0.80	1.07	0.87	0.85	0.70
Al_2O_3	14.17	16.22	14.39	19.55	17.25	14.65	17.06	18.50	17.43	16.95	12.12	17.69
FeO*	12.48	12.36	10.98	9.03	7.18	11.71	10.64	8.50	9.32	8.80	8.91	7.33
MnO	0.30	0.19	0.20	0.24	0.14	0.19	0.22	0.24	0.19	0.18	0.16	0.25
MgO	12.51	7.94	8.62	6.49	9.24	6.05	5.42	4.95	4.12	5.80	12.49	5.08
CaO	7.85	8.38	9.07	10.49	11.23	7.81	5.05	9.38	6.50	7.36	6.01	7.99
Na_2O	2.25	2.80	3.31	2.22	2.09	4.03	4.13	2.62	4.46	2.47	1.62	3.60
K_2O	0.77	1.61	2.04	0.59	0.61	1.92	2.71	1.45	2.57	1.81	1.98	0.55
BaO	0.03	0.06	0.06	0.01	0.02	0.11	0.20	0.04	0.14	0.06	0.14	0.04
P_2O_5	0.23	0.24	0.67	0.15	0.19	0.37	0.42	0.31	0.52	0.22	0.22	0.26
Total	100.00	100.00	100.00	100.00	100.00	100.00	100.00	100.00	100.00	100.00	100.00	100.00
Hydrous total	92.66	98.66	95.08	98.08	98.50	92.25	93.78	97.75	94.67	95.59	90.81	93.71
Cs	....	....	....	....	....	....	....	....	....	....	....	....
Sc	18.9	51.6	29.0	25.3	....	29.0	27.5	28.0	23.0	23.2	....	....
V	299	360	174	192	191	195	270	141	155	190	165	143
Cr	308	52	179	30	152	41	28	116	34	45	475	141
NI	55	15	71	8	82	<10	23	20	24	10	115	56
Cu	98	83	66	8	60	138	55	<10	26	82	86	45
Zn	72	69	55	88	51	96	76	65	94	69	66	83
Rb	8	14	25	3	50	25	38	23	33	20	39	6
Sr	316	710	1,129	298	461	947	2,360	555	871	405	462	565
Y	16	17	13	15	18	23	18	13	19	16	17	14
Zr	71	106	174	62	135	159	308	120	192	98	150	157
Nb	9	0	<5	5	11	<5	<5	<5	<5	6	15	6
Ba	251	539	537	124	184	896	1,670	358	1,164	546	1,094	354
La	5.48	7.61	22.00	2.80	5.00	26.00	13.90	27.00	25.00	8.75	89.00	29.00
Ce	17.60	20.30	67.00	8.10	40.00	122.00	34.10	39.00	128.00	30.30	23.00	40.00
Nd	10.80	13.20	....	6.40	....	....	19.50	....	....	19.80	....	....
Sm	2.93	3.22	....	1.97	....	....	4.69	....	....	2.72	....	....
Eu	0.92	1.14	....	0.73	....	....	1.37	....	....	0.85	....	....
Tb	0.55	0.63	....	0.42	....	....	0.56	....	....	0.34	....	....
Yb	1.85	1.83	....	1.71	....	....	2.16	....	....	1.70	....	....
Lu	0.29	0.28	....	0.28	....	....	0.34	....	....	0.28	....	....
Hf	1.57	1.43	....	1.35	....	....	2.28	....	....	2.22	....	....
Th	0.20	0.66	....	0.20	....	....	1.70	....	....	1.40	....	....
U	0.00	0.00	....	0.00	....	....	0.00	....	....	0.00	....	....

series; a calc-alkaline (CA) series, including a high-potassium (HK) subseries; and a diabase series. The PIA series occurs in the early stages of island arc evolution, whereas the CA and HK series are characteristic for the "evolved" stage of the island arc. The chemical characteristics of the island arc tholeiites are very similar to those of the PIA, whereas the shoshonites are generally the same as the HK subseries (Donnelly and Rogers, 1980). This evolution from an early tholeiitic stage to a more evolved calc-alkaline stage is complicated by the fact that tholeiitic and calc-alkaline rocks are known to extrude contemporaneously within the same arc segment (Mahlburg Kay et al., 1982; Mahlburg Kay and Kay, 1985).

To test the validity of the distinction between tholeiite and calc-alkaline suites for use to describe the evolution of the volcanic rocks of Puerto Rico, an attempt was made to classify the rocks accordingly. The terms calc-alkaline and tholeiitic magma series are defined based on several different criteria (see Gill, 1981, for a discussion). Both are defined as subalkalic and are distinguished on the basis of their iron enrichment trends (Wager and Deer, 1939); commonly, these differences are shown on an AFM diagram (e.g., Carmichael, 1964). Because the AFM diagram involves mobile alkalies, such criteria could not be applied to the rocks under study here. A different attempt to distinguish tholeiitic and calc-alkaline rocks is based on their FeO*/MgO ratios with

TABLE 2. CHEMICAL COMPOSITIONS SIP (continued - page 4)

	Río Blanco I VSA				Río Blanco II VSA							
	VP-126 Two-px Basalt	VP-162 Two-px Basalt	VP-167 Lago Garzas Fm	VP-169 Lago Garzas Fm	EC-7 Mal Paso Fm	EC-10 Tip	VP-172 TKha	VP-147 Tad	VP-144 Thad	VP-155 Anón Fm	VP-175 Anón Fm	VP-161 Anón Fm
SiO_2	57.00	58.36	61.90	68.37	46.23	46.48	47.82	51.11	52.60	56.60	56.91	57.24
TiO_2	0.83	0.92	0.64	0.42	1.09	1.05	1.13	1.00	1.34	0.72	0.75	0.73
Al_2O_3	11.87	12.20	17.26	15.53	17.09	18.05	14.14	19.25	16.55	18.81	18.18	21.33
FeO*	8.50	8.38	5.79	3.07	8.53	9.16	11.43	7.91	10.63	6.48	7.59	6.73
MnO	0.16	0.15	0.16	0.10	0.18	0.21	0.23	0.15	0.24	0.20	0.21	0.15
MgO	10.50	9.46	1.09	1.72	13.24	11.52	13.66	3.25	5.41	3.98	3.97	2.57
CaO	7.16	6.65	7.15	1.89	9.92	8.39	6.93	14.48	7.58	8.37	8.63	6.78
Na_2O	2.04	1.98	3.76	5.55	2.44	2.48	1.68	1.85	3.40	3.46	2.90	2.52
K_2O	1.57	1.56	1.94	3.12	0.98	2.22	2.23	0.70	1.94	1.08	0.61	1.65
BaO	0.14	0.12	0.04	0.06	0.03	0.08	0.14	0.02	0.05	0.05	0.02	0.03
P_2O_5	0.23	0.23	0.27	0.17	0.28	0.37	0.59	0.26	0.26	0.26	0.23	0.26
Total	100.00	100.00	100.00	100.00	100.00	100.00	100.00	100.00	100.00	100.00	100.00	100.00
Hydrous total	95.28	94.41	97.04	96.09	97.17	97.40	87.93	86.50	88.05	94.94	96.61	91.40
Cs	....	....	....	....	....	....	....	....	....	....	....	....
Sc	25.5	....	....	....				31.4				
V	165	177	118	56	32.3	26		194	248	139	145	127
Cr	438	359	68	90	157	156	224	16	130	<12	5	<12
NI	118	73	=	=	249	104	551	21	23	3	<3	3
Cu	87	83	21	13	99	67	155	58	87	22	41	bd
Zn	73	68	33	47	<10	33	93	44	77	65	75	89
Rb	22	26	22	49	68	60	81	11	39	13	16	21
Sr	562	594	459	122	8	38	33	301	600	463	862	268
Y	15	15	18	16	433	360	876	13	19	17	19	16
Zr	155	173	131	132	13	18	20	60	126	138	192	121
Nb	11	13	4	19	90	104	228	4	13	7	<3	12
Ba	1,181	996	370	502	8	12	7	119	402	384	187	235
La	21.00	24.00	16.00	23.00	269	717	1,080	5.51	<10	18	24	21
Ce	43.30	79.00	34.00	40.00	10.7	21	19	13.7	....	41	28	34
Nd	18.70	....	....	....	25.3	71	52	9.1	....	....	....	....
Sm	3.64	....	....	....	15.4	....	....	2.46	....	....	....	....
Eu	0.98	....	....	....	3.73	....	....	0.88	....	....	....	....
Tb	0.42	....	....	....	1.28	....	....	0.49	....	....	....	....
Yb	0.89	....	....	....	0.59	....	....	1.78	....	....	....	....
Lu	0.17	....	....	....	1.97	....	....	0.29	....	....	....	....
Hf	2.73	....	....	....	0.3	....	....	1.30	....	....	....	....
Th	3.40	....	....	....	1.95	....	....	0.53	....	....	....	....
U	0.00	....	....	....	1.1	....	....	....	....	....	....	....

respect to their SiO_2 content as defined by Miyashiro (1974), For most formations in Puerto Rico the distinction between calc-alkaline and tholeiitic rocks, using the latter method, does not yield unequivocal results (Fig. 3). Except in a few cases (Bermeja amphibolites, Maguayo VSA, and the Anón Formation (Lower Tertiary Río Blanco II VSA), analyses from a single formation fall in both fields, although occasionally the number of analyses for one formation is too small to be representative.

Jakes and Gill (1970) distinguished island arc tholeiites from calc-alkalic, shoshonitic, and alkalic volcanics on the basis of chondrite normalized REE. Similarly, Donnelly and Rogers (1980) mentioned that their PIA series rocks had flat REE patterns, whereas the CA series and the HK subseries rocks have LREE enriched patterns. The REE patterns for the Puerto Rican volcanic rocks are summarized in Figure 4, in which chondrite normalized La/Sm values—where the $(La/Sm)_{CN}$ of about 1 indicates that there is no LREE enrichment—are plotted against the age of the rocks. The figure shows that in all three igneous provinces the $(La/Sm)_{CN}$ suggests a flat pattern (island arc tholeiites/PIA) before 100 Ma, whereas in the younger volcanic rocks the $(La/Sm)_{CN}$ values range from low, indicating a flat or depleted pattern, to high, suggesting enriched patterns. These data suggest that the island arc terrane of Puerto Rico underwent a distinct chemical evolution with time. The cause for this

TABLE 2. CHEMICAL COMPOSITIONS SIP (continued - page 5)

	Río Blanco II VSA								
	VP-158 Anón Fm.	VP-141 TKhd	VP-176 Anón Fm.	VP-157 Anón Fm.	VP-167 Anón Fm.	VP-100 TKqd	VP-166 Anón Fm.	VP-159 Anón Fm.	EC-20 Palma Escrita
SiO_2	58.31	58.45	58.78	60.31	61.90	62.67	63.62	63.84	66.55
TiO_2	0.63	0.83	0.58	0.58	0.64	0.50	0.42	0.42	0.72
Al_2O_3	17.29	17.27	17.63	17.37	17.26	17.02	18.23	17.74	16.21
FeO*	6.80	6.61	6.54	5.45	5.79	3.46	4.33	3.52	4.17
MnO	0.24	0.16	0.22	0.21	0.16	0.14	0.13	0.15	0.12
MgO	4.03	4.46	4.16	3.35	1.09	4.45	2.72	2.99	2.02
CaO	7.50	7.08	7.16	5.83	7.15	3.31	2.56	4.20	1.07
Na_2O	3.47	3.43	3.93	4.64	3.76	5.85	4.90	4.77	6.11
K_2O	1.40	1.42	0.68	1.93	1.94	2.26	2.75	2.08	2.74
BaO	0.06	0.05	0.03	0.05	0.04	0.11	0.06	0.06	0.11
P_2O_5	0.27	0.24	0.30	0.28	0.27	0.23	0.29	0.22	0.18
Total	100.00	100.00	100.00	100.00	100.00	100.00	100.00	100.00	100.00
Hydrous total	95.54	90.93	95.54	96.84	97.04	97.29	93.19	95.04	91.81
Cs	....	....	....	....	....	....	....	....	....
Sc	....	....	8.9	....	....	....	....	....	9
V	109	151	105	97	118	95	60	64	83
Cr	7	<12	15	<12	68	34	22	1	40
NI	<3	<3	<3	4	<3	107	bd	bd	13
Cu	36	74	38	26	21	54	7	20	<10
Zn	78	54	81	70	33	74	80	64	69
Rb	16	19	10	35	22	45	32	33	42
Sr	492	443	439	532	459	763	288	484	93
Y	18	18	18	19	18	14	16	18	17
Zr	165	108	155	170	131	144	146	178	265
Nb	4	13	4	4	4	<3	11	6	34
Ba	488	376	242	440	370	940	480	551	896
La	19	<10	14.5	25	16	19	18	22.9	29
Ce	47	....	35.4	45	34	66	43	49.4	92
Nd	....	....	18.4	....	....	....	....	23.0	....
Sm	....	....	4.06	....	....	....	....	4.54	....
Eu	....	....	1.2	....	....	....	....	1.28	....
Tb	....	....	0.53	....	....	....	....	0.59	....
Yb	....	....	2.18	....	....	....	....	2.65	....
Lu	....	....	0.4	....	....	....	....	0.45	....
Hf	....	....	3.36	....	....	....	....	4.00	....
Th	....	....	3	....	....	....	....	3.97	....
U	....	....		....	....	....	....	....	....

*Only totals forced to 100%.

change will be explored using elements indicative of the source of the magmas.

Geochemical evidence for contamination in island arc magmas

$(Ce/Ce^*)_{CN}$. Pelagic sediments, sea water, and nannofossil oozes all have negative Ce anomalies (Hole et al., 1984), a characteristic that may be used to test for involvement of pelagic sediments in magma genesis (White and Dupré, 1986). The anomaly can be expressed as the ratio of the observed chondrite normalized content $(Ce)_{CN}$ over the expected chondrite normalized content $(Ce^*)_{CN}$; hence a negative anomaly will have a $(Ce/Ce^*)_{CN} < 1$. The $(Ce/Ce^*)_{CN}$ ratios for the Cretaceous and Tertiary volcanic formations are plotted in Figure 5. The Maguayo VSA shows a distinct negative anomaly, as do some of the Cretaceous Río Blanco I and the lower Tertiary Río Blanco II VSA. The pre-Robles VSAs show no anomaly, suggesting these must have formed with little or no pelagic sediment contribution. In contrast, the Robles-Orocovis VSA shows a distinct negative Ce anomaly, suggesting mixing with pelagic sediments. The $(Ce/Ce^*)_{CN}$ ratios

TABLE 3. PETROGRAPHY AND LOCATION OF ANALYZED ROCKS OF THE CENTRAL IGNEOUS PROVINCE

Number	Rock	Primary Assembly	Secondary Assembly	Location	Puerto Rico Meter Grid		Quadrangle
			PRE-ROBLES VSA (LOWER AND UPPER)				
Formation A							
VP34	Basalt	Amph.-plag	Act.-musc.	Rt 15 km 4.5	20,860	184,850	Cayey
VP35	Basalt	Amph.-plag	Act-epid-chl	Rt 15 km 6.55	22,000	184,850	Cayey
VP36	Basalt	Plag.	Chl	Rt 15 km 9.8	22,880	185,160	Cayey
VP37	Basalt	Plag.	Chl	Rt 15 km 14.0	24,250	184,000	Cayey
VP38	Bsltc. andesite	Plag	Chl	Rt 15 km 15.7	25,800	183,600	Cayey
Formation B							
VP246	Bsitc. andesite	Oox-cpx-plag	Serp-calc	3 km W Carmen	21,580	177,120	Cayey
VP247	Bsltc. andesite	Opx-cpx-plag	Alb-serp-seric	3 km W Carmen	21,580	177,120	Cayey
VP248	Dacite	Plag	Serp-calc-Qtz.	2 km W Carmen	21,800	178,120	Cayey
VP249	Basalt	Cpx-plag	Chl-calc	Rt 712 km 3.1	21,980	175,450	Cayey
VP250	Basalt	Cpx-plag	Ch-calc	Rt 712 km 7.5	23,560	177,740	Cayey
VP251	Bsltc. andesite	Plag	Chl	Rt 712 km 8.0	23,580	178,000	Cayey
VP252	Basalt	Plag	Chl-calc	Rt 712 km 8.7	23,160	178,800	Cayey
Formation C							
VP40	Basalt	Oliv-plag	Serp-seric	Rt 15 km 20.8	28,640	181,980	Cayey
VP41	Basalt	Cpx-oliv?-opx?-plag	Chl-ep-calc	Rt 15 km 21.4	29,000	181,860	Cayey
VP42	Bas. andesite	Plag-cpx	Chl-serp	Rt 15 km 22.4	29,620	181,780	Cayey
VP87	Basalt	Ol?-cpx-plag	Serp?-Qtz.	Rt 52 km 54.2	23,250	174,530	Cayey
Río Abajo Formation							
VP29	Microdiorite	Hnbl-plag-Qtz?		Rt 3	35,600	222,960	Humacao
VP30	Basalt	Cpx-plag-glass?	Chlor.-Calc	Quarry rt 3	35,540	221,820	Humacao
Torrecilla Breccia/Pitahaya Formation							
VP31	Basalt	Cpx-plag	Chl-ep-seric	Rt 926	38,700	215,850	Humacao
VP32	Basalt	Cpx-plag	Chl-ep-seric	Rt 926	28,700	216,850	Humacao
VP33	Bsltc. andesite	Cpx-plag-hbl	Ep-seric	Rt 926 vill	38,700	216,850	Humacao
			ROBLES-OROCOVIS VSA				
Lapa Lava							
VP88	Shoshonite	Plag-cpx	Calc-chl-opq-seric	Rt 52 km 59.8	20,300	172,400	Cayey
VP89	Baslt. andesite	Cpx-plag(and)	Chi-calc-opq	Rt 52 km 60.1	19,900	172,350	Cayey
VP90	Shoshonite	Plag-cpx	Chl-calc	Rt 52 km 60.3	19,760	172,300	Cayey
Las Tetas Lava							
VP90-5	Baslt. andesite	Plag(and)-cpx	Chl-calc-opq	Rt 1 km 70.2	28,820	174,220	Cayey
VP90-8	Baslt. andesite	Plag(and)-cpx	Chl-calc	Rt 1 km 70.25	28,700	174,200	Cayey
VP90-8	Baslt. andesite	Cpx-plag	Chl-epid-opq	Rt 1 km 70.32	28,600	174,260	Cayey
VP90-9	Shoshonite	Plag(olig)-cpx	Chl-calc	Rt 1 km 70.9	28,080	174,200	Cayey
VP90-11	Basalitic trachyandesit	Plag(olig)-cpxplag (olig)-cpx	Chi-calc-epid?-zeol?	Rt 1 km 72.32	28,400	173,650	Cayey
Unnamed Andesite							
VP90-2	Dacite	Plag-hbl-cpx	Chi-opq	Trail on Las Tetas	28,580	172,850	Cayey
Perchas Formation							
VP190	Shoshonite	Cpx-plag	Chl-epid-cald-opq	In Río Perchas	50,100	155,440	Ciales
VP191	Latite	Fsp-cpx	Chl-seric	In Río Perchas	49,960	155,480	Ciales
VP91	Basalt	Cpx	Chl	Rt 155 km 34.3	48,100	155,970	Ciales
Avispa Formation							
VP186	Trachydacite	Plag(oli)-Qtz-Kfsp?	Chl-seric	Rt 567	51,400	151,900	Cailes
VP187	Trachydacite	Plag(olig)	Qtz-opq	Rt 567	51,100	151,900	Ciales
Los Negros Formation							
VP213	Basalt	Cpx	Chl-epid-calc	Rt 173	47,380	187,440	Ag. Buenas
VP193	Shoshonite	Cpx	Epid	Rt 159	53,000	160,260	Corozal
VP195	Basalt	Cpx	Epid-zeol.	River/rt 568	52,340	161,430	Corozal

TABLE 3. PETROGRAPHY AND LOCATION OF ANALYZED ROCKS OF THE CENTRAL IGNEOUS PROVINCE (continued - page 2)

Number	Rock	Primary Assembly	Secondary Assembly	Location	Puerto Rico Meter Grid		Quadrangle
			VISTA ALEGRE–TETUÁN VSA				
Malo Breccia							
VP237	Basalt.and.	Opz-hbl-cpx-plag	Serp-chl-seric-opq-clc	Rt 564 L. Matrull.	41,800	147,200	Orocovis
Vista Alegre Formation							
VP241	Shoshonite	Opx-cpx-plag(and)	Chl-seric-opq-serp	Bo. Collores	44,530	146,270	Orocovis
Mameyes Formation							
VP183	K-trachybasalt	Cpx-hbl-plag	Chl-epid-opq-seric.	Rt 141 km 12.1	47,260	137,450	Florida
			POZAS-CARIBLANCO VSA				
Pozas Formation (Minguillo Lava)							
VP184	Andesite	Cpx-plag(olig)	Chl-opq	Rt 615	51,800	147,900	Ciales
VP185	Latite	Cpx-plag(olig)	Chl-opq	Rt 615 km 0.4	52,000	147,550	Cailes

for the NIP only show slight deviation from 1 in a few samples, suggesting the rocks, characteristic of this province, were formed with only a minor contribution of ocean floor sediments.

Sm, Hf, and Yb evidence. Lidiak and Jolly (this volume) used the relationship between Sm/Hf and Hf/Yb ratios to quantify the involvement of the sedimentary and mantle components in the origin of island arc magmas (Fig. 6). Sm/Hf ratios provide a measure of the sediment end-member's influence, whereas Hf/Yb ratios give an indication of the percentage of melting and the amount of mantle enrichment. On the basis of these ratios the volcanic rocks of the Río Blanco I, Robles-Orocovis, Vista-Alegre-Tetuán, and the Santa Olaya VSA display evidence for a distinct addition of a pelagic component. This confirms the interpretation of the Ce anomalies. The Maguayo VSA is distinct and the values obtained suggest a decrease in melting rather than the addition of a sedimentary component. Ratios of the other VSAs can be best explained on the basis of differing mantle compositions.

U/Th ratios. U/Th ratios of island arc volcanic rocks have been used to indicate the involvement of continental material in magma generation (see references in Defant et al., 1991). U/Th ratios lower than 2.2 are thought to indicate a primary mantle source, whereas higher ratios can be used as indicators for the involvement of continental material (Defant et al., 1991). Twenty-one of the analyzed rocks have both U and Th analyses. The Robles-Orocovis VSA show Th/U ratios above 2.2 (Fig. 7), suggesting involvement of continental material, but this is not contradicted by the isotopic evidence (Frost et al., this volume) that more evolved material was being subducted.

Isotopic evidence. Frost and Schellekens (1991) presented Rb-Sr and Sm-Nd isotopic data for three volcanic rocks of the Río Blanco II VSA (SIP), and for a flow rock and two volcaniclastic rocks intersected during drilling in the NIP. All the analyzed rocks are of Eocene age. The samples of the flow rocks have similar initial Sr ratios of $^{87}Sr/^{86}Sr = 0.7039$ to 0.7040. Initial ε_{Nd} values of the flow rocks are more variable from +2.97 to +7.02. There is no correlation between these values and SiO_2 content, and no evidence for contamination of the magma was found in the isotopic signature of the Eocene flow rocks.

Geochemical evolution of the island arc terrane

The predominant rock types occurring on the Puerto Rico part of the PRVI terrane are summarized in Figure 2. In this figure, Puerto Rico is divided into four stratigraphic sequences. These stratigraphic sequences are unconformably overlain by the early Tertiary formations. The separate Lomas Formation has not been included, because its place in the stratigraphy is unknown.

The oldest rocks found in Puerto Rico are the Jurassic abyssal cherts present in the Bermeja Complex in southwest Puerto Rico. The cherts formed at northern or southern latitudes in the Pacific and must have been deposited on ocean floor that may be present in the Bermeja Complex as the metabasite blocks incorporated in the serpentinite. A possible reason for the preservation of this part of ocean floor in a later island arc complex may be that the ocean floor represents part of a transform fault (Las Palmas Hornblende Gneiss and Amphibolite), that could have been the site of the initiation of subduction giving rise to the Aptian-Albian island arc (Las Mesas Greenstone and pre-Robles VSA), or because the cherts and ocean floor were associated with a seamount structure (Duarte Complex of Hispaniola) that was caught up in the subduction under an Aptian-Albian island arc (Draper and Lewis, 1992). In the first case the amphibolites may represent the ocean floor basement of the volcanic arc, whereas in the second case the amphibolites represent an obducted part of the ocean floor being subducted.

The first island arc volcanic rocks in Puerto Rico are of Early Cretaceous age. In central and northeast Puerto Rico, island arc volcanism is established in the pre-Robles VSA and the Daguao-

TABLE 4. CHEMICAL COMPOSITIONS CIP

	Lower and Upper Pre-Roblas VSA											
	VP-30 Río Abajo Fm.	VP-249 Fm. B	VP-32 Pltahaya Fm.	VP-87 Fm. C	VP-34 Fm. A	VP-37 Fm. A	VP-40 Fm. C	VP-36 Fm. A	VP-252 Fm. B	VP-29 Río Abajo Fm.	VP-38 Fm. A	VP-39 Fm. B
SiO_2	46.24	47.49	47.57	47.81	48.16	48.46	48.77	49.00	49.09	51.74	53.04	53.66
TiO_2	1.13	1.28	0.90	1.05	0.87	1.16	0.88	0.90	1.17	1.27	0.92	0.64
Al_2O_3	19.91	17.50	15.77	19.79	16.80	19.10	22.45	19.03	17.04	16.07	15.89	18.79
FeO*	11.05	13.99	12.33	11.66	11.32	11.11	8.80	10.51	14.34	10.49	10.27	7.92
MnO	0.24	0.24	0.16	0.24	0.28	0.19	0.16	0.21	0.22	0.18	0.23	0.19
MgO	9.33	7.22	10.14	5.50	9.15	7.57	4.33	7.77	6.57	6.67	7.62	5.67
CaO	8.63	8.82	9.47	11.03	11.18	9.48	10.71	10.01	6.60	9.90	7.38	9.61
Na_2O	2.68	2.67	2.86	2.30	1.32	2.57	3.37	1.86	2.67	2.51	4.17	3.02
K_2O	0.43	0.63	0.53	0.39	0.79	0.14	0.32	0.25	2.16	0.89	0.32	0.31
BaO	0.03	0.02	0.03	0.03	0.01	0.02	0.02	0.02	0.02	0.03	0.01	0.01
P_2O_5	0.32	0.13	0.25	0.19	0.12	0.20	0.18	0.42	0.12	0.24	0.16	0.17
Total	100.00	100.00	100.00	100.00	100.00	100.00	100.00	100.00	100.00	100.00	100.00	100.00
Hydrous total	99.99*	88.63	100.00*	97.13	100.02*	99.99*	100.00*	92.66	86.15	100.00*	100.00*	100.00*
Cs	0.6	....	....	....	0.3	0.2	0.2	....	....	....	....	....
Sc	24.8	....	46.8	....	43.0	36.4	32.2	....	....	37.3	28.7	33.0
V	290	283	232	249	273	309	215	197	239	327	205	160
Cr	50	<12	179	<12	73	52	23	33	104	111	106	79
NI	6	7	36	5	16	12	5	<12	6	38	26	20
Cu	23	140	109	71	87	189	5	72	78	245	62	109
Zn	120	69	80	72	71	79	74	111	123	93	63	78
Rb	4	3	2	<2	4	4	<2	2	29	5	3	5
Sr	330	600	626	351	181	312	310	308	227	321	180	182
Y	18	17	15	14	15	18	16	3	17	22	19	18
Zr	79	66	84	60	39	81	49	52	53	122	97	95
Nb	2	2	<2	4	4	<2	2	5	6	1	6	6
Ba	257	195	227	247	96	176	157	128	180	259	121	90
La	8.36	<10	5.68	4	2.03	6.36	1.77	....	<10	10.3	6.81	6.41
Ce	19.9	....	14.8	19	6.6	15.1	6	....	....	26.7	18.7	18
Nd	12.3	....	10.0	....	4.9	10.6	5.1	....	....	15.7	12.9	12.7
Sm	3.54	....	3.21	....	1.79	3.16	1.92	....	....	4.51	3.36	3.52
Eu	1.08	....	1.04	....	0.59	1.02	0.76	....	....	1.32	0.97	0.98
Tb	0.62	....	0.48	....	0.37	0.58	0.41	....	....	....	0.71	0.63
Yb	2.1	....	2.14	....	1.7	2.44	1.94	....	....	2.53	2.34	2.43
Lu	0.31	....	0.28	....	0.22	0.34	0.28	....	....	0.38	0.39	0.4
Hf	0	....	1.5	....	0.9	1.8	1.1	....	....	2.8	2.5	2.8
Th	1.1	....	0.6	....	0.3	0.8	....	....	....	1.3	1	1.2
U	....	....	....	....	....	....	....	....	....	....	....	....

Figuera VSA with an age of Aptian-Albian or possibly older. The geochemistry of the lavas erupted is very similar to MORB, with depleted and flat REE patterns. The Las Mesas Greenstones and a two-pyroxene microgabbro belonging to the upper Bermeja VSA have a similar age and are chemically similar to the lavas erupted in the central and northeast igneous province. Their origin in an island arc tectonic setting was based on their inferred age and composition of the clinopyroxenes (Schellekens et al., 1990). These Early Cretaceous volcanic rocks are here interpreted as belonging to an Aptian-Albian and possibly older island arc, represented in the Dominican Republic by the Los Ranchos Formation and Maimón Schists, in Jamaica by the Devil's Racecourse Formation and others, by the Water Island Formation on the U.S. Virgin Islands, and possibly by the Early Cretaceous volcanic rocks on La Désirade (Donnelly et al., 1990). If the amphibolites and serpentinites of the Bermeja Complex, at present located southwest of the volcanic arc, represent part of the subduction complex of this arc, then the arc formed as a result of Pacific ocean floor (Farallon plate?) that was consumed in a more or less northeast(?)-dipping subduction zone. This conclusion does not contradict evidence from Hispaniola (Draper and Lewis, 1992).

The environment of the first island arc volcanism is different in each of the four stratigraphic columns (Fig. 2). In the SIP, the oldest rocks—bathyal cherts and amphibolites—occur as blocks

TABLE 4. CHEMICAL COMPOSITIONS CIP (continued - page 2)

	Lower and Upper Pre-Robles VSA							Robles-Orocóvis VSA				
	VP-33 Pitahaya Fm.	VP-42 Fm. C	VP-250 Fm. B	VP-246 Fm. B	VP-247 Fm. B	VP-251 Fm. B	VP-248 Fm. B	VP-91 Perchas Fm.	VP-195 Los Negros Fm.	VP-213 Los Negros Fm.	VP-193 Los Negros Fm.	VP-190 Perchas Fm.
SiO_2	54.13	54.52	54.98	55.60	55.77	56.79	63.40	45.90	50.00	50.24	50.97	51.40
TiO_2	0.93	0.97	1.03	1.00	1.05	0.95	0.83	0.81	0.85	0.75	0.87	0.88
Al_2O_3	16.55	18.04	16.28	16.65	16.40	16.16	16.63	11.97	14.09	13.02	15.91	16.03
FeO*	8.02	9.89	10.12	9.79	9.50	8.91	6.58	9.31	10.63	10.31	10.15	9.28
MnO	0.18	0.21	0.24	0.18	0.19	0.26	0.18	0.17	0.19	0.19	0.19	0.17
MgO	7.07	4.88	5.33	4.40	4.26	5.51	2.01	10.65	7.03	10.38	6.32	4.84
CaO	9.37	7.82	6.75	8.43	8.72	6.39	5.62	16.05	9.86	10.09	9.93	8.65
Na_2O	3.16	3.39	4.16	2.72	3.19	4.24	4.15	1.82	0.76	2.56	4.98	2.95
K_2O	0.36	0.09	0.92	0.80	0.51	0.62	0.35	2.57	6.09	1.98	0.08	5.05
BaO	0.05	0.02	0.04	0.07	0.03	0.02	0.02	0.05	0.08	0.05	0.02	0.13
P_2O_5	0.20	0.18	0.14	0.36	0.38	0.16	0.22	0.71	0.42	0.44	0.58	0.62
Total	100.00	100.00	100.00	100.00	100.00	100.00	100.00	100.00	100.00	100.00	100.00	100.00
Hydrous total	100.00*	100.00*	86.28	97.37	94.31	86.75	84.90	92.94	96.63	96.11	98.02	94.80
Cs	....	....	....	....	....	....	....	....	<0.2	<0.2	<0.2	0.3
Sc	26.7	37.4	....	....	....	....	....	26.2	30	33	20	14
V	207	220	207	195	202	175	104	172	250	280	290	240
Co												
Cr	88	39	130	31	29	<12	<12	370	260	430	160	70
NI	13	<3	<3	<3	<3	<3	3	185	70	160	100	50
Cu	55	54	83	94	105	51	18	144	110	130	90	200
Zn	63	92	72	67	66	75	94	58	85	65	65	70
Rb	2	<2	18	8	6	21	6	52	76	23	5	86
Sr	578	308	577	390	491	371	325	530	1,582	286	1,085	1,050
Y	16	22	15	8	12	8	31	8	18	18	20	18
Zr	107	68	92	98	113	70	107	83	67	60	69	79
Nb	<2	<2	7	6	8	18	2	4	8	6	7	8
Sn											19	21
Ba	450	148	326	571	257	122	186	....	17	18	164	1,105
La	5.83	2.92	38	14	<10	<10	40	431	701	468	17.5	20.8
Ce	15.5	9.82	150	....	....	....	80	13.4	16.9	12.7	35.0	40.0
Nd	10.5	9.3	....	....	....	....	....	28.9	33.0	26.0	19.0	20.0
Sm	2.83	3.02	....	....	....	....	....	15.0	17.0	16.0	4.3	4.2
Eu	0.99	1.13	....	....	....	....	....	3.49	4	3.8	1.31	1.29
Tb	0.51	0.76	....	....	....	....	....	1.13	1.22	1.13	0.6	0.6
Yb	2.16	2.94	....	....	....	....	....	0.44	0.6	0.6	1.55	1.5
Lu	0.32	0.45	....	....	....	....	....	1.33	1.51	1.43	0.22	0.24
Hf	1.9	1.6	....	....	....	....	....	0.20	0.24	0.23	1.50	1.40
Th	0.8	0.2	....	....	....	....	....	1.31	1.50	1.40	2.50	3.20
U	....	....	....	....	....	....	....	1.73	2.30	1.70	0.60	1.00
								....	0.90	0.70		

in a serpentinite melange, followed by neritic cherts and the basal part of the Yauco Formation, represented by Cenomanian cherts and volcanic sandstones and conglomerates or limestones overlying serpentinites or serpentinite conglomerates (fore arc?). In the CIP, island arc volcanism was submarine, but the presence of limestone fragments, even in the oldest formations, suggests that the volcanic edifices were substantially higher. By Albian times a carbonate platform had formed, represented by the Aguas Buenas Limestone Member and other limestone lenses of the Torrecilla Breccia and Pitahaya Formation. The limestones marked the end of the lower pre-Robles VSA. The limestone platform and the evidence for local subaerial conditions suggest that the island arc crust had attained sufficient thickness to support subaerial depositional conditions. In the NIP, island arc volcanism, beginning with the Daguao-Figuera VSA, occurred in a basin that continued to sink and did not become exposed to subaerial conditions until the beginning of the Late Cretaceous with the pre–Santa Olaya VSA. These different environments are here interpreted as reflecting their location with respect to the subduction zone and axis of the island arc. The Early Cretaceous rocks in the SIP

TABLE 4. CHEMICAL COMPOSITIONS CIP (continued - page 3)

	Robles-Orocóvis VSA											
	VP-89 Lapa Lava	VP-90.6 Las Tetas	VP-90 Lapa Lava	VP-191 Perchas Fm.	VP-90.5 Las Tetas	VP-90.8 Las Tetas	VP-90.11 Las Tetas	VP-90.9 Lapa Lava	VP-88 Lapa Lava	VP-90.2 Andesite	VP-187 Avispa Fm.	VP-186 Avispa Fm.
SiO_2	52.69	52.89	53.73	54.20	54.26	54.36	54.66	56.61	57.05	63.42	65.86	66.36
TiO_2	1.01	0.86	1.09	0.80	0.85	0.83	0.87	1.01	1.17	0.53	0.81	0.58
Al_2O_3	14.36	15.53	16.10	18.22	15.70	18.97	17.58	17.62	16.78	17.28	14.79	15.07
FeO*	7.99	10.62	7.14	7.60	9.02	8.76	8.41	8.41	6.42	5.25	6.70	4.64
MnO	0.15	0.16	0.15	0.16	0.16	0.10	0.16	0.18	0.13	0.14	0.15	0.14
MgO	11.22	5.80	7.57	3.84	4.88	3.48	3.27	2.93	4.01	2.41	1.09	1.41
CaO	7.66	10.27	6.12	4.29	10.19	7.78	7.48	5.15	4.94	5.30	1.81	3.39
Na_2O	1.74	2.09	3.21	2.45	3.42	4.22	5.04	6.63	4.35	3.91	7.32	4.91
K_2O	2.70	1.48	4.23	7.34	1.23	1.19	2.19	1.08	4.52	1.57	0.96	3.27
BaO	0.12	0.09	0.20	0.19	0.10	0.09	0.15	0.06	0.14	0.06	0.02	0.11
P_2O_5	0.37	0.21	0.45	0.91	0.21	0.21	0.19	0.32	0.49	0.12	0.50	0.13
Total	100.00	100.00	100.00	100.00	100.00	100.00	100.00	100.00	100.00	100.00	100.00	100.00
Hydrous total	92.74	98.06	96.28	97.69	99.23	96.25	98.70	99.32	92.74	98.47	96.23	95.88
Cs	....	<0.2	....	0.5	1.3	3.1	0.3	<0.2	:.:	0.6	<0.2	<0.2
Sc	21.8	35	18.9	8	31	23	23	23	....	12	10	12
V	200	370	203	170	330	260	....	....	218	100	72	62
Co							7.2	<0.5	69			
Cr	342	33	190	9.1	23	5.9				3.9	<0.5	6.9
NI	219	<10	73	<10	10	<10	<10	<10	52	<10	<10	<10
Cu	223	200	254	310	200	210	170	200	266	30	80	35
Zn	61	75	54	75	70	80	95	80	65	65	100	65
Rb	83	15	52	152	18	15	29	16	65	30	13	51
Sr	337	489	562	1,620	636	372	599	333	356	459	193	227
Y	17	16	11	22	16	16	18	24	19	16	32	28
Zr	94	66	124	85	65	58	79	108	120	104	94	98
Nb	4	6	6	10	5	5	5	6	8	7	6	7
Sn	....	21	....	16	18	17	14	17	....	14	10	8
Ba	976	783	1,702	1,647	878	786	1,267	539	1,139	519	144	903
La	12.6	5.7	14.3	27.7	6.3	6.8	7.6	10.4	15.0	16.4	13.5	11.3
Ce	27.4	14.0	28.1	52.0	14.0	16.0	16.0	24.0	90.0	32.0	31.0	25.0
Nd	12.3	9.0	13.3	23.0	10.0	10.0	10.0	15.0	....	15.0	17.0	16.0
Sm	3.12	2.4	3.22	4.8	2.5	2.6	2.8	4	....	2.7	4.2	3.6
Eu	0.92	0.81	1.01	1.46	0.82	0.87	0.91	1.2	....	0.86	1.24	0.94
Tb	0.44	0.5	0.43	0.7	0.5	0.5	0.5	0.7	....	0.4	0.9	0.7
Yb	1.47	1.5	1.67	1.89	1.58	1.49	1.73	2.36	....	1.62	2.8	2.75
Lu	0.24	0.22	0.25	0.29	0.22	0.22	0.27	0.38	....	0.26	0.42	0.42
Hf	1.89	1.10	2.18	2.00	1.30	1.40	1.60	2.10	....	2.80	2.40	3.40
Th	2.30	1.00	2.96	4.80	1.00	1.00	1.10	1.40	....	3.80	1.90	2.10
U	0.00	0.50	0.00	1.70	0.40	0.30	0.50	0.60	....	1.40	0.90	0.70

formed in front of the arc (melange, fore arc), and those in the CIP correspond to the main chain of the arc, whereas the rocks in the NIP represent part of the main chain and the trailing edge of the arc.

Most tectonic reconstructions of the Caribbean (e.g., Malfait and Dinkelman, 1972; Pindell, 1985; Pindell and Dewey, 1982; Pindell and Barrett, 1990) show the Greater Antilles being swept in from the Pacific toward the east, while overriding the Atlantic Ocean floor. This requires a flipping of the subduction zone and a change in the arc from west-facing to east-facing. This reversal of the subduction direction is thought to be due to the collision of the volcanic arc with buoyant thickened Caribbean ocean floor (Donnelly et al., 1973; Burke et al., 1978). The youngest age for this thickened ocean floor, which may represent an oceanic plateau, the B″ event (Burke et al., 1978), is about 80 Ma, requiring that the arrival of the buoyant B″ and the subsequent choking of the subduction must have occurred during the Campanian or later (Burke, 1988). This scenario is supported by evidence from the chemistry, such as reduction in melting in the Maguayo VSA (Fig. 7), the unconformity before the Monte Grande–El Rayo

TABLE 4. CHEMICAL COMPOSITIONS CIP (continued - page 4)

	Vista Alegre–Tetuan VSA			Cariblanco-Pozas VSA	
	VP-183 Mameyes Fm.	VP-237 Malo Breccia	VP-241 Vista Alegre	VP-185 Minguillo Lava	VP-184 Minguillo Lava
SiO_2	51.73	54.64	54.54	56.70	58.04
TiO_2	0.97	0.77	0.93	0.72	0.76
Al_2O_3	18.32	17.97	17.07	17.09	17.00
FeO*	9.22	8.36	7.86	7.51	8.66
MnO	0.15	0.25	0.13	0.15	0.22
MgO	4.97	4.93	5.70	3.36	3.67
CaO	8.22	8.07	4.91	6.59	7.24
Na_2O	3.42	3.01	3.08	3.70	3.23
K_2O	2.52	1.55	5.18	3.52	0.67
BaO	0.07	0.05	0.09	0.17	0.04
P_2O_5	0.42	0.41	0.49	0.48	0.47
Total	100.00	100.00	100.00	100.00	100.00
Hydrous total	93.08	97.69	93.21	96.18	93.73
Cs	....	0.7	....	0.6	0.4
Sc	22.9	23.8	11.7	18	24
V	182	148	175	250	98
Co	25.3	29.9	25.9	....	....
Cr	12	3	55	9.3	150
NI	<3	<3	17	<10	20
Cu	22	77	283	180	65
Zn	48	59	67	70	65
Rb	65	30	105	63	13
Sr	548	399	601	483	551
Y	15	21	18	20	20
Zr	92	75	125	74	80
Nb	8	....	6	7	7
Sn	....	....	....	12	13
Ba	545	405	736	1,485	343
La	5.43	5.83	27.1	11.8	10.5
Ce	14.3	14.9	51.3	24	22
Nd	9.5	11.0	22.9	13	11
Sm	2.95	2.85	4.63	3.3	2.9
Eu	1.03	1.00	1.37	0.98	0.91
Tb	0.54	0.55	0.57	0.5	0.5
Yb	2.52	2.19	1.72	1.7	1.66
Lu	0.37	0.34	0.26	0.27	0.26
Hf	1.27	1.62	1.82	2.1	2
Th	0.54	0.58	4.29	2.3	1.8
U	....	....	....	0.9	0.3

*Only totals forced to 100%.

VSA and the sudden deepening of the environment of deposition after the unconformity (Sampayo, 1992), and the emplacement of plutonic rocks (Smith et al., this volume).

Volcanism continued during the Late Cretaceous with the maturing of the arc as reflected in the diversity of magmas produced from volcanoes in the Maguayo VSA in the SIP, the Robles-Orocovis and the Vista Alegre–Tetuán VSAs in the CIP, and the Hato Puerco–Toma de Agua, pre–Santa Olaya, Santa Olaya, and Martín González–Tortugas VSAs in the NIP. The volcanic arc crust continued building up in the CIP, with the first recorded intrusive ages and the extrusion of lavas in the submarine volcanic chain with locally shallow water and possibly subaerial conditions, recorded as occasional limestone lenses and possible subaerial breccias (Malo Breccia). In the NIP, subaerial conditions are recorded in the pre–Santa Olaya VSA, but in most of the NIP deposition continued in accordance with the interpre-

TABLE 5. PETROGRAPHY AND LOCATION OF ANALYZED SAMPLES OF THE NORTHEASTERN IGNEOUS PROVINCE

Number	Rock	Primary Assembly	Secondary Assembly	Location	Puerto Rico Meter Grid		Quadrangle
Daguao-Figuera Volcano-Stratigraphic association							
Daguao Formation							
VP27	Basalt	Cpx-plag(oli-lab)	Hbl-epid-chl	Hucares	39,110	229,500	Naguabo
VP50	Basalt	Cpx-plag(oli-lab)	Hbl-epid-chl-seric	Hucares	39,130	229,540	Naguabo
VP51	Basalt	Plag(and)	Hbl-epid-chl	Hucares	39,130	229,540	Naguabo
VP53	Basalt	Plag-cpx	Hbl-epid	Hucares	39,130	229,540	Naguabo
Figuera Lava							
VP26	Rhyolite	Qtz-plag(alb)	Chl-epid	Rt 982	50,310	233,990	Fajardo
VP200	Andesite	Plag(alb)hbl-Qtz	Hbl-epid-opq	Rt 975	47,490	225,590	Naguabo
VP202	Dacite	Plag(alb)-Qtz-Kfsp?	Qtz-opq-epid-seric-zeo?	Aldea Citron	51,720	236,450	Naguabo
Fajardo Formation							
VP197	Basalt	Plag(oli)	Hbl-epid-chl-opq	Rt 971 N of Duque	46,660	221,920	Naguabo
Hato Puerco–Toma de Agua VSA							
Hato Puerco Formation							
VP24	Andesite	Plag(alb)-cpx	Chl-calc	Cabeza San Juan	61,570	237,910	Cayo Icaco
VP57	Andesite	Plag(alb)-cpz	Chl-epid-cald	Cabeza San Juan	61,780	238,350	Cayo Icaco
VP58	Andesite	Plag(alb)-cpx	Chl-zeol-opq	Cabeza San JJuan	61,745	238,030	Cayo Icaco
VP222	Basalt	Plag	Chl-qtz-calc-zeol?	Rt 356 km 3.5	53,620	206,850	Gurabo
VP223	Basalt	Plag	Chl-qtz-calc-zeol	Off rt 856	53,340	206,850	Gurabo
VP224	Bslt conglom-erate	Plag-cpx	Chl-calc-zeol	Off rt 856	53,390	206,760	Gurabo
VP227	Basalt	Plag-cpx	Chl	Río Canvanillas	51,500	208,060	Gurabo
Cambalache Formation							
VP204	Andesite?	Plag-cpx	Chl-seric-opq-cald	Desvio Dolores	61,190	213,100	Río Grande
Martín González–Tortugas VSA							
Martín González Formation							
VP20	Basalt	Cpx-plag	Chl-calc-opq	Off rt 860	59,100	200,820	Gurabo
VP21	Bsl andesite	Oliv-cpx-plag	Serp	Intersection rts 185–962	57,780	208,610	Gurabo
VP207	Basalt	Cpx-plag(and)	Chl	Quarry Truj Alto	58,000	197,880	Aguas Buenas
VP208	Basalt	Cpx-plag	Chl-seric-pyrite	Quarry Truj Alto	58,000	197,880	Aguas Buenas
VP209	Basalt	Cpx-plag(oli-byt)	Chl-seric-opq-calc	Quarry Truj Alto	58,000	197,880	Aguas Buenas
VP210	Basalt	Cpx-plag(oli)	Chl	Quarry Truj Alto	58,000	197,880	Aguas Buenas
Tortugas Andesite							
VP16	Andesite	Plag(oli)-cpx	Calc-chi-zeol-seric-opq+qtz	Quarry rt 834	53,680	188,790	Aguas Buenas
Pre–Santa Olaya VSA							
Cerro Gordo Formation							
VP12	Baslt.andesite	biot-cpx-plag(and)	Chl-prehn-opq	Rt 830	56,820	179,830	Naranjito
Santa Olaya VSA							
Santa Olaya Lava							
VP13	Basalt	Plag(oli)-cpx	Chl-calc-zeol?	Rt 174R. Quarry	55,460	183,770	Naranjito
VP14	Basalt	Plag-cpx	Chl-epid-qtz-calc-malachite?	Rt 174R. Quarry	55,460	183,770	Naranjito
VP211	Andesite?	Plag-cpx-opx?	Chl-seric-opq	Rt 797 km 3.3	50,450	189,540	Aguas Buenas
VP214	Basalt	Px?-plag	Chl-seric-opq-qtz-epid	Rt 174 repr de SJ	49,450	183,540	Naranjito
VP217	Basalt	Plag	Chl-seric-calc-opq-epid	Rt 174 Bo. Sonadora	183,58 50,340	 0	Naranjito
VP218	Basalt?	Plag	Chl-epid	Qbr. Bello Gallon	51,920	183,130	Naranjito
Celado Formation							
VP18	Basalt?	Plag(and)	Epid-chl	Rt 181 quarry	49,130	201,710	Gurabo
VP19	Basalt?	Cpx	Epid-hbl-chl	Rt 181 quarry	49,130	201,710	Gurabo
Camarones Sandstone							
VP15	Basalt?	Plag	Opq-seric	Quarry rt 1	55,100	187,720	Aguas Buenas

TABLE 6. CHEMICAL COMPOSITIONS NIP

	Daguao–Figuera VSA									Hato Puerco–Toma de Agua VSA		
	VP-51 Daguao	VP-50 Daguao	VP-27 Daguao	VP-53 Daguao	VP-197 Fajardo	VP200 Figuera	VP-28 Daguao	VP-26 Figuera	VP-202 Figuera	VP-224 Hato Puerco	VP-227 Hato Puerco	VP-24 Hato Puerco
SiO_2	47.00	49.84	50.08	50.17	51.30	60.80	65.93	74.01	75.01	49.90	51.69	54.34
TiO_2	0.81	1.04	1.04	1.00	1.12	0.83	0.37	0.57	0.63	1.15	0.94	1.28
Al_2O_3	15.84	17.14	16.31	17.08	16.08	14.84	17.34	11.89	11.40	17.90	19.80	16.81
FeO*	11.12	11.21	11.52	11.10	13.58	8.99	3.91	4.19	4.10	8.67	8.44	12.87
MnO	0.26	0.18	0.18	0.17	0.23	0.19	0.09	0.07	0.08	0.18	0.16	0.23
MgO	9.55	7.17	7.68	7.17	6.23	2.20	1.87	0.81	0.85	4.80	4.57	4.94
CaO	13.95	10.57	10.47	10.58	5.74	6.86	4.86	1.36	1.95	14.74	10.28	3.28
Na_2O	1.06	2.34	2.19	2.28	5.24	4.57	4.46	5.62	4.27	2.13	3.60	5.04
K_2O	0.15	0.30	0.31	0.20	0.17	0.51	1.00	1.21	1.40	0.37	0.36	0.97
BaO	0.01	0.02	0.01	0.01	0.02	0.00	0.05	0.09	0.13	0.02	0.02	0.07
P_2O_5	0.23	0.20	0.20	0.19	0.29	0.20	0.13	0.21	0.17	0.15	0.15	0.18
Total	100.00	100.00	100.00	100.00	100.00	100.00	100.00	100.00	100.00	100.00	100.00	100.00
Hydrous total	100.01	100.00	99.97	99.99	99.16	99.02	100.00	100.00	97.34	92.01	95.67	92.04
Cs	....	....	....	....	....	<0.2	....	....	....	<0.2	0.5	....
S	....	....	....	....	....	95	....	....	....	....	275	....
Sc	....	30.8	30.2	29.6	38.6	23	....	16.6	....	32	30	32.4
V	257	279	286	2,281	251	130	56	73	96	290	330	245
Cr	96	148	172	137	40	<0.5	25	32	27	88	33	27
NI	20	56	58	51	<10	<10	<10	<10	<10	20	10	<3
Cu	188	117	129	110	175	35	5	174	62	130	160	136
Zn	118	85	85	78	94	130	65	93	65	70	65	90
Ga	....	....	....	....	....	18	....	....	....	17	21	....
Rb	<2	<2	<2	<2	<2	8	23	12	23	6	6	15
Sr	249	354	332	343	158	241	364	65	287	352	515	213
Y	13	17	19	18	6	30	14	20	17	22	20	18
Zr	34	77	83	80	49	95	98	68	76	115	78	80
Nb	....	....	....	....	6	6	5	12	11	6	5	7
Mo	....	....	....	....	....	9	....	....	....	<2	<2	....
Sn	....	....	....	....	....	15	....	....	....	16	18	....
Ba	104	210	126	133	135	320	428	779	1,115	124	179	528
La	3.02	6.34	0.75	6.74	10	6.5	....	6.45	6	7.3	6.2	6.78
Ce	8.66	17.2	17.5	17.6	4.4	18	17	17.6	....	20	16	16.8
Nd	5.7	11.6	11.6	12.0	12.1	14	....	12.1	....	15	13	10.6
Sm	1.72	2.97	3.25	3.19	10.00	3.6	....	3.5	....	3.8	3.3	3.3
Eu	0.54	1.03	1.07	1.05	2.76	1.18	....	1.02	....	1.15	1.09	1.07
Tb	0.32	0.51	0.62	0.6	0.89	0.9	....	0.66	....	0.7	0.5	0.63
Yb	1.36	2.03	2.13	2.05	0.5	3.17	....	3.17	....	2.12	1.78	2.34
Lu	0.19	0.3	0.34	0.31	1.95	0.46	....	0.45	....	0.33	0.26	0.36
Hf	0.9	1.7	2	1.7	0.26	2.3	....	2.24	....	2.5	2	2.02
Th	2	1.1	1.3	1.2	1.67	0.8	....	0.95	....	0.7	0.6	0.75
U	....	....	....	....	....	0.5	....	....	....	<0.1	<0.1	....

tation that its setting was on the trailing edge of the arc. After the alleged clogging of the subduction zone by the buoyant thickened Caribbean crust (B″), the subduction flipped, and renewed subduction of ocean floor produced volcanic centers represented in the Cariblanco-Pozas VSA. Volcanic centers that were initially on and behind the axis of the volcanic arc found themselves at the leading edge of the subduction and were uplifted, causing the unconformity at the end of the Campanian following the formation of the Martín González–Tortugas VSA.

Continued subduction from the east was associated with large intrusions and the uplift in the CIP, creating subaerial conditions in the Maastrichtian represented by the Cariblanco-Pozas VSA. Westerly directed subduction was accompanied by back-arc spreading in the Grenada basin (Pindell and Barrett, 1990), ultimately creating the basin between the Aves Ridge and the basement of the Lesser Antilles. The former fore-arc basin became a back-arc basin that was filled by the Yauco and Sabana Grande Formations. Volcanic rocks intercalated with the sediments in the

TABLE 6. CHEMICAL COMPOSITIONS NIP (continued – page 2)

	Hato Puerco–Toma de Agua VSA					Martín González–Tortugas VSA						
	VP-58 Hato Puerco	VP-57 Hato Puerco	VP-222 Hato Puerco	VP-223 Hato Puerco	VP-204 Cambalache	VP-20 Martín González	VP-207 Martín González	VP-209 Martín González	VP-210 Martín González	VP-208 Martín González	VP-21 Martín González	VP-16 Tortugas Andesite
SiO_2	54.71	55.70	55.85	60.31	64.45	48.39	50.69	50.79	51.66	52.01	54.08	58.05
TiO_2	0.97	1.02	1.33	1.23	1.08	0.88	1.03	1.10	1.30	1.40	0.97	0.83
Al_2O_3	16.14	16.11	16.50	15.19	14.35	13.72	18.31	18.18	15.58	15.75	13.48	18.07
FeO*	9.86	10.71	9.95	8.93	6.65	9.75	9.92	10.53	12.78	13.26	8.31	6.54
MnO	0.18	0.17	0.19	0.16	0.15	0.20	0.18	0.18	0.20	0.21	0.14	0.13
MgO	4.42	4.70	3.76	3.66	2.32	10.39	4.75	5.00	5.55	5.64	10.77	3.99
CaO	7.78	5.30	4.75	4.44	2.90	14.48	10.34	9.25	7.81	6.40	7.34	6.58
Na_2O	4.31	4.35	7.31	5.58	4.68	1.76	3.62	3.33	3.95	3.71	2.26	3.93
K_2O	1.19	1.58	0.15	0.30	3.00	0.28	1.01	1.19	0.78	1.22	2.20	1.50
BaO	0.07	0.08	0.01	0.02	0.11	0.01	0.03	0.03	0.02	0.06	0.08	0.07
P_2O_5	0.37	0.28	0.21	0.19	0.32	0.14	0.13	0.43	0.38	0.33	0.36	0.31
Total	100.00	100.00	100.00	100.00	100.00	100.00	100.00	100.00	100.00	100.00	100.00	100.00
Hydrous total	95.01	92.16	96.31	95.81	92.46	93.27	96.51	97.25	95.11	94.05	97.64	94.11
Cs	....	....	<0.2	<0.2	....	....	<0.2	....	....	....	7.0	....
S	....	....	....	....	....	....	....	....	....	....	....	....
Sc	....	....	30	28	16.1	53.1	31.00	....	....	....	....	16.3
V	184	185	270	270	142	200	320	219	250	265	200	154
Cr	30	30	<0.5	<0.5	2	401	32	36	61	65	364	....
NI	<3	<3	<10	<10	<3	109	10	<3	12	10	270	2
Cu	127	141	250	130	54	<2	190	185	181	202	172	107
Zn	64	77	90	75	95	72	65	70	80	83	65	69
Ga	....	....	14	18	....	....	19	....	....	....	....	....
Rb	14	19	5	6	41	<2	18	17	11	25	18	21
Sr	318	120	129	248	134	153	581	697	222	874	700	512
Y	9	10	28	26	27	11	24	11	10	12	16	16
Zr	78	62	130	114	155	40	85	136	83	171	142	140
Nb	6	11	7	5	15	2	6	5	6	7	5	8
Mo	....	....	<2	<2	....	....	<2	....	....	....	....	....
Sn	....	....	16	16	....	....	16	....	....	....	....	....
Ba	603	645	57	191	888	104	263	236	152	519	703	612
La	12	4	7.7	7.6	18.1	3.2	5.10	19.00	6.00	6.00	15.3	12.9
Ce	....	....	20	22	44.1	8.5	14.00	....	....	....	30.9	30.5
Nd	....	....	15	17	29.9	6.1	10.00	....	....	....	16.2	16.4
Sm	....	....	4.3	4.1	7.25	1.88	3.00	....	....	....	3.96	3.97
Eu	....	....	1.26	1.32	1.87	0.68	0.95	....	....	....	1.17	1.13
Tb	....	....	0.7	0.8	1.12	0.29	0.60	....	....	....	0.48	0.62
Yb	....	....	2.67	2.38	3.87	1.40	2.18	....	....	....	1.86	1.99
Lu	....	....	0.41	0.38	0.87	0.19	0.35	....	....	....	0.27	0.29
Hf	....	....	3	2.6	4.93	1.15	2.20	....	....	....	2.42	2.82
Th	....	....	0.7	0.8	2.00	<0.2	0.90	....	....	....	2.47	1.76
U	....	....	0.8	<0.1	....							

top of the Yauco Formation (Río Blanco I VSA) have chemical characteristics, such as high Ti, Zr, Sr, Ba, and higher alkalies, that suggest their origin in a within-plate (back-arc) tectonic setting. This basin may have been the northernmost extension of the Grenada back-arc basin. This implies that the rocks of the Maguayo VSA could represent the northernmost extension of the Aves Ridge. The Parguera Limestone and the Cotui Limestone are then extensions of the limestone cover of the Aves Ridge, which is capped by limestones of similar age (Holcombe et al., 1990). Subsequent compression during the collision of the Greater Antilles arc with the Bahamas brought this northern extension close to the Late Maastrichtian–Eocene volcanic arc. Part of the PRVI terrane remained in an extensional setting as is inferred from basic dike intrusions in the NIP.

The first magmas produced as a result of subduction of Pacific ocean floor are the island arc tholeiites characterized by flat REE patterns as expressed by $(La/Sm)_{CN}$ ratios of about 1 or lower, suggesting that they were generated by mixing of melts

TABLE 6. CHEMICAL COMPOSITIONS NIP (continued – page 3)

	Pre Santa Olaya VSA	Santa Olaya VSA								
	VP-12 Carro Gordo Fm.	VP-218 Santa Olaya Fm.	VP-217 Santa Olaya Fm.	VP-13 Santa Olaya Fm.	VP-19 Celado Fm.	VP-14 Santa Olaya Fm.	VP-15 Camarones Sst	VP-18 Celado Fm.	VP-211 Santa Olaya Fm.	VP-214 Santa Olaya Fm.
SiO_2	54.54	48.17	48.81	51.53	51.98	52.02	54.95	58.55	57.24	63.20
TiO_2	1.02	0.81	0.98	1.03	1.02	1.04	0.81	0.78	0.99	1.02
Al_2O_3	17.47	19.95	15.98	16.97	19.74	16.65	20.56	17.00	16.38	15.28
FeO*	8.52	9.32	11.24	9.94	8.99	9.63	6.48	6.85	7.83	7.81
MnO	0.16	0.18	0.16	0.18	0.14	0.17	0.13	0.14	0.19	0.12
MgO	6.57	6.45	5.67	4.33	3.29	3.62	2.35	5.37	5.12	2.36
CaO	7.38	10.21	13.08	12.13	7.39	11.18	7.79	9.03	5.97	4.55
Na_2O	3.29	4.36	3.57	3.60	4.75	5.18	4.47	3.39	3.31	4.80
K_2O	0.59	0.37	0.00	0.13	2.27	0.32	1.99	0.67	2.46	0.54
BaO	0.30	0.04	0.01	0.01	0.10	0.02	0.10	0.02	0.10	0.08
P_2O_5	0.17	0.13	0.51	0.13	0.32	0.17	0.37	0.20	0.41	0.23
Total	100.00	100.00	100.00	100.00	100.00	100.00	100.00	100.00	100.00	100.00
Hydrous total	100.27	93.22	93.95	94.00	91.38	94.09	98.17	95.76	95.01	97.00
Cs	....	1.3	0	<0.2	5.70	0.4	<0.2	....	....	<0.2
S	....	....	....	....	....	....	....	....	....	....
Sc	29.6	28	0	31	23	31	15	0	....	19
V	221	320	219	340	200	360	190	166	176	190
Cr	84	24	32	28	8	28	5.30	16.00	45	13
NI	27	10	0	10	7	10	<10	<10	<10	10
Cu	238	210	178	180	193	150	150	4	154	150
Zn	84	60	55	80	61	80	65	56	72	65
Ga	....	17	....	15	0	16	20	....	....	16
Rb	5	7	....	5	33	6	50	4	35	11
Sr	474	252	117	179	602	153	1,030	368	298	429
Y	20	14	1	20	16	20	20	14	25	26
Zr	172	50	22	81	112	81	94	100	102	148
Nb	0	<2	1	5	4	5	6	6	....	7
Mo	0	<2	....	<2	....	<2	<2	....	....	2
Sn	0	20	....	18	....	14	13	....	....	16
Ba	0	321	49	70	787	137	845	202	846	651
La	11.4	3.9	....	6.2	10.8	6.3	11.6	14.0	23.0	11.6
Ce	30.3	10.0	....	17.0	24.7	16.0	26.0	21.0	....	25.0
Nd	18.50	8.00	....	12.0	14.10	11.0	13.0	....	....	16.00
Sm	4.72	2.20	....	3.20	3.38	3.00	3.50	....	....	3.90
Eu	1.16	0.80	....	0.97	1.11	0.98	1.10	....	....	1.07
Tb	0.58	0.50	....	0.60	0.58	0.50	0.60	....	....	0.60
Yb	2.57	1.17	....	1.72	1.67	1.66	1.62	....	....	2.44
Lu	0.38	0.19	....	0.26	0.24	0.24	0.24	....	....	0.39
Hf	4.23	0.80	....	1.90	1.89	1.90	2.20	....	....	4.30
Th	2.55	0.30	....	0.40	1.71	0.40	9.00	....	....	1.80
U	....	<0.1	....	0.60	0.00	0.30	1.00	....	....	1.00

with an N-type MORB composition formed through partial melting in the mantle wedge enriched by dehydration fluids derived from the downgoing slab. There is no chemical evidence for involvement of either continentally derived material or pelagic oozes. If such material was in fact absent from the ocean floor being subducted beneath Puerto Rico, that suggests that the ocean floor was both remote from any continental source and also possibly deep, because it did not have any discernible amounts of pelagic sediments.

During continuing subduction of this ocean floor from the Albian to Campanian, the lava compositions of the Robles-Orocovis VSA and the Vista Alegre–Tetuán VSA have chemical compositions that suggest the involvement of pelagic oozes, as based on negative Ce anomalies and increased Sm/Hf ratios. In

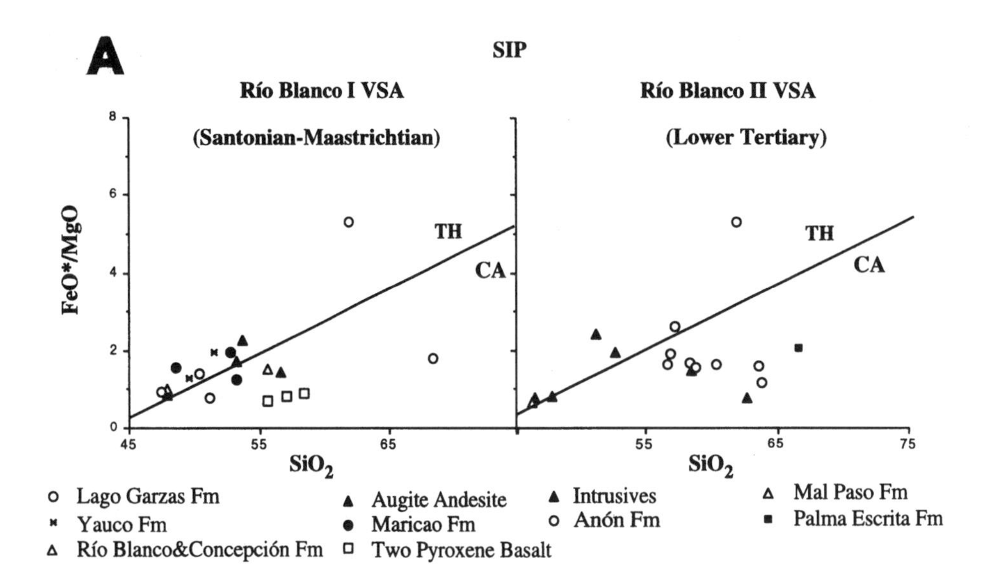

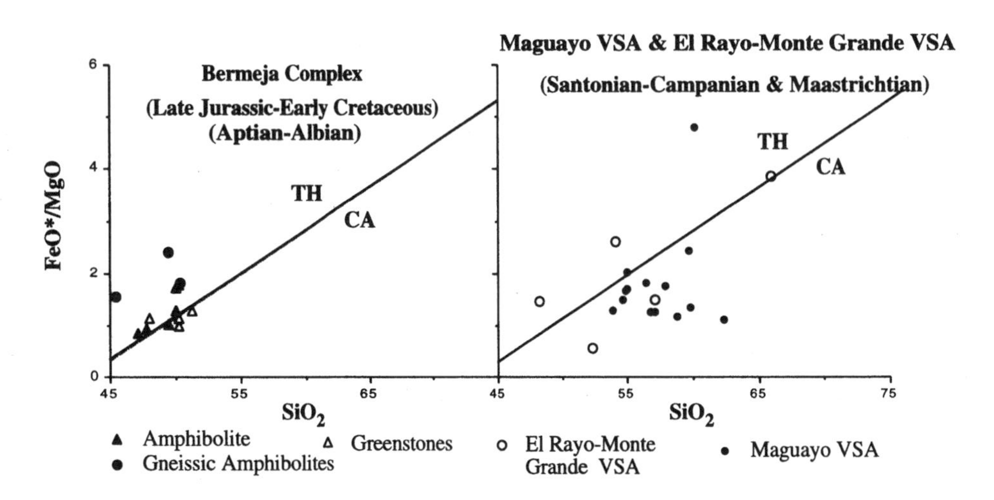

Figure 3 (this and facing page). A, FeO*/MgO versus SiO_2 for volcanic rocks of the Southwestern Igneous Province. FeO* = (Fe_2O_3 + FeO). Fields for calc-alkaline (CA) and tholeiitic (TH) volcanic rocks from Miyashiro (1974). B, FeO*/MgO versus SiO_2 for volcanic rocks of the Central and Northeastern Igneous Province. FeO* = (Fe_2O_3 + FeO). Fields for calc-alkaline (CA) and tholeiitic (TH) volcanic rocks from Miyashiro (1974).

addition, the Robles-Orocovis VSA has Th/U ratios, suggesting involvement of continental material. The involvement of pelagic oozes and the possible contamination with continentally derived debris are consistent with the subduction of older oceanic crust and the approach of South America (Pindell and Barrett, 1990). The increase of the Hf/Yb ratios for the Maguayo VSA suggests a decrease in melting, a similar feature found in the plutonic rocks of the same age (Smith et al., this volume). This decrease in melting is compatible with the slowing down of subduction due to the attempted subduction of the oceanic plateau.

After the choking of the subduction zone at the Pacific side of the island arc, subduction was initiated from the Atlantic side. The

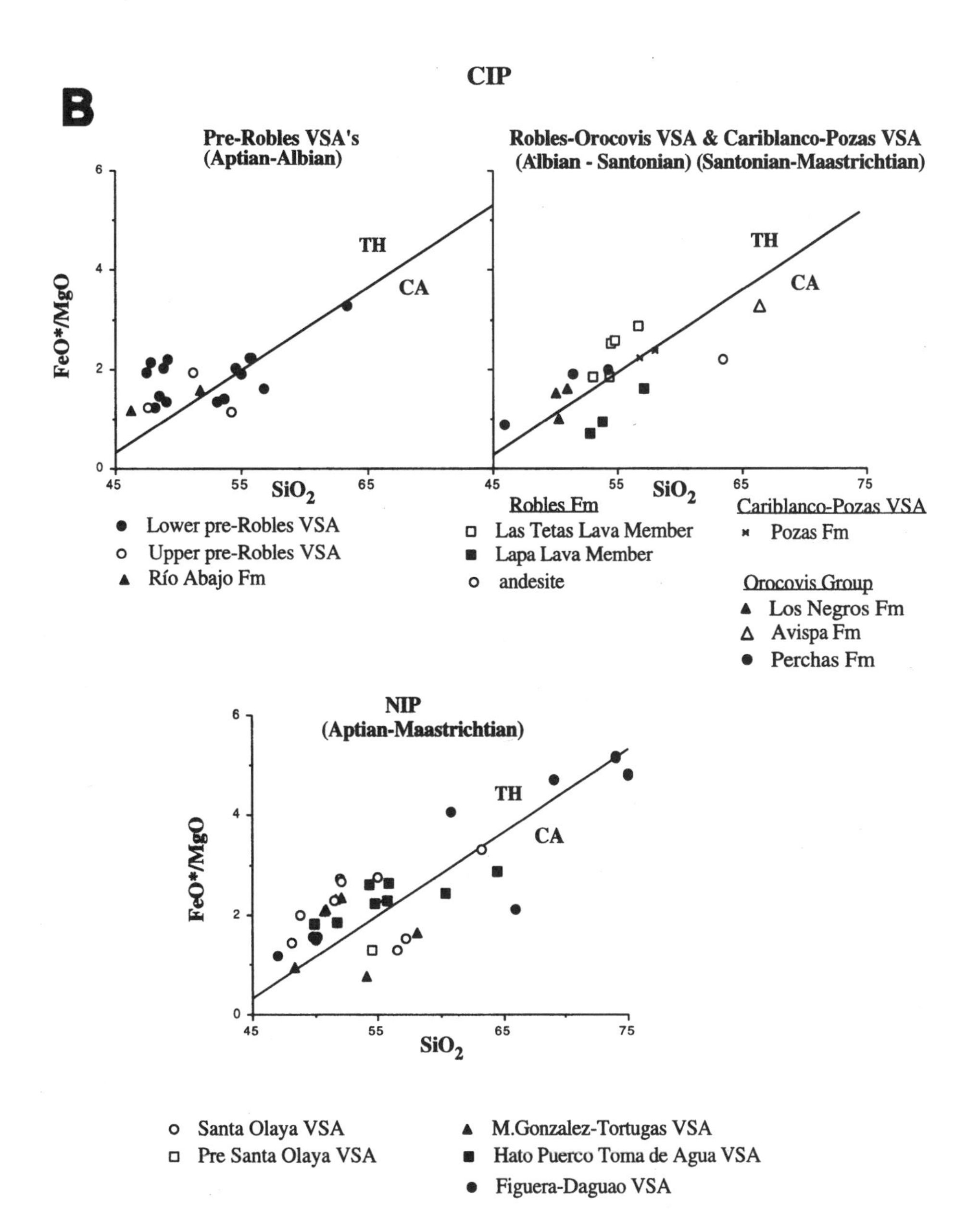

first ocean floor consumed was probably ocean floor of the proto-Caribbean, which must have formed during the separation of the North American and South American plates; this was followed by the subduction of Atlantic ocean floor that is still continuing today. Insufficient data are available from the Maastrichtian Cariblanco-Pozas VSA to draw conclusions concerning the involvement of continental and pelagic components in the magma genesis, although the one analysis obtained suggests some contribution of pelagic sediments. The contemporaneous lavas in the Late Cretaceous Río Blanco VSA I have negative Ce anomaly and higher Sm/Hf ratios suggestive of magma generation that included a pelagic component. The presence of alkaline rocks is not uncommon in island arcs (Box and Flower, 1989), and are found associated with arc rifting (e.g., Fiji: Gill and Whelen, 1989), arc-continent collision (e.g., Timor:

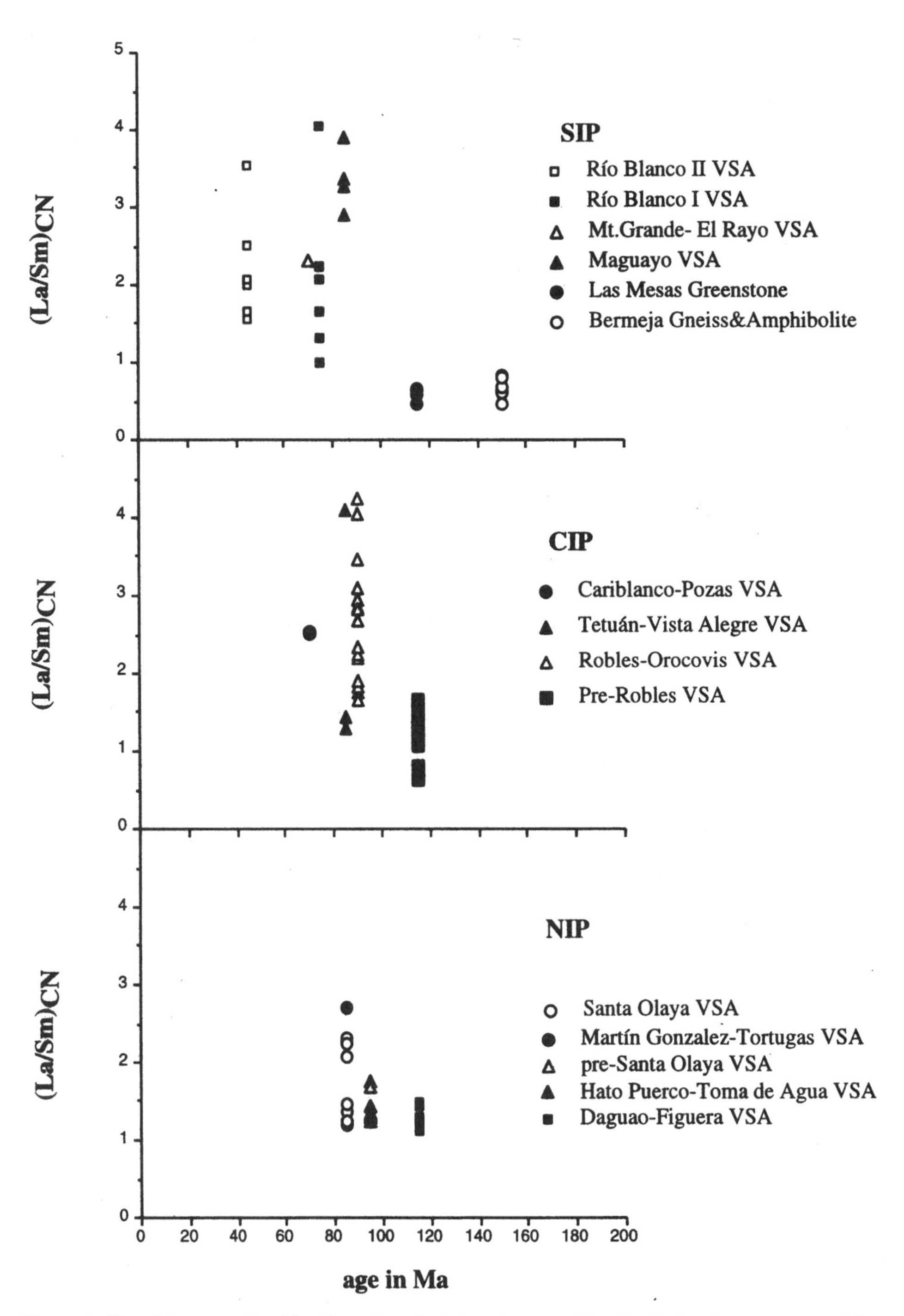

Figure 4. Chondrite normalized La/Sm ratios plotted against age. The $(La/Sm)_{CN}$ is a measure of the enrichment of the La with respect to the Sm, and illustrates the difference between tholeiitic rocks (flat, nonenriched patterns), and calc-alkaline rocks (enriched patterns), following Jakes and Gill (1970).

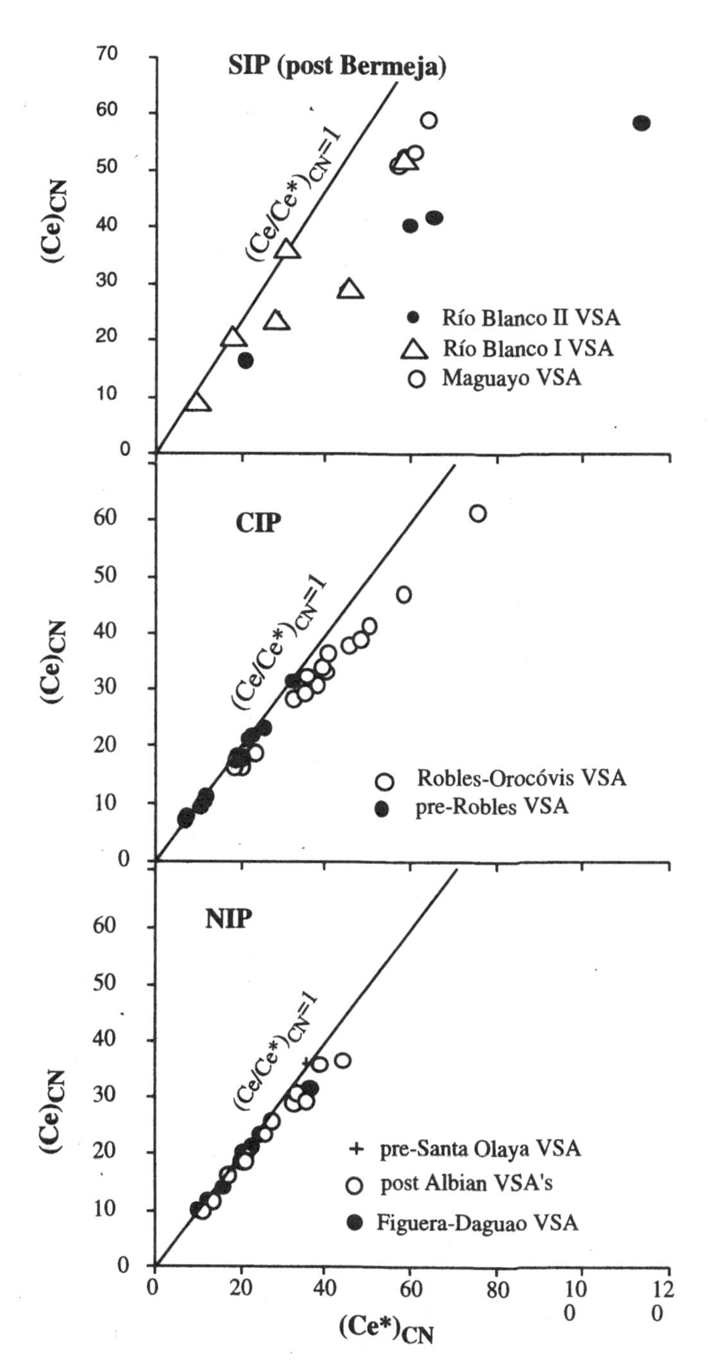

Figure 5. Ratio of observed chondrite normalized Ce content $(Ce)_{CN}$ over expected chondrite normalized Ce content $(Ce^*)_{CN}$. Negative Ce anomalies will fall below $(Ce/Ce^*) = 1$.

Varne, 1985), and near an arc-terminus (e.g., Japan: Nakamura et al., 1989). The cause for their occurrence in the Río Blanco I VSA could be any of those but awaits a more detailed study of the Maricao Formation. There is, however, no chemical indication for the involvement of continentally derived material. This would imply an older oceanic crust (proto-Caribbean?) remote from continents in concordance with the tectonic models (e.g., Pindell and Barrett, 1990).

In the lower Tertiary rocks belonging to the Río Blanco II VSA a distinct negative Ce anomaly is suggestive of the involvement of pelagic sediments; however, isotopic data of volcanic rocks show no evidence for contamination (Frost and Schellekens, 1990).

Alternate models for the origin and history of the Caribbean Plate exist (for a discussion of stabilist versus mobilist view, see Donnelly, 1985), but the occurrence of Early Jurassic radiolarians in the cherts of the Greater Antilles (Montgomery et al., 1994a,b), requires an origin outside the present-day Caribbean region. The Pacific provenance of the Caribbean plate has been widely accepted; however, the timing of the eastward motion of the plate, and hence the initiation of westward-directed subduction, is still being debated.

In the models of Mattson (1979), Burke (1988), Pindell and Barrett (1990), and Lebron and Perfit (1993), the reversal of subduction direction is caused by the attempted subduction of the oceanic plateau. Mattson (1979) has suggested that the reversal occurred around 120 to 130 Ma and renewed subduction occurred around 110 Ma. Burke (1988) has suggested a collision of the arc with the oceanic plateau to be between 84 and 60 Ma (the oldest age is the age of the intercalated sediment at the top of the plateau; Donnelly et al., 1973), with renewed subduction between 70 and 40 Ma. Lebron and Perfit (1993) proposed an arc-plateau collision in the Aptian-Albian, followed by a reversal. These authors have interpreted the cessation of primitive island arc (PIA) magmas and the renewed eruption of the calc-alkaline magmas after the Albian as the record of this reversal.

In the model proposed here, the attempted subduction of the oceanic plateau is considered to have caused the reversal, which could not have happened before 84 Ma, the age of the oldest intercalated sediments. This is in agreement with the timing proposed by Burke (1988). It is remarkable that this period between collision and renewed subduction coincides with uplift, emplacement of the major batholiths, and erosion of the arc plateau in the early Paleocene (see also Jolly et al., Chapter 1, this volume, and Smith et al., this volume). The unconformity invoked by Lebron and Perfit (1993) between the primitive island arc eruptive event (pre-Robles VSAs in this study) and the calc-alkaline event (Robles-Orocovis and contemporaneous VSAs) occurs only locally. Although the addition of pelagic oozes, as seen in the chemistry of the Albian to Campanian volcanic rocks, does not contradict this model.

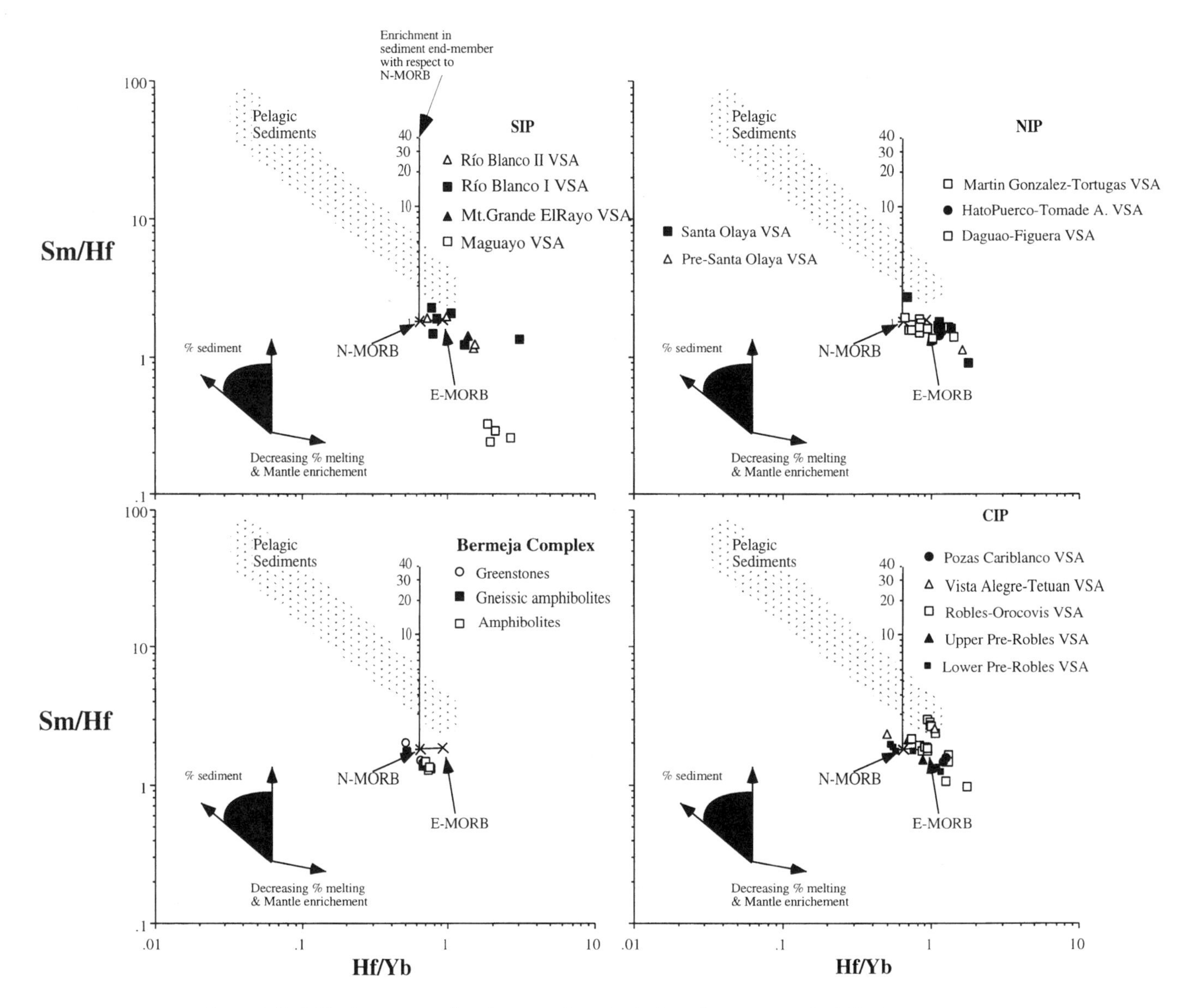

Figure 6. Sm/Hf ratios, representing the proportion of pelagic sediment versus Sm/Hf ratios, representing the degree of melting. Diagram from Lidiak and Jolly, this volume. Field for pelagic sediments from Hole et al. (1984); White and Dupré, (1986); Ben-Othman et al., (1989).

ACKNOWLEDGMENTS

This research was part of my Ph.D. dissertation work at Syracuse University. I thank my advisors, John S. Dickey, Jr., and Gary McG. Boone, for their guidance. I also thank Alan L. Smith for his advice, support, and contributions that improved the manuscript. Wayne Jolly, Edward Lidiak, and an anonymous reviewer are thanked for their comments and suggestions on earlier versions of the manuscript. This research was supported by a leave of absence with economic assistance and several grants of the Faculty of Arts and Sciences of the University of Puerto Rico at Mayagüez, a Senate Research Grant from Syracuse University, and National Science Foundation Grants RII–85–13533 and HRD93–53549.

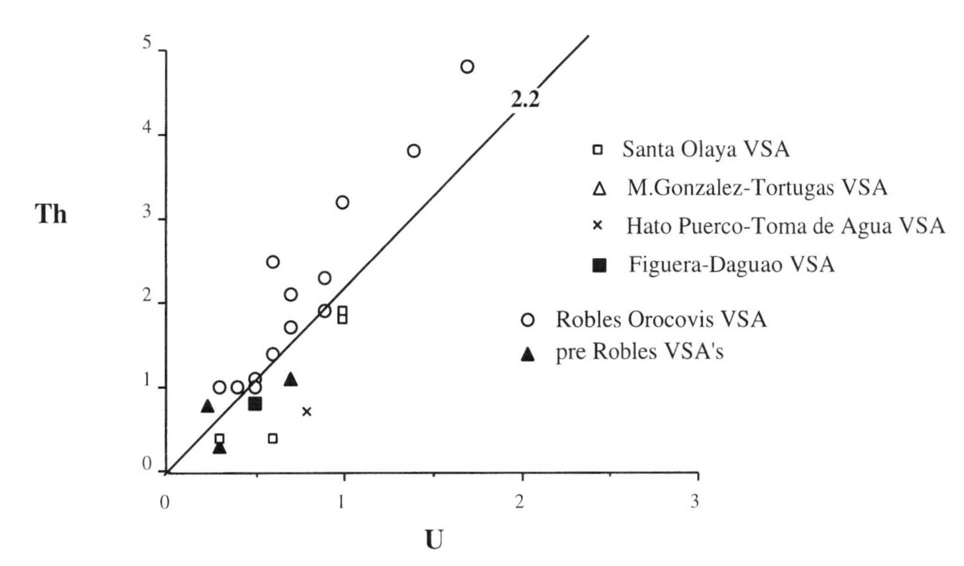

Figure 7. Th versus U. The upper limit of the MORB range and island arc volcanic rocks (Th/U = 2.2) from Defant et al. (1991).

REFERENCES CITED

Almy, C. C., Jr., 1965, Parguera Limestone, Upper Cretaceous Mayagüez Group, southwest Puerto Rico [Ph.D. thesis]: Houston, Texas, Rice University, 203 p.

Almy, C. C., Jr., 1969, Sedimentation, tectonism in the Upper Cretaceous Puerto Rican portion of the Caribbean island arc: Transactions, Gulf Association Geological Sciences, v. XIX, p. 269–279.

Barabas, A. H., 1982, Potassium-argon dating of magmatic events and hydrothermal activity associated with porphyry copper mineralization in west central Puerto Rico: Economic Geology, v. 77, p. 109–126.

Ben-Othman, D., White, W. M., and Patchett, J., 1989, The geochemistry of marine sediments, island arc magma genesis, and crustal-mantle recycling: Earth and Planetary Science Letters v. 94, p. 1–21.

Berryhill, H. L., Jr., 1961, Ash-flow deposits, Ciales quadrangle, Puerto Rico and their significance: U.S. Geological Survey Professional Paper 424–B, p. B224–B226.

Berryhill, H. L., Jr., 1965, Geology of the Ciales quadrangle, Puerto Rico: U.S. Geological Survey Bulletin, v. 1184, 116 p.

Berryhill, H. L., Jr., and Glover, L., III, 1960, Geology of the Cayey quadrangle, Puerto Rico: U.S. Geological Survey Miscellaneous Geologic Investigations Series Map I–319, scale 1:20,000.

Box, S. E., and Flower, M. F., 1989, Introduction to Special Section on alkaline arc magmatism: Journal of Geophysical Research, v. 94, B4, p. 4467–4468.

Briggs, R. P., 1967, The Malo Breccia and Cotorra Tuff in the Cretaceous of central Puerto Rico, *in* Cohee, G. V., West, W. S., and Wilkie, L. C., eds., Changes in stratigraphic nomenclature by U.S.G.S. 1966: U.S. Geological Survey Bulletin, 1254–A, p. A23–A29.

Briggs, R. P., 1969, Changes in the nomenclature Cretaceous System east-central Puerto Rico: U.S. Geological Survey Bulletin v. 1274–O, p. O1–O31.

Briggs, R. P., 1971, Geologic map of the Orocóvis quadrangle, Puerto Rico: U.S. Geological Survey Miscellaneous Geologic Investigations Map I–615, scale 1:20,000.

Briggs, R. P., 1973, The Lower Cretaceous Figuera Lava and Fajardo Formation in the stratigraphy of northeastern Puerto Rico: U.S. Geological Survey Bulletin, v. 1372–G, p. G1–G10.

Briggs, R. P., and Aguilar-Cortés, E., 1980, Geologic map of the Fajardo and Cayo Icacos quadrangles, Puerto Rico: U.S. Geological Survey Miscellaneous Geologic Investigations Map I–1153, scale 1:20,000.

Briggs, R. P., and Akers, J. P., 1965, Hydrogeologic map of Puerto Rico and adjacent islands: U.S. Geological Survey Hydrologic Investigations Atlas HA–197, 1965, scale 1:240,000.

Briggs, R. P., and Gelabert, P. A., 1962, Preliminary report of the geology of the Barranquitas quadrangle, Puerto Rico: U.S. Geological Survey Miscellaneous Geologic Investigations Map I–336, scale 1:20,000.

Briggs, R. P., and Pease, M. H., 1968, Large- and small-scale wrench faulting in an island arc segment, Puerto Rico [abs.]: Geological Society of America Special Paper 115, p. 24.

Broedel, C. H., 1961, Preliminary geologic map showing iron and copper prospects in the Juncos quadrangle, Puerto Rico: U.S. Geological Survey Miscellaneous Geologic Investigations Map I–326, scale 1:20,000.

Burke, K., 1988, Tectonic evolution of the Caribbean: Annual Review of Earth and Planetary Sciences, v. 16, p. 201–230.

Burke, K., Fox, P. J., and Sengör, A. M. C., 1978, Buoyant ocean floor and the evolution of the Caribbean: Journal of Geophysical Research, v. 83, p. 3949–3954.

Byrne, D. B., Suarez, G., and McCann, W. R., 1985, Muertos Trough subduction—Microplate tectonics in the northern Caribbean: Nature, v. 317, p. 420–421.

Carmichael, I. S. E., 1964, The petrology of Thingmuli, a Tertiary volcano in eastern Iceland: Journal of Petrology, v. 5, p. 435–460.

Cox, D. P., and Briggs, R. P., 1973, Metallogenic map of Puerto Rico: U.S. Geological Survey Miscellaneous Geologic Investigations Map I–721, scale 1:240,000.

Cox, D. P., Marvin, R. F., M'Gonigle, J. W., McIntyre, D. H., and Rogers, C. L., 1977, Potassium-argon geochronology of some metamorphic, igneous, and hydrothermal events in Puerto Rico and the Virgin Islands: U.S. Geological Survey Journal of Research, v. 5, p. 689–703.

Curet, A. F., 1986, Geologic map of the Mayagüez and Rosario quadrangles, Puerto Rico: U.S. Geological Survey Miscellaneous Geologic Investigations Map I–421, scale 1:20,000.

Defant, M. J., Maury, R. C., Ripley, E. M., Feigenson, M. D., and Jacques, D.,

1991, An example of island-arc petrogenesis: Geochemistry and petrology of the southern Luzon arc, Philippines: Journal of Petrology, v. 32, p. 455–500.

Donnelly, T. W., 1985, Mesozoic and Cenozoic plate evolution of the Caribbean region, *in* Stehli, F. G., and Webb, S. D., eds., The great American biotic interchange: New York, Plenum Press, p. 89–121.

Donnelly, T. W., and Rogers, J. J. W., 1980, Igneous series in island arcs: the northeastern Caribbean compared with worldwide island-arc assemblages: Bulletin Volcanologique, v. 3, p. 347–382.

Donnelly, T. W., Melson, W., Kay, R., and Rogers, J. J. W., 1973, Basalts and dolerites of Late Cretaceous age from the Central Caribbean, *in* Edgar, N. T., Saunders, J. B., et al., Initial Report Deep Sea Drilling Project, Volume XV: Washington, D.C., Government Printing Office, p. 989–1011.

Draper, G., and Lewis, J. F., 1992, Metamorphic belts in central Hispaniola: Geological Society of America Special Paper 262, p. 29–46.

Donnelly, T. W., and 11 others, 1990, History and geology of Caribbean igneous rock series, *in* Dengo, G., and Case, J., eds., The Caribbean region: Boulder, Colorado, Geological Society of America, The Geology of North America, v. H., p. 339–374.

Fiske, R. S., 1969, Recognition and significance of pumice in marine pyroclastic rocks: Geological Society of America Bulletin, v. 80, p. 1–8.

Frost, C. D., and Schellekens, J. H., 1991, Rb-Sr and Sm-Nd isotopic characterization of Eocene volcanic rocks from the Toa Baja borehole and the Eocene volcanic sequence, Puerto Rico: Geophysical Research Letters, v. 18, p. 545–548.

Garrison, L. E., Martin, R. G., Jr., Berryhill, H. L., Jr., Buell, M. W., Jr., Ensminger, H. R., and Perry, R. K., 1972, Preliminary tectonic map of the eastern Greater Antilles region: U.S. Geological Survey Miscellaneous Geologic Investigations Map I–732, scale 1:500,000.

Gill, J. B., 1981, Orogenic andesites and plate tectonics: New York, Springer-Verlag, 390 p.

Gill, J., and Whelan, P., 1989, Early rifting of an oceanic island arc (Fiji) produced shoshonitic to tholeiitic basalts: Journal of Geophysical Research, v. 94, B4, p. 4561–4579.

Glover, L., III, 1971, Geology of the Coamo area, Puerto Rico and its relation to the volcanic arc-trench association: U.S. Geological Survey Professional Paper 636, 102 p.

Glover, L., III and Mattson, P. H., 1967, The Jacaguas Group in central-southern Puerto Rico, *in* Cohee, G. V., West, W. S., and Wilkie, L. C., eds., Changes in stratigraphic nomenclature by U.S.G.S. 1966: U.S. Geological Survey Bulletin, v. 1254–A, p. A29–A39.

Glover, L., III, and Mattson, P. H., 1973, Geologic map of the Río Descalabrado quadrangle, Puerto Rico: U.S. Geological Survey Miscellaneous Investigations Map I–735, scale 1:20,000.

Hanson, G. W., 1980, Rare earth elements in petrogenic studies of igneous systems: Annual Review of Earth and Planetary Sciences, v. 8, p. 371–406.

Holcombe, T. L., Ladd, J. W., Westbrook, G., Edgar, N. T., and Bowland, C. L., 1990, Caribbean marine geology; ridges and basins of the plate interior, *in* Dengo, G., and Case, J., eds., The Caribbean region: Boulder, Colorado, Geological Society of America, The Geology of North America, v. H, p. 231–260.

Hole, M. J., Saunders, A. D., Marriner, G. F., and Tarney, J., 1984, Subduction of pelagic sediments: implications for the origin of Ce anomalous basalts from the Mariana Islands: Journal of the Geological Society of London, v. 141, p. 453–472.

Ila, P., and Frey, F., 1984, Utilization of neutron activation analysis in the study of geologic material, *in* Harling, O., et al., eds., Use in development of low and medium flux research reactors: v. 44 (suppl.), Atomkern Energie Kerntechnik, p. 710–716.

Jakes, P., and Gill, J., 1970, Rare earth elements and the island arc tholeiitic series: Earth and Planetary Science Letters, v. 9, p. 17–22.

Jolly, W. T., 1970a, Petrological studies of the Robles Formation, south central Puerto Rico [Ph.D. thesis]: Binghamton, State University of New York, 150 p.

Jolly, W. T., 1970b, Zeolite and prehnite-pumpellyite facies in southcentral Puerto Rico: Contributions to Mineralogy and Petrology, v. 27, p. 204–224.

Jolly, W. T., 1971, Potassium-rich igneous rocks from Puerto Rico: Geological Society of America Bulletin, v. 82, p. 399–408.

Kaye, C. A., 1959, Geology of the San Juan Metropolitan area, Puerto Rico: U.S. Geological Survey Professional Paper 317-A, 48 p.

Krushensky, R. D., 1978, Unconformity between the Cretaceous and Eocene rocks in central western Puerto Rico, a concept rejected, *in* MacGillavry, H. J., and Beets, D. J., eds., Transactions, 8th Caribbean Geological Conference, Willemstad, 1977: Geologie en Mijnbouw, v. 57, p. 227–232.

Krushensky, R. D., and Curet, A. F., 1984, Geologic map of the Monte Guilarte quadrangle, Puerto Rico: U.S. Geological Survey Miscellaneous Investigations Series Map I–1556, scale 1:20,000.

Krushensky, R. D., and Monroe, W. H., 1975, Geologic map of the Ponce quadrangle, Puerto Rico: U.S. Geological Survey Miscellaneous Geologic Investigations Map I–863, scale 1:20,000.

Krushensky, R. D., and Monroe, W. H., 1978, Geologic map of the Peñuelas and Punta Cucharra quadrangles, Puerto Rico: U.S. Geological Survey Miscellaneous Geologic Investigations Map I–1142, scale 1:20,000.

Krushensky, R. D., and Monroe, W. H., 1979, Geologic map of the Yauco and Punta Verraco quadrangles, Puerto Rico: U.S. Geological Survey Miscellaneous Geologic Investigations Map I–1147, scale 1:20,000.

Lebron, M. C., and Perfit, M. R., 1993, Stratigraphic and petrochemical data support subduction polarity reversal of the Cretaceous Caribbean island arc: Journal of Geology, v. 101, p. 389–396.

Mahlburg Kay, S., and Kay, R. W., 1985, Aleutian tholeiitic and calc-alkaline magma: Series I: The mafic phenocrysts: Contribution to Mineralogy and Petrology, v. 90, p. 276–290.

Mahlburg Kay, S., Kay, R. W., and Citron, G. P., 1982, Tectonic controls on the tholeiitic and calc-alkaline magmatism in the Aleutian arc: Journal of Geophysical Research, v. 87, p. 4051–4072.

Malfait, B. T., and Dinkelman, M. G., 1972, Circum-Caribbean tectonic and igneous activity and the evolution of the Caribbean Plate: Geological Society of America Bulletin, v. 83, p. 251–272.

Mattson, P. H., 1960, Geology of the Mayagüez area, Puerto Rico: Geological Society of America Bulletin, v. 71, p. 319–362.

Mattson, P. H., 1964, Petrography and structure of serpentinite from Mayagüez, Puerto Rico, *in* Burke, C. A., ed., A study of serpentinite: NAS-NRC Publication, v. 1188, p. 7–24.

Mattson, P. H., 1967, Cretaceous and lower Tertiary stratigraphy in west-central Puerto Rico: U.S. Geological Survey Bulletin, v. 1254–B, p. 1–35.

Mattson, P. H., 1968a, Geologic map of the Adjuntas quadrangle, Puerto Rico: U.S. Geological Survey Miscellaneous Geologic Investigations Map I–519, scale 1:20,000.

Mattson, P. H., 1968b, Geologic map of the Jayuya quadrangle, Puerto Rico: U.S. Geological Survey Miscellaneous Geologic Investigations Map I–520, scale 1:20,000.

Mattson, P. H., 1973, Middle Cretaceous nappe structures in Puerto Rican ophiolites and their relation to the tectonic history of the Greater Antilles: Geological Society of America Bulletin, v. 84, p. 21–38.

Mattson, P. H., 1979, Subduction, buoyant braking, flipping, and strike-slip faulting in the northern Caribbean: Journal of Geology, v. 87, p. 293–304.

M'Gonigle, J. W., 1977, The Río Abajo, Pitahaya, and Daguao Formations in eastern Puerto Rico: U.S. Geological Survey Bulletin, v. 1435–B, p. B1–B10.

M'Gonigle, J. W., 1978, Geologic map of the Humacao quadrangle, Puerto Rico: U.S. Geological Survey Miscellaneous Investigations Series Map I–1070, scale 1:20,000.

M'Gonigle, J. W., 1979, Geologic map of the Naguabo and part of the Puerto Puerca quadrangles, Puerto Rico: U.S. Geological Survey Miscellaneous Investigations Series Map I–1099, scale 1:20,000.

McIntyre, D. H., 1971, Geologic map of the Central La Plata quadrangle, Puerto Rico: U.S. Geological Survey Miscellaneous Investigations Series Map I–660, scale 1:20,000.

McIntyre, D. H., 1974, Concepción and Palma Escrita Formations, western Puerto Rico: U.S. Geological Survey Bulletin, v. 1394–D, p. D1–D9.

McIntyre, D. H., 1975, Geologic map of the Maricao quadrangle Puerto Rico: U.S. Geological Survey Miscellaneous Geologic Investigations Map I–918, scale 1:20,000.

McIntyre, D. H., Aaron, J. M., and Tobisch, O. T., 1970, Cretaceous and Lower Tertiary stratigraphy of northwestern Puerto Rico: U.S. Geological Survey Bulletin, v. 1294–D, 16 p.

Miyashiro, A., 1974, Volcanic rock series in island arcs and active continental margins: American Journal of Science, v. 274, p. 321–355.

Monroe, W. H., 1980, Geology of the middle Tertiary formations of Puerto Rico: U.S. Geological Survey Professional Paper 953, 93 p.

Montgomery, H. M., Pessagno, E. A., Jr., Pindell, J. L., 1994a, A 195 Ma Terrane in a 165 Ma sea: Pacific origin of the Caribbean Plate: GSA Today, v. 4, no. 1, p. 1, 3–6.

Montgomery, H. M., Pessagno, E. A., Jr., Lewis, J. F., and Schellekens, J. H., 1994b, Paleogeographic history of Jurassic terranes in Puerto Rico and Hispansiola: Tectonics, v. 13, p. 725–732.

Moussa, M. T., and Seiglie, G. A., 1970, Revision of mid-Tertiary stratigraphy of southwestern Puerto Rico: American Association of Petroleum Geolotists Bulletin, v. 53, p. 1887–1898.

Moussa, M. T., and Seiglie, G. A., 1975, Stratigraphy and petroleum possibilities of the middle Tertiary rocks in Puerto Rico (discussion): American Association of Petroleum Geolotists Bulletin, v. 59, p. 163–168.

Nakamura, E., Campbell, I. H., McCulloch, M. T., and Sun, S.-S., 1989, Chemical geodynamics in a back-arc region around the Sea of Japan: implications for the genesis of alkaline basalts in Japan, Korea, and China: Journal of Geophysical Research, v. 94, B4, p. 4634–4654.

Nelson, A. E., 1967a, Geologic map of the Corozal quadrangle, Puerto Rico: U.S. Geological Survey Miscellaneous Geologic Investigations Map I–473, scale 1:20,000.

Nelson, A. E., 1967b, Geologic map of the Utuado quadrangle, Puerto Rico: U.S. Geological Survey Miscellaneous Geologic Investigations Map I–480, scale 1:20,000.

Nelson, A. E., and Monroe, W. H., 1966, Geology of the Florida quadrangle, Puerto Rico: U.S. Geological Survey Bulletin, v. 1221–C, p. C1–C22.

Pearce, J. A., 1982, Trace element characteristics of lavas from destructive plate boundaries, *in* Thorpe, R. S., ed., Andesites: New York, John Wiley & Sons, p. 525–548.

Pearce, J. A., and Cann, J. R., 1973, Tectonic setting of basic volcanic rocks using trace element analyses: Earth and Planetary Science Letters, v. 129, p. 290–300.

Pease, M. H., 1968a, Cretaceous and Lower Tertiary stratigraphy of the Naranjito and Aguas Buenas quadrangles and adjacent areas, Puerto Rico: U.S. Geological Survey Bulletin, v. 1253, 57 p.

Pease, M. H., Jr., 1968b, Geologic map of the Aguas Buenas quadrangle, Puerto Rico: U.S. Geological Survey Miscellaneous Geologic Investigations Map I–479, scale 1:20,000.

Pease, M. H., Jr., 1968c, Geologic map of the Naranjito quadrangle, Puerto Rico: U.S. Geological Survey Miscellaneous Geologic Investigations Map I–508, scale 1:20,000.

Pease, M. H. and Briggs, R. P., 1960, Geology of the Comerío quadrangle, Puerto Rico: U.S. Geological Survey Miscellaneous Geologic Investigations Map I–320, scale 1:20,000.

Pease, M. H., and Briggs, R. P., 1972, Geologic map of the Río Grande quadrangle, Puerto Rico: U.S. Geological Survey Miscellaneous Geologic Investigations Map I–733, scale 1:20,000.

Pease, M. H., and Monroe, W. H., 1977, Geologic map of the San Juan quadrangle, Puerto Rico: U.S. Geological Survey Miscellaneous Investigations Map I–1010, scale 1:20,000.

Pindell, J. L., 1985, Alleghenian reconstruction and the subsequent evolution of the Gulf of Mexico, Bahamas, and proto-Caribbean: Tectonics, v. 4, p. 1–39.

Pindell, J. L., and Barrett, S. F., 1990, Geological evolution of the Caribbean region: a plate tectonic perspective, *in* Dengo, G., and Case, J., eds., The Caribbean region: Boulder, Colorado, Geological Society of America, The Geology of North America, v. H, p. 405–432.

Pindell, J. L., and Dewey, J. F., 1982, Permo-Triassic reconstruction of western Pangea and the evolution of the Gulf of Mexico/Caribbean region: Tectonics, v. 1, p. 179–212.

Ringwood, A. E., 1974, The petrological evolution of island arc systems: Geological Society of London Journal, v. 130, p. 183–204.

Rogers, C. L., 1977, Geologic map of the Punta Guayanés quadrangle, Puerto Rico: U.S. Geological Survey Miscellaneous Investigations Series Map I–998, scale 1:20,000.

Rogers, C. L., 1979, Geologic map of the Caguas quadrangle, Puerto Rico: U.S. Geological Survey Miscellaneous Geologic Investigations Map I–1152, scale 1:20,000.

Rogers, C. L., Cram, C. M., Pease, M. H., Jr., and Tischler, M. S., 1979, Geologic map of the Yabucoa and Punta Tuna quadrangles, Puerto Rico: U.S. Geological Survey Miscellaneous Investigations Series Map I–1086, scale 1:20,000.

Rose, W. I., Jr., Bornhorst, T. J., and Sivonen, S. J., 1986, Rapid, High quality major and trace element analysis of powdered rock by x-ray fluorescence spectrometry: X-Ray Spectrometry, v. 15, p. 55–60.

Sampayo, M. M., 1992, Stratigraphy and sedimentology of the Monte Grande Formation, southwest Puerto Rico [M.S. thesis]: Boulder, University of Colorado, 109 p.

Santos, H., 1990, The stratigraphy, paleoenvironments, and biofacies of the Cotui Limestone: Cretaceous of southwest Puerto Rico [M.S. thesis]: Boulder, University of Colorado.

Schellekens, J. H., 1991, Late Jurassic to Eocene geochemical evolution of volcanic rocks of Puerto Rico: Geophysical Research Letters, v. 18, p. 553–556.

Schellekens, J. H., 1993, Geochemical evolution of the volcanic rocks in Puerto Rico [Ph.D. thesis]: Syracuse, New York, Syracuse University, 289 p.

Schellekens, J. H., Montgomery, H., Joyce, J., and Smith, A. L., 1990, Late Jurassic to Late Cretaceous development of island arc crust in southwestern Puerto Rico, *in* Larue, D. K., and Draper, G., eds., Transactions, 12th Caribbean Geological Conference, St. Croix, U.S. Virgin Islands, August 1989, p. 268–281.

Seiders, V. M., 1971a, Geologic map of the Gurabo quadrangle Puerto Rico, U.S. Geological Survey Miscellaneous Geologic Investigations Map I–657, scale 1:20,000.

Seiders, V. M., 1971b, Geologic map of the El Yunque quadrangle, Puerto Rico: U.S. Geological Survey Miscellaneous Geologic Investigations Map I–658, scale 1:20,000.

Seiders, V. M., 1971c, Cretaceous and Lower Tertiary stratigraphy of the Gurabo and El Yunque quadrangles, Puerto Rico: U.S. Geological Survey Bulletin, v. 1294–F, 58 p.

Seiglie, G. A., and Bermúdez, P. J., 1969, Informe preliminar sobre los foramineferos del terciario del sur de Puerto Rico: Caribbean Journal Science, v. 9, p. 67–80.

Seiglie, G. A., and Moussa, M. T., 1984, Late Oligocene–Pliocene transgressive-regressive cycles of sedimentation in northwestern Puerto Rico, *in* Schlee, J. S., ed., Interregional unconformities and hydrocarbon accumulation: American Association of Petroleum Geologists Memoir 36, p. 89–95.

Sohl, N. F., and Kollmann, H. A., 1985, Cretaceous Actaeonellid gastropods from the western hemisphere: U.S. Geological Survey Professional Paper 1304, 104 p.

Tobisch, O. T., and Turner, M. D., 1971, Geologic map of the San Sebastian quadrangle, Puerto Rico: U.S. Geological Survey Miscellaneous Investigations Map I–661, scale 1:20,000.

Varne, R., 1985, Ancient subcontinental mantle: A source for K-rich orogenic volcanics: Geology, v. 13, p. 405–408.

Volckmann, R. P., 1984a, Upper Cretaceous stratigraphy of southwest Puerto Rico, *in* Stratigraphic notes 1983: U.S. Geological Survey Bulletin, v. 1537–A, p. A73–A83.

Volckmann, R. P., 1984b, Geologic map of the Cabo Rojo and Parguera quadrangles, southwest Puerto Rico: U.S. Geological Survey Miscellaneous Geologic Investigations Map I–1557, scale 1:20,000.
Volckmann, R. P., 1984c, Geologic map of the San German quadrangle, southwest Puerto Rico: U.S. Geological Survey Miscellaneous Geologic Investigations Map I–1558, scale 1:20,000.
Volckmann, R. P., 1984d, Geologic map of the Puerto Real quadrangle, southwest Puerto Rico: U.S. Geological Survey Miscellaneous Geologic Investigations Map I–1559, scale 1:20,000.
Wager, L. R., and Deer, W. A., 1939, Geological investigations in East Greenland, Pt. III. The petrology of the Skaergaard intrusion, Kangerdlugssuaq, East Greenland: Medd. Grønland, v. 105, no. 4, p. 1–352.
Weaver, J. D., 1958, Utuado pluton, Puerto Rico: Geological Society of America Bulletin, v. 69, p. 1125–1142.
Weiland, T. J., 1988, Petrology of volcanic rocks in Lower Cretaceous formations of northeastern Puerto Rico [Ph.D. thesis]: Chapel Hill, University of North Carolina, 295 p.
White, W. M., and Dupré, B., 1986, Sediment subduction and magma genesis in the Lesser Antilles: isotopic and trace element constraints: Journal of Geophysical Research, v. 91, p. 5927–5941.

Manuscript Accepted by the Society June 20, 1997

Printed in U.S.A.

Geological Society of America
Special Paper 322
1998

Geochemical diversity of Mesozoic island arc tectonic blocks in eastern Puerto Rico

Wayne T. Jolly
Department of Earth Sciences, Brock University, St. Catherines, Ontario L2S 3A1, Canada
Edward G. Lidiak
Department of Geology and Planetary Science, University of Pittsburgh, Pittsburgh, Pennsylvania 15260
Alan P. Dickin
Department of Geology, McMaster University, Hamilton, Ontario L8S 4M1, Canada
Tsai-Way Wu
Department of Geology, University of Western Ontario, London, Ontario N6A 5B7, Canada

ABSTRACT

Eastern Puerto Rico is composed of two distinctive volcanic terranes, the northeastern and central volcanic provinces, that represent independent tectonic blocks assembled in mid-Santonian time by left-lateral strike-slip faulting with displacement of at least 50 km. Volcanic strata in the juxtaposed tectonic blocks occur in five successive volcanic phases: (I) Upper Aptian to Lower Albian island arc tholeiites (IAT); (II) Upper Albian cal-calkaline (CA) volcanic rocks; (III) Cenomanian to Lower Santonian shoshonites (SHO, central block) and cal-calkaline (northeastern block) volcanic rocks; (IV) Upper Santonian to Maastrichtian cal-calkaline to shoshonitic volcanic rocks; and (V) Lower Tertiary, predominantly felsic, cal-calkaline volcanic rocks. The geochemical evolution is marked by progressive increases in ratios of large-ion lithophile (LILE) and light rare earth (LREE) elements relative to high field strength (HFSE) and heavy rare earth (HREE) elements. Compositional changes with time are also evident in the Nd isotope ratios of the volcanics of the central tectonic block, which are MORB-like and display a gradual decrease in ε_{Nd} from +8 to about +6 between phases I and IV. In contrast, Sr and Pb isotope ratios show no evidence of compositional evolution. Initial (*i*) Sr isotope compositions overlap the field of Mesozoic MORB with $i^{87}Sr/^{86}Sr$ ratios exhibiting a broad range from about 0.7034 to 0.7044 (ε_{Sr} from −12 to +1.0) and an average of 0.7037 (−10.0). Pb isotope compositions form a trend emanating from the MORB field and oriented along or subparallel to the Northern Hemisphere Reference Line (NHRL).

HFSE ratios in Puerto Rican basalts overlap the MORB trend at all concentrations, consistent with incompatible behavior. As in modern island arcs, low absolute HFSE abundances compared with MORB indicate the wedge was more depleted in incompatible elements than a MORB-type source. Uniformly flat normalized HREE patterns, together with wide ranges in Nb/Hf ratios reflecting variation in degree of melting, indicate magma generation at relatively low P_t. Cooling of the shallow wedge during the 35-Ma eruption period is inferred to have produced the observed geochemical shifts. Superimposed on the magmas are effects of low-P_t gabbroic and, in

Jolly, W. T., Lidiak, E. G., Dickin, A. P., and Wu, T.-W., 1998, Geochemical diversity of Mesozoic island arc tectonic blocks in eastern Puerto Rico, *in* Lidiak, E. G., and Larue, D. K., eds., Tectonics and Geochemistry of the Northeastern Caribbean: Boulder, Colorado, Geological Society of America Special Paper 322.

phase II of the northeast tectonic block, high-P_t two-pyroxene fractional crystallization (fc). Many lavas, particularly in early volcanic phases, display flat chondrite-normalized LREE patterns, consistent with widespread sequential batch melting (SBM) processes.

Trends displayed by isotope and trace element ratios are consistent with incorporation of a subduction-related component (SDC) dominated by a fluid phase with slightly high ε_{Sr}-values and Th/Nb and La/Nb ratios compared to MORB, and with MORB-like Pb isotope ratios. In the central tectonic block, basalts from volcanic phases III and IV exhibit slightly elevated $^{208}Pb/^{204}Pb$ ratios and lower ε_{Nd} values, compared to phases I and II, consistent with an additional small pelagic sediment contribution (about 0.1 to 0.2%) to the SDC.

INTRODUCTION

The Greater Antilles (including Cuba, Jamaica, Hispaniola, Puerto Rico, and the Virgin Islands) contains an island arc volcanic record encompassing at least 80 Ma (Donnelly, 1989; Donnelly et al., 1990; Larue et al., 1991; Larue, 1994; Jolly et al., Chapter 1, this volume), extending from Lower Cretaceous (120 Ma) to Eocene (40 Ma) in age. In Puerto Rico (Fig. 1) posteruptive uplift and erosion of the deformed volcanic complex since Oligocene time has exposed representative strata from the entire arc sequence. Moreover, the geographic distribution of individual volcanic units and their relative ages and stratigraphic correlations have been firmly established through detailed stratigraphic, paleontologic, and structural studies by the U.S. Geological Survey during the Puerto Rico mapping project (1960–1986). Therefore, the island is ideally suited to detailed geochemical investigation of petrologic processes operating in a major ancient island arc system throughout its development.

Geologic limitations on geologic investigations

Although investigation of an ancient island arc produces a stratigraphic perspective not accessible in modern arcs, in which older strata are buried by recent eruptives, a number of limitations are inherent to study of an extinct arc. First, the orientation and tectonic history of the subduction zone generating the arc must be determined indirectly, since geophysical evidence has been obliterated by destructive plate margin tectonism. Second, stratigraphic relations have been disrupted by extensive postvolcanic deformation of the arc platform. In Puerto Rico much of the faulting involved vertical displacements that have been evaluated in many areas by detailed stratigraphic investigations. Tectonism associated with abundant strike-slip faulting (Fig. 1), however, produced displacement of uncertain magnitude, particularly along boundaries between tectonic blocks. In eastern Puerto Rico, trends of major strike-slip faults tend to be oriented subparallel with or deflected around major volcanic axes and thick volcanic sequences, and consequently faulting produced minimal displacement in relative positions of lateral lithofacies.

An additional constraint on geochemical investigation of ancient arcs is the pervasive mobilization and redistribution of large-ion lithophile elements (LILE: Rb, Ba, K, Sr) during low-grade metamorphism, devitrification, and other alteration processes in the volcanic pile. As a result of alteration, the behavior of the more soluble elements in ancient arc petrogenesis cannot be convincingly evaluated. This is a lamentable loss, because the highly soluble LILE, which tend to be enriched in arc basalts with respect to other incompatible elements (Hawkesworth and Powell, 1980; Pearce, 1983; White and Patchett, 1984), play a critical role in modern arc processes. Instead, it is necessary to emphasize less soluble rare earth and high field strength elements (REE, HFSE); (Dickin and Jones, 1983; Dickin, 1988; Brennan and Watson, 1991) and the highly incompatible but insoluble element Th (Baily and Ragnursdotter, 1994). Together these components provide useful constraints on the magnitude of the ubiquitous subduction-related component (SDC) in the arc magmas.

Scope and objectives

The focus of this chapter is restricted to geochemical relations in the eastern part of the island, with particular reference to the distribution of diagnostic incompatible trace elements. Objectives include comparison of Puerto Rican lavas with modern island arcs, and investigation of evidence regarding the nature of the mantle wedge source of the arc, the roles of fractional crystallization and sequential batch melting processes, and the magnitude and degree of variation of the subduction-related component (SDC) in arc petrogenesis. Additionally, vertical geochemical variations within various sectors of the arc are investigated.

GEOLOGIC SETTING

Tectonic subdivision of eastern Puerto Rico

Puerto Rico is composed of three independent tectonic terranes (Figs. 1 and 2), one in the west, another occupying the central core of the island, and a third smaller member in the northeastern corner (Larue et al., 1991; Schellekens et al., 1991; Larue, 1994; Jolly et al., Chapter 1, this volume). The terms tectonic blocks (in discussion of structural elements) and volcanic provinces (when describing stratigraphic, petrographic, and geochemical features) are used interchangeably in referring to these

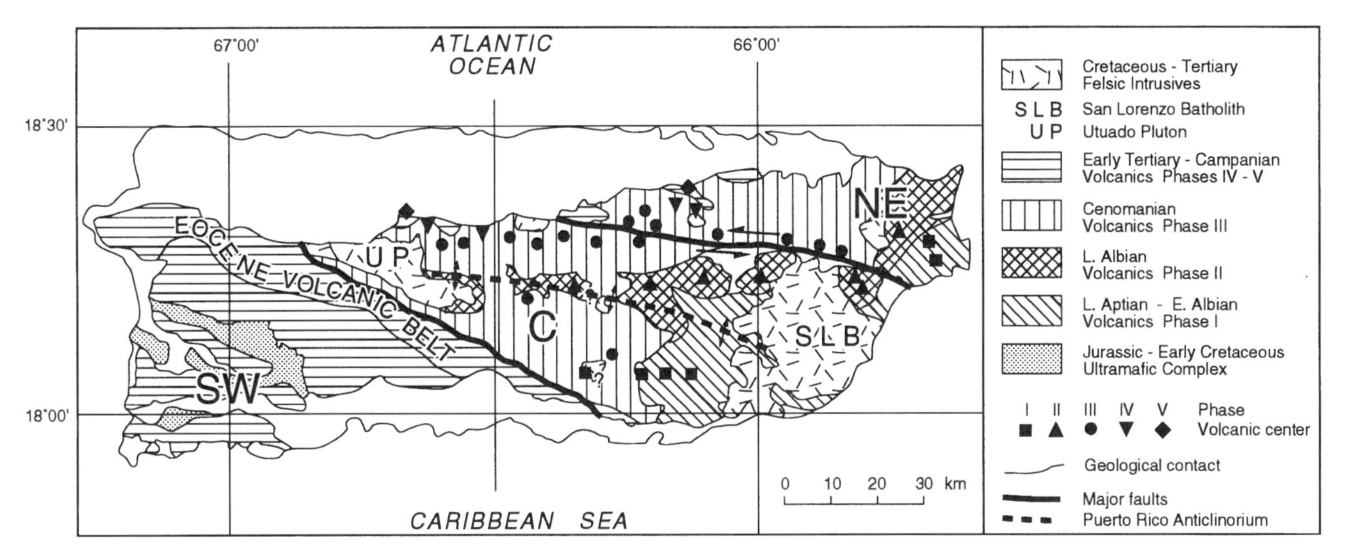

Figure 1. Distribution of volcanic strata in Puerto Rico modified from Briggs and Akers (1965) and U.S. Geological Survey 7.5' quadrangle maps. NE, northeastern tectonic block; C, central block; SW, southwestern block. Lower Albian (phase I) volcanic centers in east from Berryhill and Glover (1960); those in western subsurface inferred from data of Glover (1961). Upper Albian (II) centers from data of Briggs (1973) and M'Gonigle (1977). Upper Cretaceous (III) centers modified from Glover (1971). For clarity volcanic rocks of the Upper Santonian to Maastrichtian (volcanic phase IV) are included with Upper Cretaceous phase III strata in the central province. SLB = San Lorenzo batholith; UP = Utuado pluton.

terranes. The central and northeastern blocks to which this discussion is restricted were assembled during the Upper Cretaceous (Pease, 1968; Seiders, 1971) by left-lateral transcurrent faulting along the prominent Cerro Mula Fault Zone, which forms the major strand of the 50-km-long Northern Puerto Rico Fault Zone (NPRFZ), (Glover, 1971). Stratigraphic units on either side of this fault are lithologically unrelated prior to mid-Santonian time, and total displacement is inferred to be greater than 50 km (Pease, 1968).

It has long been recognized that Cenomanian volcanic rocks on opposite sides of this tectonic boundary exhibit contrasting geochemistry (Lidiak, 1965, 1972; Nelson, 1966; Glover, 1971; Donnelly and Rogers, 1980). Island arc tholeiitic and cal-calkaline lavas comprise Albian assemblages in both tectonic blocks (Weiland, 1988; Donnelly et al., 1990), and cal-calkaline types dominate all volcanic phases in the northeastern block (Lidiak, 1965; Nelson, 1966; Weiland, 1988; Schellekens, this volume). In contrast, shoshonitic lavas with highly elevated concentrations of incompatible elements comprise Cenomanian volcanic assemblages in central Puerto Rico (Jolly, 1971; Jolly et al., Chapter 1, this volume; Schellekens, this volume). Mid- Santonian to Campanian volcanic strata in both the central and northeastern tectonic blocks display closely similar geochemistry, and because the host strato-volcanic accumulations occur in a continuous belt that crosses the Cerro Mula fault, it is inferred that displacement took place in mid-Santonian time.

The boundary between the central and western tectonic blocks is formed by the complex and poorly understood Southern Puerto Rico Fault Zone (SPRFZ), which trends southeastward across the western third of the island (Glover, 1971). This fault zone ranges in age from Maastrichtian to Eocene (Jolly et al., Chapter 1, this volume), and effectively truncates geological features in the adjacent central tectonic block.

Distribution of major volcanic centers

Volcanic strata in the central tectonic block are subdivided (Fig. 1) into five volcanic phases that are generally separated by unconformities and reefoidal limestone units that formed in the elevated parts of the platform (Jolly et al., Chapter 1, this volume): (I) Upper Aptian to Lower Albian island arc tholeiitic basalts; (II) Upper Albian cal-calkaline basaltic volcanic rocks; (III) Cenomanian to Lower Santonian shoshonites; (IV) Upper Santonian to Maastrichtian cal-calkaline to shoshonitic intermediate volcanic materials; and (V) following an island-wide volcanic hiatus, Lower Tertiary, predominantly felsic, cal-calkaline volcanic basalts (Frost and Schellekens, 1991). These volcanic phases are extended into the northeast block (Fig. 1) on the basis of recognized stratigraphic correlations (Jolly et al., Chapter 1, this volume). Eastern Puerto Rico is not well suited to investigation of Eocene volcanism because there are only three poorly exposed units (Guaracanal Andesite, Jobos Lava, Yunes Tuff) (Fig. 1 of Jolly et al., Chapter 1, this volume). Hence, this survey is restricted to the first four volcanic phases. More extensive Tertiary volcanic basins are buried beneath the postvolcanic platform sedimentary cover along the north coast (Frost and Schellekens, 1991; Montgomery, this volume).

Cretaceous volcanic centers in the central province are characterized by accumulations of several kilometers of lavas and proximal volcanic breccia that occur in three parallel belts (Fig.

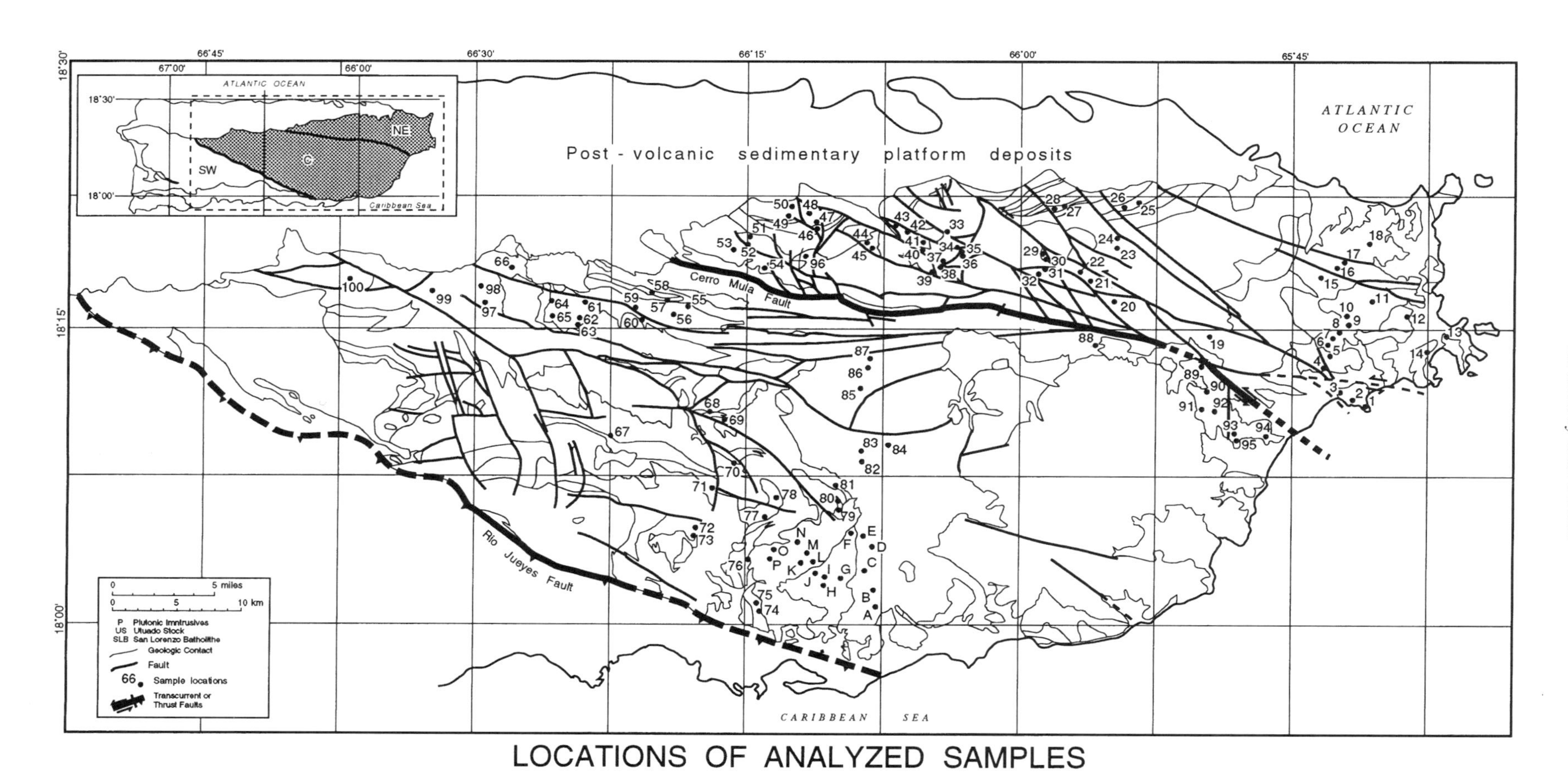

LOCATIONS OF ANALYZED SAMPLES

Figure 2. Locations of analyzed samples; see Table 1 for key to sample numbers. Geologic boundaries are from Figure 1 of Jolly et al., Chapter 1, this volume.

1). The centers are oriented along east-southeast trends and are aligned in a manner that is physiographically analogous to the characteristic linear pattern of modern volcanic arc fronts (see, for example, Carr et al., 1990). The position of successive Cretaceous volcanic chains migrated 5 to 15 km northward, such that each generation of strato-volcanic centers formed along the northern flank of precursors.

Petrography of Puerto Rican lavas

Metamorphism. Postdepositional burial metamorphism of zeolite and prehnite-pumpellyite facies has recrystallized some of the original groundmass mineralogy of Puerto Rican strata (Otalora, 1964; Jolly, 1971; Cho, 1991), but augite and partly albitized plagioclase phenocrysts and relict textures are preserved in most specimens. Stratigraphic reconstructions and mineralogic compositions indicate metamorphism occurred at shallow levels, normally less than about 1.5 to 3 km. Jolly (1970) and Cho (1991) suggested geothermal gradients were elevated during metamorphism by subvolcanic plutonic activity associated with volcanism.

Central volcanic province. Lavas are characteristically devitrified basalts with abundant, commonly well-developed phenocrysts of plagioclase, clinopyroxene, and olivine (normally pseudormorphed by chlorite), all characteristic products of low P_t (subvolcanic) gabbroic fractionation (see Tables 1 and 2). Hornblende is *absent* from all of the eruptive rocks in volcanic phases I through IV, but is present in Eocene materials (Pease, 1968) and in a few stocks and sills of Late Cretaceous age (Glover, 1971). Accessory minerals in Puerto Rican units include abundant subhedral magnetite grains and common apatite, and in a few Perchas samples, rare pseudomorphs of orthopyroxene.

Northeastern volcanic province and Campanian volcanic rocks. Daguao and Figuera (volcanic phase I) and Santa Olaya (phase III) lavas and lateral equivalents (Hato Puerco, Infierno, and Lomas Formations), like their counterparts in central Puerto Rico, carry augite, plagioclase, olivine, and minor magnetite phenocrysts (Table 2), consistent with shallow fractionation within the upper parts of the arc basement. Phase II lavas, including the Fajardo Formation (Weiland, 1988) and Cerro Gordo Lava (Lidiak, 1965), however, carry an orthopyroxene-rich assemblage, indicative of high-pressure crystal fractionation processes (Weiland, 1988). Orthopyroxene is invariably degraded to chlorite, but characteristic blocky, square-shaped pseudomorphs are readily recognizable. Augite is present, but normally comprises less than a few percent of a given specimen.

Eruptive centers of plagioclase-augite-rich Campanian volcanic rocks occur along a discontinuous belt that crosses (Fig. 1) both the central and northeastern blocks (Pease 1968; Berryhill, 1965; Nelson, 1966). An unconformity is present between the phase IV Río de la Plata Sandstone (Lidiak, 1965; Pease, 1968) and the underlying phase III Santa Olaya Lava.

VOLCANIC GEOCHEMISTRY IN EASTERN PUERTO RICO

Analytic methods

Major and trace element x-ray fluorescence (XRF) analyses of 80 representative Puerto Rican lavas (Tables 1 and 2) were determined on a Philips PW1450 automated XRF spectrometer at Brock University (Jolly et al., 1992) and 95 samples by D. Clarke at Memorial University of Newfoundland; accuracy is considered better than 5% of the amount of an element present, as illustrated by comparison of simultaneous analyses of international standards AGV-1 and DNC-1 (cols. 20 and 21, Table 2), which bracket most elemental abundances in the Puerto Rican suite. Rb, Ba, Sr, Th, REE, Nb, Ta, Zr, Hf, and Y determinations for 53 basalts were determined by ICP-MS techniques by S. Jackson at Memorial University of Newfoundland (Longerich et al., 1990). Precision ranges from 2 to 4% of the amount of an element present, except Nb and Ta, with relative standard deviations (RSD) of 6 and 11%, respectively. REE, Cs, U, Th, Ta, Hf, and Sc data from 122 specimens were determined by instrumental neutron activation (INAA) techniques by T.-W. Wu at the University of

TABLE 1. KEY TO ANALYZED SAMPLE LOCALITIES IN EASTERN PUERTO RICO*

1. DG-12	26. MGZ-14	51. RDP-500	76. CAR-33
2. DG-13	27. MGZ-15	52. RDP-499	77. LL-38
3. DG-14	28. MGZ-9	53. SO-502	78. LT-27
4. DG-16	29. INF-7A	54. SO-329	79. LT-60
5. DG-15	30. INF-7B	55. SO-349	80. TOR-40
6. FG-17	31. INF-6	56. AV-56	81. TOR-42
7. FG-9	32. INF-5	57. AV-74	82. TOR-43
8. FG-8	33. TTG-21	58. AV-54	83. J-44
9. FG-7	34. MAM-22	59. AV-43	84. J-45
10. FG-10	35. TTG-24	60. PE-115	85. J-77-81
11. FG-2	36. TTG-28	61. PE-111	86. TOR-46
12. DG-26	37. MAM-30	62. PE-239	87. TOR-47
13. DG-22	38. MAM-31	63. PE-230	88. TOR-48
14. DG-21	39. TTG-26	64. PE-229	89. PTH-23
15. FJ-25	40. GUR-16	65. AV-154	90. PTH-22
16. FJ-28	41. GUR-17	66. PE-182	91. PTH-50
17. FJ-29	42. GUR-18	67. AV-148	92. PTH-52
18. FJ-24	43. GUR-19	68. LL-11	93. PTH-51
19. LOM-24	44. SO-412	69. LL-16	94. RAB-53
20. LOM-11	45. SO-480A	70. HS-18	95. RAB-54
21. LOM-8	46. GC-450	71. LL-54	96. RAB-55
22. LOM-12	47. CG-447	72. LLL-9	97. POZ-1
23. HP-49C	48. CG-441	73. CAR-32	98. POZ-58
24. HP-49A	49. CG-440	74. LL-37J	99. POZ-67
25. TDA-10	50. CG-444	75. LL-37D	100. ALZ-798
A. A-8	E. A-3	I. B-4	M. C-14
B. A-7	F. B-1	J. B-3	N. C-13
C. A-5	G. B-7 and 8	K. C-10	O. C-3
D. A-4	H. B-5	L. G-11	P. C-2

*See Figure 1 of Jolly et al., Chapter 1, this volume, for identification of stratigraphic units.

TABLE 2. GEOCHEMICAL DATA FROM REPRESENTATIVE EASTERN PUERTO RICAN BASALTS*

	1	2	3	4	5	6	7	8	9	10	11	12
Sample	A-5	A-8	B-5	C-11A	CG-444	DG-12	DG-14	DG-16	FG-17	FG-7	FG-9	FJ-25
Desig.	CI	CI	CI	CI	NEII	NEI	NEI	NEI	NEI	NEI	NEI	NEII
Method	P	P	P	P	N	P	N	P	P	N	N	P
Major element oxides (Wt. %)												
SiO_2	53.36	55.30	55.30	51.07	54.96	49.10	56.50	65.72	49.60	51.10	65.80	53.37
TiO_2	0.92	1.06	0.73	0.71	0.75	0.60	0.97	0.81	0.81	0.84	0.68	0.66
Al_2O_3	17.87	15.98	17.59	19.52	6.44	19.59	19.06	15.72	18.08	17.53	15.87	17.42
Fe_2O_3	0.98	12.32	9.70	10.29	8.98	9.63	9.56	6.11	11.75	10.35	4.27	9.55
MnO	0.19	0.25	0.21	0.19	0.09	0.21	0.33	0.12	0.20	0.31	0.12	0.19
MgO	5.21	4.56	4.94	6.05	3.97	4.09	6.72	2.15	5.13	4.87	2.75	6.75
CaO	9.76	5.47	7.45	9.62	7.04	7.47	9.01	2.00	11.63	8.72	2.63	7.26
Na_2O	2.46	4.19	3.39	2.53	3.50	4.50	2.61	4.60	2.82	2.83	5.26	4.29
K_2O	0.37	1.36	0.78	0.23	1.66	0.21	0.51	1.85	0.19	0.70	0.82	0.47
P_2O_5	0.13	0.22	0.10	0.12	0.32	0.34	0.41	0.23	0.11	0.14	0.29	0.12
Total	100.25	100.71	100.19	100.43	97.59	99.67	98.06	99.31	100.32	98.72	99.49	100.08
H_2O^+	....	....	....	3.25	2.02	....	3.22	....	....	0.89	0.79	....
MG#	50.8	42.3	50.2	53.6	46.7	45.7	58.2	41.1	46.4	48.2	56.1	58.3
Incompatible lithophile elements (ppm)												
Cs	....	....	....	....	0.69	....	....	....	....	....	0.44	....
Rb	6	18	16	1	33	2	7	21	2	15	16	6
Ba	132	417	169	103	364	194	237	990	91	315	299	226
Th	0.92	0.86	0.30	0.42	1.60	0.24	0.82	3.00	0.18	0.31	0.66	0.62
U	....	....	....	....	0.50	....	....	....	....	....	....	....
K	3,071	11,290	6,475	4,256	13,780	1,743	4,234	15,357	1,577	5,811	6,807	3,902
Nb	0.9	1.1	0.6	0.8	1.6	0.7	1.2	5.4	0.6	1.1	1.9	0.5
La	6.16	7.29	3.39	4.10	14.00	2.77	5.71	20.68	2.68	5.00	5.77	6.77
Ce	14.97	17.00	7.98	9.91	30.44	6.46	13.60	46.01	7.16	11.90	16.70	17.71
Pb	6	5	....	....	5	13	....	7	7	....	....	5
Sr	294	280	200	318	406	423	239	275	272	226	241	429
Pr	3.26	2.69	1.25	1.57	....	1.07	....	6.88	1.18	....	....	2.79
Nd	10.61	13.93	6.20	7.75	19.50	5.38	9.00	29.83	6.24	8.38	13.40	13.42
Sm	2.87	3.90	2.03	2.32	5.12	1.65	2.70	6.41	1.92	2.64	4.33	3.11
Zr	72	71	34	36	124	37	67	262	41	45	102	63
Hf	2.51	2.27	0.99	1.42	4.11	1.16	1.79	5.40	1.43	1.19	3.17	1.63
Eu	0.92	1.32	0.80	0.79	1.20	0.66	0.94	1.31	0.66	0.89	1.14	0.95
Ti	5,515	6,355	4,376	4,256	4,496	3,597	5,815	4,856	4,856	5,036	4,077	3,957
Gd	3.39	4.63	2.07	2.73	....	1.93	....	5.69	2.23	....	....	2.76
Tb	0.51	0.72	0.34	0.43	0.60	0.32	0.51	0.88	0.37	0.55	0.89	0.39
Y	20	25	13	16	22	12	18	33	14	17	29	11
Dy	3.44	4.84	2.20	2.97	....	2.10	....	5.30	2.43	....	....	2.19
Ho	0.75	1.06	0.50	0.63	....	0.49	....	1.14	0.52	....	....	0.43
Er	2.26	3.25	1.39	1.81	....	1.36	....	3.30	1.59	....	....	1.19
Tm	0.32	0.44	0.20	0.27	....	0.21	....	0.49	0.23	....	....	0.16
Yb	2.12	2.90	1.29	1.79	1.87	1.31	1.99	1.55	1.51	1.90	3.80	1.09
Lu	0.34	0.46	0.26	0.27	....	0.22	....	0.27	0.24	0.28	0.59	0.17
Compatible trace elements												
Ni	20	5	4	23	20	6	....	12	19	27	....	62
Cr	93	....	....	20	71	14	....	....	20	31	....	139
V	277	279	263	259	223	241	....	113	372	289	....	236
Sc	33	40	30	27	26	16	35	17	42	38	25	34
Phenocryst modes												
Plag	1.7	5.9	9.3	5.4	5.6	6.4	4.2	17.6	12.2	9.8	11.3	8.4
Augite	0.6	4.7	6.4	0.2	0.5	2.2	3.4	4.1	6.8	7.1	6.7	2.3
Opx	0	0	0	0	2.6	0	0	0	0	0	0	6.8
Olivine	tr	0.1	0	1.6	0.5	1.2	0	0	0	0	0	0.2
Mag.	0.2	0.5	0.6	0.2	0.2	0.4	1.1	0.2	0.1	0.3	0.4	0.3

TABLE 2. GEOCHEMICAL DATA FROM REPRESENTATIVE EASTERN PUERTO RICAN BASALTS* (continued - page 2)

	13	14	15	16	17	18	19	20	21	22	23	24
Sample	FJ-28	HP-49A	INF-7	J-77	LL-11B	LOM-12	MGZ-15	POZ-1	PTH-51	Pe-239	RDP-499	SO-329
Desig.	NEII	NEIII	NEIII	CI	CIII	NEIII	NEIV	CIV	CII	CIII	NEIV	NEIII
Method	P	N	N	P	N	P	P	N	P	N	P	P
Major element oxides (Wt. %)												
SiO_2	55.84	48.60	49.14	57.00	54.60	53.10	52.10	53.90	49.81	51.87	52.09	55.15
TiO_2	0.75	0.58	0.84	0.85	0.84	0.82	0.83	0.84	0.76	0.91	0.84	0.93
Al_2O_3	17.94	15.67	17.26	17.80	16.20	17.80	16.70	16.80	18.83	15.45	19.17	17.41
Fe_2O_3	9.31	6.45	10.83	8.11	5.78	8.90	8.11	7.87	6.45	6.93	8.20	9.56
MnO	0.16	0.17	0.16	0.19	0.09	0.22	0.21	0.20	0.17	0.15	0.15	0.81
MgO	4.16	6.79	8.05	4.06	2.10	5.43	5.26	5.56	5.51	2.98	3.08	3.62
CaO	3.77	9.85	9.85	7.90	6.10	8.30	8.70	8.10	8.97	9.85	7.52	6.07
Na_2O	5.72	2.75	3.45	3.11	4.05	3.97	4.09	3.93	3.48	1.75	3.28	3.62
K_2O	1.30	1.21	0.47	0.39	5.75	0.55	4.45	2.40	1.30	0.41	3.52	2.02
P_2O_5	0.17	0.10	0.15	0.21	0.49	0.19	0.20	0.18	0.22	0.50	0.51	0.47
Total	100.12	96.25	100.20	99.62	96.20	99.28	100.65	99.78	99.87	96.80	99.36	99.03
H_2O^+	....	3.27	0.56	....	3.91	....	....	0.87	1.50	4.33	....	....
MG#	47.0	56.3	59.6	49.8	55.5	54.7	56.2	58.3	50.2	45.6	42.7	42.9
Incompatible lithophile elements (ppm)												
Cs	....	....	0.20	....	0.58	....	....	0.81	0.25	0.16	0.10	0.52
Rb	17	9	3	6	103	9	75	41	19	94	72	32
Ba	642	201	147	94	2,164	135	836	775	420	1,413	1,036	713
Th	1.02	0.46	0.54	0.40	4.10	0.69	2.98	2.70	0.77	3.06	3.20	1.40
U	....	....	....	....	1.70	....	....	2.96	....	3.40	2.80	1.10
K	10,792	10,045	3,902	3,238	47,732	4,566	36,941	19,923	10,792	5,455	29,221	16,769
Nb	1.3	0.8	0.9	0.7	5.8	3.0	5.1	2.9	0.8	....	3.1	3.7
La	10.43	6.21	7.35	4.50	16.10	5.93	15.45	14.80	7.46	21.10	19.30	15.61
Ce	23.39	15.21	17.90	12.08	33.70	13.80	31.57	28.80	16.50	44.90	39.20	37.70
Pb	22	....	....	....	29	....	....	....	5	7	....	....
Sr	350	209	596	198	502	255	836	651	420	988	1,649	574
Pr	3.50	2.30	....	1.80	....	2.20	4.16	....	....	....	....	....
Nd	16.42	16.01	12.80	8.46	17.50	10.86	17.81	16.80	11.70	22.20	22.60	20.00
Sm	3.90	2.87	3.86	2.54	3.63	3.09	4.28	4.15	3.28	4.80	5.02	4.78
Zr	91	45	49	82	97	72	92	75	44	58	65	97
Hf	2.58	1.33	1.90	2.15	2.77	1.99	2.16	2.67	1.87	1.77	2.44	3.13
Eu	1.11	1.04	1.12	0.81	1.11	0.92	1.23	1.12	1.00	1.48	1.48	1.40
Ti	4,496	4,077	5,036	5,096	5,036	4,916	4,976	5,036	4,556	5,455	5,036	5,575
Gd	3.94	2.79	....	2.91	....	3.36	4.45	....	....	....	....	....
Tb	0.58	0.37	0.46	0.49	0.49	0.50	0.56	0.52	0.46	0.60	0.59	0.66
Y	21	12	14	19	16	19	19	16	17	15	17	23
Dy	3.54	2.32	....	7.09	....	3.46	3.68	....	....	....	....	....
Ho	0.79	0.45	....	0.73	....	0.69	0.72	....	....	....	....	....
Er	2.21	1.26	....	2.15	....	2.12	2.17	....	....	....	....	....
Tm	0.31	0.18	....	0.33	....	0.31	0.30	....	....	....	....	....
Yb	2.07	1.12	1.55	2.22	1.72	2.04	1.92	1.57	1.64	1.69	1.55	1.98
Lu	0.31	0.18	0.27	0.36	0.27	0.30	0.30	....	0.16	0.28	....	....
Compatible trace elements												
Ni	23	....	58	....	29	....	29	26	21	39	17	107
Cr	82	....	158	....	51	....	19	122	100	99	12	262
V	286	....	337	24	297	....	302	347	343	299	270	251
Sc	31	....	50	13	12	....	24	16	32	20	16	21
Phenocryst modes												
Plag	12.6	1.8	3.6	6.6	19.0	8.6	17.5	10.2	4.7	7.6	4.3	5.7
Augite	0.8	2.2	2.8	2.7	7.0	6.4	8.4	7.6	15.4	15.7	6.7	1.2
Opx	8.6	0	0	0	0.0	0	0.2	0	0	0.5	0	tr
Olivine	0.4	0	0	0	4.0	0.1	1.2	0.4	0	0.7	0	0.1
Mag.	0.1	0.8	0.5	0	0.6	2.4	1.7	2.4	0.9	0.2	0.3	1.1

Western Ontario; details of analytic methods are outlined in Jolly et al. (1992). Accuracy by INAA ranges from 1 to 4% (see, for comparison, analyses of international standards AGV-1 and DNC-1 in Table 2), whereas precision, calculated from replicate analyses of an in-house standard (UWO-1), is better than 3% for all elements except Sm (3.4%), Lu (3.6%), and U (7.0%) (Table 3). Samples powders were routinely ground in a tungsten carbide shatterbox for 30 sec; results for Ta are not used due to possible contamination. Selected duplicate samples were ground by hand in sintered alumina to ensure there was no significant Nb contamination. Duplicate Nb analyses by XRF and ICP-MS techniques, both corrected for interelement interferences, yielded almost identical Nb results (correlation coefficient 0.98). Full analyses of 33 representative lavas are presented in Table 2; sample locations are given in Figure 2.

Sr and Nd isotope analyses were performed by A. P. Dickin by dynamic multiple collection on a VG Isolab 54T machine at McMaster University. Analysis of the NBS 987 Sr standard (normalized to $^{86}Sr/^{88}Sr = 0.1194$) during the course of this work yielded an average $^{87}Sr/^{86}Sr$ value of 0.710251 ± 0.000024 (2σ). Average within-run precision on Sr standards and samples was 0.0024% (2σ). Analysis of the La Jolla Nd standard (normalized to 146/144 = 0.729) yielded an average $^{143}Nd/^{144}Nd$ value of 0.511862 ± 0.000015 (2σ), with average within-run precision of 0.0026% (2σ). Nd analyses for samples are quoted relative to a value of 0.51185 for La Jolla. Duplicate Sr-isotope analyses were made of four samples treated by strong hot acid leaching according to the following procedures: the samples were leached in hot 3 molal HCl overnight, washed, and treated again overnight by leaching in a cold acid solution of HF, HCl, and HNO_3; comparisons of the two sets of results (Table 4) reveal minimal differences. Initial $(i)^{87}Sr/^{86}Sr$ ratios are given in the text, followed by ε_{Sr}-values.

Pb was separated in 0.2-ml exchange columns using HBr. After loading on Re filaments, using silica gel and H_3PO_4, Pb was analyzed on a VG354 spectrometer with a Faraday collector at McMaster University. Pb isotope data (Table 4) are corrected for mass fractionation of 0.08% per atomic mass unit (amu), based on analyses of the NBS 981 standard. Estimated 2σ reproducibility, based on standard analyses and replicate analysis of samples, is as follows: $^{206}Pb/^{204}Pb$, (±0.020; $^{207}Pb/^{204}Pb$, ±0.015; $^{208}Pb/^{204}Pb$, ±0.040. Data are not age corrected for radiogenic Pb growth since eruption, because the magnitude of this small effect is expected to be similar to radiogenic growth of mantle reference sources over the same time period.

Major element geochemistry

Major element distribution in Puerto Rican lavas is dominated by subvolcanic gabbroic fractionation processes (Weiland, 1988), which produced continuous trends on variation diagrams. SiO_2 abundances (Fig. 3B-C) range from 46 to 76%, but the lavas are dominantly basaltic, with a mean of 53.6% (median 53.2%). Only 8% of the samples analyzed for this project contain more

TABLE 2. GEOCHEMICAL DATA FROM REPRESENTATIVE EASTERN PUERTO RICAN BASALTS* (continued - page 3)

	25	26	27	28
Sample	SO-412	TOR-40	TOR-42	TTG-26
Desig.	NEIII	CII	CII	NEIV
Method	P	N	N	P
Major element oxides (Wt. %)				
SiO_2	54.45	53.70	48.06	51.80
TiO_2	0.81	0.85	0.70	0.75
Al_2O_3	18.16	18.20	14.56	15.90
Fe_2O_3	10.00	8.50	11.30	10.11
MnO	0.14	0.19	0.35	0.17
MgO	4.71	4.21	8.07	5.68
CaO	5.38	8.27	9.51	7.80
Na_2O	6.07	3.42	3.25	3.98
K_2O	0.26	0.35	1.38	2.26
P_2O_5	0.19	0.23	0.24	0.14
Total	100.17	97.92	97.42	98.59
H_2O^+	....	2.36	2.54	....
MG#	48.3	49.5	58.6	52.6
Incompatible lithophile elements (ppm)				
Cs	0.10	....	0.37	....
Rb	3	9	40	658
Ba	60	152	730	51
Th	0.70	0.42	1.33	2.25
U	0.50	....	0.22	....
K	2,158	2,905	11,456	18,761
Nb	1.3	0.9	2.3	4.8
La	7.35	3.26	10.46	13.57
Ce	16.80	9.04	24.30	27.08
Pb	....	....	5	9
Sr	239	340	1,086	658
Pr	....	1.48	....	3.45
Nd	11.40	7.54	14.45	14.04
Sm	5.16	2.63	3.75	3.37
Zr	70	55	58	79
Hf	2.26	1.57	1.79	2.21
Eu	0.93	0.98	1.22	0.82
Ti	4,856	5,096	4,197	4,496
Gd	....	3.40	....	3.47
Tb	0.39	0.53	0.58	0.44
Y	16	20	17	16
Dy	....	3.75	....	2.85
Ho	....	0.77	....	0.58
Er	....	2.24	....	1.71
Tm	....	0.33	....	0.25
Yb	1.49	2.16	1.82	1.78
Lu	....	0.36	0.28	0.27
Compatible trace elements				
Ni	8	....	173	....
Cr	45	....	393	....
V	274	....	289	....
Sc	31	....	28	....
Phenocryst modes				
Plag	4.3	1.2	13.2	6.5
Augite	4.3	0.9	9.7	3.3
Opx	0	0	0	0
Olivine	0	0	0.5	0
Mag.	0.6	0.1	1.7	0.5

TABLE 2. GEOCHEMICAL DATA FROM REPRESENTATIVE EASTERN PUERTO RICAN BASALTS* (continued - page 4)

Sample	29 AMPH	30 AMPH	31 AMPH	32 AMPH	33 AMPH	34 CP3	35 DNG-1
Desig.	30	102	105	126	135	103B	STD
Method	P	P	P	P	P	P	
Major element oxides (Wt. %)							
SiO_2	48.79	50.91	53.36	51.76	47.42	51.45	44.46
TiO_2	0.71	1.53	1.05	0.88	2.14	1.05	0.44
Al_2O_3	12.09	13.17	15.13	15.54	14.65	15.09	18.16
Fe_2O_3	9.64	12.05	10.51	9.43	14.58	9.96	10.03
MnO	0.15	0.18	0.18	0.17	0.22	0.19	0.15
MgO	17.04	12.10	6.90	8.00	7.77	7.70	10.05
CaO	9.40	6.60	8.65	10.90	9.66	10.03	11.21
Na_2O	1.46	3.26	3.84	2.86	2.95	3.09	2.15
K_2O	0.05	0.41	0.27	0.47	0.51	0.77	0.27
P_2O_5	0.05	0.14	0.09	0.07	0.19	0.08	0.08
Total	99.38	100.38	99.98	100.08	100.09	99.41	
MG#	77.78	66.54	56.53	62.69	51.35	60.49	
Incompatible lithophile elements (ppm)							
Rb	0	2	3	7	7	12	3.4
Ba	116	108	56	129	53	217	109
Th	0.02	0.17	0.09	0.16	0.34	0.18	
K	415	3,403	2,241	3,901	4,234	6,392	
Nb	0.4	1.9	2.2	0.9	5.9	1.5	1.4
La	1.09	3.11	2.39	2.00	5.00	2.62	
Ce	3.88	9.76	7.24	6.15	15.44	7.83	
Sr	296	141	176	511	143	257	139
Pr	0.68	1.60	1.13	1.02	2.50	1.31	
Pb	2	0	0	2	4	1	9
Nd	3.13	9.83	6.06	5.52	13.73	7.19	
Sm	1.60	3.25	2.07	2.03	4.97	2.65	
Zr	29	95	66	50	130	65	34
Hf	1.08	2.53	1.98	1.50	3.41	1.86	
Eu	0.58	1.14	0.66	0.79	1.82	0.91	
Ti	4,256	9,172	6,295	5,276	12,829	6,295	
Gd	2.08	4.31	2.98	2.71	6.76	3.24	
Tb	0.33	0.72	0.50	0.46	1.06	0.54	
Dy	2.54	5.43	3.72	3.33	8.01	4.12	
Y	15	30	21	19	44	22	
Ho	0.53	1.13	0.80	0.72	1.66	0.85	
Er	1.57	3.37	2.40	2.11	4.86	2.30	
Tm	0.24	0.48	0.35	0.31	0.70	0.36	
Yb	1.55	3.14	2.38	2.07	4.05	2.33	
Lu	0.24	0.48	0.36	0.31	0.72	0.37	
Compatible trace elements							
Ni	701	458	65	76	84	50	
Cr	801	504	182	178	102	125	
V	216	324	271	254	234	201	
Sc	39	31	30	31	59	39	25.1
Phenocryst modes							
Hb	74	67	0	84	63	0	
Ca-pl	14	24	0	10	19	0	
Cpx	12	9	18	3	8	14	
Act	0	0	43	0	0	0	
Ab	0	0	12	0	0	6	

*N = trace elements by INAA techniques; P = ICP-MS techniques. Loss on ignition given as H_2O^+ for the INAA data set; ICP-MS data set given on a water-free basis. Total Fe is listed as Fe_2O_3; Mg# = mole prop. Mg/Mg≠fe. Unit designations for island arc basalts (columns 1–28) as in Figure 2; C = central tectonic block; NE = northeast block, I, II, III, IV = volcanic phases. MORB-like altered basalts from the pre-arc complex in western Puerto Rico (cols. 29–34) are identified as follows: 1 and 5, massive amphibolites; 2, gneissic amphibolite; 3 nonfoliated dike that cross-cuts gneissic amphibolite; 4, hornblende schist; 6, albite basalt; sample locations are given in Figure 10B of Jolly et al., Chapter 1, this volume. Modes based on thin-section counts of 700 points; norms calculated with $FeO/FeO+Fe_2O_3$ ratio set at 0.8.

than 58% SiO_2. More fractionated andesitic end-members are commonly highly aluminous, with over 20% Al_2O_3. Mg# (molecular proportion Mg/Mg + Fe), used as a differentiation index, displays a complementary range from 70 to 30. Reflecting the role of olivine fractionation, the abundance of Ni ranges between 100 and 200 ppm in the least fractionated basalts to about 20 or less in evolved end-members. Many of the trends display considerable scatter, resulting from such petrologic processes as crystal accumulation, variation in degree of melting, and other processes. Normative compositions of lavas (Table 2) are dominantly hypersthene-quartz–bearing, but high alkali contents in shoshonitic basalts of phase III in the central tectonic block commonly produce abundant normative olivine and normative nepheline. Norms must be viewed with caution, because they are sensitive to K-Na–redistribution during alteration; several specimens contain normative corundum, perhaps due to leaching of alkalis.

Incompatible trace element geochemistry

N-MORB–normalized elemental distribution diagrams (Fig. 4) display strong overenrichment in large-ion lithophile elements (LILE), moderate enrichment in light rare earth elements (LREE) and Th, negative anomalies for high field strength elements (HFSE) with respect to REE, prominent positive K, Pb, and Sr spikes, and flat heavy rare earth element segments (HREE), all typical features of island arc associations (Pearce, 1983; McCullough and Gamble, 1991; Hawkesworth et al., 1993a,b). Compared with other members of the Puerto Rican volcanic assemblage, phase I basalts are the least enriched in incompatible elements, and exhibit lowest LILE/HFSE and HFSE/HREE ratios (Fig. 4). In addition, they have lowest LREE/HFSE and LREE/HREE ratios. All of these ratios increase in succeeding volcanic phases, reaching highest levels in shoshonites from phase III of the central volcanic province.

TABLE 3. PRECISION OF INAA ANALYSES*

Element	Average (5)	SD	RV (%)	AGV-1	GXR-1
La	45	0.58	1.30	39	8
Ce	93	2.00	2.24	69	28
Nd	42	1.10	2.64	36	18
Sm	8.3	0.28	3.37	5.9	2.7
Eu	1.15	0.02	1.74	1.42	0.61
Tb	1.13	0.01	0.88	0.60	0.67
Yb	3.72	0.06	1.61	1.52	1.87
Lu	0.56	0.02	3.57	0.21	0.27
Hf	8.62	0.07	0.81	5.50	1.25
Cs	7.9	0.19	2.42	1.3	....
Th	25.17	0.57	2.26	6.80	2.53
U	7.5	0.52	6.98	1.6	33.0

*Determined using replicate analyses of an in-house standard (UWO-1); analyses of international standards AGV-1 and GXR-1 are also listed for comparison.

Geochemical classification of Puerto Rican island arc basalts

Th/Hf-Hf/Yb ratios. Ratios between Th, HFSE, and HREE, which express the total incompatible element enrichment of the magmas, have been used by Pearce (1983) to subdivide arc lavas into island arc tholeiites (IAT), cal-calkaline volcanic rocks (CA), and shoshonites (SHO). Variations in the Puerto Rico arc extend across all three series (Fig. 5), with IAT dominating volcanic phase I, and CA dominating phase II. Calcalkaline types continue to dominate in phase III of the northeastern block, but shoshonites are common in central Puerto Rico during phase III and, to a lesser extent, phase IV. Phase I lavas overlap compositions of sediment-poor oceanic arcs (New Britain, Marianas, Oman), while phase III lavas are similar to continental margin materials (Aeolian Islands, Philippines). The Th/Hf ratio of the average South Pacific island arc basalt (0.6) (McCullough and Gamble, 1991) is in the middle of the Puerto Rican range (Fig. 5C).

Sr, Nd, and Pb isotopes

Puerto Rican basalts from the three earliest volcanic phases in the central volcanic province form overlapping fields on variation diagrams of Sr and Nd isotope ratios (Fig. 6A). Sr isotope ratios display similar ranges in the three phases, with initial (*i*) $^{87}Sr/^{86}Sr$ ratios averaging of 0.7037 (ε_{Sr} = –10.0) and extending from about 0.7034 to 0.7044 (–11.5 to +1), while ε_{Nd}-values decrease from about 8 to 6 from phases I to III. Arc lavas from the northeastern volcanic province (Fig. 6B) are more restricted in radiogenic Sr and Nd, forming a small cluster centered within the field of phase I lavas from the central province. Younger volcanic materials from phase IV in eastern Puerto Rico form a field largely overlapping phase III in central Puerto Rico (Fig. 6A). Additional data from Eocene (phase V) lavas from northern Puerto Rico (Frost and Schellekens, 1991) exhibit slightly elevated Sr isotope ratios; two stratified tuffs display lower ε_{Nd} values (+2.97 and +5.17) possibly due to contamination by postvolcanic authigenic sediment or low-T alteration.

Pb-isotope data from Puerto Rican lavas, including eight from the central volcanic province (Table 4; Fig. 6D, E), seven from the northeast province, and four from volcanic phases IV and V, partly overlap the field of temporally equivalent arc rocks from Hispaniola (Lebron and Perfit, 1994). Samples from individual volcanic phases form small fields aligned along a trend originating within the MORB field (Zindler and Hart, 1986) and trending parallel to the Northern Hemisphere Reference Line (NHRL of Hart, 1984). Basalts from phase III in the central province are anomalous compared with other units, and their Pb and Nd isotope compositions more closely approach the field of oceanic pelagic sediments. A sample of Cajul Basalt, a MORB-like basalt from the pre–arc complex in western Puerto Rico, has a similar Pb isotope composition as phase I–III basalts from the northeastern tectonic block.

TABLE 4. SR, ND, AND PB ISOTOPE DATA FROM CRETACEOUS ISLAND ARC BASALTS FROM CENTRAL PUERTO RICO*

Sample	$i^{87}Sr/^{86}Sr$	$i^{144}Nd/^{143}Nd$	ε_{Nd}	$m^{206}Pb/^{204}Pb$	$m^{207}Pb/^{204}Pb$	$m^{208}Pb/^{207}Pb$
			CENTRAL VOLCANIC PROVINCE			
Volcanic phase I						
Volcanic front (VF), Río Majada Group						
Formation A						
A-4	0.703399	0.512865	7.19	....	....	....
A-5	0.703627	0.512931	8.48	19.033	15.606	38.473
A-8	0.703703	0.512918	8.22	....	....	....
Formation B						
B-1	0.704023	0.512954	8.94	....	....	....
B-3	0.704582	....	....	....	....	....
B-5	0.704140	....	....	....		
Formation C						
C-3	0.703887	0.512847	6.85	....	....	....
C-10	0.704646	....	....	....	....	....
C-11A	0.703839	0.512905	7.97	19.050	15.608	38.458
Volcanic phase II						
Volcanic front (VF)						
Pitahaya Formation						
PTH-22	0.703700	0.512843	6.52	18.870	15.590	38.320
PTH-50	0.703913	0.512824	6.49	18.792	15.578	38.262
PTH-51	....	....	....	18.702	15.561	38.261
Torrecilla Breccia						
TOR-46	0.704165	0.512922	8.06	....	....	....
Volcanic phase III						
Volcanic front (VF), Río Orocovis Group						
Perchas Lava						
PE-111	0.703998	....	....	....	....	....
PE-115	0.703998	0.512832	6.04	19.193	15.614	39.956
PE-229A	0.703998	0.512783	5.09	19.213	15.618	38.982
PE-230A	0.703927	....	....	....	....	....
PE-239	0.704005	....	....	....	....	....
Avispa Lava						
AV-148	0.703605	0.512884	7.05	....	....	....
AV-159	0.704361	0.512842	6.24	....	....	....
AV-54A	0.704065	....	....	....	....	....
AV-56	0.703757	....	....	....	....	....
AV-43	0.704156	....	....	....	....	....
Lateral beside the arc basin (BSA), Robles Formation						
Honduras Sill						
HS-18C	0.704063	....	....	....	....	....
Lapa Lava Member						
LL-11B	0.703897	....	....	....	....	....
LL-16D	0.703972	....	....	....	....	....
LL-37D	0.704212	....	....	....	....	....
LL-37J	0.704129	....	....	....	....	....
LL-38D	0.703841	0.512842	6.24	19.245	15.641	39.073
LL-54A	0.703831	....	....	....	....	....
Lapa-like lava						
LLL-9	0.703654	0.512829	5.99	....	....	....
Las Tetas Lava Member						
Lt-27A	0.703588	0.512869	6.86	....	....	....
LT-60F	0.704116	....	....	....	....	....
Volcanic phase IV						
Pozas Formation						
POZ-1	0.703707	0.512912	7.35	19.626	15.614	38.925
POZ-58	0.703584	....	....	....	....	....
POZ-67	0.703996	....	....	....	....	....

TABLE 4. SR, ND, AND PB ISOTOPE DATA FROM CRETACEOUS ISLAND ARC BASALTS FROM CENTRAL PUERTO RICO* (page 2)

Sample	$i^{87}Sr/^{86}Sr$	$i^{144}Nd/^{143}Nd$	ε_{Nd}	$m^{206}Pb/^{204}Pb$	$m^{207}Pb/^{204}Pb$	$m^{208}Pb/^{207}Pb$
			CENTRAL VOLCANIC PROVINCE			
Volcanic phase V						
Jobos Formation						
JOB-97	0.704327	0.512884	6.05	18.832	15.611	38.457
JOB-100	0.703966	0.512910	6.56	....	....	....
Yunes Formation						
YUN-97	0.705746	0.512846	8.70	....	....	....
			NORTHEASTERN VOLCANIC PROVINCE			
Volcanic phase I						
Daguao Formation						
DG-12	0.703842	0.512865	7.18	18.507	`15.559	38.060
DG-15B	0.703745	....	....	....	....	....
DG-16	0.703622	....	....	19.002	15.542	38.267
Figuera Lava						
FG-7	0.703664	0.512844	6.78	....	....	....
FG-9	0.703526	0.512923	8.33	....	....	....
FG-17	0.703757	....	....	18.527	15.562	38.076
Volcanic phase II						
Fajardo Formation						
FJ-24	0.703832	0.512947	8.55	....	....	....
FJ-25	0.703724	0.512946	8.53	18.463	15.547	37.990
FJ-28	....	....	....	18.791	15.604	38.312
Volcanic phase III						
Cerro Gordo Lava						
CG-444	0.703541	0.512968	8.69	18.482	15.724	38.170
Hato Puerco Formation						
HP-49C	0.703498	....	....	....	....	....
Infiemo Formation						
INF-6	0.703876	....	....	....	....	....
INF-7	0.704040	....	....	....	....	....
Lomas Formation						
LOM-11	0.703856	0.512894	7.25	....	....	....
LOM-24	0.703912	0.512919	7.74	....	....	....
Santa Olaya Lava						
SO-329	0.703635	0.512890	7.18	18.826	15.574	38.369
SO-399	0.703990	....	....	....	....	....
SO-412	0.703951	0.512953	8.40	18.639	15.565	38.189
SO-502	0.703582	....	....	....	....	....
Volcanic phase IV						
Mamey Lava						
MAM-27	0.703745	0.512922	7.55	....	....	....
Martin Gonzáles Lava						
MGZ-9	0.703604	....	....	....	....	....
MGZ-15	0.703931	....	....	....	....	....
Río de la Plata Formation						
RdP-500	0.703820	....	....	19.193	15.592	38.747
Tortugas Andesite						
TTG-21	0.704103	....	....	....	....	....
TTG-26	0.703692	0.512881	6.50	....	....	....
Volcanic phase V						
Guaracanal Andesite						
Gur-17	0.704663	0.512859	5.82	....	....	....
Gur-18	0.073987	0.512855	5.74	18.892	15.615	38.494

TABLE 4. SR, ND, AND PB ISOTOPE DATA FROM CRETACEOUS ISLAND ARC BASALTS FROM CENTRAL PUERTO RICO* (page 3)

Sample	$i^{87}Sr/^{86}Sr$	$i^{144}Nd/^{143}Nd$	ε_{Nd}	$m^{206}Pb/^{204}Pb$	$m^{207}Pb/^{204}Pb$	$m^{208}Pb/^{207}Pb$
			PRE-ARC COMPLEX (WESTERN VOLCANIC PROVINCE)			
Amphibolite						
Media Ouijada						
AMPH-30	0.703355	0.512822	8.50	....	....	....
Sierra Bermeja						
AMPH-102	0.704266	0.512905	10.10	....	....	....
AMPH-105	0.703707	0.512831	8.66	....	....	....
AMPH-126	0.703820	....	....	....	....	....
AMPH-135	0.703958	0.512748	7.04	....	....	....
Altered MORB-like basalt						
Cajul Basalt						
CAJ-103B	0.704255	....	....	18.704	15.545	38.162
Las Mesas Greenstone						
LMG-91	0.703236	....	....	....	....	....

*Determined by A. P. Dickin at McMaster University. *i* and *m* denote initial and measured isotope values, respectively; *i* and ε_{Nd}-values calculated for T = 110 Ma (volcanic phase I), 100 Ma (phase II), and 90 Ma (phase III). All analyzed samples were leached prior to analysis. Sample locations and additional isotope and other chemical data from central Puerto Rican shoshonites and from northeastern Puerto Rico are given in Jolly et al., Chapter 1, this volume.

Geochemical variation in the central volcanic province

Volcanic phase I. Variation diagrams reveal that the more incompatible elements are systematically depleted in Río Majada lavas from Formations B and C compared with Formation A. For example, Hf/Yb ratios of Formation C form clusters at about 0.8 (Fig. 5A), compared to average a value of 0.9 in Formation A. Similarly, Th/Hf (Fig. 5A) and Th/Nb ratios in Formation C (averaging 0.2 and 0.3) are systematically lower than in Formation A (0.4, 0.9). LREE is also depleted in Formation C, such that average values of La/Yb ratios decrease upward from about 2.5 to 2.0, respectively. Variations in REE abundances are displayed by chondrite-normalized patterns in Figure 4, where Formation A lavas tend to exhibit moderate LREE abundances, whereas Formation B and C have intermediate to flat La/Sm segments. The variations are similar to patterns reported in MORB basalts generated by incremental or sequential batch melting processes (Wood, 1979).

Volcanic phase II. Trace element concentrations from lavas of volcanic phase II overlap those of phase I, but average incompatible element abundances are consistently higher than their older counterparts (see Table 2). For example, the average Th/Hf ratio in Formation A is about 0.4, while in phase II lavas it is 0.6 (Fig. 5A). Also, La/Yb ratios increase from about 2.5 in Formation A to an average of 4 in phase II. In general, phase II lavas are intermediate in composition between those of phases I and III, and normally fall within the cal-calkaline field, while phase III representatives are, with the exception of Las Tetas lavas, dominantly shoshonitic (Fig. 5A). In marked contrast to older Formation B and C lavas, normalized LREE segments from the majority of phase II basalts display considerable enrichment, and only two samples display flat LREE patterns (samples TOR-47 and TOR-40).

Volcanic phase III. Basalts of phase III in central Puerto Rico are the most incompatible element-enriched lavas reported in the island, and samples from the Perchas and Lapa lavas (Lidiak, 1965; Jolly, 1971; Jolly et al., Chapter 1, this volume) are predominantly shoshonitic in the terminology of Peccerillo and Taylor (1976) (Fig. 5A). Th/Nb and La/Nb ratios of phase III are as high as 2.0 and 10 compared with maximum values in other phases of about 1.0 and 8.0. Hf/Yb and Nb/Hf ratios are also slightly higher (Fig. 5A) in these lavas than in phases I and II. Normalized REE distribution diagrams reveal there is no flattening of LREE segments in any of the analyzed lavas from phase III.

Temporal trends in central Puerto Rico. Volcanism in central Puerto Rico evolved progressively during phases I, II, and III through all three distinctive island arc suites. The initial phase, erupted in an ocean floor environment, produced a thick pile of island arc tholeiite lava and associated volcanic breccia. The rocks contain low incompatible element concentrations, only slightly higher than N-MORB, resembling island arc basalts from modern intraoceanic arcs (Fig. 5C). The second volcanic phase is characterized by slightly more incompatible element-enriched cal-calkaline basalts of intermediate LILE/HREE and LREE/HREE ratios, while the third phase contains abundant, incompatible element-enriched shoshonites (Fig. 5A). The gradual geochemical progression is accompanied by a persistent rise in HFSE/HREE, Nb/Hf, and La/Yb ratios. Volcanic products from phase III are widely distributed both along the main axis of volcanism and in lateral basins. Apart from a progressive southward increase in Hf/Yb ratios, reflecting decreasing degrees of fusion, diagnostic ratios are relatively constant along a north-south traverse perpendicular to the main axis.

Geochemical trends in the northeastern volcanic province

Volcanic phase I. Daguao basalts fall within the broad field of island arc tholeiites on variation diagrams, although a few samples with higher incompatible element concentrations are classified as calcalkaline basalts (Fig. 5B). The rocks are predominantly basaltic with from 46 to about 54% SiO_2, but they display widely variable HFSE/HREE ratios. Hf/Yb ratios, for example, range from about 0.50 to 2 in the more SiO_2-enriched end-members (Fig. 5B), compared to a range in Formation A in central Puerto Rico from 0.8 to 1.2. In contrast to the basaltic composition of the Daguao Formation, Figuera lavas are predominantly highly evolved with SiO_2 as high as 75% (Weiland, 1988). A large variation of La/Yb ratios, from 2 to 6, is reflected in a wide range in normalized REE slopes, from slight (La/Yb ratio = 3 in sample DG-12) to moderate (La/Yb = 6 in sample DG-21C).

Volcanic phase II. Fajardo lava flows are unusual in the Puerto Rican volcanic sequence in their plagioclase-orthopyroxene mineralogy. Augite is present (modal volumes of 1 to 3%), but is distinctly subordinate to orthopyroxene pseudomorphs, which comprise up to 10% of the total volume. Plagioclase is also abundant (up to 12%). Similar phenocryst assemblages occur in Cerro Gordo lavas in the far northwestern corner of the block (Fig. 1). These unfossiliferous strata were originally assigned to the Cenomanian by Pease (1968), because some of the earliest flows contain cruciform plagioclase phenocrysts similar to those of the Lapa Lava in the central tectonic block. However, the unusual low SiO_2, high Hf/Yb compositions and unique phenocryst assemblages are likely correlated with Upper Albian Fajardo strata (Fig. 5B).

Volcanic phase III. Almost all phase III volcanic rocks in northeastern Puerto Rico are cal-calkaline basalts with relatively low degrees of LILE enrichment (Fig. 5). Hato Puerco lavas are the most enriched in LILE (Fig. 5B), while Santa Olaya Lava, which form several thick interfingering strato-volcanic accumulations along the north side of the Cerro Mula Fault Zone (Fig. 1), tend to display flattened chondrite-normalized REE patterns. One specimen from the upper part of the unit (sample SO-502) exhibits extreme LREE depletion and negative LREE anomalies, including depleted Sm concentrations relative to HREE. Pease (1968) estimated maximum thickness of Santa Olaya Lava exceeds 3 km. The lavas are basaltic with a narrow range of Hf/Yb ratios averaging about 1.7 (Fig. 5B). Lavas from the

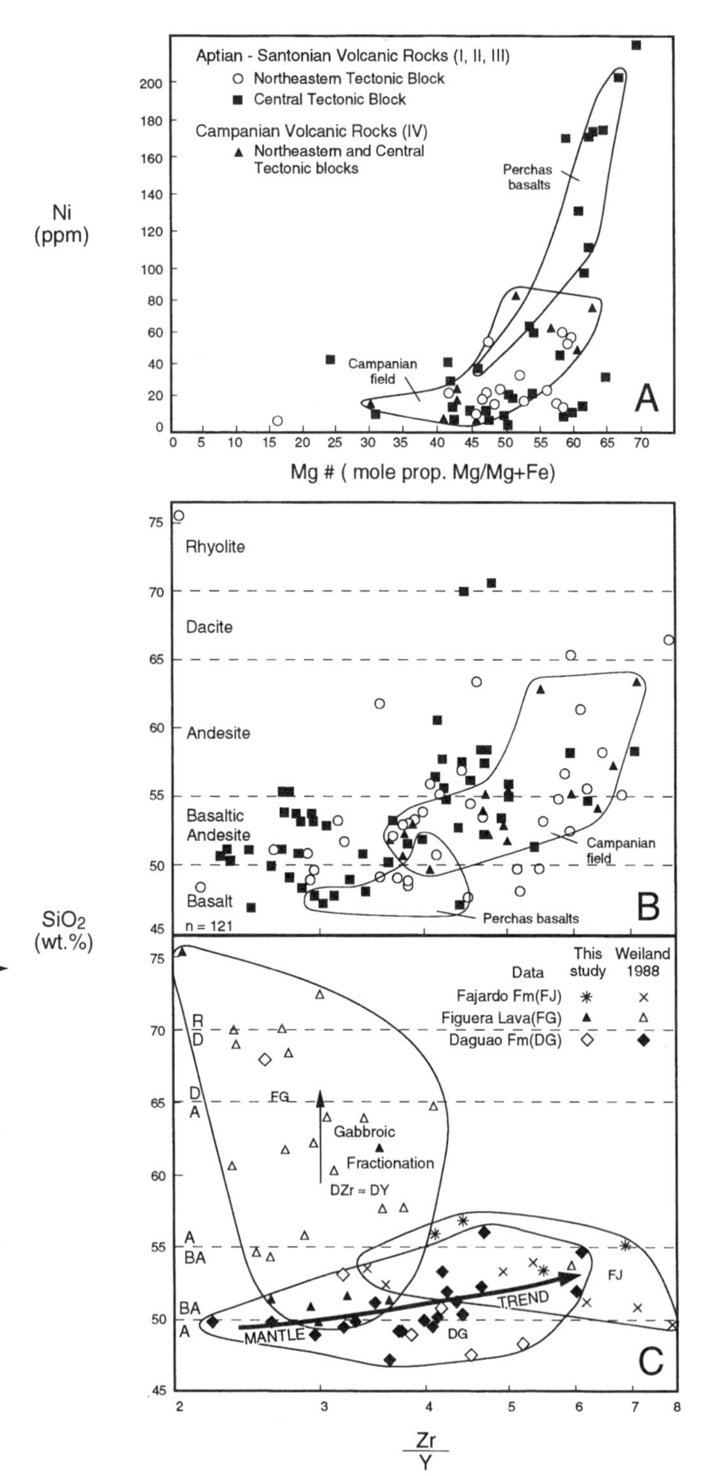

Figure 3. Relations between major and trace element geochemistry and fractional crystallization in Puerto Rican arc lavas. A, Positive relations between Ni (in parts per million) and Mg# and low absolute Ni abundances in the majority of Puerto Rican lavas are indicative of extensive olivine fractionation. Fields for the most incompatible element enriched unit (Perchas lavas) and late-stage Campanian lavas are included for comparison. B and C, Relations between SiO_2 and Zr/Y ratios. In B, SiO_2 content of all analyzed lavas are used to subdivide the rocks into volcanic classes, based on SiO_2 subdivision of Taylor et al., 1969). Puerto Rican lavas are predominantly basalts and basaltic andesites, but fractionated end-members form up to 25% of the total population. In C, SiO_2 content of lavas from the northeastern tectonic block is illustrated. During volcanic phase I, numerous Daguao parental magmas (mantle trend) underwent extensive subvolcanic gabbroic fractionation, producing the evolved Figuera lava suite. Subsequent Fajardo lavas (phase II) carry an orthopyroxene-plagioclase–bearing phenocryst mineralogy, consistent with higher P_t fractional crystallization. Data include analyses from Weiland (1988).

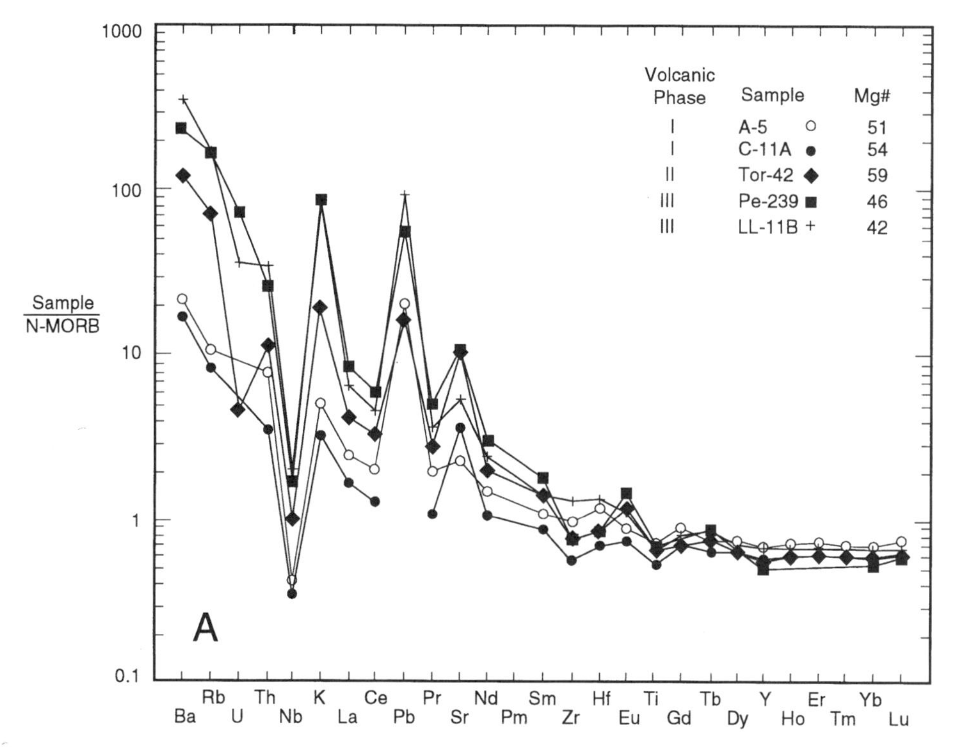

Figure 4. N-MORB–normalized incompatible element patterns in representative Puerto Rican arc basalts from the central tectonic block, illustrating the complete spectrum of lava types. Normalization factors and the elemental sequence are from Sun and McDonough (1989); more incompatible elements appear at left. For clarity Pr concentrations are interpolated for INAA analyses.

Infierno Formation characteristically exhibit strong depletion in the more incompatible elements, with low Hf/Yb (Fig. 5) and La/Yb ratios.

Temporal trends in northeastern Puerto Rico. Lavas of northeastern Puerto Rico form two somewhat overlapping geochemical groups. The first includes phase I lavas of the Daguao and Figuera lavas, which display wide ranges in HFSE/HREE ratios, covering almost the entire observed range (Fig. 5). For example, Hf/Yb ratios in basalts from volcanic phase I range from 0.7 to 2.0, compared with a range of 0.6 to 1.1 in the central block. The second group includes phase II and III lavas that display consistently higher incompatible element ratios (Fig. 5B). Normalized REE patterns from lower Daguao and Figuera Lavas from the northeastern block exhibit enriched LREE patterns with variable slopes.

Geochemical variation in Campanian volcanic rocks

Campanian lavas from volcanic phase IV all display similar compositions, with Hf/Yb ratios ranging from about 1 to 2. Th/Hf ratios range from 0.4 to 1.5 (Fig. 5A, B), overlapping the boundary between cal-calkaline and shoshonitic compositions. Eu anomalies are minimal except in the Tortugas andesite, consistent with extensive subvolcanic fractional crystallization of plagioclase.

GEOCHEMICAL PROCESSES IN PUERTO RICAN VOLCANISM

Behavior of the mantle wedge source

Composition of Atlantic and Caribbean Mesozoic MORB. Altered basalts associated with partly serpentinized peridotite and chert deposits in western Puerto Rico are thought to represent Jurassic pre-arc oceanic crust (Schellekens et al., 1991; Montgomery et al., 1994; Jolly et al., 1994). Several of these basalts (sample locations and descriptions are given in Fig. 9B of Jolly et al., Chapter 1, this volume) display MORB-like ε_{Nd}-values (average about 9.0) and elevated $i^{87}Sr/^{86}Sr$ ratios (average of 0.7038 [–8.2]) (Fig. 6C), overlapping the field of unleached altered Cretaceous Atlantic MORB (averaging 9.0 and 0.7040 [–7.4], respectively) (Jahn et al., 1980). The pre-arc basalts also exhibit depleted normalized incompatible element patterns and low La/Sm and La/Nb ratios, averaging about 0.90 and 1.50, respectively, similar to values exhibited by Cretaceous Atlantic MORB and N-MORB values (0.95 and 1.07) of Sun and McDonough (1989). Although the tectonic history and polarity of subduction of the Greater Antilles arc is uncertain (cf. Donnelly, 1989, and Pindell and Barrett, 1990), subduction of either the Pacific or Atlantic Plates must have involved fusion in a depleted mantle source.

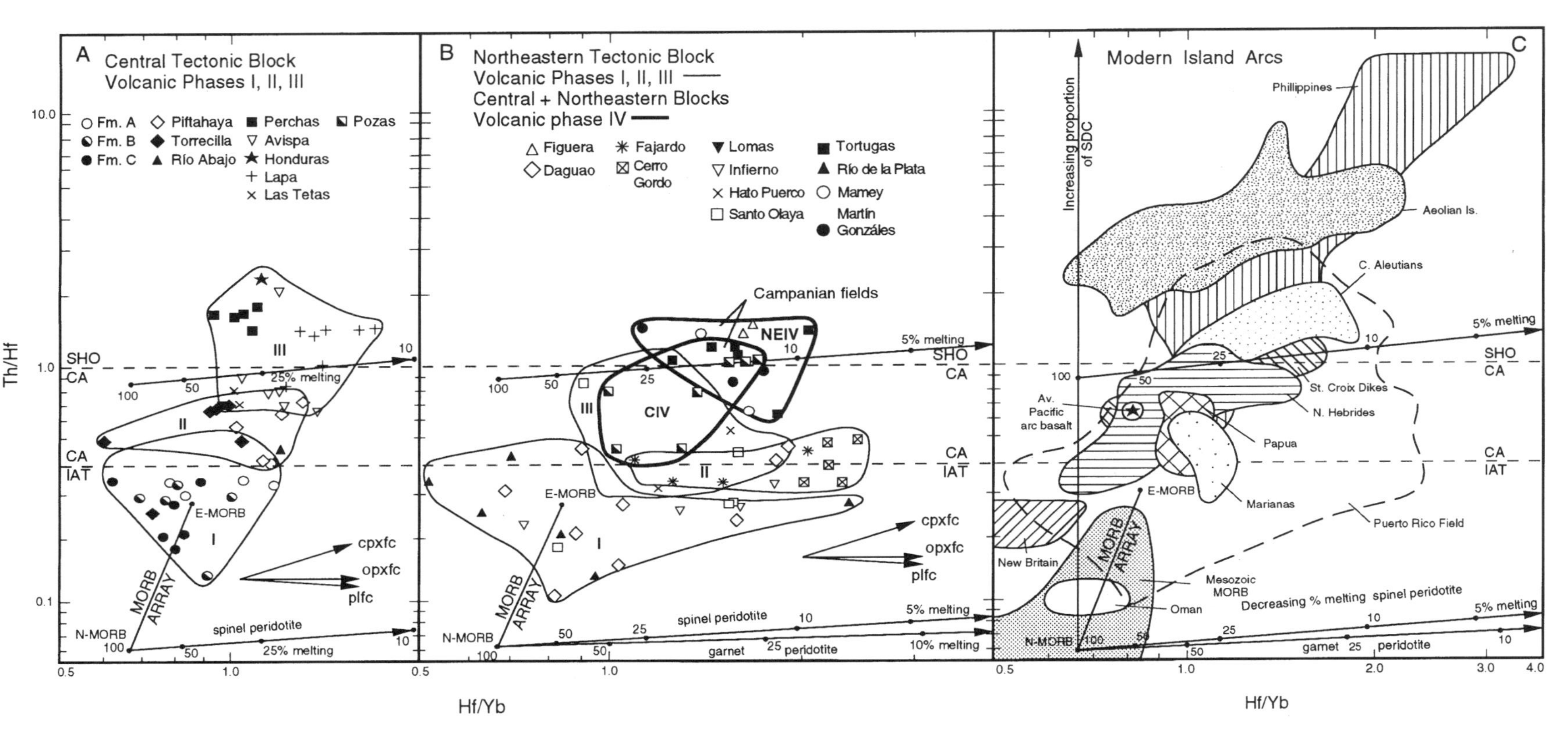

Figure 5. Classification of arc lavas in eastern Puerto Rico from Th/Hf-Hf/Yb ratios. SHO, shoshonites; CA, cal-calkaline volcanic rocks; IAT, island arc tholeiites (boundaries modified from Pearce, 1983). References to arc data used are as follows: Aeolian Islands: Ellam et al. (1988); Central Aleutians: Romick et al. (1992); Grenada: Hawkesworth and Powell (1980), Thirlwall and Graham (1984); Japan: Tatsumi et al. (1988); Northern Lesser Antilles: Davidson (1986), White et al. (1985); Marianas: Woodhead (1989), McCullough and Gamble (1991); New Britain: DePaulo and Johnson (1979), Woodhead and Johnson (1993), McCullough and Gamble (1991); New Hebrides: Dupuy et al. (1982); Oman: Alabaster et al. (1982); Papua New Guinea: Kennedy et al. (1990); Philippines: Defant et al. (1990), McDermott et al. (1993); South Sandwich: Cohen and O'Nions (1982), Hawkesworth et al. (1977), Barreiro (1983); Tonga: Ewart and Hawkesworth (1987); St. Croix: Upper Cretaceous dikes, Lidiak and Jolly (this volume). A, Central Puerto Rican lavas; B, northeastern and Campanian Puerto Rican lavas; s, fields of some representative modern island arcs compared to the Puerto Rican field (this study); also shown is the field of Mesozoic MORB (Table 4). The average island arc basalt composition (using the conversion factor Hf = Zr/36.2 from Sun and McDonough, 1989) is from McCullough and Gamble (1991). Hf and Yb play a minimal role in the subduction related component (SDC), and the vertical vector represents relative degree of SDC enrichment. Melting curves for spinel and garnet peridotite, calculated from an N-MORB–type source and other hypothetical sources with various Th/Hf ratios, represent relative melting factors rather than actual estimated degree of melting, because the composition of the source is uncertain.

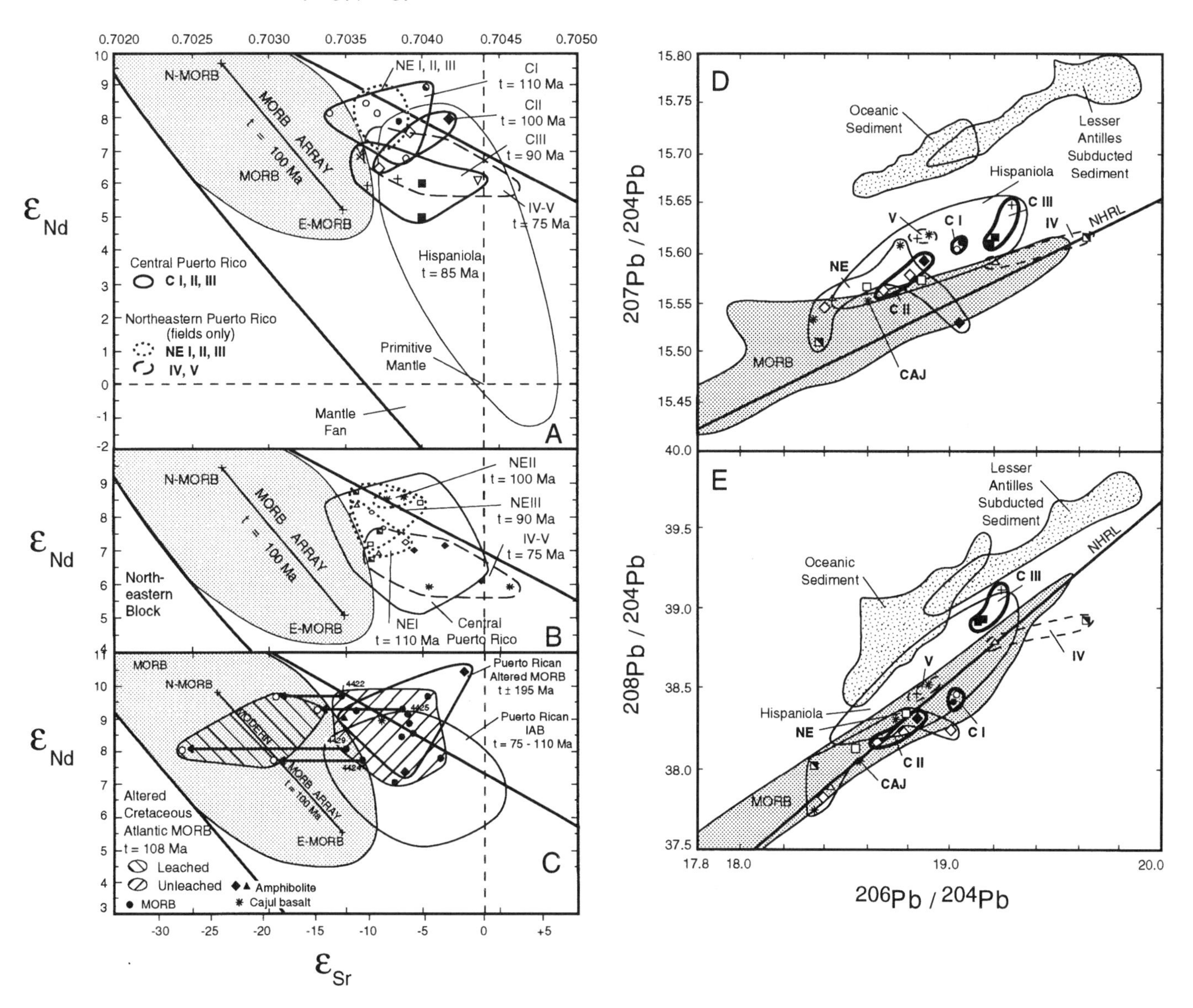

Figure 6. Sr, Nd, and Pb isotopes in Puerto Rican lavas. A, Sr-Nd isotopes in lavas from central Puerto Rico. B, Northeastern and Campanian Puerto Rican lavas. C, Sr-Nd isotope compositions of altered MORB-like pre-arc basalts and amphibolites from western Puerto Rico (sample locations given in Jolly et al., Chapter 1, this volume), and altered Atlantic Cretaceous MORB (Jahn et al., 1980). The leached Puerto Rican samples resemble unleached altered oceanic basalt. D and E, Pb isotopes in Puerto Rican Basalts. NE, Northeast block (sample locations given in Jolly et al. (Chapter 1, this volume); C, central block; I, II, III, IV, V, volcanic phases; CAJ, pre-arc MORB-like basalt from western Puerto Rico; A-5 designates composition of a sample from Formation A (phase I) used in mixing models. MORB fields in all diagrams are from (Zindler and Hart, 1986); pelagic oceanic sediment field as in Hawkesworth et al. (1993b); field of sediments (contaminated by continental detritus supplied by the Río Oronoco) from the Demarara Plain, Atlantic Ocean are from White et al. (1985); Northern Hemisphere Reference Line (NHRL) is from Hart (1984); Hispaniola field is from Lebron and Perfit (1994).

Parameters used in mantle melting models. Melting models in MORB-like depleted mantle sources are constructed using estimated trace element source compositions, assumed for consistency to be an order of magnitude lower than observed basalt compositions (Wood, 1979b). Bulk partition coefficients for garnet and spinel peridotite (Table 5) were calculated from mineral/melt partition coefficients modified from McKenzie and O'Nions (1991) and Hawkesworth et al. (1993b). It is assumed the degree of fusion was sufficiently high to eliminate hornblende from the source (Stolper and Newman, 1994). Melting vectors produced by the model calculations represent maximum degrees of melting rather than actual values, because evidence from high field strength elements (HFSE), discussed below, suggest mantle wedge compositions were more depleted in incompatible elements than a MORB-like source.

Distribution of HFSE in Puerto Rican arc basalts. The origin of characteristic negative normalized HFSE anomalies in island arc basalts (see Fig. 4) is controversial. The anomalies have been attributed (Davidson and Wolff, 1989; Ringwood, 1990) to residual behavior of titanate and other oxide phases within the mantle source. Considerable experimental (Ryerson and Watson, 1987) and observational (McCullough and Gamble, 1991) data, however, cast doubt on the stability of such titanates in most modern arc environments, and suggest instead that the HFSE depletions reflect low abundances in the wedge source (Pearce, 1983) or processes within the wedge (Keleman et al., 1992). HFSE are investigated using Hf and Nb; Nb is considerably more incompatible than H (Fig. 4).

McCullough and Gamble (1991) demonstrated that South Pacific island arc basalts exhibit Zr/Nb ratios almost identical to MORB basalts, regardless of the Nb content, indicating the parental melts were generated without the presence of a residual Nb-rich titanate oxide phase. Hence, these authors considered HFSE independent of flux from the descending slab, and suggested that, at the degrees of melting characteristic of island arcs, these elements behave incompatibly (see also White and Patchett, 1984). McCullough and Gamble (1991) further noted that most arc basalts, particularly those generated by higher degrees of melting, carry lower absolute abundances of both Nb and Zr, and concluded that the wedge source of arcs is more depleted than a MORB-type source. Depleted upper mantle compositions are also expected to be generated by MORB melting associated with diapiric activity along mid-ocean ridges during plate formation (Ringwood, 1990).

HFSE patterns in Puerto Rican volcanic rocks are consistent with these observations. For example, in Figure 7A, which includes only basalts and basaltic andesites with SiO_2 <55.0%, Hf/Nb ratios overlap the MORB trend, consistent with incompatible behavior. Additionally, in samples with low concentrations, Hf and Nb display depletions up to 30 and 50%, respectively, compared with N-MORB (Fig. 7A, B), indicative of a depleted mantle source. A calculated melting curve, derived from a spinel peridotite source with an N-MORB-like Hf/Yb ratio of 0.68 and an Hf content of 1.5 ppm, is subparallel to the Puerto Rican field. This curve represents maximum degrees of melting, since the depleted mantle source has a lower Hf/Yb ratio than N-MORB; the best fit to the data is obtained when the curve is translated leftward to a starting Hf/Yb ratio of 0.52 (dashed curve in Fig. 7B). The latter curve coincides with 25 to less than 10% melting.

Ti also exhibits deeper negative anomalies in normalized incompatible element patterns (Fig. 4) than Ta, Zr, and Hf. Modes of rocks studied in this chapter (Table 2) reveal magnetite is an abundant accessory of basalts from all volcanic phases, which, in conjunction with low correlations between Ti and Y, is consistent with subvolcanic oxide fractionation.

Distribution of heavy rare earth elements (HREE). Flat chondrite normalized HREE (including HREE-like Y) patterns in elemental distribution diagrams (see Fig. 4) are characteristic of Puerto Rican arc basalts and other island arc lavas. Kay (1980) and Pearce (1983) demonstrated that such patterns are produced routinely (see Fig. 3, Pearce, 1983) by moderate degrees of melting (about 15%) of a MORB-source, but that at lower degrees of fusion in the garnet peridotite facies, residual garnet controls HREE concentrations producing fractionated HREE patterns. On the contrary, fusion at lower P_t in the in spinel peridotite facies, where distribution of HREE is controlled by clinopyroxene rather than garnet, produces flat HREE patterns at all degrees of melting. The flat HREE signature, together with a wide range in Nb/Hf ratios reflecting variation in degree of fusion (Fig. 7A, B), is consistent with generation of the Puerto Rican suite at relatively low P_t, in spinel peridotite. In this model low Yb contents (less than N-MORB) (Fig. 4) reflect, in part, the presence of residual clinopyroxene in the source.

TABLE 5. PARAMETERS USED IN MANTLE MELTING MODELS*

	D-Values						Peridotite Modes	
Phase	Th	Nb	La	Hf	Y	Yb	Spinel	Garnet
Ol	0.0015	0.0004	0.0005	0.0020	0.0050	0.0040	0.578	0.598
Opx	0.0015	0.0004	0.0005	0.0030	0.0030	0.0290	0.270	0.211
Cpx	0.0110	0.0150	0.0200	0.1200	0.2000	0.2000	0.119	0.076
Gt	0.0100	0.0150	0.0010	0.0450	2.0000	4.0000	....	0.115
Sp	0.0100	0.0100	0.0100	0.0500	0.0100	0.0100	0.133	....
Bulk D-values								
Gt perid	0.0032	0.0031	0.0020	0.0149	0.2458	0.4837		
Sp perid	0.0029	0.0023	0.0030	0.0180	0.0278	0.0272		

*Peridotite modes from McKenzie and O'Nions, 1991; peridotite/melt partition coefiicients (D) modified from Hawkesworth et al., 1993b.

Variation in degree of melting

As indicated above, the distribution of Nb and Hf is consistent with incompatible behavior for both of these components during melt generation. Moreover, these elements play an insignificant role in phenocryst phases associated with the basaltic melts and are highly insoluble in aqueous fluids (Pearce, 1983; Brennan and Watson, 1991). Hence, Nb/Hf ratios are little affected by fractional crystallization processes and by the proportion of the subduction-related component (SDC) introduced into the wedge by slab-derived fluids. The ratio thus provides relative degree of melting factors for the parental magmas (Fig. 7B).

The widest variation in Nb/Hf ratios is displayed by the central volcanic province, where they range from 0.3 to about 2 (Fig. 8B), and increase progressively from an average of 0.4 in Formation A of volcanic phase I to about 0.75 in phase II, and finally to about 1.5 in Perchas lavas of phase III, reflecting a systematic decrease in degree of fusion with time. Phase IV basalts overlap the field of phases II and III, and the average Nb/Hf ratio (about 1.0) is intermediate between these two groups (Fig. 8A). The range of variation is similar in the northeastern province, but averages are much more restricted and less systematic, ranging from 0.6 in phase I, 0.4 in phase II, to 0.7 in phase III. Fajardo and Cerro Gordo lavas from phase II were derived from some of the highest degree melts recognized in eastern Puerto Rico. Only samples from the Lomas Formation and a few from the Santa Olaya Lava display Nb/Hf ratios greater than 1.0 in phase III. The distribution suggests that few Puerto Rican lavas were co-genetic and that all volcanic phases were formed from multiple discrete parental magmas.

Fractional crystallization

General characteristics. When plotted against Nb/Hf ratios, concentrations of SiO_2 and highly incompatible trace elements in Puerto Rican lavas form elongate to oval shaped fields aligned along the SiO_2 axis due to fractional crystallization. Phase I lavas from both volcanic provinces contain abundant andesitic, dacitic, and rhyolitic fractionates (Fig. 8A, B), especially in later stages of the phase (Figuera lavas), and as clasts in volcanic breccia from Formation A of the Río Majada Group. Lesser degrees of fractionation occurred in other volcanic phases.

Parameters used in basalt fractionation models. Trace element fractionation vectors for clinopyroxene, orthopyroxene, and plagioclase were determined for the diagnostic elements Th, Nb, La, Hf, and Yb using mineral/melt partition coefficients (D-values, Table 6) modified from the compilation of G. A. Jenner (NEWPET Program Package, 1991, Center for Earth Resources Research, Memorial University of Newfoundland); D-values for Hf are inferred to be identical to Zr. The vectors were calculated from N-MORB-type starting compositions, but also represent fractionation trends for other compositions.

High pressure orthopyroxene-rich fractionation. The plagioclase-orthopyroxene dominated phenocryst mineralogy of Cerro Gordo and Fajardo lavas from volcanic phase II in the northeastern tectonic block (Table 2) are unique in eastern Puerto Rico. The abundance of orthopyroxene is indicative of relatively high-pressure fractional crystallization, perhaps within the upper mantle lithosphere (Weiland, 1988) or near the crust-mantle discontinuity. Major element mixing calculations in the Fajardo Formation (Weiland, 1988) suggest an increase in silica from about 50 to 58% SiO_2 was accompanied by fractionation of about 25% labradorite, 12% hypersthene, and less than 4% augite and magnetite. High silica content of orthopyroxene produced limited enrichment in SiO_2, averaging 56% and ranging only as high as about 62% (Fig. 8A). Fractionation of abundant pyroxene also had a pronounced effect on REE abundances in the evolved lavas, especially HREE as illustrated by fractionation vectors in Figure 9C.

Subvolcanic gabbroic fractionation. Most basalts in Puerto Rico carry low-P_t gabbroic phenocryst assemblages dominated by olivine, augite, and plagioclase (Table 2); orthopyroxene is rare and hornblende is absent from all lavas investigated. Mixing models demonstrate gabbroic fractionates are rapidly enriched in SiO_2 (Fig. 8) (Jolly, 1971; Weiland, 1988), and phase I units commonly contain evolved dacitic and rhyolitic end-members. In the Figuera Lavas, for example, a rise in silica from 53 to 73% is accompanied by fractionation of about 40% labradorite, 12% augite, 5% olivine, and 5% magnetite (Weiland, 1988). In other volcanic phases (II, III, IV), fractionation normally reached only the andesitic range, and dacites and rhyolites are rare or absent.

In Figure 9A, B effects of gabbroic fractionation on LREE are illustrated for the entire Puerto Rican suite (a) and for an individual volcanic phase (phase III of the central block) (b). In contrast to the field of Atlantic MORB, which is broadly parallel to a 1:1 enrichment vector on Th-La element-element plots, the field of Puerto Rican lavas has a lower slope more closely related to fractionation vectors for plagioclase and clinopyroxene (Fig. 9A) than to the MORB melting trend. Similarly, flows from the Río Orocovis Group and Robles Formation form least-square trends with intercepts on the La axis (Fig. 9B). Effects of fractionation on the main element groups (including LREE [La], HREE [Yb], HFSE [Nb, Hf], and Th) are shown in Figure 9C, D). Hf/Yb ratios of analyzed lavas fall between vectors representing augite and plagioclase fractionation, suggesting the evolved end-members can be derived primarily through removal (or accumulation) of a combination of these two phases. It is noted, however, that there is wide variation in starting trace-element ratios, indicating fractional crystallization patterns were superimposed on a range parental melt compositions. This is revealed in Figure 9D, in which each unit displays a broad range in Nb/Hf ratios inconsistent with a co-magmatic origin.

Sequential batch melting

Several lava units in the Puerto Rican volcanic sequence display a pronounced flattening of LREE segments in chondrite normalized distribution diagrams. The most systematic variations

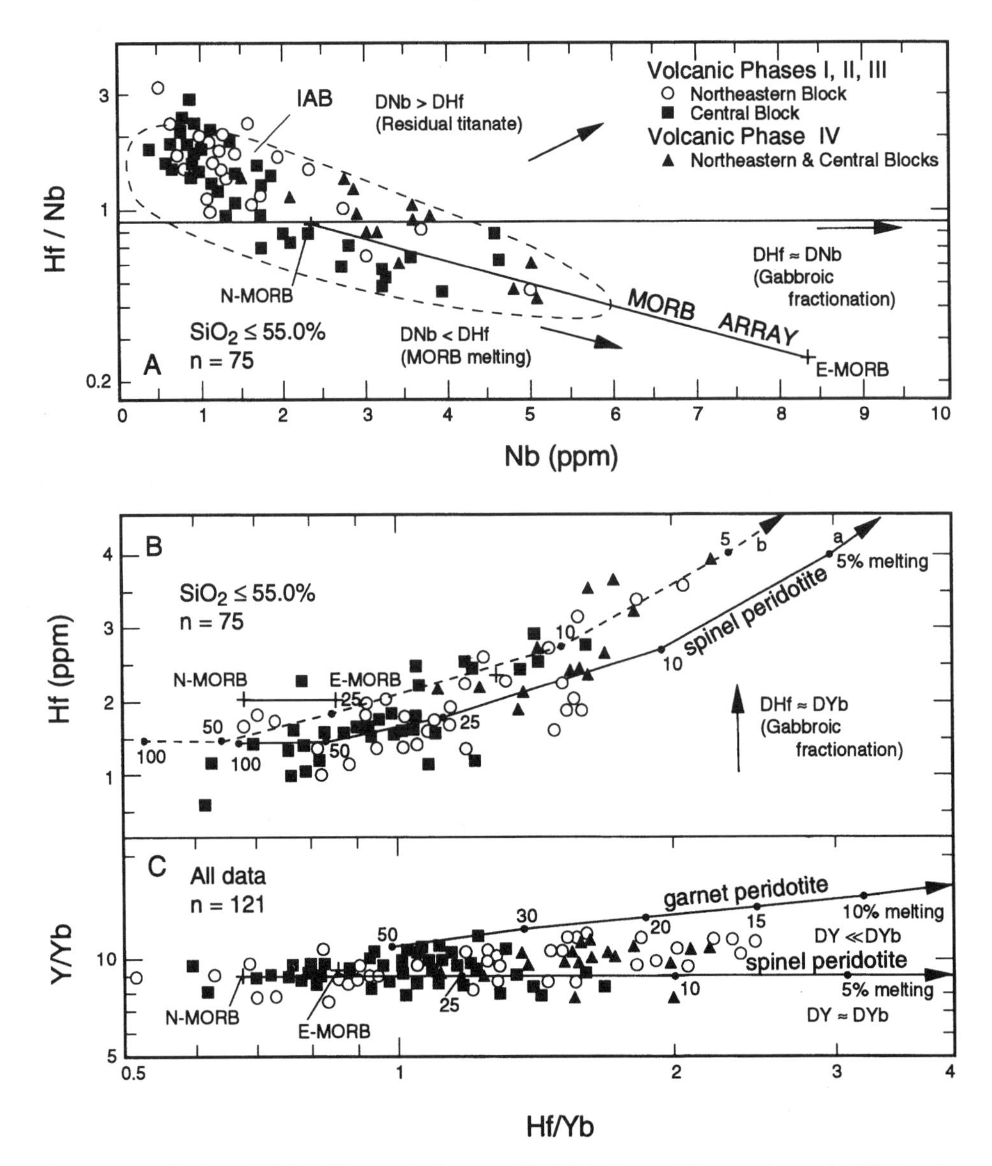

Figure 7. Distribution of high field strength elements (HFSE) in Puerto Rican arc lavas. A, Hf/Nb ratios and Nb abundances platted according to the method of McCullough and Gamble (1991). Puerto Rican basalts follow the MORB trend, regardless of Nb concentration, consistent with incompatible behavior of HFSE. IAB field from data of McCullough and Gamble (1991) using the factor Hf = Zr/36.2 (Sun and McDonough, 1989). B, Hf and Hf/Yb ratios, illustrating low absolute Hf abundances compared with MORB, and suggesting the source was more depleted than an N-MORB–type source; plotted samples contain SiO_2<55.0%. Spinel peridotite melting curve (solid line a) was calculated using parameters in Table 5 and an N-MORB–type source as the starting composition. The dashed line (b) is a best fit leftward translation of the melting curve, and estimates actual melting patterns in a depleted wedge source with Hf concentration of 0.52 ppm. C, Y/Yb and Hf/Yb ratios in Puerto Rican arc basalts, shown with calculated melting curves for spinel and garnet peridotite. The flat pattern of Y/Yb ratios at relatively low degrees of melting is consistent with fusion of spinel peridotite at relatively low P_t, i.e., in a low-angle subduction zone. MORB values from Sun and McDonough (1989).

occur within the sequence of Río Majada basalts from volcanic phase I of the central tectonic block, and these basalts are selected for detailed investigation.

Distribution of incompatible trace elements in Río Majada basalts. Stratigraphic variation of selected incompatible elements is illustrated in Figure 10, where east-west distances across the Cayey quadrangle (Fig. 3, Jolly et al., Chapter 1, this volume) are correlated with height in the volcanic pile. La/Sm ratios decrease upward, from an average of about 2.0 in Formation A to about 1.75 in Formation B, and finally to about 1.5 in the upper part of Formation C (Fig. 10A). Other incompatible elements display similar depletions, including Zr/Sm and Th/Sm ratios, which decline from 0.38 to

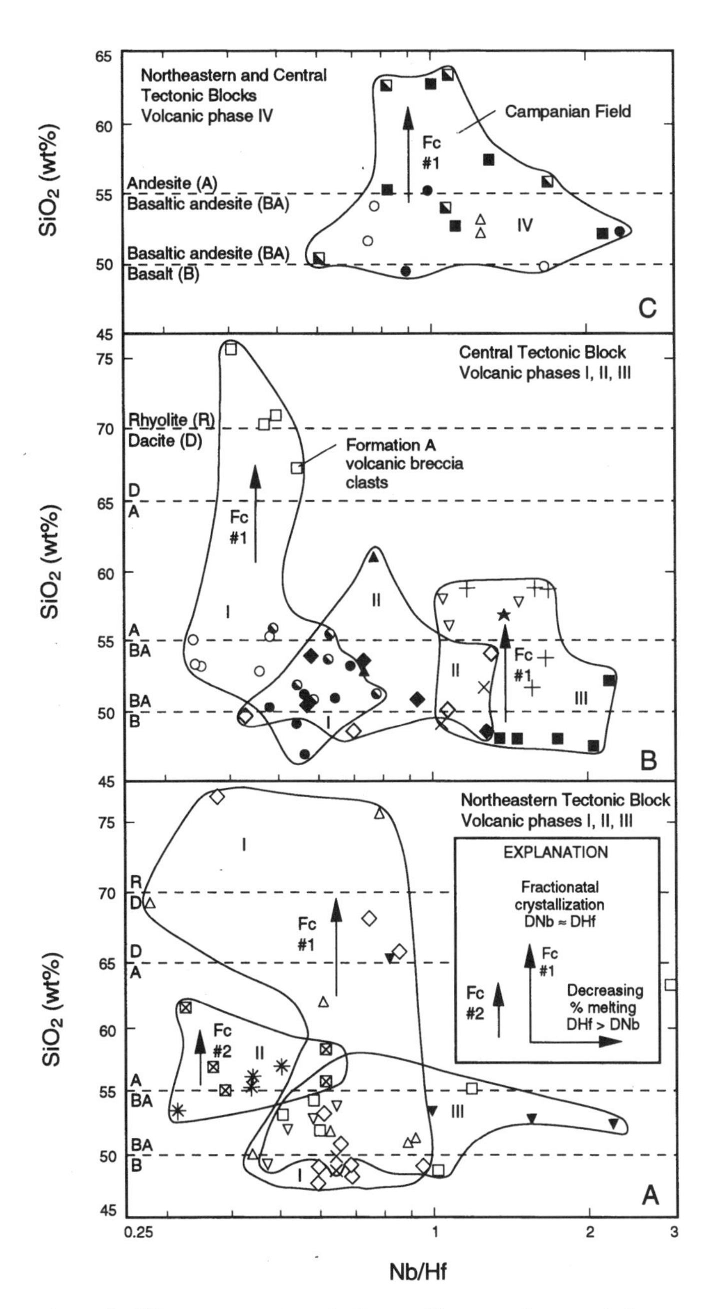

Figure 8. SiO_2 concentrations in Puerto Rican arc lavas, relative to Nb/Hf ratios, which are insensitive to fractional crystallization processes (see schematic vectors). The diagram compares relative degree of fusion (Nb/Hf) with fractional crystallization processes (SiO_2). Phase I lavas in both tectonic blocks display extensive plagioclase-augite-olivine-based gabbroic subvolcanic fractionation patterns (Fc#1), characterized by rapid increase in SiO_2. Lavas from phase II in northeastern Puerto Rico display limited increases in SiO_2 content despite their elevated Hf/Yb ratios (Fig. 5), and carry a plagioclase–two pyroxene–olivine-dominated phenocryst mineralogy, consistent with higher pressure fractionation (Fc#2).

TABLE 6. PARAMETERS USED IN BASALT CRYSTAL FRACTIONATION MODELS*

Element	Pl	Cpx	Opx
La	0.1800	0.2880	0.0260
Yb	`0.0670	0.7190	0.4700
Hf	0.0100	0.2500	0.0200
Th	0.0100	0.4584	0.0150
Nb	0.0100	0.2160	0.0150

*Mineral/basalt melt partition coefficients (D) modified from compilation of G. A. Jenner, Newpet Petrological Program, 1991, Center for Earth Resources Research, the Memorial University of Newfoundland.

about 0.10, and 11.5 to 10.0, respectively (Fig. 10C, D). The degree of depletion increases with the relative incompatibility of an element with respect to Yb, ranging from about 11% for Zr, 24% for La, and over 53% for Th, while average ratios of less incompatible elements, including Sm/Yb (Fig. 10B), remain similar throughout Formations A, B, and C. Conversely, Sr/Sm ratios are progressively enriched upward from about 84 to 130. A change in slope in the lower part of Formation B naturally subdivides the basalts into two populations. An early group, consisting of Formation A and the oldest flows from Formation B, exhibits relatively constant and high incompatible element ratios, whereas a later group, containing Formations B and C, has lower incompatible element ratios.

Depletion of LREE from basalts of Formations B and C is reflected in chond rite-normalized distribution diagrams by flattening of the LREE segment. To facilitate comparisons, patterns in Figure 11A-C have been subdivided into three types: (1) $(La/Sm)_N$ ratios greater than unity, including all Formation A lavas and one from the lower third of Formation B (Fig. 11A); (2) relatively flat LREE segments and $(La/Sm)_N$ ratios averaging about one, including remaining Formation B basalts and most samples from Formation C (Fig. 11B); and (3) an LREE depleted basalt with $(La/Sm)_N$ ratios less than one (Fig. 11C) from the top of Formation C. Río Majada basalts, with Mg# restricted to the range 49 to 53, exhibit a 50% depletion in HREE in late units (Formations B and C), which contain only four to eight times the chondrite abundances compared with enrichment ranging from 8 to 10 times in Formation A (Fig. 11A-C).

Distribution of Sr, Nd, and Pb isotopes. While many incompatible trace elements are strongly depleted from basalts comprising upper parts of the Río Majada volcanic sequence, concentrations of radiogenic Sr are strongly enriched. Basalts from Formation A have some of the lowest Sr isotope ratios in the entire Puerto Rican suite, with a range of ε_{Sr}-values from –13.8 to –9.5 (0.7034 to 0.7037) and averaging –12.00 (0.7035), compared with a range from –8 to as high as about –3.0 (0.7038 to 0.7042) and an average of –5.5 (0.7038) in Formations B and C. Pb isotope ratios are also MORB-like, and, except for anomalous shoshonitic basalts from volcanic phase III in central Puerto Rico (Fig. 6D, E), plot along or subparallel to the Northern Hemisphere Reference Line (NHRL) of Hart (1984). Two Río Majada basalts, from Formations A and C, have almost identical Pb-isotope compositions.

Relative degree of incompatible element depletion. The degree of depletion exhibited by Río Majada basalts is approximated using differences in incompatible element/Sm ratios between average values of the four samples from the base of Formation A and the two uppermost samples from Formation C (Fig. 12A). The maximum variation of these six samples with respect to average values, are lowest (between ±6 and 11%) for REE and Nb, and moderate (±13 to 21%) for other elements (Th, Sr, Zr, Hf). The order of decreasing depletion (Th, La, Ce, Nd, Zr, Hf, Nb) is similar to the generalized sequence for island arc volcanic rocks suggested by McCullough and Gamble (1991), with Th and Sr exhibiting the most, LREE intermediate, and HFSE the least incompatibility with respect to Yb. The sequence also resembles (Fig. 12A, B) the order of partition coefficients for spinel peridotite/melt (Hawkesworth et al., 1993a). Nb is anomalous and falls near HREE, consistent with lower degrees of fusion for Formation C basalts.

Many of the above discussed features of incompatible trace elements and isotope data from Puerto Rican basalts are similar to patterns developed during sequential or incremental batch melting in oceanic basalts (Wood, 1979). The process is more complicated in arc settings due to contamination of the wedge with the ubiquitous subduction-related component (SDC), which acts as a flux and controls the degree of melting (Stolper and Newman, 1994). Sr/Sm ratios (Fig. 10E), for example, suggest a 35% Sr enrichment in Formations B and C, with respect to Formation A, consistent with incorporation of additional slab-derived flux. Melting depletes a peridotite source in mantle-derived Sr, while refluxing produces a source containing a higher proportion of Sr supplied by the flux. Furthermore, an increase in ε_{Sr}-values from –12 to –5.5 (0.7035 to 0.7038) upward in the sequence (Fig. 11D), is consistent with sequential batch melting.

Trace element melting models. The objective of modelling is to reproduce the characteristic flattened chondrite-normalized La-Sm segments while preserving the fractionated slopes of the Sm-Yb segment in Formation C by multiple melting events in source material incorporating small proportions of residua from previous melts. The simplest model of the melting regime in island arc environments (McCullough and Gamble, 1991; Hawkesworth et al., 1993A, B; Stolper and Newman, 1994) involves fusion in the mantle wedge in response to fluxing by the subduction-related component (SDC). MORB-like Pb and Nd isotope ratios in Río Majada and other Puerto Rican basalts are indicative of a minimal sediment component and low REE abundances in the fluxing fluid. Thus, REE had minimal involvement in refluxing of residua during sequential batch melting. Nb/Hf ratios indicate Formation A basalts were generated by about 15% fusion (Fig. 7B), and in conformity with relatively stable Sm/Yb ratios (Fig. 13B), melting is held constant at this level (f = 0.15).

The source composition for the initial melt was estimated using a representative Formation A basalt (sample A-4, Table 7), but other samples yield similar results. The initial step in the process, 15% fusion of the calculated source, generates a hypothetical liquid with an La/Sm ratio of 1.80, similar to the actual value in the sample (1.78; Fig. 13A). The residue is highly depleted in LREE, and La decreases almost 95% from 0.530 ppm in the original source to 0.025 ppm, compared with a 30% decrease in Yb from 0.215 to 0.064. Sr is also highly depleted, from 25 to about 4 ppm, representing an 86% decrease.

Source mixtures used to model the second fusion event consist of various proportions of pristine source material and depleted residuum from the initial melt. Residua/original source ratios in mixtures range from 1:9, 2:8, to 3:7, reflecting contribution of 10, 20, and 30% residua, respectively, most closely resemble patterns in Formation C basalts (Table 7). Hypothetical basalts produced by a mixture containing 30% residuum, for example, reproduces lower La/Sm ratios of Formations B and C (about 1.60; Fig. 13B). Models with lower degrees of melting require a higher proportion of residuum to produce similar results, whereas addition of higher proportions of residuum produces melts with Sm/Yb ratios that are too low. Addition of a minute LREE fraction to residua between melting events overprints earlier elemental depletions, effectively masking sequential batch melting. REE distribution suggests these elements are relatively independent of the refluxing process during the sequential batch melting process in Río Majada basalts. Sr isotopes, in contrast, were strongly dependent on the flux, because Formation C basalts have higher Sr isotope ratios than Formation A.

Figure 9. Effects of fractional crystallization (fc) on distribution of trace elements. Fractional crystallization paths were calculated using parameters in Table 6; also included are melting vectors for spinel peridotite melting patterns, calculated using parameters in Table 5. Symbols as in Figure 5. A, Th-La element-element plot of Puerto Rican data and Mesozoic MORB (which includes Puerto Rican pre-arc MORB-like basalts and amphibolites together with altered Atlantic Cretaceous MORB of Jahn et al. (1980). In contrast to the MORB field, which follows a 1:1 enrichment path, the Puerto Rican trend intersects the La axis at about the 5-ppm level. The latter trend is subparallel to pyroxene fractionation vectors (cpxfc, opxfc), consistent with removal of La from Puerto Rican melts during fractional crystallization. B, Similar trends are present for individual volcanic units. For example, shoshonitic lavas from phase III of the central block form two groups, one including Río Orocovis lavas from the north and another including lavas from the southern Robles basin. Both groups have least-square trends exhibiting lower slopes than expected during ideal incompatible behavior (represented by the heavy lines), consistent with pyroxene fractionation or accumulation; r = correlation coefficient. C, Hf/Yb and Th/La ratios are sensitive to fractional crystallization of both plagioclase (plfc) and clinopyroxene (cpxfc), and compositions of Puerto Rican basalts fall between fractionation vectors for these phases. When plotted against Nb/Hf ratios (D), which are insensitive to fractionation, however, Th/La ratios reveal that few of the shoshonites are co-magmatic. Instead they were probably formed from numerous similar batches of parental magmas derived by various degrees of partial fusion and each subsequently modified by fractional crystallization.

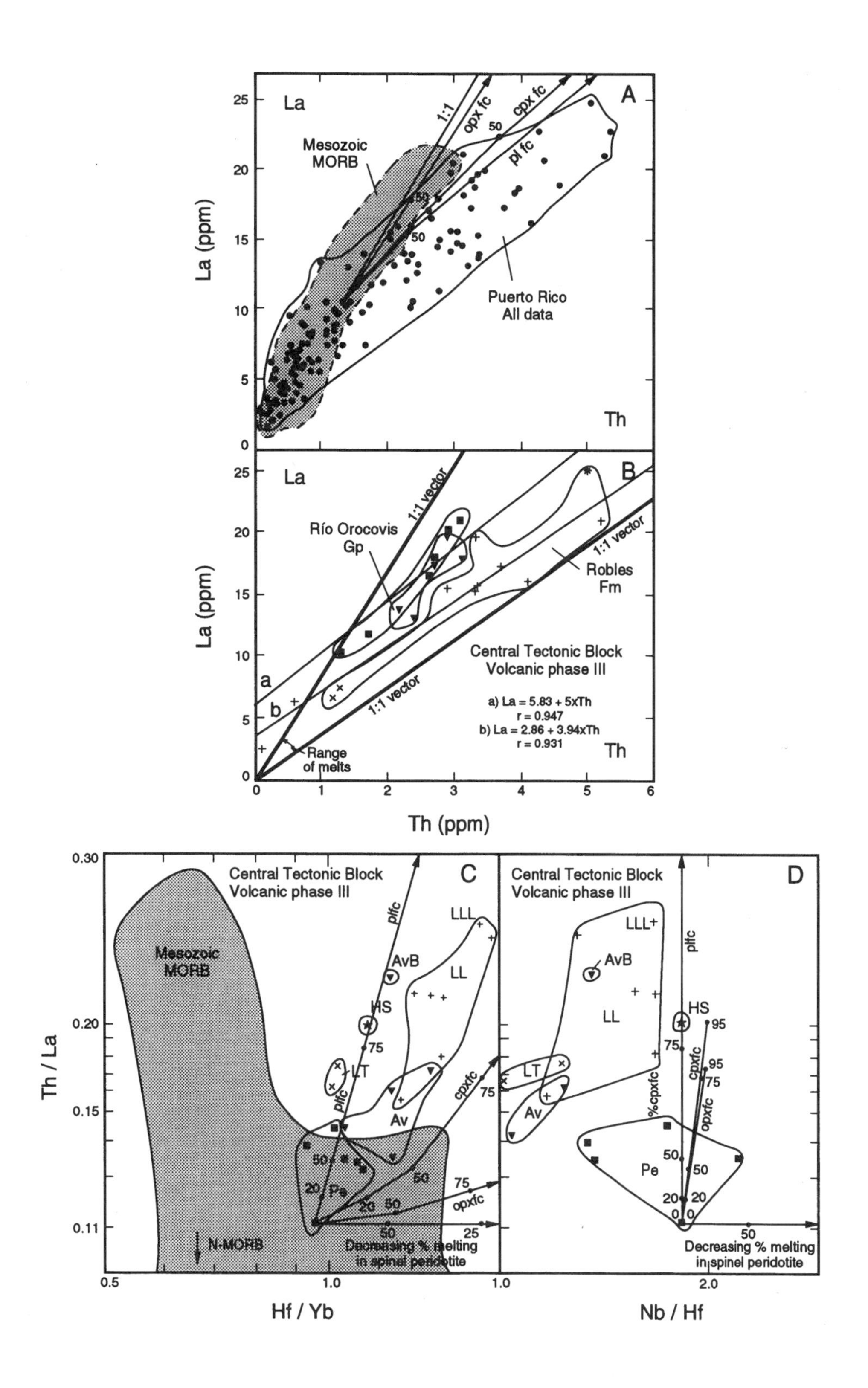
La
Mesozoic MORB
1:1
opx fc
cpx fc
pl fc
A
Puerto Rico All data
Th
La (ppm)
Río Orocovis Gp
1:1 vector
B
Robles Fm
Central Tectonic Block Volcanic phase III
a) La = 5.83 + 5xTh
r = 0.947
b) La = 2.86 + 3.94xTh
r = 0.931
Range of melts
Th (ppm)
Central Tectonic Block Volcanic phase III
C
Mesozoic MORB
N-MORB
Decreasing % melting in spinel peridotite
Th / La
Hf / Yb
D
Nb / Hf

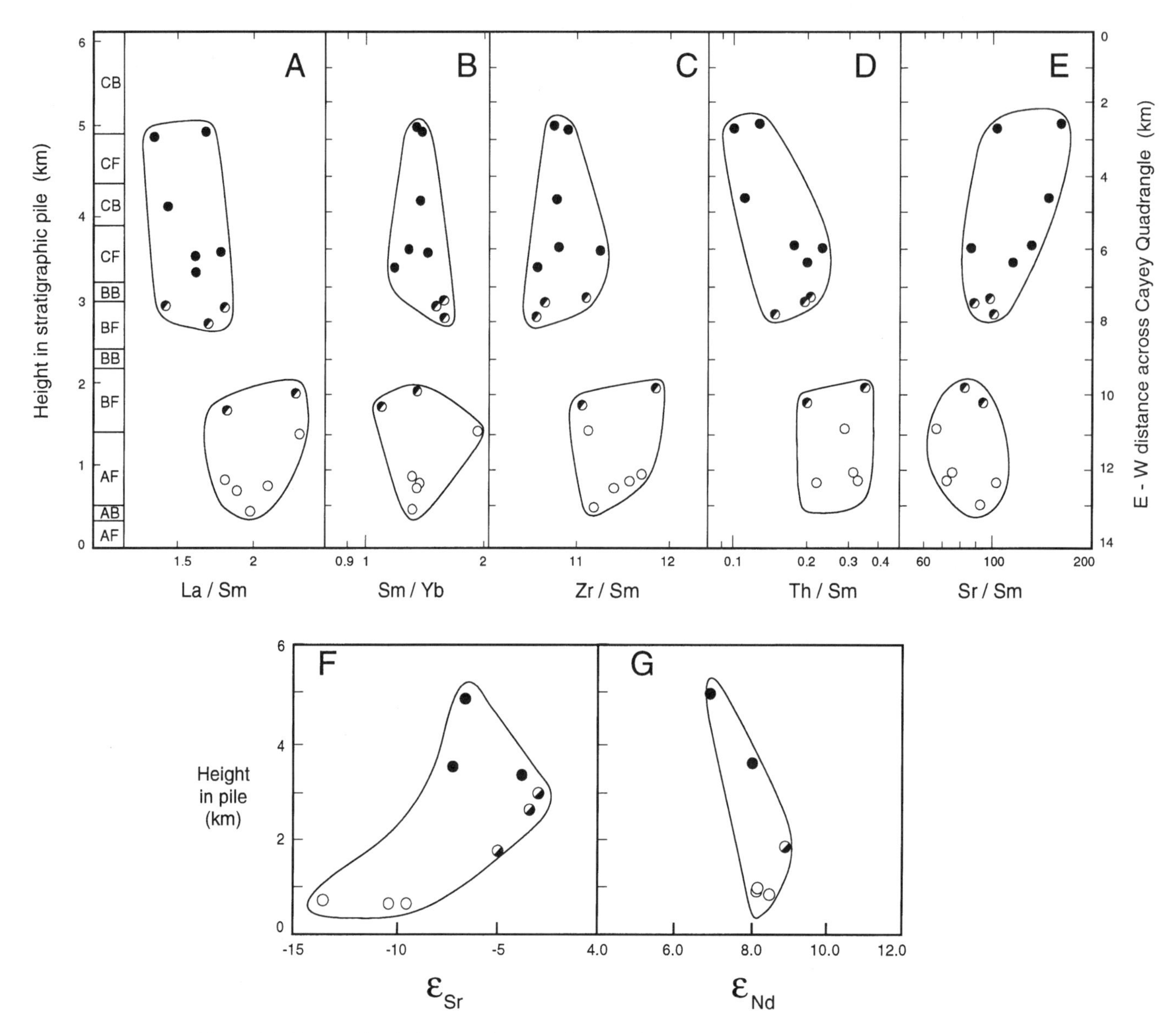

Figure 10. Geographic distribution of selected incompatible element and isotope ratios in basalts of the Río Majada Group relative to east-west distance from the western border of the Cayey quadrangle, and equivalent height in the stratigraphic pile; all data in kilometers. Circles, Formation A; half-circles, Formation B; filled circles, Formation C. A, La/Sm ratios; B, Sm/Yb ratios; C, Zr/Sm ratios; D, Th/Sm ratios; E, Sr/Sm ratios; F, Sr isotope ratios; G, Nd isotope ratios. B, breccia; F, flow; symbols as in Figure 5. Fields for the Río Majada geochemical subdivisions are indicated.

Variation in magnitude of subduction-related component

Dehydration reactions in the descending slab in subduction zone settings generate fluids that supply the overlying wedge with incompatible elements derived from altered oceanic basalt and scavenged from the wedge itself (Pearce, 1983; McCullough and Gamble, 1991; Hawkesworth et al., 1985; 1993a,b; Peacock, 1990; Stolper and Newman, 1994). Low Nd and elevated Pb isotope ratios in many island arcs suggest an additional pelagic sediment component was also introduced into the source (Kay, 1980; Pearce, 1983; Hawkesworth et al., 1993a). Together, these materials comprise the subduction-related component (SDC), the magnitude of which is investigated in this section using Sr, Nd, and Pb isotopes.

Sr-Nd isotope ratios. Initial (*i*) $^{87}Sr/^{86}Sr$ ratios (Table 4) ranging from about 0.7034 to 0.7044 (–11.5 to +1.0) are similar to modern intraoceanic arcs (Hawkesworth et al., 1993a), and most values overlap altered Cretaceous Atlantic MORB (Jahn et al., 1980). In central Puerto Rico, Sr isotope ratios (Fig. 6C) tend to increase with decreasing age such that basalts from volcanic phase I, especially the oldest lavas from Formation A, carry slightly lower

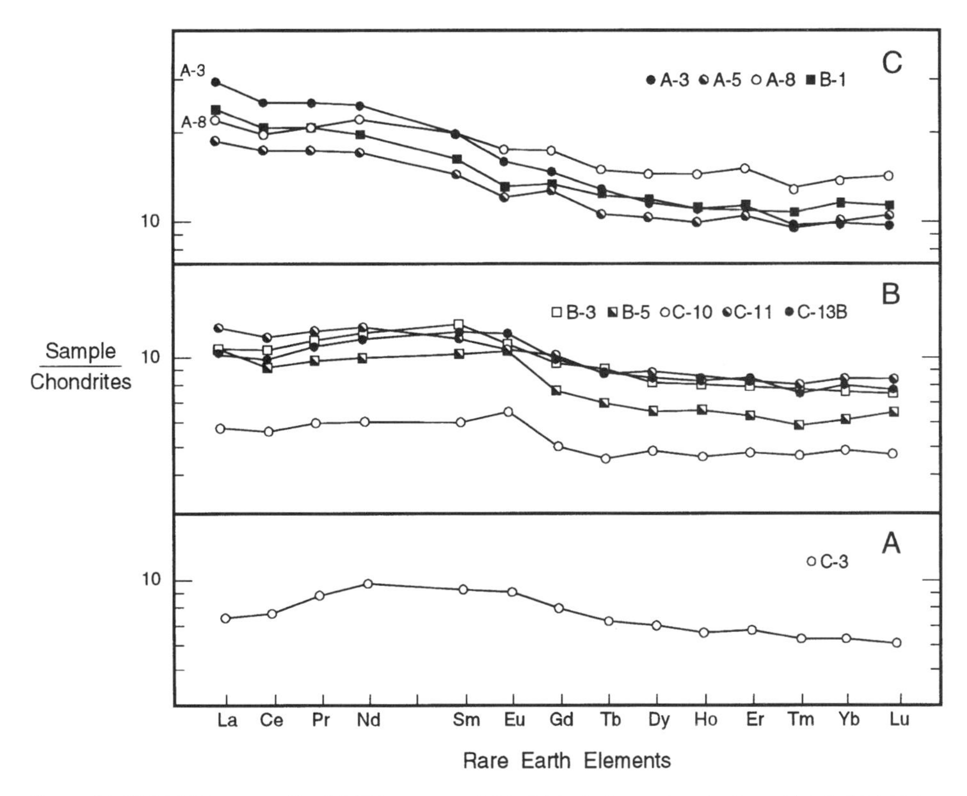

Figure 11. N-MORB–normalized REE patterns of Río Majada Group basalts for which full REE data (ICP-MS [induced coupled plasma–mass spectrometry] analyses) are available. Patterns include types with La/Sm_N ratios greater than unity (A); flat LREE segments (B); La/Sm_N ratios significantly less than unity (C).

values ranging from 0.7034 to 0.7038 (–12.0 to –5.5) than their counterparts in phase III, ranging from 0.7036 to 0.7044 (–11.0 to about 0). Nd isotope ratios ($i^{144}Nd/^{143}Nd$ from 0.5130 to 0.5128; ε_{Nd} 8.94 to 5.09) are relatively high (Fig. 6A, B), particularly in basalts from volcanic phases I and II. Fields of basalts from phases III, IV, and V are displaced toward lower ε_{Nd} values, reaching levels characteristic of E-MORB. Eocene lavas (Guarabo and Jobos Formations; Fig. 6B) exhibit the highest Sr and Nd isotope ratios ($i^{87}Sr/^{86}Sr$ up to 0.7050 and ε_{Nd} as low as –8.0). Together the data are indicative of minimal incorporation of sediment in phase I and II magmas, while slightly lower ε_{Nd}-values in phases III through V are consistent with small sediment contributions. Sr-Nd isotope variation in the northeastern block is much more restricted, and phases I, II, and III all exhibit essentially overlapping fields (Fig. 6B, C) centered on that of phase I in the central block.

Pb isotope ratios. Pb isotope ratios exhibit little apparent systematic temporal variation except that basalts from phases I and II are the least and those from phases III and IV tend to be the most radiogenic. An analysis of pre-arc MORB-like Cajul Basalt from western Puerto Rico displays low Pb isotope ratios similar to lavas of volcanic phases I and II. The MORB-like slope of the Puerto Rican data suggests the mantle source was MORB-like, and that the wedge was inhomogeneous with respect to Pb isotopes. The distribution is inconsistent with incorporation of large proportions of sediment in any of the samples, although slightly elevated $^{208}Pb/^{204}Pb$ ratios are indicative of a small pelagic sediment contribution in lavas from phase III, in agreement with Nd-isotope data. The data suggest Pb in the subduction-related component (SDC) was dominated by a fluid with a MORB-like Pb-isotope composition similar to that expected in the descending basaltic crust. This interpretation is confirmed by high total Pb abundances (Table 4), averaging about 5 ppm in Puerto Rican basalts, which, when coupled with MORB-like Pb isotope ratios, preclude the presence of appreciable Pb derived from typical pelagic sediments (see Fig. 6D, E), including carbonate-rich types.

Isotope mixing models. Sr, Nd, and Pb isotope data are all indicative of incorporation of material dominated by altered oceanic crust rather than oceanic sediments; only basalts from phase III exhibit evidence of a minor additional sediment contribution. The distribution resembles relations in the sediment-poor New Britain arc (Woodhead and Johnson, 1993) rather than modern arcs with an appreciable sediment component (White and Patchett, 1984; Hawkesworth et al., 1993A, B). To determine if Puerto Rican basalts of volcanic phase III can be produced by simple addition of pelagic sediments to earlier sediment-poor basaltic types, two component mixing calculations were performed between representative pelagic sediment compositions and the source of Formation A.

Sample A-5 (Table 8), a typical volcanic phase I basalt, is used in this analysis, but other samples and average compositions

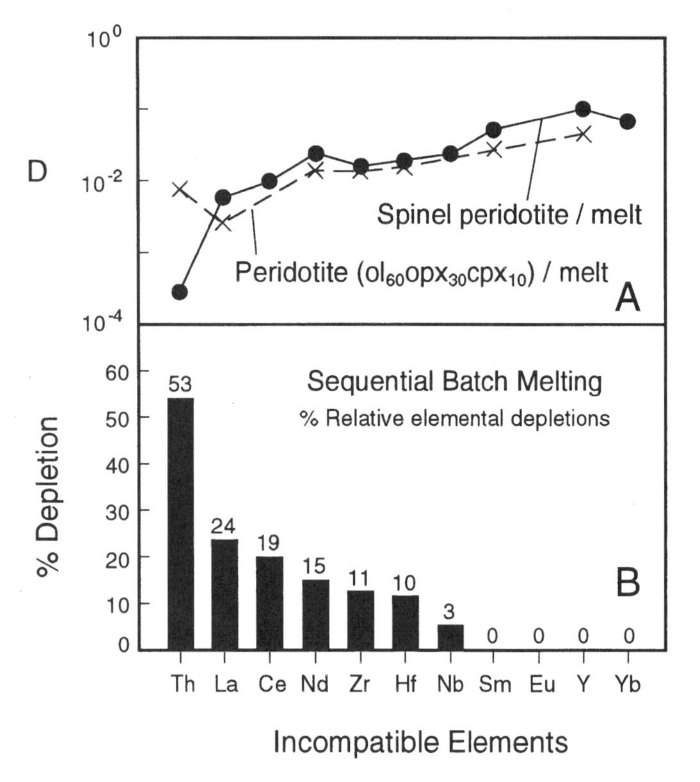

Figure 12. A, Bulk distribution coefficients (D) for spinel peridotite/melt (filled circles, Hawkesworth et al., 1993b) and peridotite ($ol_{60}opx_{30}cpx_{10}$)/melt (x—x), (Stolper and Newman, 1994). B, Relative degree of depletion (in percent) of less soluble incompatible elements in Río Majada basalts during sequential batch melting; maximum variations for each element are given in the text.

produce similar results. Interactions between the wedge and the sediment component during transport (Hawkesworth et al., 1993b) are not considered, and it is inferred that sediment was transported to the melting zone in bulk. White et al. (1985) demonstrated that compositions of pelagic sediments are highly variable, and Ben-Othman et al. (1989) subdivided modern pelagic sediments into two principal varieties (Table 8), which are considered to represent the spectrum of compositional variation. These include clay-rich pelagic sediments with low carbonate content, and biogenic carbonate-rich pelagic oozes (similar to the Pacific authigenic weighted mean sediment [PAWMS] of Hole et al., 1984). Both display high Sr and low Nd isotope ratios, elevated Pb isotope ratios compared to MORB, and low Th, Nb, Zr, and Hf abundances (Table 8).

Sr and Nd isotope results reveal (Fig. 14A) that mixing lines between the source of Formation A sample A-5 and Atlantic pelagic sediments forms a hyberbolic mixing curve with a high slope at low sediment proportions. A similar but lower slope curve is produced by mixtures containing PAWMS. The fields of Puerto Rican basalts are oriented along a trend between the two curves relating the hypothetical source and compositions of the two predominant pelagic sediment types. The trend is characterized by decreasing ε_{Nd} and slightly increasing $i^{87}Sr/^{86}Sr$ ratios, and is compatible with addition of a small proportion (up to 0.1 to 0.2%) of either type of sediment to the source of the shoshonites from phase III of central Puerto Rico. Perchas basalts (squares, Fig. 14) and the field of phase IV and V lavas (dashed) are closely associated with the PAWMS mixing curve. The broad range in Sr-isotope ratios at all ε_{Nd}-values suggest wide variation in isotope composition of the subduction-related component independent of sediment proportions.

As indicated previously, Pb isotope ratios of Puerto Rican basalts lie along an extension of the MORB field (Fig. 6D, E). The distribution is consistent with inhomogeneity of the wedge source with respect to Pb isotopes, and suggests the source of each volcanic phase had it own characteristic Pb-isotope composition. Mixing between N-MORB and pelagic sediments, therefore, cannot explain the high Pb isotope ratios of many lavas from the central tectonic block, including those from volcanic phases I, III, and V, as illustrated using ε_{Nd}-values and $^{206}Pb/^{204}Pb$ isotope ratios in Figure 14B (lines a and b). Instead, mixing between sources of low-sediment units, such as phase I basalts from the central tectonic block (lines c and d). Phase II basalts are displaced slightly toward the field of pelagic sediments. The amount of displacement, relative to the source of basalt A-5 (Table 8), is consistent with a small sediment contribution (0.2 to 0.5%), in agreement with Sr-Nd isotope models.

Origin of interprovincial geochemical variations

Although the Cretaceous basalts of eruptive phases I, II, and III in eastern Puerto Rico share general tectonic provenance, temporal subdivision, eruptive histories, and many petrographic characteristics (Nelson, 1966), there are substantial geochemical

TABLE 7. PARAMETERS USED IN SEQUENTIAL BATCH MELTING MODELS

Element	La	Sm	Yb	Sr
N-MORB-type source	0.246	0.263	0.309	9.07
A-4 source	0.530	0.330	0.215	25.29
A-4	5.45	3.06	2.34	235.00
First melt (f = 0.15)	3.39	1.84	1.34	146.06
Residue of first melt	0.025	0.063	0.064	3.98
Second melt (f = 0.15)				
a. 10% residue	3.07	1.73	1.04	133.75
b. 20% residue	2.74	1.62	0.97	121.44
c. 30% residue	2.42	1.58	0.89	109.12
Residue of second melt				
a. 10% residue	0.023	0.060	0.050	3.64
b. 20% residue	0.021	0.056	0.046	3.31
c. 30% residue	0.018	0.083	0.043	2.97

*Data in parts per million; bulk spinel peridotite/melt partition coefficients given in Table 5. Second melt results calculated from mixtures of the original (A-4) source and various proportions (10, 20, 30%) of residue from the first melt.

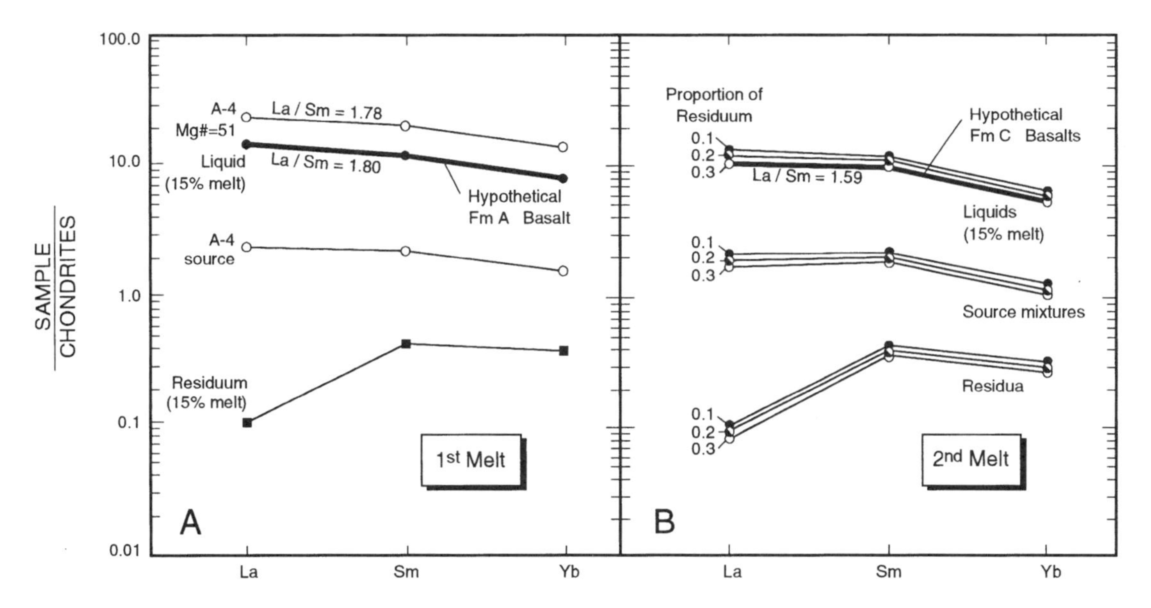

Figure 13. Evaluation of chondrite-normalized patterns of La-Sm and Sm-Yb segments produced by sequential batch melting models: A, First melt: the normalized REE configuration of sample A-4 is reproduced by a 15% melt of the calculated whole rock source. B, Second melt: the source compositions contain two components: residuum from the first melt and the whole rock source for basalt A-4. A 15% melt of such sources generates hypothetical basalts similar to Formation C (heavy lines in b) when small to moderate proportions (19 to 30%) of residuum are included.

distinctions between lavas in the northeastern and central tectonic blocks (Lidiak, 1972; Schellekens, 1993, this volume). Geochemical and temporal trends of representative incompatible trace element and isotope ratios are plotted against the approximate age, estimated from stratigraphic position within individual units (Fig. 2), are illustrated in Figure 15A-L.

There is a progressive increase in La/Sm and Th/Y ratios, representing the proportion of SDC, and Nb/Y ratios, indicative of decreasing degrees of melting, during the first three volcanic phases (I, II, III) in both the central and northeastern tectonic blocks. Moreover, the degree of enrichment is considerably more pronounced in the central block (Fig. 15A, B, E-H). Effects of sequential batch melting processes in Río Majada basalts of phase I in the central block, are also evident, and exhibit pronounced temporal depletion patterns (denoted by arrows). These effects are minimized in Figure 15C-D where samples with Sm/Yb <1.2 are omitted. ε_{Sr}-values display relatively constant ranges in both tectonic blocks, but the range of variation is much greater in the central block. When basalts from anomalous Formations B and C are considered separately (Fig. 15I), the range of ε_{Sr}-values increases dramatically from phases I to III. ε_{Nd}-values are virtually constant throughout the northeast tectonic block, but decrease slightly in the central block, reaching minimum values in phase III and IV shoshonites (Fig. 15K, L) both of which display similar geochemical patterns in both northeastern and central Puerto Rico.

Considered collectively, geologic and geochemical data suggest basalts in the northeastern and central volcanic provinces erupted simultaneously at various points along a single subduction zone. Evidence for this conclusion includes similarities in Pb, Sr, and Nd isotope compositions, geochemical similarities in initial phase I basalts, progressive shifts in geochemical compositions, and uniformly flat normalized HREE segments, together with similar temporal and stratigraphic correlations and tectonic setting. Basalts from volcanic phase III in the central province are anomalous and exhibit relatively high Pb and low Nd isotope ratios (Fig. 6). Incorporation of higher proportions of slab-derived fluid and sediment, more rapid compositional evolution, and higher Th/Nb and Nb/Hf ratios in the central volcanic province are consistent with melt generation at slightly lower temperatures than in the northeastern province. The contrasts are inferred to arise from undulations or other tectonic irregularities

TABLE 8. PARAMETERS USED IN MIXING CALCULATIONS*

	A-5	A-5	PAWMS (source)	Atlantic Sediment	N-MORB
$i^{144}Nd/^{143}Nd$	0.5129	0.5129	0.5120	0.5121	0.5131
ε_{Nd}	8.48	8.48	-12	-12	10.77
$i^{87}Sr/^{86}Sr$	0.7036	0.7036	0.7150	0.7200	0.7026
$^{208}Pb/^{204}Pb$	19.033	19.033	18.71	19.04	18.25
Nd	10.6	1.06	19.3	35	0.73
Sr	220	22.0	1,144	140	9.00
Pb	6.0	0.6	55.4	34	0.043

*PAWMS is from Hole et al., 1984; Atlantic pelagic sediment is from Ben-Othman et al., 1989; elemental data in parts per million; source composition by method of Wood, 1979.

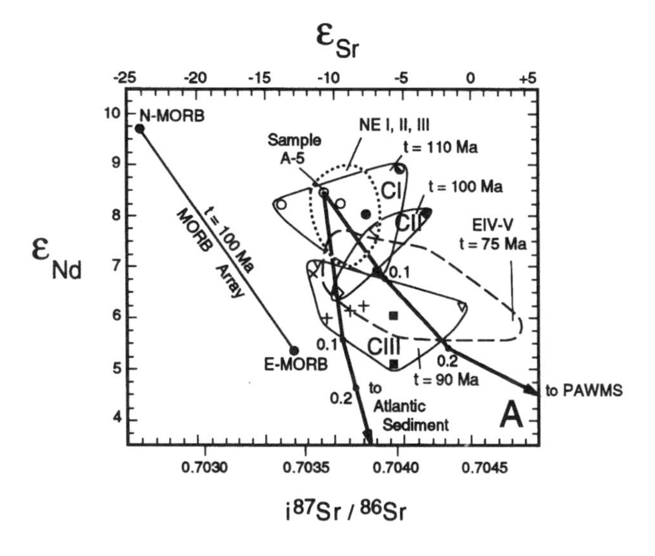

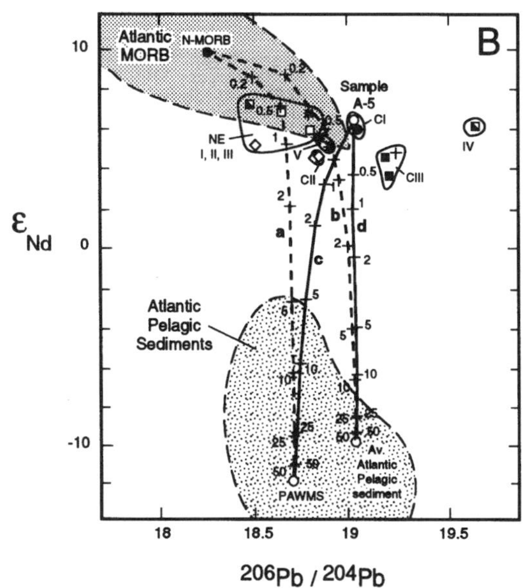

Figure 14. Isotope mixing between hypothetical wedge sources and pelagic sediment calculated using parameters in Table 8. Hyperbolic curves with mixing intervals represent results of mixing calculations. Fields of analyzed samples are identified as follows: C, central tectonic block; NE, northeast tectonic block; I, II, III, IV, V represent Puerto Rican volcanic phases. *A*, ε_{Nd}-$i^{87}Sr/^{86}Sr$ values. End-members (Table 2) include (1) hypothetical source of sample A-5 (see analysis in Table 2, column 1, and normalized REE pattern from volcanic phase I (representing the composition of the wedge plus slab-derived aqueous fluid with a minimal sediment component); (2) PAWMS-type carbonate-rich pelagic sediment (Hole et al., 1984); (3) Atlantic low-carbonate pelagic sediment from Ben-Othman et al. (1989). MORB values are from Sun and McDonough (1989). *B*, ε_{Nd}-$^{206}Pb/^{204}Pb$ isotope values. Sediment field from White et al. (1985); MORB field from Zindler and Hart (1986). Compositions of Puerto Rican basalts lie along an extension of the MORB trend, indicating inhomogeneity in the wedge with respect to Pb isotopes. Curves a and b reveal that mixing between an N-MORB-type source (White et al., 1985) and pelagic sediments cannot account for the highest Pb isotope values (fields labeled CIII and IV. Curves c and d suggest that mixing between 0.2 to 0.5% sediment and a source similar to that of sample A-5 produces compositions similar to those of shoshonitic basalts of phase III in the central block.

along the original length of the subduction zone and resultant lateral funnelling of fluids toward shallower, low temperature zones. Progressive wedge modification by fluxing fluids may also have played a role in the central block, permitting concentration of fluids in the wedge.

Uniformly flat HREE patterns and variable Nb/Hf ratios suggest low degrees of fusion at relatively low P_t within the spinel rather than garnet peridotite facies. Geophysical models of subduction zones (Arkani-Hamed and Jolly, 1989) reveal that geothermal gradients in the wedge decline rapidly, especially at shallower levels, where temperatures fluctuate several hundred degrees within a few tens of millions of years. The 35-Ma-transition from island arc tholeiites (volcanic phase I) to calc-alkaline basalts (phase II) to shoshonites (phase III) is therefore consistent with thermal cooling of the wedge. This interpretation is supported by gradually increasing Nb/Hf (Fig. 7A) ratios in younger units, reflecting decreasing degrees of fusion.

CONCLUSIONS

Geochemical data from Puerto Rican lavas are consistent with the following conclusions:

1. Constraints on mantle wedge source composition. Compositions of pre-arc basalts in southwest Puerto Rico, thought to represent the pre-arc oceanic crust (Schellekens et al., 1991), display depleted normalized incompatible element patterns and MORB-like La/Sm ratios, high ε_{-Nd}- values, and slightly elevated ε_{Sr}-values resembling Cretaceous Atlantic MORB (Jahn et al., 1980). These features indicate the mantle wedge had an N-MORB-type composition at the time of formation (Jolly et al., 1994). MORB-like HFSE-Hf/Nb at all degrees of fusion throughout Puerto Rican basalts, as in other island arcs (McCullough and Gamble, (1991), are consistent with compatible behavior of these components during partial fusion of the wedge. Moreover, low absolute abundances of HFSE, especially Nb, suggest the wedge source was more depleted in incompatible elements than a MORB-type source.

2. Constraints on polarity of subduction. With the exception of shoshonite basalts from phase III of the central tectonic block, Pb isotope data from all volcanic phases in eastern Puerto Rico form a trend that plots along or subparallel to the northern hemisphere reference line (NHRL) (Hart, 1984), indicating the subduction-related component (SDC) was dominated by material contributed by aqueous fluids from the basaltic oceanic crust

Figure 15. Geochemical stratigraphy in eastern Puerto Rico. Ages of samples, estimated from relative position within individual units, are illustrated relative to La/Y, Sm/Yb, Th/Y, Nb/Y, and Sr-Nd isotope ratios. Arrowed lines denote sequential batch melting trend in phase I of the central block. A slight geochemical discontinuity between phases III and IV was contemporaneous with strike-slip displacement along the boundary separating the two tectonic blocks. Campanian lavas are similar in both blocks and have compositions intermediate between central and northeastern lavas. Isotope ratios of lavas from phase V are given for comparison.

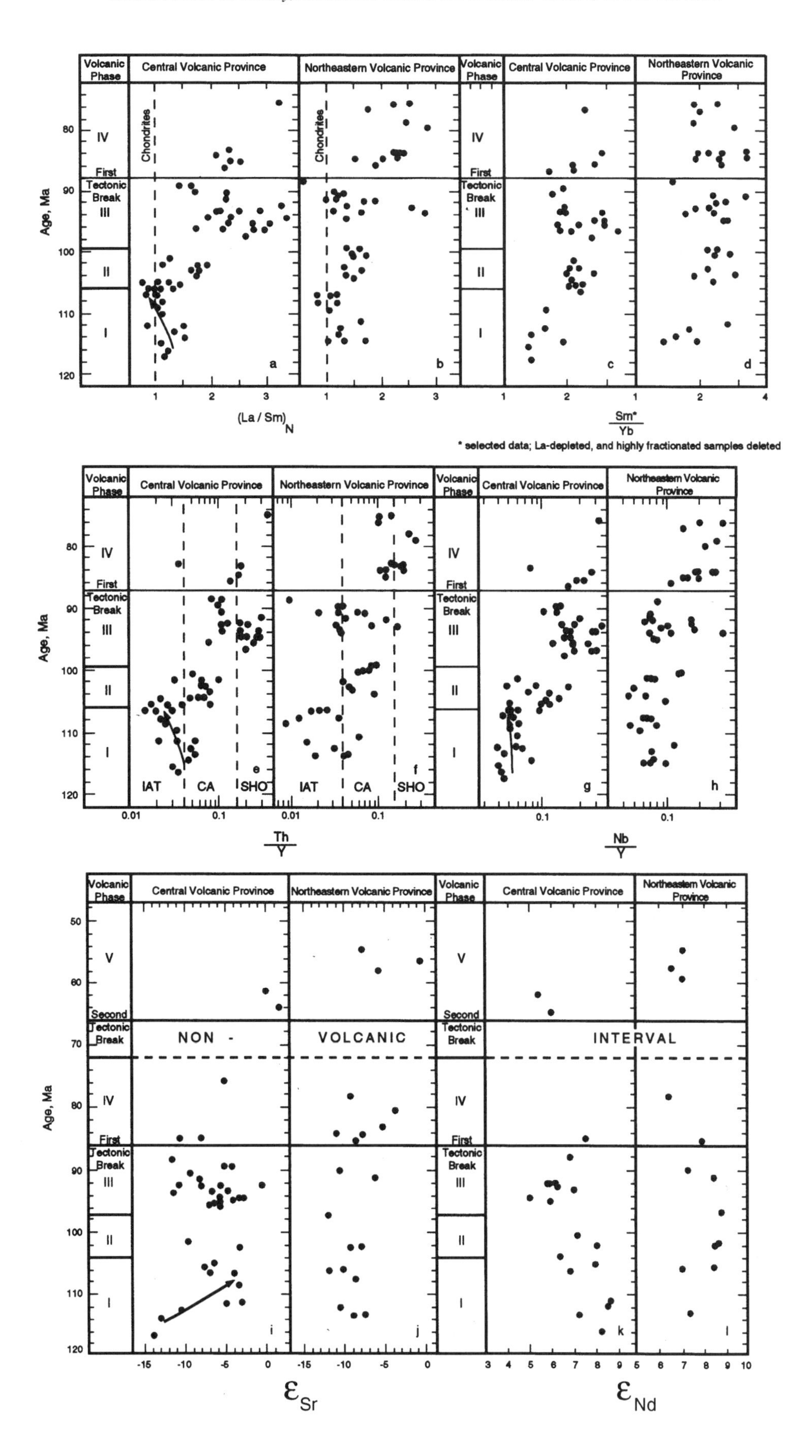

Volcanic Phase
Central Volcanic Province
Northeastern Volcanic Province
IV
III
II
I
V
First Tectonic Break
Second Tectonic Break
Age, Ma
Chondrites
(La / Sm)N
Sm* / Yb
* selected data; La-depleted, and highly fractionated samples deleted
IAT
CA
SHO
Th / Y
Nb / Y
NON - VOLCANIC INTERVAL
εSr
εNd

rather than by sediments. The data are inconsistent with east-dipping subduction of the pelagic sediment-rich Pacific plate, since such subduction would presumably lead to incorporation of higher proportions of sediment than observed. Instead, the Pb data are consistent with east- or west-dipping subduction of the relatively young, sediment-poor proto-Caribbean plate according to models such as those proposed by Draper et al. (1996), Donnelly (1989, 1994), and Donnelly et al., 1990). Tectonic or geochemical discontinuities reflecting profound change in orientation of the subduction zone are not recognized within the sequence that includes volcanic phases I, II, and III. The gradual northward shift of volcanism throughout this period is suggestive of trenchward accretionary processes accompanying west- or northwest-dipping subduction. Hence, changes in polarity of subduction in Puerto Rico appear to have either predated the preserved volcanic strata, or to have occurred following phase III during latest Cretaceous or early Tertiary time. If so, the Greater Antilles arc is possibly analogous to the Scotia arc (Upper Jurassic to Recent) (Keller et al., 1992), which was also generated by long-term westerly subduction of the Atlantic plate.

3. Constraints on configuration of subduction zone. Flat normalized HREE segments in all Puerto Rican basalts together with highly variable HFSE/HREE ratios are consistent with fusion at relatively low P_t (i.e., in a low-angle subduction zone), where distribution of HREE is controlled by clinopyroxene, and where all degrees of melting produce flat HREE patterns. Low subduction angles deflect high temperatures out of the wedge core above dehydration reactions, promoting generation of melts at lower P_t (in the spinel peridotite facies) than normal in modern arc environments. Heat flow from mantle plates is rapidly conducted to the surface and lost by mantle plates as they age, especially at shallow levels (Arkani-Hamed and Jolly, 1989). Therefore, thermal cooling of the shallow Puerto Rican wedge, together with incorporation of increasing proportions of slab-derived fluid flux (SDC) and declining degrees of melting, are inferred to have produced the observed shifts in basalt compositions with decreasing age.

4. Geochemical evolution. During the initial 35 Ma, basalt compositions in the central tectonic block shifted progressively from predominantly island arc tholeiites (volcanic phase I) to calcalkaline basalts (phase II), and finally to shoshonites (phase III). These changes were accompanied by increases in LILE/LREE, LILE/HFSE, LREE/HFSE, HFSE/HREE, and Nb/Hf ratios, slight increases in ε_{Sr} values, and slight decreases in ε_{Nd} values. In addition, Pb-isotope ratios are relatively enriched in phase III basalts compared to all other units. Like their counterparts in the central block, phase I basalts in the northeastern block are also island arc tholeiites. However, all subsequent phases II and III basalts in the northeast display calcalkaline compositions, and exhibit relatively constant Sr and Nd isotope compositions.

5. Isotope and trace element constraints on composition of subduction-related component (SDC). Trends displayed by combined isotope and trace element ratios are consistent with incorporation of a subduction-related component (SDC) dominated by a fluid phase with slightly elevated ε_{Sr}-values similar to altered MORB, and MORB-like Pb isotope ratios. In the central tectonic block, basalts from phase III also exhibit elevated $^{208}Pb/^{204}Pb$ ratios and lower ε_{Nd}-values, compared to phases I and II, consistent with a small pelagic sediment contribution (0.1 to 0.5%).

6. Origin of geochemical diversity in eastern Puerto Rico. Geologic and geochemical data suggest basalts in the northeastern and central tectonic blocks were erupted simultaneously at various points along a single subduction zone. Evidence for this conclusion includes similarities in Pb, Sr, and Nd isotope compositions, geochemical similarities in initial phase I basalts, progressive shifts in geochemical compositions, and uniformly flat normalized HREE segments, together with similar temporal and stratigraphic correlations and tectonic setting. Thus, this suite is considered an integral part of the Puerto Rican island arc volcanic front assemblage (VF). Incorporation of higher proportions of slab-derived aqueous fluids and sediment, more rapid compositional evolution, and less abundant evidence of sequential batch melting in the central tectonic block are consistent with melt generation at slightly lower temperatures than in the northeastern block. The contrasts are inferred to arise from undulations or other tectonic irregularities along the original length of the subduction zone and resultant lateral funnelling of fluids toward shallower, low temperature zones.

ACKNOWLEDGMENTS

This project is supported by operating grants from the National Science and Engineering Research Council of Canada (NSERC). Samples were prepared by C. Kramer and S. Habib, and graphics by M. Lozon. Detailed reviews of the manuscript by Glen Mattiola, James Joyce, Mark S. Drummond, and Dave Larue, who contributed numerous thoughtful suggestions for improving the text and figures, are gratefully acknowledged. Discussions with Charles Almy, Pete Briggs, Nick Donnelly, the Hon. Pedro Gelabert, Lynn Glover, John Lewis, Hernan Santos, Hans Schellekens, Al Smith, and many others through the years have substantially contributed to our understanding of stratigraphy and geochemistry in Puerto Rico.

REFERENCES CITED

Alabaster, J., Pearce, J. A., and Malpas, J., 1982, The volcanic stratigraphy and petrogenesis of the Oman Complex: Contributions to Mineralogy and Petrology, v. 81, p. 168–183.

Arkani-Hamed, J., and Jolly, W. T., 1989, Generation of Archean tonalites: Geology, v. 17, p. 307–310.

Baily, E. H., and Ragnursdotter, K. V., 1994, U and Th solubility in subduction zone liquids: Earth and Planetary Science Letters, v. 124, p. 119–129.

Barreiro, B., 1983, Lead isotope compositions of South Sandwich Island volcanic rocks and their bearing on petrogenesis: Geochemica et Cosmochemica Acta, v. 47, p. 812–822.

Ben-Othman, D. B., White, W. M., and Patchett, J., 1989, The geochemistry of marine sediments, island arc magma genesis, and crust-mantle recycling: Earth and Planetary Science Letters, v. 94, p. 1–21.

Berryhill, H. L., Jr., 1965, Geology of the Ciales quadrangle, Puerto Rico: U.S. Geological Survey Bulletin, 1184, 116 p.

Berryhill, H. L., and Glover, L., 1960, Geology of the Cayey quadrangle, Puerto Rico: U.S. Geological Survey Miscellaneous Investigations Map I–319, scale 1:20,000.

Berryhill, H., Briggs, R., and Glover, L., 1960, Stratigraphy, sedimentation and structure of Late Cretaceous rocks, eastern Puerto Rico: American Association of Petroleum Geologists Bulletin, v. 44, p. 137–155.

Brennan, J. M., and Watson, E. B., 1991, Partitioning of fluid between olivine and aqueous fluid at high P-T conditions: Earth and Planetary Science Letters, v. 107, p. 672–688.

Briggs, R. P., 1973, The Lower Cretaceous Figuera lava and Fajardo Formation in the stratigraphy of northeastern Puerto Rico: U.S. Geological Survey Bulletin, 1372–G, 10 p.

Briggs, R. P., and Akers, A., 1965, Hydrogeologic map of Puerto Rico and adjacent islands: U.S. Geological Survey Hydrogeologic Atlas Map HA–197, scale 1:240,000.

Carr, M.J., Feigenson, M.D., and Bennett, E.A., 1990, Incompatible element and isotopic evidence for tectonic control of source mixing and melt extraction along the Central American arc: Contributions to Mineralogy and Petrology, v. 105, p. 369–380.

Cho, M., 1991, Zeolite to prehnite-pumpellyite facies metamorphism in the Toa Baja drill hole, Puerto Rico: Geophysical Research Letters, v. 18, p. 525–528.

Cohen, R. S., and O'Nions, R. K., 1982, Identification of recycled continental material in the mantle from Sr, Nd, and Pb isotope investigations: Earth and Planetary Science Letters, v. 61, p. 73–84.

Davidson, J. P., 1986, Isotopic and trace element constraints on the petrogenesis of subduction-related lavas from Martinique, Lesser Antilles: Journal of Geophysical Research, v. 91 (B6), p. 5943–5962.

Davidson, J. P., and Wolff, J. A., 1989, On the origin of the Nb-Ta "anomaly" in arc magmas: Eos (Transactions, American Geophysical Union), v. 70, p. 1387.

Defant, M. J., Maury, R. C., Joron, J. L., Feigenson, M. D., and Leterrier, J., 1990, The geochemistry and tectonic setting of the northern section of the Luzon Arc (the Philippines and Taiwan): Tectonophysics, v. 183, p. 187–205.

DePaulo, D. J., and Johnson, R. W., 1979, Magma genesis in the New Britain island arc: constraints from Nd and Sr isotopes and trace element patterns: Earth and Planetary Science Letters, v. 70, p. 367–379.

Dickin, A. P., 1988, Evidence for limited REE leaching from the Roffna Gneiss, Switzerland—A discussion of the paper by Vock et al. (1987)(CMP95:145-154): Contributions to Mineralogy and Petrology, v. 99, p. 73–275.

Dickin, A. P., and Jones, N. W., 1983, Relative mobility during hydrothermal alteration of a basic sill, isle of Skye, N.W. Scotland: Contributions to Mineralogy and Petrology, v. 82, p. 147–153.

Donnelly, T.W., 1989, Geologic history of the Caribbean and Central America, *in* Bally, A. W., and Palmer, A. R., eds., Geology of North America—An overview: Boulder, Colorado, Geological Society of America, The Geology of North America, v. A, p. 299–321.

Donnelly, T. W., 1994, The Caribbean basalt association: a vast igneous province that includes the Nicoya Complex of Costa Rica, *in* Seyfried, H., and Hellman, W., eds., Geology of an evolving arc: the isthmus of southern Nicaragua, Costa Rica, and western Panama: Stuttgart, Germany, Profile (Band 7), Institut fur Geologie und Palaontologie, p. 17–45.

Donnelly, T. W., and Rogers, J. J. W., 1980, Igneous series in island arcs: Bulletin of Volcanology; v. 43, p. 347–382.

Donnelly, T. W., and 9 others, 1990, History and tectonic setting of Caribbean magmatism, *in* Case, J. E., and Dengo, G., eds., Caribbean region: Boulder, Colorado, Geological Society of America, The Geology of North America, v. H, p. 339–374.

Draper, G., Guitierrez, G., and Lewis, J. F., 1996, Thrust emplacement of the Hispaniola peridotite belt: orogenic expression of the mid-Cretaceous Caribbean arc polarity reversal?: Geology v. 24, p. 1143-1146.

Dupuy, C., Dostol, J., Marcelot, G., Bougault, H., Joron, J. L., and Treuil, M., 1982, Geochemistry of basalts from southern New Hebrides arc: implications for their source rock compositions: Earth and Planetary Science Letters, v. 60, p. 207–225.

Ellam, R. M., Menzies, M. A., Hawkesworth, C. J., Leeman, W. P., Rosi, M., and Serri, G., 1988, The transition from calc-alkaline to potassic orogenic magmatism in the Aeolian Islands, southern Italy: Bulletin of Volcanology, v. 50, p. 386–398.

Ewart, A. W., and Hawkesworth, C. J., 1987, Pleistocene to recent Tonga-Kermadec arc lavas: interpretation of new isotope and rare earth data in terms of a depleted mantle source model: Journal of Petrology, v. 28, p. 495–530.

Frost, C. D. and, Schellekens, J. H., 1991, Rb-Sr and Sm-Nd isotopic characterization of Eocene volcanic rocks from Puerto Rico: Geophysical Research Letters, v. 18, p. 545–548.

Glover, L., III, 1971, Geology of the Coamo area, Puerto Rico, and its relation to the volcanic arc-trench association: U.S. Geological Survey Professional Paper 636, 102 p.

Hart, S. R., 1984, A large-scale isotope anomaly in the southern hemisphere mantle: Nature, v. 309, p. 753–757.

Hawkesworth, C. J., and Powell, M., 1980, Magma genesis in the Lesser Antilles island arc: Earth and Planetary Science Letters, v. 51, p. 297–308.

Hawkesworth, C. J., O'Nions, R. K., Pankhurst, P. J., Hamilton, P. J., and Evenson, N. M., 1977, A geochemical study of island-arc and back-arc tholeiites from the Scotia Sea: Earth and Planetary Science Letters, v. 36, p. 253–262.

Hawkesworth, C. J., Rogers, N. W., and van Calsteren, P., 1985, Mantle enrichment processes: Nature, v. 311, p. 331–335.

Hawkesworth, C. J., Gallagher, K., Hergt, J. M., and McDermott, F., 1993a, Mantle and slab contributions in arc magmas: Annual Reviews of Earth and Planetary Science, v. 21, p. 175–204.

Hawkesworth, C. J., Gallagher, K., Hergt, J. M., and McDermott, F., 1993b, Trace element fractionation processes in the generation of island arc basalts: Philosophical Transactions of the Royal Society of London, Series A, v. 342, p. 179–191.

Hole, M. J., Saunders, A. D., Marriner, G. F., and Tarney, J., 1984, Subduction of pelagic sediments: implications for the origin of Ce-anomalous basalts from the Mariana islands: Journal of the Geological Society of London, v. 141, p. 453–472.

Jahn, B., Bernard-Griffiths, J., Charlot, R., Cornichet, J., and Vidal, F., 1980, Nd and Sr isotopic compositions and REE abundances of Cretaceous MORB (Holes 417D and 418A, Legs 51, 52, and 53): Earth and Planetary Science Letters, v. 48, p. 171–184.

Jolly, W. T., 1970, Zeolite and prehnite-pumpellyite facies in south-central Puerto Rico: Contributions to Mineralogy and Petrology, v. 27, p. 204–224.

Jolly, W. T., 1971, Potassium-rich igneous rocks from Puerto Rico: Geological Society of America Bulletin, v. 82, p. 399–408.

Jolly, W. T., Dickin, A. P., and Wu, T.-S., 1992, Geochemical stratigraphy of the Huronian continental volcanic rocks at Thessalon, Ontario: Contributions of two stage crustal contamination: Contributions to Mineralogy and Petrology, v. 110, p. 411–428.

Jolly, W. T., Lidiak, E. G., Dickin, A. P., Wu, T.-W., and Schellekens, S. H., 1994, Pre-island arc oceanic crust in Puerto Rico: example of altered Jurassic MORB from the proto-Caribbean (Farallon) plate: Geological Society of America Abstracts with Programs, v. 26, p. A39–A40.

Kay, R. W., 1980, Volcanic arc magmas: implications of a melting-mixing model for element recycling in the crust-upper mantle system: Journal of Geology, v. 88, p. 497–522.

Keleman, P. B., Johnson, K. T. M., Kinzle, R. J., Irving, A. J., 1992, High field strength element depletion in arc basalts due to mantle-magma interactions: Nature, v. 345, p. 521–524.

Keller, R. A., Fisk, M. R., White, W. M., and Birkenmajer, K., 1992, Isotope and trace element constraints on mixing and melting models of marginal basin volcanism, Barnsfield Strait, Antarctica: Earth and Planetary Science Letters, v. 111, p. 287–303.

Kennedy, A. W., Hart, S. R., and Frey, F. A., 1990, Compositions and isotope constraints on the petrogenesis of alkaline arc lavas: Lihir Islands, Papua New Guinea: Journal of Geophysical Research, v. 95, p. 6929–6942.

Larue, D. K., 1994, Puerto Rico and the Virgin Islands, *in* Donovan, S. K., and Jackson, T. A., eds., Caribbean geology: an introduction: Kingston, Jamaica, University of the West Indies Publishers' Association, p. 151–161.

Larue, D. K., Smith, A. L., and Schellekens, J. H., 1991, Ocean island arc stratigraphy in the Caribbean region: Sedimentary Geology, v. 74, p. 289–308.
Lebron, M. C., and Perfit, M. R., 1994, Petrochemistry and tectonic significance of Cretaceous island arc rocks, Cordillera Oriental, Dominican Republic: Tectonophysics, v. 229, p. 60–100.
Lidiak, E. G., 1965, Petrology of andesitic, spilitic, and keratophyric flow rock, north central Puerto Rico: Geological Society of America Bulletin, v. 76, p. 57–88.
Lidiak, E. G., 1972, Spatial and temporal variations of potassium in the volcanic rocks of Puerto Rico: 6th Caribbean Geological Conference Transactions, Margarita, Venezuela, p. 203–209.
Longerich, H. P., Jenner, G. A., Fryer, B. J., and Jackson, S. E., 1990, Inductively coupled plasma–mass spectrometric analysis of geological samples: A critical evaluation based on case studies: Chemical Geology, v. 83, p. 105-118.
McCullough, M. T., and Gamble, J. A., 1991, Chemical and geodynamical constraints on subduction zone magmatism: Earth and Planetary Science Letters, v. 102, p. 358–374.
McDermott, F., Defant, M. J., Hawkesworth, C. J., Maury, R. C., and Joron, J. I., 1993, Isotope and trace evidence for three component mixing in the genesis of the North Luzon arc lavas (Philippines): Contributions to Mineralogy and Petrology, v. 113, p. 9–33.
McKenzie, D. and O'Nions, R. K., 1991, Partial melt distributions from inversion of rare earth element concentrations: Journal of Petrology, v. 32, p.1021–1091.
M'Gonigle, J. W., 1977, The Río Abajo, Pitahaya, and Daguao Formations in eastern Puerto Rico: U.S. Geological Survey Bulletin, 1435–B, 10 p.
Montgomery, H., Pessagno, E. A., Jr., and Pindell, J. L., 1994, A 195 Ma terrane in a 165 Ma sea: Pacific origin of the Caribbean plate: GSA Today, v. 4, p. 1–4.
Nelson, A. E., 1966, Significant changes in volcanism during the Cretaceous in north-central Puerto Rico: U.S. Geological Survey Professional Paper, v. 550–D, p. D172–D177.
Otalora, G., 1964, Zeolite and related minerals in Cretaceous rocks of east-central Puerto Rico: American Journal of Science, v. 2632, p. 726–734.
Peacock, S. M., 1990, Fluid processes in subduction zones: Science, v. 248, p. 329–337.
Pearce, J. A., 1983, Role of sub-continental lithosphere in magma genesis at active continental margins, *in* Hawkesworth, C. J., and Norry, M. J., eds., Continental basalts and mantle xenoliths: Cheshire, UK, Shiva Publishing Ltd, p. 230–249.
Pease, M. H., Jr., 1968, Cretaceous and lower Tertiary stratigraphy of the Naranjito and Aguas Buenas quadrangles: U.S. Geological Survey Bulletin, v. 1253, 57 p.
Peccerillo, A., and Taylor, S.R., 1976, Geochemistry of Eocene calc-alkaline volcanic rocks from the Kastamonu area, northern Turkey: Contributions to Mineralogy and Petrology, v. 58, p. 63–91.
Pindell, J. L., and Barrett, S. F., 1990, Geological evolution of the Caribbean region: a plate tectonic perspective, *in* Dengo, G. and Case, J. E., eds., The Caribbean region: Boulder, Colorado, Geological Society of America, The Geology of North America, v. H, p. 179–212.
Ringwood, A. E., 1990, Slab-mantle interactions 3: Petrogenesis of intraplate magmas and the structure of the upper mantle: Chemical Geology, v. 82, p. 187–207.
Romick, J. D., Perfit, M. R., Swanson, S. E., and Shuster, R. D., 1992, Magmatism in the eastern Aleutian Arc: temporal characteristic of igneous activity on Akutan Island: Contributions to Mineralogy and Petrology, v. 104, p. 700–721.
Ryerson, F. J., and Watson, E. B., 1987, Rutile saturation in magmas: implications for Ti-Nb-Ta depletion in island arc basalts: Earth and Planetary Science Letters, v. 86, p. 225–239.
Schellekens, J. H., 1993, Geochemical evolution of volcanic rocks in Puerto Rico [Ph.D. thesis]: Syracuse, New York, Syracuse University, 289 p.
Schellekens, J. H., Montgomery, H., Joyce, J., and Smith, A.L., 1991, Late Jurassic to Late Cretaceous development of island arc crust in southwest Puerto Rico: Transactions, 12th Caribbean Geological Conference, St Croix, Virgin Islands, p. 268–281.
Seiders, V. M., 1971, Cretaceous and lower Tertiary stratigraphy of the Gurabo and El Yunque quadrangles, Puerto Rico: U.S. Geological Survey Bulletin, 1294–F, 58 p.
Stolper, E., and Newman, S., 1994, The role of water in the petrogenesis of Marianas trough magmas: Earth and Planetary Science Letters, v. 121, p. 293–325.
Sun, S.-S., and McDonough, W. F., 1989, Chemical and isotopic systematics of oceanic basalts: implications for mantle composition and processes, *in* Saunders, A., and Norry, M., eds., Magmatism in ocean basins: Geological Society of London Special Publication, v. 42, p. 313–345.
Tatsumi, Y., Nohoda, S., and Ishazaka, K., 1988, Secular variation in magma source compositions beneath the northeast Japan Arc: Chemical Geology, v. 68. p. 309–316.
Taylor, S. R., Capp, A. C., and Graham, A. L., 1969, Trace elements in andesites II: Contributions to Mineralogy and Petrology, v. 23, p. 177–195.
Thirlwall, M. F., and Graham, A. M., 1984, Evolution of high-Ca, high-Sr C-series basalts from Grenada, Lesser Antilles: the effects of intra-crustal contamination: Journal of the Geological Society of London, v. 141, p. 427–445.
Weiland, T. J., 1988, Petrology of volcanic rocks in Lower Cretaceous formations of northeastern Puerto Rico [Ph.D. thesis]: Chapel Hill, University of North Carolina, 205 p.
White, W. M., and Patchett, J., 1984, Hf-Nd-Sr isotopes and incompatible element abundances in island arcs: implications for magma origins and crust-mantle evolution: Earth and Planetary Science Letters, v. 67, p. 167–186.
White, W. M., Dupre, B., and Vidal, Ph., 1985, Isotope and trace element geochemistry of sediments from the Barbados Ridge–Demarara Plain region, Atlantic Ocean: Geochimica et Cosmochimica Acta, v. 49, p. 1875–1886.
Wood, D. A., 1979, Geochemistry of basalts drilled in the North Atlantic by Leg 49: implications for mantle heterogeneity: Earth and Planetary Science Letters, v. 42, p. 77–97.
Woodhead, D. A., 1989, Geochemistry of the Mariana arc (western Pacific): source composition and processes: Geochemica et Cosmochemica Acta, v. 53, p. 1607–1619.
Woodhead, J. D., and Johnson, R. W., 1993, Isotopic and trace-element profiles across the New Britain island arc, Papua New Guinea: Contributions to Mineralogy and Petrology, v. 113, p. 479–491.
Zindler, A., and Hart, S., 1986, Chemical geodynamics: Annual Reviews of Earth and Planetary Sciences, v. 14, p. 493–471.

MANUSCRIPT ACCEPTED BY THE SOCIETY JUNE 20, 1997

Printed in U.S.A.

Geological Society of America
Special Paper 322
1998

Batholiths as markers of tectonic change in the northeastern Caribbean

Alan L. Smith and Johannes H. Schellekens
Department of Geology, University of Puerto Rico, Mayagüez, Puerto Rico 00681-5000
Amalys-Luz Muriel Díaz
Department of Geological Sciences, State University of New York, Binghamton, New York 13902-6000

ABSTRACT

Plutonic rocks from the northeastern Caribbean can be subdivided into two distinct groups on the basis of their relationship with associated volcanic rocks. The first group comprises small stocks, which have geochemical affinities with surrounding volcanic rocks of similar age. Examples on Puerto Rico, all of Cretaceous age, include possibly the oldest bodies in the San Lorenzo batholith, the Maguayo Porphyry, and the Morovis/Ciales stock. These are thought to be the intrusive equivalents of the pre-Robles, the Maguayo, and the Robles–Rio Orocovis volcano-stratigraphic associations, respectively. The Fountain stock on St. Croix, also of Cretaceous age, is intruded into sedimentary rocks similar to the Yauco Formation of Puerto Rico, and shows geochemical affinities to small intrusions in this formation, suggesting a displacement of the St. Croix terrane. Tertiary intrusives, including those associated with the Anón–Mal Paso Formations, and stocks such as Tanamá, Río Viví, Cuyon, Barranquitas, and Río Blanco of Puerto Rico, as well as the intrusives on St. Martin, also fall within this category. The second group consists of large (>200 km^2), granodiorite–quartz monzonite–diorite–gabbro bodies, which do not appear to be associated with volcanic activity, and were intruded in several stages spanning millions of years. This group includes the San Lorenzo batholith (79 to 59 Ma), the Utuado pluton (72 to 58 Ma), and the Virgin Islands batholith (45 to 24 Ma). The Cretaceous stocks and their related volcanic associations are thought to have been formed above a south-verging subduction zone, whereas the Tertiary stocks are related to a northerly or easterly verging zone. In contrast, the large batholiths, which were emplaced in a period of little or no volcanism, were generated by different conditions of formation as a consequence of a dramatic change in the tectonic setting. This chapter is a contribution to International Geological Correlation Program project 364.

INTRODUCTION

The northeastern Caribbean is described here to include the easternmost islands of the Greater Antilles and the northern islands of the Lesser Antilles (Fig. 1). The former is composed of the islands of Puerto Rico, the northern Virgin Islands, and St. Croix, and the latter of the islands of Saba, St. Eustatius, St. Kitts, Nevis, Montserrat, Guadeloupe, Anguilla, St. Martin, St. Barthélémy, Barbuda, and Antigua. Puerto Rico and the northern Virgin Islands represent the subaerially exposed parts of the Puerto Rico–Virgin Islands microplate (Byrne et al., 1985) that lies within the seismically active Caribbean–North American plate

Smith, A. L., Schellekens, J. H., and Muriel Díaz, A.-L., 1998, Batholiths as markers of tectonic change in the northeastern Caribbean, *in* Lidiak, E. G., and Larue, D. K., eds., Tectonics and Geochemistry of the Northeastern Caribbean: Boulder, Colorado, Geological Society of America Special Paper 322.

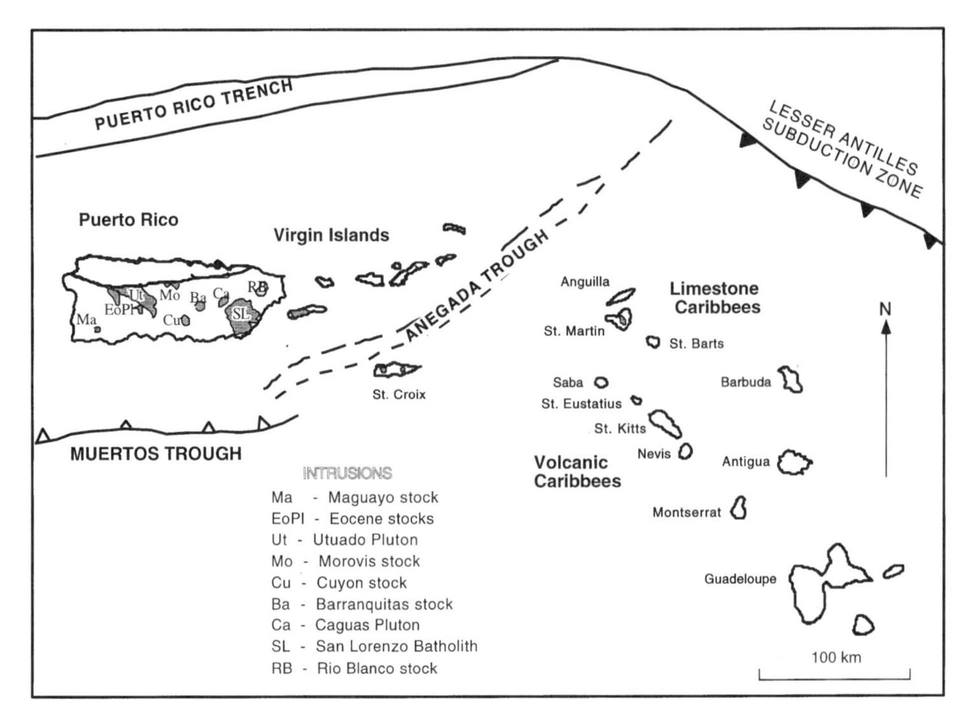

Figure 1. Location map of the northeastern Caribbean with major tectonic features mentioned in the text. Greater Antilles includes Puerto Rico, Virgin Islands, and St. Croix; the Lesser Antilles includes Anguilla, Antigua, Barbuda, St. Eustatius, Guadeloupe, Montserrat, Nevis, Saba, St. Barthélémy, and St. Kitts.

boundary zone. The northern margin of this boundary zone is the Puerto Rico Trench, and the southern margin is represented by the Muertos Trough, where Caribbean oceanic crust is subducted beneath the Puerto Rico–Virgin Islands block (Byrne et al., 1985). Puerto Rico and the northern Virgin Islands are separated by the Virgin Islands Trough and the Anegada Passage from the St. Croix ridge, which is dominantly a deformed Cretaceous terrane (Speed, 1989; Speed and Joyce, 1989). East and south of St. Croix lies the Lesser Antilles island arc, which in its northern segment is composed of an eastern group of islands, the Limestone Caribbees, that are separated from a western group, known as the Volcanic Caribbees, by an inter-arc basin. The former are composed of Miocene and younger limestones and marls overlying Eocene to Oligocene igneous and sedimentary rocks, although dredge samples indicate the presence of a Late Cretaceous basement to these islands (Bouysse et al., 1980). The latter are made up of Pliocene to Recent volcanic rocks, and include a number of potentially active volcanoes (Roobol and Smith, 1989).

With the exception of the Volcanic Caribbees, all of the other islands from the northeastern Caribbean have been subjected to sufficient erosion to expose intrusive rocks of varying size, age, and composition. Although a considerable amount of work has been undertaken on the volcanic rocks of this region (see Donnelly et al., 1990, for references), very little is known about their plutonic equivalents. This study tries to fill this gap by supplementing the initial works of Weaver (1958), Longshore (1965), Chen (1967), Nelson (1968), and Kesler and Sutter (1979), with trace and rare earth element data. A separate chapter (Frost et al., this volume) discusses recent isotopic data for both volcanic and plutonic rocks of the northeastern Caribbean.

GEOLOGIC SETTING OF THE PLUTONIC ROCKS OF THE NORTHEASTERN CARIBBEAN

A summary of the geology of the different islands from which plutonic rocks were studied is shown diagrammatically in Figure 2. For more background information, the reader is referred to Dengo and Case (1990).

As part of this study, 24 samples were dated at the University of California at Los Angeles (Table 1). (All data tables and related plots can be obtained from *http://oro.ess.ucla.edu/argon.html.)* Total gas ages were calculated from incremental step heating with model ages calculated using York regression of the $^{39}Ar/^{40}Ar^*$ versus $^{36}Ar/^{40}Ar^*$ results. In general, York regression indicates near atmospheric $^{40}Ar/^{36}Ar$ ratios for the trapped components for biotites and slightly radiogenic compositions for the hornblendes. The perceptibly younger hornblende ages (relative to biotite) can be explained by either the presence of a younger K/Ca-rich contaminant, possibly represented by a low-temperature alteration product, or an underestimation of the Ca correction factors for ^{36}Ar and ^{39}Ar, with the latter probably being the more likely explanation (M. Heizler, personal communication, 1996). The age spectra yielded by both the biotites and hornblendes tend to lack significant age gradients, in contrast many of the potassium feldspars show significant age gradients. Based on the data provided by the age dating it would appear that all dated samples

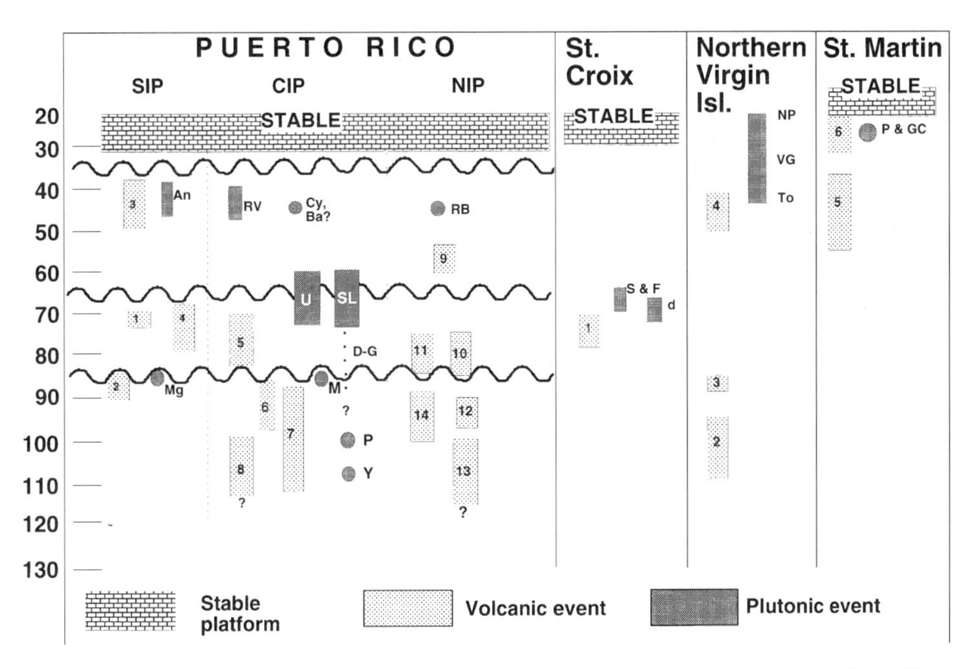

Figure 2. Stratigraphic summary of selected islands in the northeastern Caribbean. Puerto Rico: SIP = Southwestern Igneous Province; CIP = Central Igneous Province; NIP = Northeastern Igneous Province. 1: Monte Grande–El Rayo VSA; 2: Maguayo VSA; 3: Rio Blanco II VSA; 4: volcanic rocks of Río Blanco I VSA; 5: Pozas and Alonso Formations; 6: volcanic rocks of Tetuan–Vista Alegre VSA; 7: Robles–Río Orocovis VSA; 8: pre-Robles VSA; 9: Guaracanal Andesite; 10: volcanic rocks of the Martin Gonzalez–Tortugas VSA; 11: Santa Olaya VSA; 12: volcanic rocks of the Hato Puerco–Toma de Agua VSA; 13: Daguao-Figuera VSA; 14: pre–Santa Olaya VSA; An: early Tertiary stocks in the Anon Formation: Mg: Maguayo Porphyry; RV: Rio Vivi and other Tertiary intrusives associated with the Utuado pluton; Cy: Cuyon stock; Ba: Barranquitas stock; U: Utuado pluton; SL: San Lorenzo batholith; D-G: diorite-gabbro intrusives in the San Lorenzo batholith; M: Morovis stock; P: diorite in the Patillas quadrangle; Y: diorite in the Yabucoa quadrangle; RB: Rio Blanco stock. St. Croix 1: Lava flows in the Judith Fancy Formation and clasts in the Caledonia Formation; S & F: Southgate and Fountain stocks; d: dikes. Northern Virgin Islands: 2: Water Island Formation; 3: Louisenhoj Formation; 4: Andesitic pyroclastics of the Necker Formation; VG: Virgin Gorda batholith; NP: Narrows pluton; To: Tortola pluton; St. Martin: 5: volcanic rocks of the Point Blanche Formation; 6: volcanics of the pre–Lowlands Formation; P & GC: Philipsburg and Grand Case. (Sources of data: Table 1; Andreieff et al., 1988; Christman, 1953; Cox et al. , 1977; Davidson et al., 1993; Donnelly, 1966; Helsey, 1971; Jolly et al., Chapter 1, this volume; Kesler and Sutter, 1979; Nagle et al., 1976; Schellekens et al., 1991; Schellekens, this volume; Speed et al., 1979 ; Whetten, 1966, 1974.)

probably formed at a relatively high level (5 to 10 km) in the crust, thus making the model ages from both biotite and hornblende approximate the date of the intrusion. The significant age gradients recorded by the older potassium feldspars in contrast appear to be more consistent with reheating due to adjacent intrusions (M. Grove, personal communication, 1996).

Puerto Rico

Puerto Rico is a complex island arc terrane with a preserved geologic record of about 195 Ma (Montgomery et al., 1994; Schellekens, 1993, this volume; Jolly et al., Chapter 1, this volume). The basement rocks of the island have been divided on the basis of differences in stratigraphy, lithology, petrology, and geochemistry into three igneous provinces: Southwestern (SIP), Central (CIP), and Northeastern (NIP), (Schellekens, 1991).

The geology of SIP (Fig. 2) is distinct from the remainder of Puerto Rico in that it has serpentinite belts containing rafts of chert and metabasalts that make up the Bermeja Complex (Mattson, 1960, 1973). Lying unconformably on the Bermeja Complex rocks in the southern part of the province are volcanic and volcaniclastic rocks of the Maguayo volcano-stratigraphic association (Maguayo VSA; see Schellekens, 1991, 1993, this volume, for a description of the term volcano-stratigraphic association), which is inferred to be of Santonian-Campanian age on the basis of its stratigraphic position below the Cotui Limestone (Schellekens et al., 1991; Schellekens, 1993). Intruding through the southernmost belt of the Bermeja Complex in southwestern Puerto Rico is the Maguayo Porphyry (Mattson, 1973; Volckmann, 1984a,b). The small size of this stock and its porphyritic texture has led to the interpretation that it represents a subvolcanic intrusion (Volckmann, 1984 a,b), which, based on geochemical similarities, is

TABLE 1. Ar–Ar AGES FOR PLUTONIC ROCKS FROM THE NORTHEASTERN CARIBBEAN

Sample	Mineral	Total Gas Age (Ma)
St. Martin		
SM-11	Potassium feldspar	27
Virgin Islands		
DL3	Hornblende	38
DL3	Potassium feldspar	37
TO15	Hornblende	39
TO15	Biotite	42
TO15	Potassium feldspar	40
Rio Blanco		
PRP16	Hornblende	47
PRP16	Biotite	47
PRP14	Hornblende	48
PrP14	Biotite	48
6513	Hornblende	47
6513	Biotite	48
6513	Potassium feldspar	47
PRP13	Hornblende	46
PRP13	Biotite	48
St. Croix		
V26	Hornblende	67
V26	Biotite	66
V36	Potassium feldspar	57
San Lorenzo		
PP1	Potassium feldspar	57
SL1	Hornblende	75
SL1	Potassium feldspar	65
Utuado		
8690	Hornblende	76
8690	Potassium feldspar	69
Morovis		
MOR1	Hornblende	86

thought to be related to the surrounding Maguayo VSA (Schellekens et al., 1991; Schellekens, 1993). Cox et al. (1977) obtained a K-Ar age of 86.1 ± 2.1 for this intrusion, which also yielded an Ar-Ar age of 83 Ma (Schellekens et al., 1991). Overlying the Maguayo VSA are alternating sequences of limestones and volcanic-volcaniclastic rocks (Monte Grande–El Rayo VSA), which are in turn overlain by stratified rocks of Late Cretaceous and Early Tertiary age (Río Blanco I and Río Blanco II VSA) (Schellekens, 1993, this volume). Intruding these Cretaceous and Tertiary stratified rocks in a northwest-southeast belt (Nelson, 1967; Nelson and Tobisch, 1968; Mattson, 1968a,b; Krushensky and Monroe, 1975, 1978, 1979; Krushensky and Curet, 1984; Cox, 1985) are a number of small stocks that, based on their texture and mineralogy, have been assigned names such as aphyric dacite, hornblende dacite, hornblende augite dacite, hornblende dacite porphyry. (Krushensky and Monroe, 1975, 1978, 1979; Krushensky and Curet, 1984; Cox, 1985). These stocks are lithologically and chemically similar to the flow rocks of the Anón Formation (Río Blanco II VSA), but with an intrusive relationship, and probably represent domes or stocks and sills that were the feeders for the extrusive rocks (Cox et al., 1977; Barabas, 1982).

The volcanic rocks of the CIP range in age from Aptian-Albian to Eocene (Fig. 2), and include the dominantly submarine pre-Robles (Río Majada Formation of Jolly et al., Chapter 1, this volume) and Robles–Río Orocovis VSA, and the partly subaerial Pozas Formation (Schellekens, 1993, this volume). Intruding into these stratified sequences of volcanic-volcaniclastic rocks with interbedded limestone lenses are two large felsic intrusions, the San Lorenzo batholith and the Utuado pluton, as well as a number of smaller stocks.

The largest of these felsic intrusions is the San Lorenzo batholith (Fig. 1), which has been described and mapped with varying degrees of detail in the Juncos (Broedel, 1961), Punta Guayanés (Rogers, 1977), Humacao (M'Gonigle, 1978), Yabucoa–Punta Tuna (Rogers et al., 1979), and Caguas quadrangles (Rogers, 1979). The oldest rocks described from the batholith are from a small body of dark amphibole-rich tonalite enclosed within younger more felsic tonalite (Rogers et al., 1979), and from a small diorite stock west of the main batholith that is petrographically similar to the dated mafic tonalite. These rocks have been K-Ar dated at 109 ± 9 and 100 ± 16 Ma, respectively (Cox et al., 1977). The main batholithic body, on the basis of field relationships (Rogers, 1977) and K-Ar age dating (Cox et al., 1977), has been divided into a granodiorite–quartz diorite and associated tonolite unit that makes up about 75% in area of the batholith, and has an average age of approximately 73 Ma (Cox et al., 1977); a quartz monzonite–quartz diorite unit that extends in a zone from the center of the batholith to the coast at Punta Guayanés, and has an age of approximately 66 Ma (Cox et al., 1977), and small bodies of diorite and gabbro that usually occur enclosed in the first unit close to the border zone of the batholith. The dates obtained from this group, which are around 78 Ma, are interpreted to represent minimal ages as the rocks are thought to have been reheated by the younger units (Cox et al., 1977). This group could therefore represent intrusive bodies as old as Early Cretaceous.

Two samples from the San Lorenzo batholith were dated as part of this study (Table 1). One sample (SL-1) gave a total gas age on hornblende of 75 Ma and an age of 65 Ma on K-feldspar. The other date was from a late stage porphyry at Punta Guayanés that gave a total gas age of 57 Ma from a K-feldspar, suggesting that the late stage activity associated with the batholith may have extended into the Tertiary.

The Caguas stock is exposed 7 km north of the San Lorenzo batholith, and is considered, based on the similar composition of the granodiorite and associated tonalite, the presence of small diorite bodies at or near the periphery of both intrusions, and the presence in the stock of small amounts of light gray felsic porphyry resembling the late stage differentiates of the San Lorenzo batholith at Punta Guayanés, to be a satellite of the San Lorenzo batholith (Rogers, 1979). Small tonalite bodies, resembling both the Caguas and San Lorenzo intrusions, occur between both outcrop areas.

The Utuado pluton (Fig. 1), which crops out in northwest central Puerto Rico, was studied by Weaver (1958) and Chen (1967). It is contained in the U.S. Geological Survey maps of the

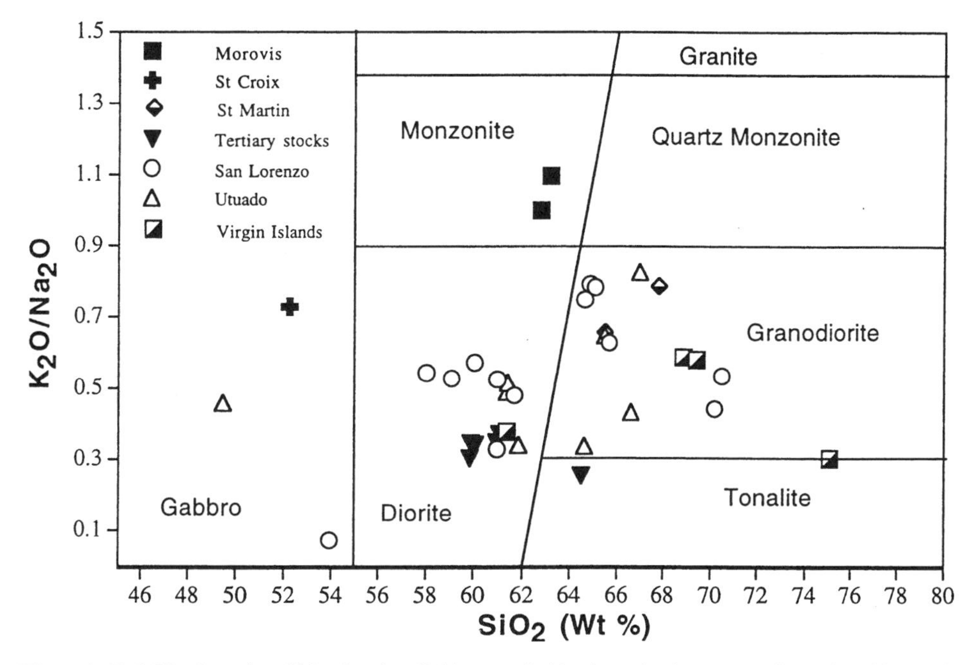

Figure 3. K_2O/Na_2O against SiO_2 showing fields occupied by intrusive igneous rocks and positions of samples studied. Adapted from Kesler, 1978, and Kesler and Sutter, 1979.

Adjuntas (Mattson, 1968a), Bayaney (Nelson and Tobisch, 1968), Jayuya (Mattson, 1968b), and Utuado (Nelson, 1967) quadrangles. Weaver (1958) distinguished four main petrographic suites: (1) granodiorite and quartz monzonite, (2) quartz diorite, (3) quartz porphyrite, and (4) gabbro. About 75% of the pluton consists of granodiorite and quartz monzonite (Weaver, 1958), locally grading into tonalite (Barabas, 1982). The remaining 25% consists of quartz diorite that, locally, especially along the western border of the pluton, grades into small bodies of porphyritic quartz diorite (quartz porphyrite of Weaver, 1958). Gabbro occurs as small bodies at two localities near the edge of the pluton (Weaver, 1958).

Only one sample of the Utuado pluton was dated as part of this study (Table 1). This sample, from a dioritic outlier to the southeast of the main body, yielded a total gas age of 76 Ma from hornblende, and 69 Ma for K-feldspar, consistent with previous K-Ar ages of 73.2 to 71 Ma obtained by Cox et al. (1977). The hornblende ages obtained from this outlier are similar to those from the main intrusive event of the San Lorenzo batholith, whereas the younger K-feldspar age is similar to the K-Ar hornblende ages of 69 to 58 Ma (Cox et al., 1977) assigned to the main phase of the Utuado pluton. On the basis of these dates, the outlier appears to have been intruded at the same time as the main phase of the San Lorenzo batholith with the K-feldspar ages having been reset as a result of the intrusion of the Utuado pluton. Young ages of around 46 Ma obtained from the main Utuado pluton also probably represent dates that were reset by the intrusion of the surrounding Eocene stocks. Further evidence for such effects is shown by discordant hornblende-biotite ages obtained from three samples from the Utuado pluton representing Late Cretaceous ages reset during the Eocene (Cox et al., 1977; Barabas, 1982).

The Morovis and Ciales stocks in north-central Puerto Rico are two small (18 and 2 km^2, respectively) intrusions that occur within about 1 km of each other. A total gas age on hornblende of 86 Ma was obtained from the Morovis stock (Table 1), which is similar to the K-Ar age 88.1 $\pm$ 2.1 Ma age obtained by Cox et al. (1977) from the same pluton, and within the range of error of the lead alpha age of 70 $\pm$ 20 Ma quoted by Berryhill (1965) for the Ciales stock. Both intrusions show sharp contacts with the surrounding country rock and, along the southern contact of the Morovis stock, migmatitic textures and evidence of contact metamorphism have been observed. Autoliths and xenoliths occur in both stocks, with the Ciales stock also containing roof pendants of the Avispa Formation (Berryhill, 1965). Based on their close proximity and similar petrography and chemistry, it is suggested that these two stocks are the surface expression of a single intrusion.

A number of intermediate size Eocene stocks intruding Cretaceous rocks have been mapped in the CIP. These include the hornblende quartz diorite Cuyon stock (Berryhill and Glover, 1960; Kesler and Sutter, 1979) , the porphyritic hornblende diorite Los Panes stock, and the quartz diorite Barranquitas stock (Briggs and Gelabert, 1962). The latter two stocks have been inferred to be of Eocene age on the basis of their stratigraphic position (Glover, 1971), and resemblance with other Eocene stocks (Scott Monroe, personal communication, 1994). Similar stocks, which intrude along the southern margin of the Utuado pluton, have dates of 48 to 41 Ma and are associated with copper mineralization (Barabas, 1982).

TABLE 2. REPRESENTATIVE MODES OF PLUTONIC ROCKS FROM THE NORTHEASTERN CARIBBEAN*

Mineral	Morovis	San Lorenzo			Utuado			Virgin Islands	Rio Blanco	St. Martin
	MOR 1	PRP 104	PP 1	PRP 7	SU 16	PRP 27	8690	TO 15	PRP 14	SM 11
Quartz	14.2	23.0	7.6	20.7	np	15.0	14.5	28.5	25.7	33.5
Orthoclase	22.7	0.7	39.0	2.5	np	7.2	5.7	17.5	1.5	tr
Plagioclase	43.7	59.5	13.6	46.2	74.7	66.7	52.7	36.0	54.5	61.5
Hornblende	13.7	11.0	np	14.2	9.5	3.0	15.2	10.7	14.7	2.5
Biotite	tr	3.7	0.8	13.5	np	np	1.0	6.0	2.0	2.2
Iron Oxides	2.0	1.2	0.4	2.5	4.0	0.7	2.7	1.0	0.7	np
Sphene	1.2	tr	tr	tr	np	0.5	np	np	tr	np
Chlorite	2.0	0.7	np	0.2	10.2	4.7	8.0	0.2	0.5	np
Epidote	0.2	np	np	np	1.5	2.0	np	np	np	0.2
Pyroxene	np	np	np	np	tr	np	tr	np	np	tr
Groundmass	np	np	38.6	np	np	np	np	np	np	np

*tr = trace; np = not present.

In the NIP (Fig. 2), island arc volcanism started in the Lower Cretaceous with the Daguao-Figuera VSA. This volcanism in the eastern part of the province occurred in a basin that continued to sink until the beginning of the Late Cretaceous when it was uplifted above sea level (Schellekens, 1993). In contrast, in the west the volcanogenic sequences are interrupted by unconformities probably representing frequent subaerial conditions. This igneous province can therefore be divided into two sequences, a distal one of continuous basinal sedimentation composed of turbidites and interbedded submarine lavas, and a proximal, discontinuous one that provides evidence for the presence of volcanic centers that generated the materials deposited in the basin.

Intruding middle Cretaceous rocks of NIP is the Río Blanco stock (Fig. 1). Ar-Ar total gas ages from this intrusion (Table 1) range between 49 and 42 Ma, and are similar to those obtained by Cox et al. (1977). Locally, diorite occurs as a border phase, and apophyses of the stock invade the surrounding Albian-Cenomanian country rock. Similar diorites occur as dikes elsewhere in the area. The stock has a sharp contact and is associated with a considerable contact aureole (Seiders, 1971).

For all three igneous provinces two major periods of erosion and deformation occurred during the Cretaceous, one around 85 Ma and the other toward the end of the Maastrichtian. A third period of deformation, which occurred at the end of the Eocene and the beginning of the Oligocene, marked the end of igneous activity in the region, as younger rocks are entirely sedimentary being dominantly stable platform limestones (Fig. 2).

St. Croix

The island of St. Croix (Figs. 1 and 2) represents an exposed part of the St. Croix ridge. The island is predominantly composed of Cretaceous volcaniclastic rocks, which are overlain unconformably by Oligocene-Miocene limestones and marls (Whetten, 1966, 1974). A volcanic fragment in the entirely clastic Caledonia Formation gave a K-Ar age of 75.2 ± 4.3 Ma (Speed et al., 1979), indicating the age of probably contemporaneous volcanism from an as yet unknown source. The only igneous rocks described from St. Croix are two lava flows, one andesitic and the other basaltic, from the Campanian-Maastrichtian Judith Fancy Formation (Whetten, 1966), and two small intrusions, the Fountain and Southgate stocks. The Fountain stock, which intrudes the Judith Fancy Formation (Whetten, 1974), has yielded total gas ages on hornblende, biotite, and K-feldspar, which show considerable scatter (Table 1), probably due to contrasts in bulk Ar retentivity during thermal relaxation following emplacement (M. Grove, personal communication, 1996). The hornblende age from this intrusion is similar to that obtained from the Southgate stock, a coarse-grained poikilitic hornblende gabbro, that intrudes the Late Cretaceous Caledonia Formation (Speed et al., 1979).

Northern Virgin Islands

The northern Virgin Islands (Figs. 1 and 2) form the exposed eastern part of the Puerto Rico–Virgin Islands Platform. The oldest exposed rocks are spilites and keratophyres of the Albian Water Island Formation (Donnelly, 1966). This formation is unconformably overlain by the Louisenhoj Formation composed of a thick series of andesitic pyroclastics that have been dated, using microfossils, as Turonian to early Santonian (Pessagno, 1976). Volcanism continued into the Tertiary as suggested by the presence of andesitic pyroclastics in the middle Eocene Tortola and Necker Formations (Helsley, 1971). Intruding the rocks of the northern Virgin Islands is the Virgin Island batholith, which petrographically consists of approximately 65% tonalite, 25% granodiorite, and 10% gabbro, with granite occurring as late stage dike rocks (Longshore, 1965). The batholith intruded and metamorphosed the early Cretaceous Water Island Formation, the Late Cretaceous Tutu Formation, and the middle Eocene Necker and Tortola Formations. Plutonic rock fragments, possibly derived from the batholith, have been described from the upper

Necker Formation (Helsley, 1971). Total gas ages on hornblende, biotite, and K-feldspar from a diorite on the island of Tortola range from 39 to 42 Ma (Table 1). The granodiorite of Virgin Gorda gave ages of 38 Ma for hornblende and 37 Ma for K-feldspar (Table 1), which are slightly older than the ages of 32 to 36 Ma obtained by previous workers (Cox et al., 1977; Kesler and Sutter, 1979) for this intrusion. A much younger age of 24 Ma was obtained from an outcrop of tonalite from the Narrows pluton on the island of St. John (Kesler and Sutter, 1979).

St. Martin

The stratigraphy of St. Martin has been divided into the Pointe Blanche Formation, a volcanic and sedimentary sequence, composed of siliceous tuffs and occasional andesitic flows, that extends into the upper Eocene, although volcanism appears to have ceased by the late middle Eocene; a series of basaltic, andesitic, and dacitic flows that were intruded during the Oligocene by diorite, quartz diorite, and granodiorite stocks, and early Miocene limestones and marls of the Lowlands Formation (Christman, 1953; Andreieff et al., 1988; Dagain et al., 1989; Davidson et al., 1993). The stocks, which have been hydrothermally altered to varying degrees, have yielded Ar-Ar amphibole ages of 26.8 ± 0.4 and 26.7 ± 0.44 Ma (Davidson et al., 1993), and a total gas age on K-feldspare of 27 Ma (Table 1).

PETROGRAPHY OF THE ANALYZED SAMPLES

In their studies of the plutonic rocks of the northeast Caribbean, Kesler (1978) and Kesler and Sutter (1979) used a classification based on the relationship between the K_2O/Na_2O ratio and SiO_2. In order to maintain consistency in the naming of these rocks we have followed the same classification. Figure 3 shows the fields assigned to the different intrusive rocks and the positions of the samples studied here.

Modal analyses of representative plutonic rocks from Puerto Rico, the Virgin Islands, and St. Martin are given in Table 2. All rocks are composed of various combinations of quartz, plagioclase, alkali feldspar, hornblende, and biotite, with accessory magnetite and sphene. Alkali feldspars were distinguished on the basis of staining. Almost all of the samples show some evidence of alteration or low-grade metamorphism, as illustrated by sericitization of the feldspars, chloritization of biotite and hornblende, and growth of epidote. Quartz and alkali feldspar occur only interstitially, whereas rare pyroxene grains are found as cores to larger hornblende crystals.

The majority of the rocks studied have a fine- to medium-grained subhedral granular texture. The exceptions are the Maguayo porphryry, the Tertiary stocks from western Puerto Rico, the Baranquitas stock, and the sample from Punta Guayanés (PP-1) of the San Lorenzo batholith. These all show distinctive porphyritic textures with phenocrysts of quartz, plagioclase, alkali feldspar with or without hornblende, and biotite in a granular groundmass of feldspar and quartz.

TABLE 3. CHEMICAL COMPOSITION OF ROCKS FROM CRETACEOUS STOCKS

Sample	Maguayo VP-118†	Morovis PRP-23†	Morovis MOR-1†	St. Croix V-26†
SiO_2	62.36	62.78	63.18	52.22
TiO_2	0.69	0.46	0.48	1.00
Al_2O_3	17.14	17.27	16.96	21.35
FeO*	4.51	4.38	4.19	7.30
MnO	0.18	0.12	0.12	0.14
MgO	4.03	1.92	1.90	2.74
CaO	4.25	4.80	4.60	8.25
Na_2O	3.86	4.05	4.02	3.73
K_2O	2.53	4.05	4.41	2.72
P_2O_5	0.28	0.16	0.14	0.54
Anhydrous Total	95.98	97.96	100.10	98.94
Cs	nd§	0.8	1.0	0.4
SC	md	0	9	11
V	117	92	88	210
Cr	35	9	11	3
Ni	13	10	<10	<10
Cu	28	45	70	60
Zn	116	65	55	65
Ga	nd	12	24	19
Pb	53	108	93	65
Sr	489	718	793	853
Y	17	28	20	18
Zr	153	115	107	25
Nb	24	12	12	9
Ba	1,263	1,276	1,341	1,129
La	13	18.8	17.2	16.7
Ca	91	38	33	35
Nd	nd	18	16	18
Sm	nd	4.0	3.3	3.9
Eu	nd	0.90	0.90	1.29
Tb	nd	0.6	0.5	0.6
Yb	nd	2.22	1.71	1.28
Lu	nd	0.36	0.28	0.20
Hf	nd	2.8	2.9	0.8
Pb	nd	7	20	10
Th	nd	4.6	4.4	2.9
U	nd	2.1	2.0	1.0

*Total iron as FeO.
†VP-118, south of Barrio Maguayo; PRP-29, Rte. 155, km 43.5; MOR-1, Rte. 155, where road crosses river; V-26, scenic route, St. Croix.
§nd = not determined.

GEOCHEMISTRY

Major, trace, and REE analyses were carried out by ICP (induced coupled plasma emission spectrometry) and INAA (instrumental neutron activation analyses) at Actlabs, Ancaster, Ontario, (see Schellekens, 1993, for detection limits). Additional analyses by x-ray fluorescence and INAA were carried out at Michigan Technological University and Massachusetts Institute of Technology, respectively. Analytical procedures for the former are described in Rose et al. (1986), and for the latter in Ila and Frey (1984). Analyses of the rocks studied are given in Tables 3

TABLE 4. CHEMICAL COMPOSITIONS OF ROCKS FROM TERTIARY STOCKS

	Anon						Rio Vivi	Barran-quitas	Rio Blanco			
	EC-10[†]	VP-172[†]	VP-147[†]	VP-144[†]	VP-141[†]	VP-100[†]	PRP-23[†]	VP-59[†]	PRP-17[†]	PRP-16[†]	PRP-14[†]	6513[†]
SiO_2	46.46	47.82	51.11	52.60	58.45	62.67	64.48	58.41	59.86	59.90	60.07	60.95
TiO_2	1.05	1.13	1.00	1.34	0.83	0.50	0.39	0.68	0.50	0.55	0.54	0.49
Al_2O_3	18.05	14.14	19.25	16.55	17.27	17.02	17.39	18.49	17.73	17.27	17.51	17.71
FeO*	9.16	11.43	7.91	10.63	6.61	3.46	4.51	6.66	6.54	7.13	6.52	6.02
MnO	0.21	0.23	0.15	0.24	0.16	0.14	0.17	0.21	0.16	0.16	0.17	0.16
MgO	11.52	13.66	3.25	5.41	4.46	4.45	1.58	5.52	3.12	3.01	2.77	2.80
CaO	8.39	6.93	14.48	7.58	7.08	3.31	6.15	7.19	7.53	7.38	7.37	7.35
Na_2O	2.48	1.68	1.85	3.40	3.43	5.85	4.17	3.50	3.43	3.36	3.64	3.31
K_2O	2.22	2.23	0.70	1.94	1.42	2.26	1.06	1.16	1.04	1.16	1.24	1.15
P_2O_5	0.37	0.59	0.26	0.26	0.24	0.23	0.10	0.16	0.10	0.08	0.08	0.06
Anhydrous Total	97.40	87.93	86.50	88.05	90.93	97.29	98.28	99.98	97.79	100.16	98.07	100.44
Cs	nd[§]	nd	nd	nd	nd	nd	0.3	nd	1.2	1.4	1.1	1.0
Sc	26	nd	31	nd	nd	nd	5	nd	12	12	12	12
V	156	224	194	248	151	95	58	162	110	140	120	110
Cr	104	551	16	130	<12	34	6	35	6	5	3	8
Ni	67	155	21	23	<3	107	<10	5	20	<10	<10	<10
Cu	33	93	58	87	74	54	15	27	45	25	20	30
Zn	60	81	44	77	54	74	65	71	65	70	70	75
Ga	nd	nd	nd	nd	nd	nd	13	nd	12	13	11	26
Rb	38	33	11	39	19	45	19	25	28	31	27	25
Sr	360	876	301	600	443	763	436	558	239	234	248	265
Y	18	20	13	19	18	14	20	nd	20	22	20	20
Zr	104	228	60	126	106	144	84	131	125	63	92	100
Nb	12	7	4	13	13	<3	7	6	7	8	8	7
Ba	717	1,080	119	402	376	940	384	nd	251	297	323	307
La	21	19	5.51	<10	<10	19	9.7	21	5	5.1	5.3	5.1
Ce	71	52	13.7	nd	nd	66	21	23	12	12	13	13
Nd	nd	nd	9.1	nd	nd	nd	11	nd	8	7	7	8
Sm	nd	nd	2.46	nd	nd	nd	2.5	nd	2.0	2.1	2.0	2.0
Eu	nd	nd	0.88	nd	nd	nd	0.75	nd	0.67	0.68	0.65	0.69
Tb	nd	nd	0.49	nd	nd	nd	0.5	nd	0.4	0.4	0.4	0.4
Yb	nd	nd	1.78	nd	nd	nd	2.16	nd	1.84	1.89	1.77	1.95
Lu	nd	nd	0.29	nd	nd	nd	0.34	nd	0.31	0.32	0.30	0.31
Hf	nd	nd	1.3	nd	nd	nd	2.4	nd	1.9	1.8	1.7	2.0
Pb	nd	nd	nd	nd	nd	nd	<5	nd	<5	<5	<5	<5
Th	nd	nd	0.53	nd	nd	nd	1.0	nd	0.8	0.7	0.9	0.9
U	nd	nd	nd	nd	nd	nd	0.5	nd	0.7	0.5	0.5	0.6

*Total iron as FeO.

[†]EC-10 = Rio Grande de Añasco; VP-172 = Rte. 128; VP-147 = east of Barrio Marueno; VP-144 = Rte. 391; VP-141 = Rte. 372; VP-100 = Rte. 318, km 1.9; PRP-23 = Rte. 10, intersection of Rio Pellejas–Rio Grande Arecibo; VP-59 = Barranquitas; PRP-17 = Rte. 191, km 13.3; PRP-16 = Rte. 191, km 13.3; PRP-14 = Rte. 191, km 17.5; 6513 = Rte. 191, km 82.

[§]nd = not determined.

through 7. The following discussion is based on both these new analyses and on those already published.

Plutonic rocks from the northeastern Caribbean range in silica content from 45 to 78 wt %. A characteristic feature, for those suites for which sufficient data exist, is that both major and trace elements generally show coherent linear tends, with TiO_2, Al_2O_3, FeO(Total), MgO, CaO, P_2O_5, Sc, and V showing decreasing values, and Na_2O, K_2O, Hf, Rb, Zr, Ba, and Th showing increasing values with increasing silica content. Sr is somewhat ambiguous, with a decreasing trend being characteristic of the Tertiary stocks (Table 4), and possibly two trends being shown by the larger batholiths (Fig. 4) (Utuado and San Lorenzo show increasing trend of Sr, and the Virgin Islands a decreasing trend with increasing silica). The larger scatter shown by the alkalis compared to other major elements (e.g., Fig. 4*A*) could possibly be the result of the mobility of these elements during low-grade metamorphism.

The Cretaceous stocks studied include the Maguayo and the Morovis-Ciales stocks from Puerto Rico, and the Fountain stock

TABLE 4. CHEMICAL COMPOSITIONS OF ROCKS FROM TERTIARY STOCKS (continued - page 2)

	Rio Blanco	St. Martin	
	PRP-12†	SM-12†	SM-11†
SiO_2	61.07	65.48	67.80
TiO_2	0.51	0.55	0.46
Al_2O_3	17.34	15.57	15.13
FeO*	6.22	4.93	4.06
MnO	0.16	0.12	0.07
MgO	2.89	2.40	1.98
CaO	7.02	4.87	4.07
Na_2O	3.45	3.52	3.56
K_2O	1.28	2.38	2.80
P_2O_5	0.06	0.08	0.06
Anhydrous Total	99.96	100.19	97.95
Cs	1.2	2.8	1.4
Sc	13	12	11
V	110	96	75
Cr	13	25	18
Ni	10	<10	<10
Cu	10	90	20
Zn	70	96	55
Ga	11	21	22
Rb	31	61	61
Sr	232	255	201
Y	20	22	20
Zr	72	131	129
Nb	8	8	9
Ba	337	558	541
La	4.5	10.2	8.4
Ce	11	23	19
Nd	7	12	10
Sm	1.8	2.9	2.5
Eu	0.63	0.71	0.63
Tb	0.4	0.5	0.5
Yb	2.01	1.97	1.98
Lu	0.31	0.31	0.32
Hf	2.1	3.6	3.9
Pb	<5	7	7
Th	0.8	3.3	4.6
U	0.6	1.6	1.7

All major elements have been recalculated to 100 wt % volatile free.
*Total iron as FeO.
†PRP-12 = Rte. 191, km 13.9; SM-12 = Philipsburg; SM-11 = Quarry, Philipsburg.
§nd = not determined.

from St. Croix (Table 3) (Kesler and Sutter, 1979; Schellekens, 1993). The first two have somewhat similar compositions and are characterized by relatively high values of Ba (1250 to 1350 ppm) and Zr (100 to 150 ppm). The rocks of the Morovis stock are, however, richer in K_2O (4%), and Rb (100 ppm) than those of Maguayo (K_2O = 2.8%; Rb = 50 ppm) for similar silica contents. The similarity of the Ciales and Morovis major element compositions support the earlier suggestion that they actually represent one intrusion (Table 3) (Berryhill, 1965).

The Late Cretaceous Fountain stock on St. Croix has relatively high values of Ba (1100 ppm), Sr (900 ppm), Rb (75 ppm), and Th (3 ppm) for its silica content of 50% (Table 3).

Stocks of Tertiary age have been described from the Eocene of Puerto Rico and the Oligocene of St. Martin (Table 4) (Kesler and Sutter, 1979; Barabas, 1982; Schellekens, 1993; Davidson et al., 1993). The rocks from all of the Eocene stocks from Puerto Rico show linear trends, which are relatively well defined for the major elements, and somewhat more scattered for trace elements, over a range of 25 wt % SiO_2. Some of the small stocks from western Puerto Rico are characterized by relatively high values of MgO, CaO, and K_2O, suggesting that they may represent cumulative rocks. In comparison with the Late Cretaceous stocks from Puerto Rico, those from the Tertiary have much lower values of K_2O, Na_2O, and Ba (Tables 3 and 4).

The Oligocene stocks on St. Martin also show relatively well-defined linear trends for both major and trace elements with values for most major elements being similar to those obtained from the Eocene stocks of Puerto Rico. K_2O, however, is distinctly higher for St. Martin, as are Rb, Zr, and Th (Table 4) (Davidson et al., 1993).

As previously described for the stocks, the rocks of the batholiths also show well-defined linear trends with trace elements again showing a greater scatter. The two Cretaceous batholiths from Puerto Rico appear to be geochemically similar, and somewhat distinct from the Virgin Islands batholith (Fig. 4).

One sample from the San Lorenzo batholith (PRP-4) has low values of K_2O, P_2O_5, Rb, Ba, Zr, Sr, and Th, and is chemically distinct from the rest of the batholith. This sample was collected from a small diorite intrusion near the western border of the batholith, and appears to be lithologically similar to the dated intrusive rocks of Lower Cretaceous age included within the batholith.

The Virgin Islands batholith with its relatively low values of K_2O, Ba, and Zr appears to be more similar in composition to the Tertiary stocks of Puerto Rico than to its Cretaceous equivalents from Puerto Rico (Tables 4 through 7). The high values of MgO and CaO for the more basic rocks from this intrusion suggest that the gabbros from the batholith are probably of cumulative origin (Longshore, 1965).

Of the two Late Cretaceous stocks analyzed from Puerto Rico REE data are only available from the Morovis stock. These samples are LREE enriched with a flat or slightly depleted HREE pattern and a slight negative Eu anomaly (Fig. 5*A*). A similar pattern is shown by the volcanic rocks associated with the Maguayo stock (Schellekens, 1993, this volume). In contrast, the Fountain stock on St. Croix shows strong enrichment of the LREE and depletion of the HREE (La/Lu = 9.47) (Fig. 5*B*).

The Tertiary stocks from Puerto Rico and St. Martin have similar patterns to those already described for the Morovis stock, that is, LREE enrichment with relatively flat HREE (Figs. 5*C-E*), with

TABLE 5. CHEMICAL COMPOSITIONS OF ROCKS FROM CRETACEOUS BATHOLITHS – I

	San Lorenzo												
	PRP-4†	PRP-5†	PRP-6†	PRP-104†	PRP-103†	PRP-2†	SL-1†	PRP-100†	PRP-1†	PRP-10†	PRP-11†	PRP-105†	PP-1†
SiO_2	53.94	58.03	59.08	60.05	60.98	61.68	62.76	64.62	64.84	65.05	65.66	70.18	70.49
TiO_2	0.60	0.71	0.61	0.57	0.58	0.59	0.70	0.46	0.45	0.45	0.49	0.36	0.19
Al_2O_3	19.39	17.68	17.67	17.21	17.49	17.07	16.26	16.10	16.07	16.26	16.41	15.25	16.62
FeO*	7.15	7.07	6.51	6.37	5.81	5.59	5.98	4.55	4.27	4.37	4.27	3.29	1.50
MnO	0.18	0.17	0.16	0.16	0.15	0.16	0.13	0.15	0.14	0.14	0.14	0.06	0.04
MgO	4.26	3.24	3.04	2.96	2.54	2.27	2.36	1.92	1.93	1.80	1.75	1.20	0.59
CaO	9.71	7.39	7.13	6.86	6.40	6.69	5.84	5.63	5.73	5.39	4.41	4.98	2.77
Na_2O	4.44	3.59	3.70	3.57	3.87	3.94	3.49	3.70	3.60	3.60	4.14	3.19	5.05
K_2O	0.32	1.95	1.95	2.04	2.03	1.89	2.32	2.77	2.85	2.82	2.60	1.41	2.70
P_2O_5	0.02	0.16	0.14	0.12	0.14	0.12	0.16	0.10	0.12	0.12	0.12	0.06	0.04
Anhydrous Total	100.91	99.65	100.36	99.73	99.38	100.48	100.73	99.20	99.97	100.30	100.87	99.73	99.96
Cs	<0.2	0.9	0.9	0.8	0.8	0.3	0.6	0.5	0.4	0.5	<0.2	0.6	0.7
Sc	33	17	17	14	12	11	14	9	8	9	7	7	2
V	260	210	190	150	110	110	120	84	78	84	80	68	40
Cr	38	4	5	7	6	4	8	5	3	5	6	6	5
Ni	10	<10	<10	<10	<10	<10	<10	<10	<10	<10	10	<10	<10
Cu	5	85	80	80	50	30	150	30	20	20	<5	<5	55
Zn	75	130	80	80	80	80	75	80	80	75	70	55	60
Ga	10	11	11	10	10	14	25	10	10	12	10	8	25
Rb	5	31	31	33	35	25	39	44	47	51	40	24	69
Sr	172	475	485	413	456	510	319	421	429	426	403	266	832
Y	18	22	22	24	20	24	28	26	24	20	16	22	6
Zr	47	75	76	95	113	91	174	104	75	112	161	141	97
Nb	6	7	7	8	8	9	11	8	8	8	7	8	8
Ba	106	865	794	807	886	764	1,001	1,045	1,018	1,001	973	530	1,441
La	1	6.9	7.0	7.7	7.1	9.3	14.8	9.9	10.1	10.0	7.3	8.4	8.0
Ce	4	15	16	18	16	20	32	21	21	20	16	20	14
Nd	3	10	10	11	9	12	18	11	11	10	8	12	5
Sm	1.0	2.5	2.6	2.7	2.2	3.1	4.3	2.8	2.6	2.5	1.9	2.8	1.1
Eu	0.42	0.81	0.80	0.78	0.71	0.94	0.92	0.79	0.79	0.79	0.65	0.55	0.34
Tb	0.3	0.5	0.5	0.5	0.4	0.6	0.8	0.5	0.5	0.5	0.4	0.5	0.2
Yb	1.50	1.94	1.98	2.25	1.79	2.32	2.65	2.09	2.04	2.00	1.80	2.38	0.51
Lu	0.23	0.31	0.29	0.34	0.29	0.38	0.41	0.35	0.34	0.34	0.28	0.38	0.08
Hf	0.9	1.8	1.9	2.6	2.7	2.5	4.2	2.8	2.9	2.8	2.4	3.8	2.6
Pb	<5	8	<5	6	<5	6	<5	8	8	8	5	12	24
Th	<0.1	1.2	1.3	2.0	1.4	1.7	3.2	2.3	2.4	2.6	2.1	4.0	3.5
U	<0.1	0.6	0.7	1.3	0.8	1.2	1.5	1.6	1.2	1.6	1.4	2.5	2.6

All major elements have been recalculated to 100 wt % volatile free.
*Total iron as FeO.
†PRP-4 = Rte. 181, km 23; PRP-5 = Rte. 3, km 97.0; PRP-6 = Rte. 3, km 97.2; PRP-104 = Rte. 183, km 7.5; PRP-103 = Rte. 183, km 5.6; PRP-2 = Rte. 181, km 8.3; SL-1 = Rte. 3, km 118; PRP-100 = Rte. 183, km 2.8; PRP-1 = Rte. 181, km 62; PRP-10 = Rte. 2, 1 km after Juncos; PRP-11 = Rte. 189, km 26.8; PRP-105 = Rte. 183, km 12.1; PP-1 = Punta Guyanes.

the samples from St. Martin (Fig. 5*E*) showing a more distinct negative Eu anomaly than those from Puerto Rico (Figs. 5*C*, *D*).

Unlike the smaller stocks that show relatively limited variations in REE patterns, the batholiths show at least five distinct trends (Fig. 6). One group of rocks are LREE enriched with flat HREE (Figs. 6*A*—San Lorenzo, 6*C*—Utuado, 6*F*—Virgin Islands); a second group shows a similar pattern but with a distinct negative Eu anomaly (Figs. 6*B*—San Lorenzo, 6*C*—Utuado); a third group has essentially flat REE patterns with a pronounced negative Eu anomaly (Fig. 6*E*—Virgin Islands), and a fourth group displays LREE enrichment and varying degrees of HREE depletion (Figs. 6*B*, *C*—San Lorenzo, 6*D*—Utuado, 6*F*—Virgin Islands). This HREE depletion varies from relatively small in rocks from Utuado (Eu/Lu = 6.38) (Fig. 6*C*) to extreme in the youngest rocks from the San Lorenzo batholith (Eu/Lu = 29.01) (Fig. 6*B*) and from the Peter Island intrusion of the Virgin Islands batholith (Eu/Lu = 19.09) (Fig. 6*F*). The final pattern, that of LREE depletion with slight HREE enrichment, is shown by the

TABLE 6. CHEMICAL COMPOSITION OF ROCKS FROM CRETACEOUS BATHOLITHS – II

	Utuado								
Sample	SU-16†	6358†	PRP-30†	8690†	PRP-27†	PRP-21†	PRP-28†	PRP-24†	8710†
SiO_2	49.46	60.97	61.41	61.37	61.85	64.61	65.46	66.60	66.97
TiO_2	0.95	0.49	0.56	0.54	0.51	0.43	0.39	0.39	0.48
Al_2O_3	20.51	17.41	16.99	17.31	17.87	16.92	16.49	16.23	15.60
FeO*	8.82	6.31	6.42	6.22	4.82	3.61	3.73	3.80	3.54
MnO	0.19	0.15	0.14	0.14	0.15	0.13	0.09	0.11	0.08
MgO	5.20	2.68	2.80	2.80	2.36	1.62	2.12	1.79	1.92
CaO	9.25	7.21	6.49	6.65	4.74	6.20	4.42	5.19	4.23
Na_2O	3.60	3.53	3.34	3.25	4.88	4.75	4.35	4.05	3.86
K_2O	1.65	1.16	1.72	1.59	1.66	1.60	2.62	1.75	3.19
P_2O_5	0.37	0.08	0.12	0.14	0.14	0.12	0.12	0.08	0.12
Anhydrous Total	100.25	100.63	100.53	100.26	100.21	100.75	99.27	100.41	100.20
Cs	0.6	1.1	0.8	0.7	0.5	0.5	0.5	1.1	0.6
Sc	22	11	16	16	9	6	7	8	7
V	430	110	120	110	98	76	82	72	80
Cr	11	7	6	7	20	9	15	9	14
Ni	20	<10	<10	<10	10	<10	<10	<10	10
Cu	60	10	30	35	100	25	80	20	120
Zn	85	55	70	75	65	70	60	65	60
Ga	25	22	12	22	16	16	13	12	12
Rb	36	29	27	25	33	34	66	37	73
Sr	1,008	246	313	302	711	739	559	483	518
Y	18	20	2	22	14	14	10	16	20
Zr	72	71	88	214	109	99	94	87	105
Nb	9	8	7	8	8	9	7	8	13
Ba	412	292	661	617	704	870	757	591	891
La	9.9	5.0	8.9	9.7	9.9	9.1	12.7	6.5	20.6
Ce	20	13	19	20	19	18	22	15	47
Nd	12	8	11	11	10	9	9	8	23
Sm	3.1	2.1	2.6	2.8	2.2	2.0	1.6	1.9	4.3
Eu	1.02	0.70	0.74	0.74	0.69	0.61	0.52	0.53	0.93
Tb	0.5	0.5	0.6	0.5	0.4	0.3	0.3	0.4	0.6
Yb	1.31	2.05	2.22	2.03	1.29	1.07	1.00	1.61	1.92
Lu	0.20	0.33	0.33	0.33	0.20	0.18	0.16	0.24	0.27
Hf	1.2	2.0	2.4	2.1	2.4	2.4	3.1	2.6	2.9
Pb	<5	<5	<5	<5	9	8	13	<5	16
Th	1.0	1.3	1.9	1.8	1.3	1.9	5.1	1.6	6.8
U	0.4	0.4	0.6	0.6	0.8	1.1	2.5	0.9	2.8

All major elements have been recalculated to 100 wt % volatile free.
*Total iron as FeO.
†SU-16 = Rio Caonillas, near power plant; 6358 = Rte. 144 near Jayuya; PRP-30 = Rte. 143, km 13.5; 8690 = Rte. 143, km 14.0; PRP-27 = Caonillas power plant; PRP-21 = Caonillas power plant; PRP-28 = Rte. 140, km 11.6; PRP-24 = Ramal Rte. 141, km 0.7; 8710 = Rte. 140, km 11.0.

diorite sample (PRP-4) from the San Lorenzo batholith (Fig. 6*B*), which is also distinct from the rest of the batholithic rocks in terms of its major and trace elements (Fig. 4).

Discussion

The intrusive rocks in the northeastern Caribbean can be subdivided into two groups. The first group is composed of stocks that range in size from a few hundred meters to a few kilometers in diameter. Compositional variations shown by these stocks are similar to those shown by associated volcanic rocks, suggesting that the stocks may represent subvolcanic intrusive equivalents of the more abundant volcanic rocks. Intrusives belonging to this type are the Late Cretaceous Maguayo and Morovis-Ciales stocks from western and central Puerto Rico (Fig. 7), the Eocene stocks of Puerto Rico and the Oligocene stocks of St. Martin. (Fig. 8). The St. Martin igneous rocks show especially well-defined linear trends with the intrusive rocks

TABLE 7. CHEMICAL COMPOSITION OF ROCKS FROM TERTIARY BATHOLITHS

	Virgin Islands			
Sample	TO-15†	DL-3†	V-25†	DL-2†
SiO_2	61.37	68.86	69.41	75.07
TiO_2	0.67	0.31	0.22	0.31
Al_2O_3	15.97	15.36	16.75	12.88
FeO*	7.09	3.70	1.75	2.78
MnO	0.15	0.10	0.04	0.04
MgO	3.22	1.61	0.75	0.32
CzO	6.53	4.15	3.58	2.01
Na_2O	3.58	3.68	4.69	5.02
K_2O	1.35	2.16	2.72	1.52
P_2O_5	0.06	0.06	0.09	0.04
Anhydrous Total	100.15	100.04	97.67	97.80
Cs	1.0	0.9	1.2	0.3
Sc	22	7	3	11
V	190	58	34	16
Cr	18	8	9	8
Ni	<10	20	<10	<10
Cu	40	70	5	5
Zn	80	65	65	65
Ga	14	17	17	15
Rb	27	58	66	20
Sr	191	215	743	135
Y	28	14	6	52
Zr	110	80	60	145
Nb	7	7	8	7
Ba	264	380	770	305
La	6.1	5.5	5.2	9.4
Ce	16	12	10	25
Nd	10	6	5	16
Sm	2.7	1.4	1.1	4.5
Eu	0.69	0.47	0.37	0.94
Tb	0.6	0.3	0.2	1.1
Yb	3.00	1.26	0.38	5.00
Lu	0.48	0.20	0.06	0.77
Hf	2.8	2.4	2.0	4.4
Pb	<5	<5	10	9
Th	1.5	3.5	1.1	2.0
U	0.6	1.8	0.9	0.9

All major elements have been recalculated to 100 wt % volatile free.
*Total iron as FeO.
†TO-15 = Tortola; DL-3 = Virgin Gorda, near Copper Mine Point; V-25 = Peter Island; DL-2 = Virgin Gorda, Leverick Bay.

forming silica-rich and their associated extrusive rocks the more mafic end (Davidson et al., 1993).

The second group of intrusive rocks include the San Lorenzo, Utuado, and Virgin Islands batholiths, which represent composite intrusions of predominantly diorite-granodiorite composition, with areal extents measured in hundreds of square kilometers. In contrast to the smaller stocks these larger intrusions do not appear to be associated with co-magmatic volcanic rocks (Fig. 2).

The REE patterns, showing LREE enrichment and flat or slightly enriched HREE with or without a negative Eu anomaly, suggest that the processes for the formation of both the stocks and the batholiths could either have been fractionation of hornblende plus variable amounts of plagioclase, or partial melting leaving an amphibolite residue (Hanson, 1980). In contrast, the flat REE patterns with a pronounced negative Eu anomaly for two samples from the Virgin Islands batholith suggest that plagioclase was the dominant fractionating phase for these rocks. The steep negative slopes of the REE patterns shown by the Fountain stock on St. Croix, the late stage Punta Guayanés intrusion of the San Lorenzo batholith, and the Peter Island intrusion of the Virgin Islands batholith suggest that pyroxene could have been the dominant fractionating phase, or that they were formed by partial melting of either a basic source leaving a garnet residue or a high-grade metamorphosed sedimentary source (Hanson, 1980). The final pattern, that of PRP-4 with its negative LREE, is very similar to that shown by the lavas of the pre-Robles VSA (Schellekens, 1993, this volume; Jolly written communication, 1995), suggesting a similar origin of partial melting of a mantle source (Hanson, 1980). As the composition of this sample is similar to that shown by the Lower Cretaceous volcanic rocks surrounding the batholith (Fig. 7) and distinct from the rest of the batholith (Figs. 4*A*, *B* and 6), it is possible that this sample may represent an example of an Early Cretaceous intrusion associated with the pre-Robles volcanics.

The generation of island arc magmas depends on the interrelationship of three main components, the subducted lithosphere, the mantle wedge, and the arc crust. To evaluate the roles played by these components in the origin of intrusive rocks from the NE Caribbean, chondrite-normalized Ba/La ratios were plotted against chondrite-normalized La/Sm ratios (melting-mixing model of Kay [1980], as modified by Defant et al. [1991]). Figure 9 shows that the Cretaceous and Tertiary stocks generally lie along mixing curves involving N-MORB, pelagic sediments (represented by PAWMS), and dehydration fluids. In contrast, best-fit curves through the data from the batholiths appear to cross-cut these mixing curves and do not seem to have their origin at N-MORB, suggesting a different origin for the batholiths than for the stocks. PRP-4 is again distinct from the rest of the San Lorenzo batholith. Its high Ba/La and low La/Sm ratios suggest it could have formed by partial melting of an N-MORB source that had only been modified by the incorporation of dehydration fluids.

Similar origins to those just discussed for the stocks and batholiths are suggested by Nd and Sm data. On a plot of Nd versus Sm/Nd (Davidson, 1987), the Cretaceous and Tertiary stocks and their associated volcanic rocks show trends compatible with an origin by partial melting of a MORB source modified by bulk mixing of "crustal" material on which has been superimposed fractional crystallization (Fig. 10*A*). In contrast, the samples from the San Lorenzo and Utuado batholiths do not follow such trends

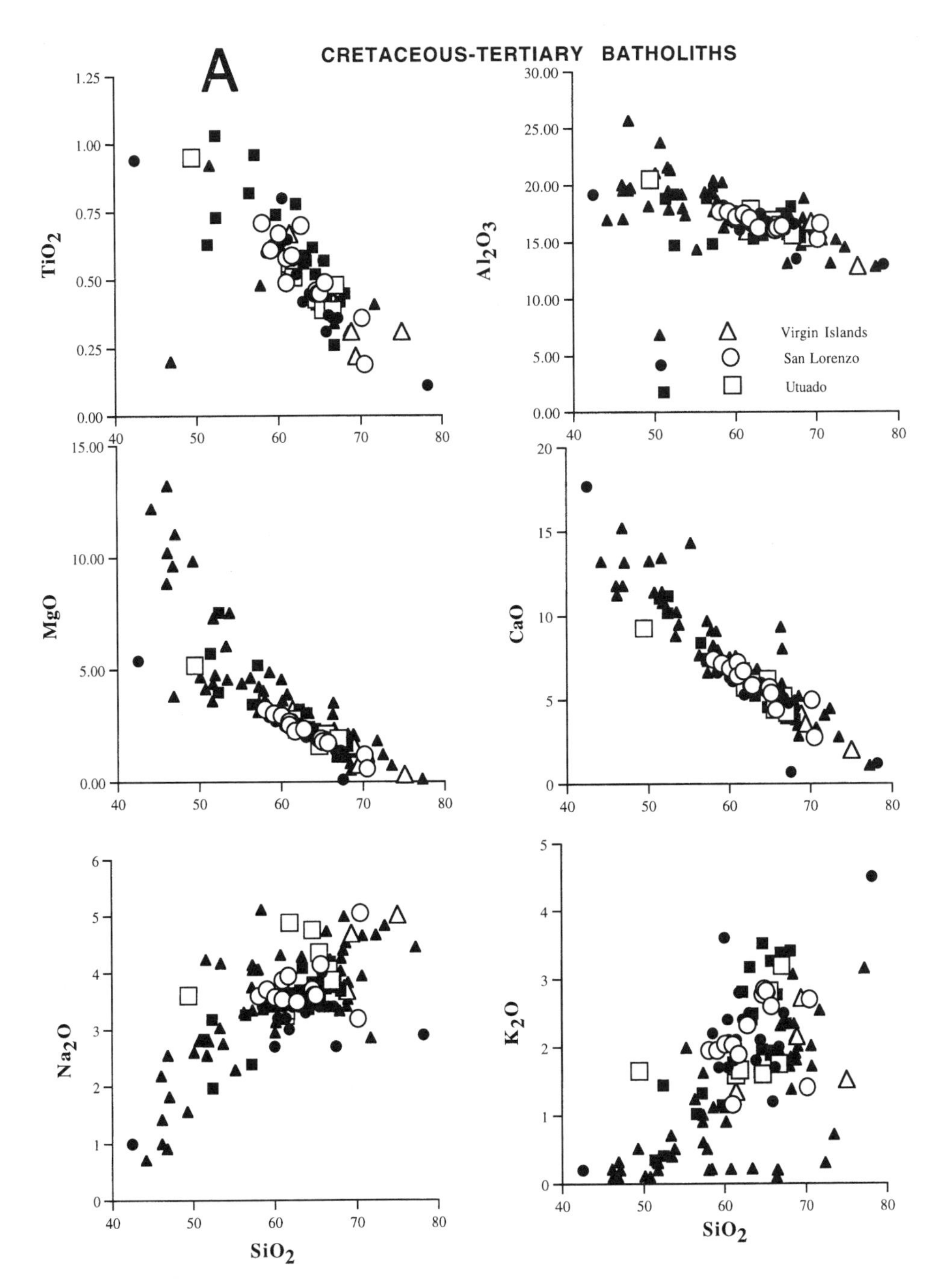

Figure 4*A*. Representative major element variations (in weight percent) against SiO_2 (wt %) for Cretaceous and Tertiary batholiths. Large open symbols from Tables 5, 6, and 7. Small closed symbols from Barabas, 1982; Kesler and Sutter, 1979; Longshore, 1965.

but show considerable scatter centered around the mid-point of the bulk mixing curve between MORB and "crust." A possible origin for these batholithic rocks could therefore involve partial melting of a source with a composition similar to the Lower Cretaceous volcanics of Puerto Rico followed by fractional crystallization of hornblende (Fig. 10*B*).

IGNEOUS ACTIVITY AND THE TECTONIC EVOLUTION OF THE CARIBBEAN

The present-day ocean floor of the Caribbean is thought to have been formed at the Farallon-Phoenix-Pacific triple junction between 136 and 130 Ma (Ghosh et al., 1994). Subduction of this

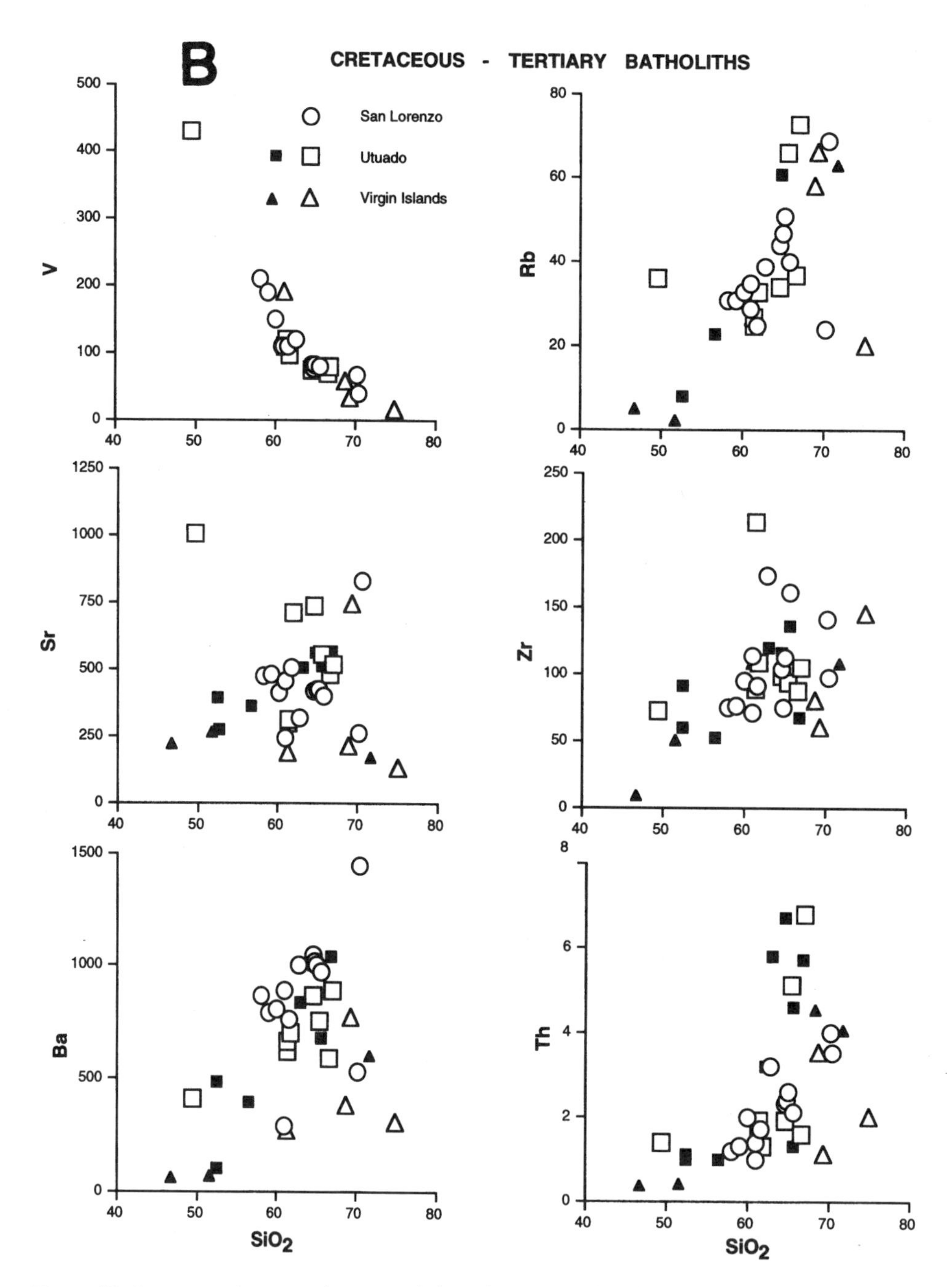

Figure 4*B*. Representative trace element variations (in ppm) against SiO_2 (wt %) for Cretaceous and Tertiary batholiths. Large open symbols from Table 5, 6, and 7. Small closed symbols from Barabas, 1982; Kesler and Sutter, 1979; Longshore, 1965.

ocean floor, together with older segments as early as Jurassic in age (Montgomery et al., 1994), is thought to have generated the Early and Late Cretaceous igneous suites of the Greater Antilles island arc. For Puerto Rico the present-day location of the Cretaceous stocks and associated volcanics north of the serpentinite melange of the Bermeja Complex, suggests that the Cretaceous Benioff zone for the island arc was northward dipping (Fig. 11). The earliest exposed igneous products associated with this subduction zone are the pre-Robles (Río Majada of Jolly et al., Chapter 1, this volume) and Daguayo-Figuera VSAs of Aptian-Albian or older age (Schellekens, 1993, this volume; Jolly et al., Chapter 1, this volume). These rocks, are characterized by flat to depleted LREE patterns and low values of incompatible elements (Schellekens, 1993, this volume; Jolly et al., Chapter 3, this vol-

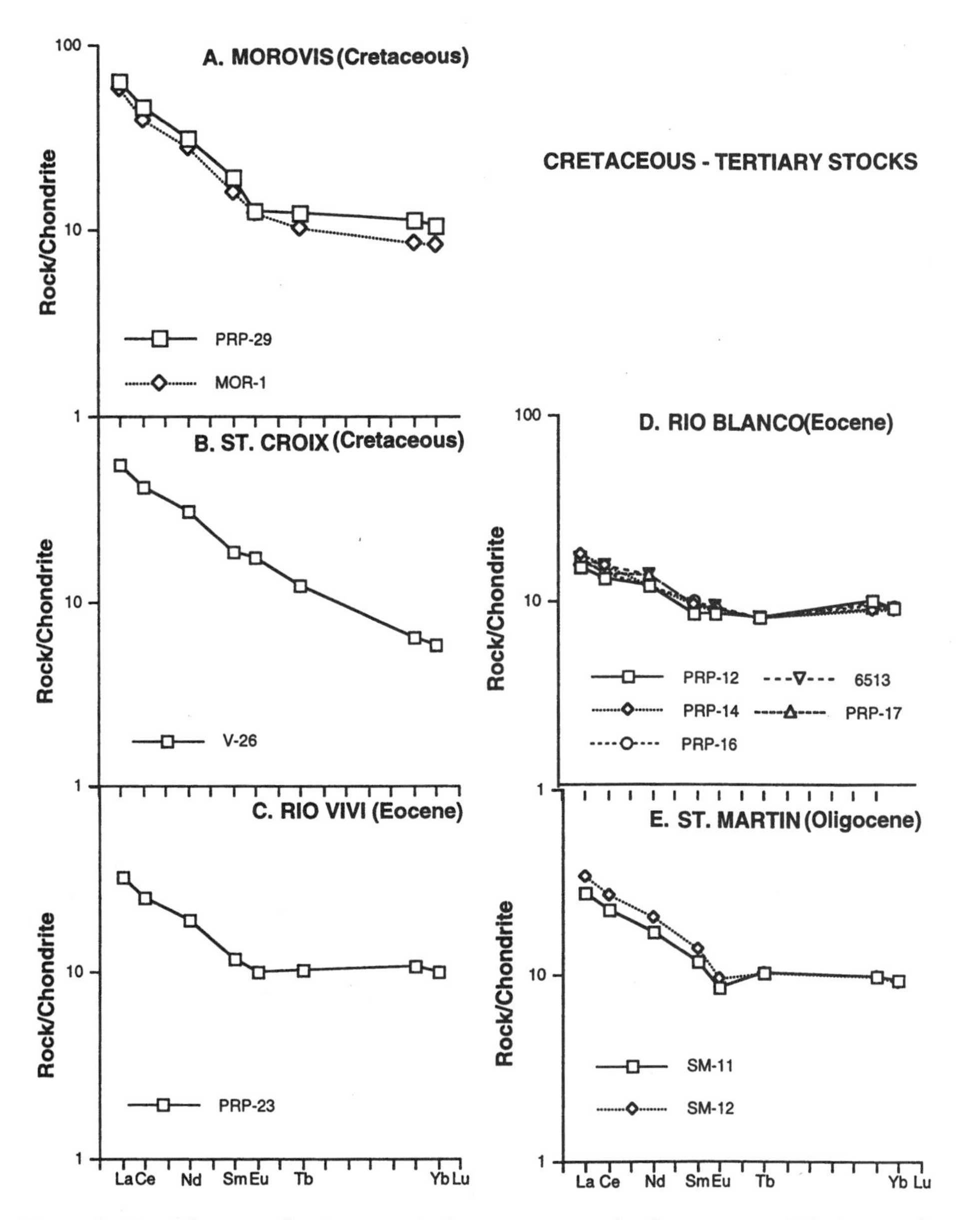

Figure 5. Chondrite-normalized rare earth elements patterns for Cretaceous and Tertiary stocks. (Chondrite normalizing factors from Taylor, *in* Donnelly and Rogers, 1980.)

ume). Jolly has suggested that the Lower Cretaceous Formation A (belonging to the pre-Robles VSA) was generated by approximately 4 to 17% melting of a spinel peridotite mantle (Jolly, written communication, 1995). As has been noted previously, one of the samples from the San Lorenzo batholith (PRP-4) is geochemically similar to these Lower Cretaceous volcanic rocks, and it has been postulated that it represents their intrusive equivalent. Based on its Zr/Yb ratio, PRP-4 could have been generated by approximately 10% melting from such a mantle (Fig. 12).

The Upper Cretaceous volcanic rocks and their associated stocks show much higher values for incompatible elements and are LREE enriched compared to those of the Lower Cretaceous (Fig. 7), suggesting lower degrees of partial melting or derivation from a previously enriched source. For example, the Upper Cretaceous Morovis stock could have been formed by only 1 to 4% melting of the same spinel peridotite source that generated PRP-4 (Fig. 12). These low values for partial melting are probably only a minimum, however, as the mantle wedge would have become enriched in incompatible elements introduced from the slab during the 15- to 20- evolution of the arc, as can be seen from the trends of the Morovis stock and its associated volcanic rocks in Figures 9 and 10.

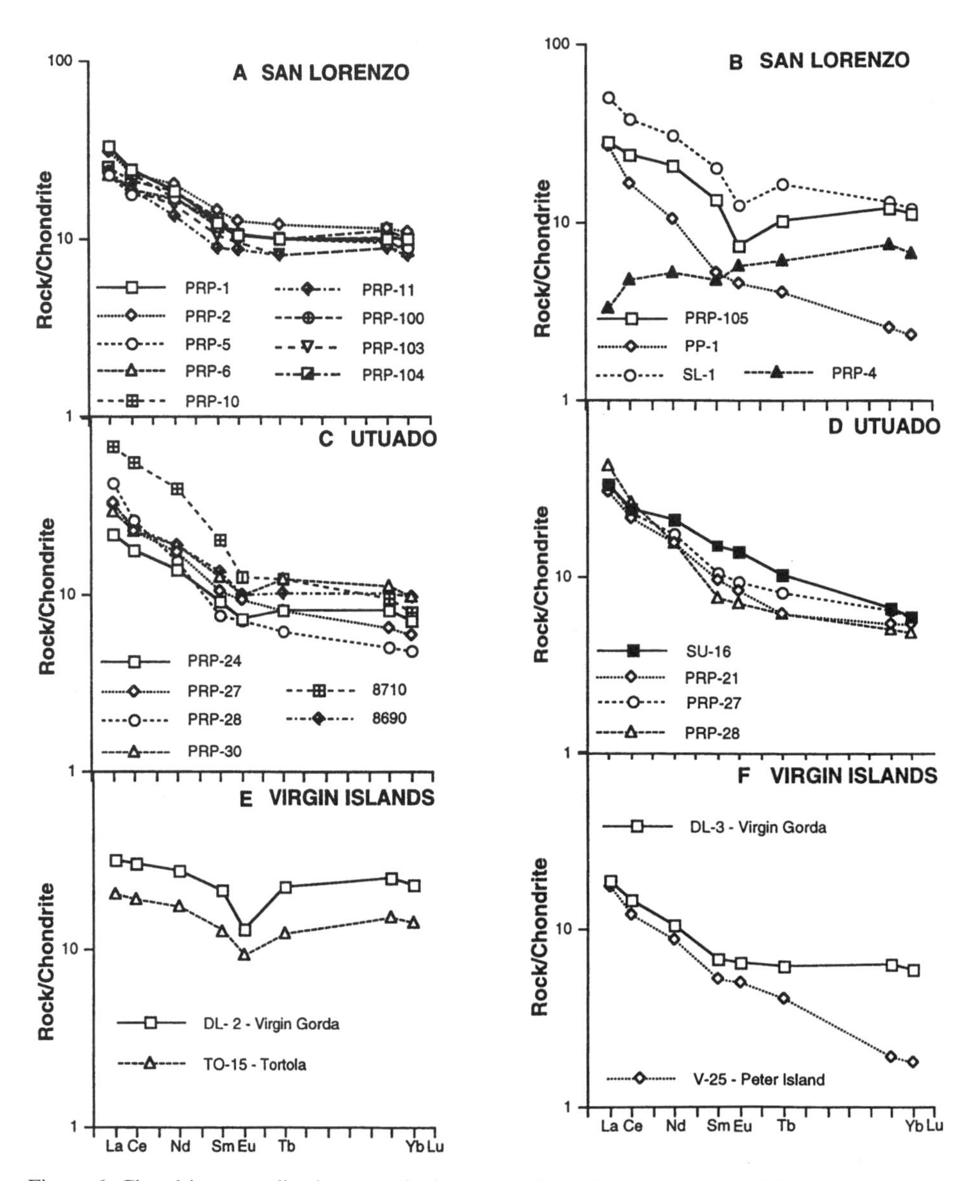

Figure 6. Chondrite-normalized rare earth elements patterns for Cretaceous and Tertiary batholiths. (Chondrite normalizing factors from Taylor, *in* Donnelly and Rogers, 1980.)

The ocean floor generated at the Farallon-Phoenix-Pacific triple junction, which is postulated to have moved northward and eastward while rotating through an angle of 45° (Ghosh et al., 1994), is thought to have passed over the Galapagos mantle plume around 89 to 88 Ma (Sinton and Duncan, 1992). The interaction of this plume with the "Caribbean" lithosphere is thought to have caused extensive melting and the generation of large amounts of basaltic magma to form the Cretaceous Caribbean Basaltic Province (CCBP) (Duncan and Donnelly, 1994). This large outpouring of basalt on the ocean floor thickened the oceanic crust forming an oceanic plateau, the remnant of which is now represented by the B″ reflector of the Colombian and Venezuelan basins. This thickened oceanic crust probably reached the subduction zone of the Greater Antilles island arc around 85 Ma (Fig. 13), and it is suggested that as it moved into the northward directed subduction zone the rate of subduction decreased and finally stopped entirely (Burke, 1988; Burke et al., 1978; Ghosh et al., 1994). Such a situation could explain the apparent decrease in the amount of partial melting of the mantle wedge that has been postulated above to explain the differences between the Early and Late Cretaceous igneous suites of Puerto Rico.

As the Greater Antilles island arc could no longer subduct

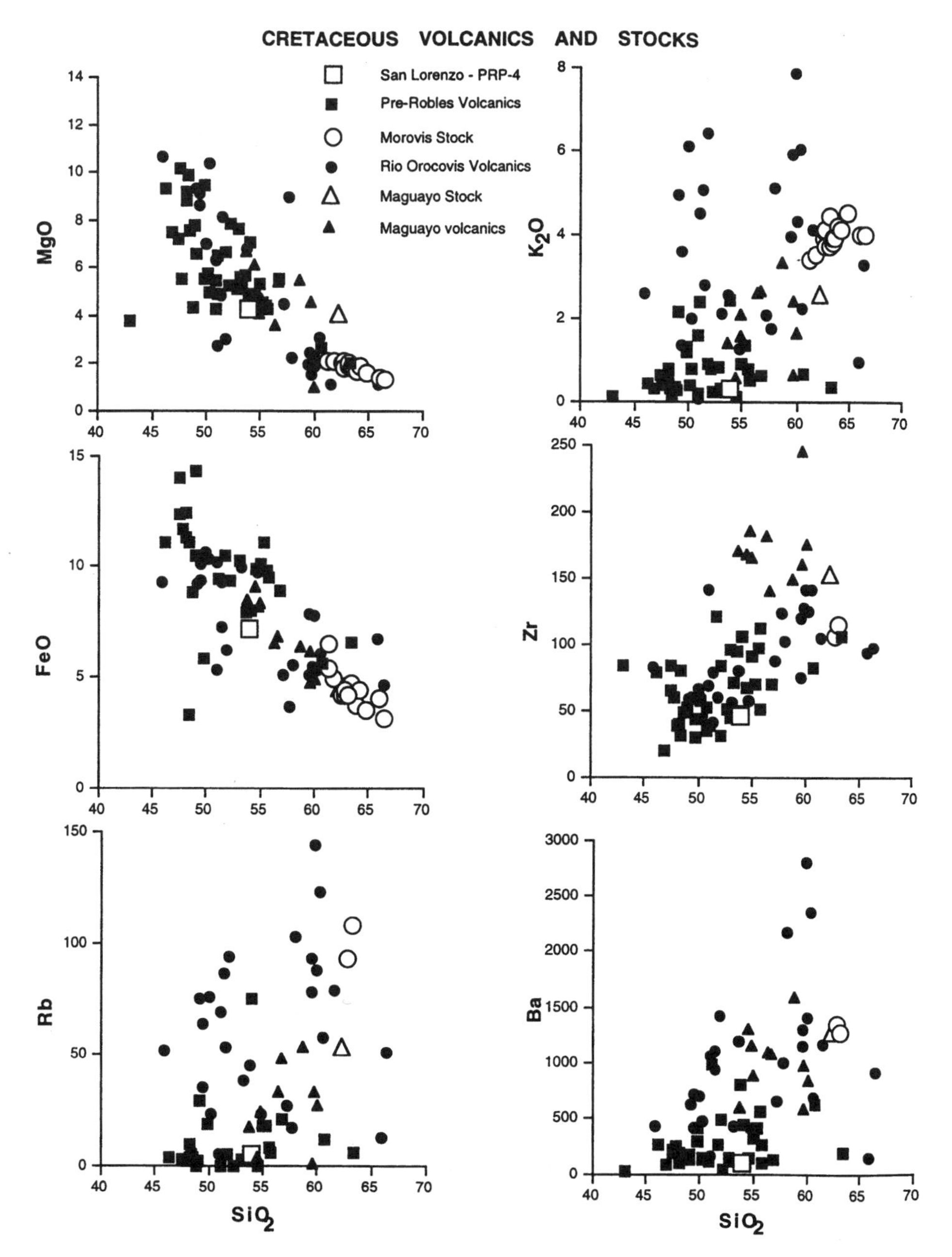

Figure 7. Major and trace element variations compared with SiO_2 for Cretaceous stocks and associated volcanic rocks. Major elements in weight percent, trace elements in parts per million. Large open symbols intrusive rocks, small closed symbols extrusive rocks. (Data sources: Table 3; Berryhill, 1965; T. W. Donnelly, unpublished data; W. T. Jolly, unpublished data; Kesler and Sutter, 1979; Schellekens, 1993.)

the buoyant, thickened Caribbean ocean floor, it is suggested that a new subduction zone was initiated on the opposite side of the arc causing the subduction of the Atlantic ocean floor (Fig. 13). The major tectonic break recorded between 85 and 80 Ma throughout Puerto Rico (Fig. 2) (Schellekens, 1993; Jolly et al., Chapter 1, this volume; H. Santos, personal communication, 1996), and the occurrence of a subduction complex dated at between 100 and 80 Ma on the Samana Peninsula, Dominican Republic (Joyce and Aronson, 1987) could provide evidence for this flip.

The initiation of a new subduction zone at around 80 Ma on the opposite side to that which had been active throughout most of the Cretaceous placed the Greater Antilles island arc in a vice-like situation. On the northside of the arc was the newly developed

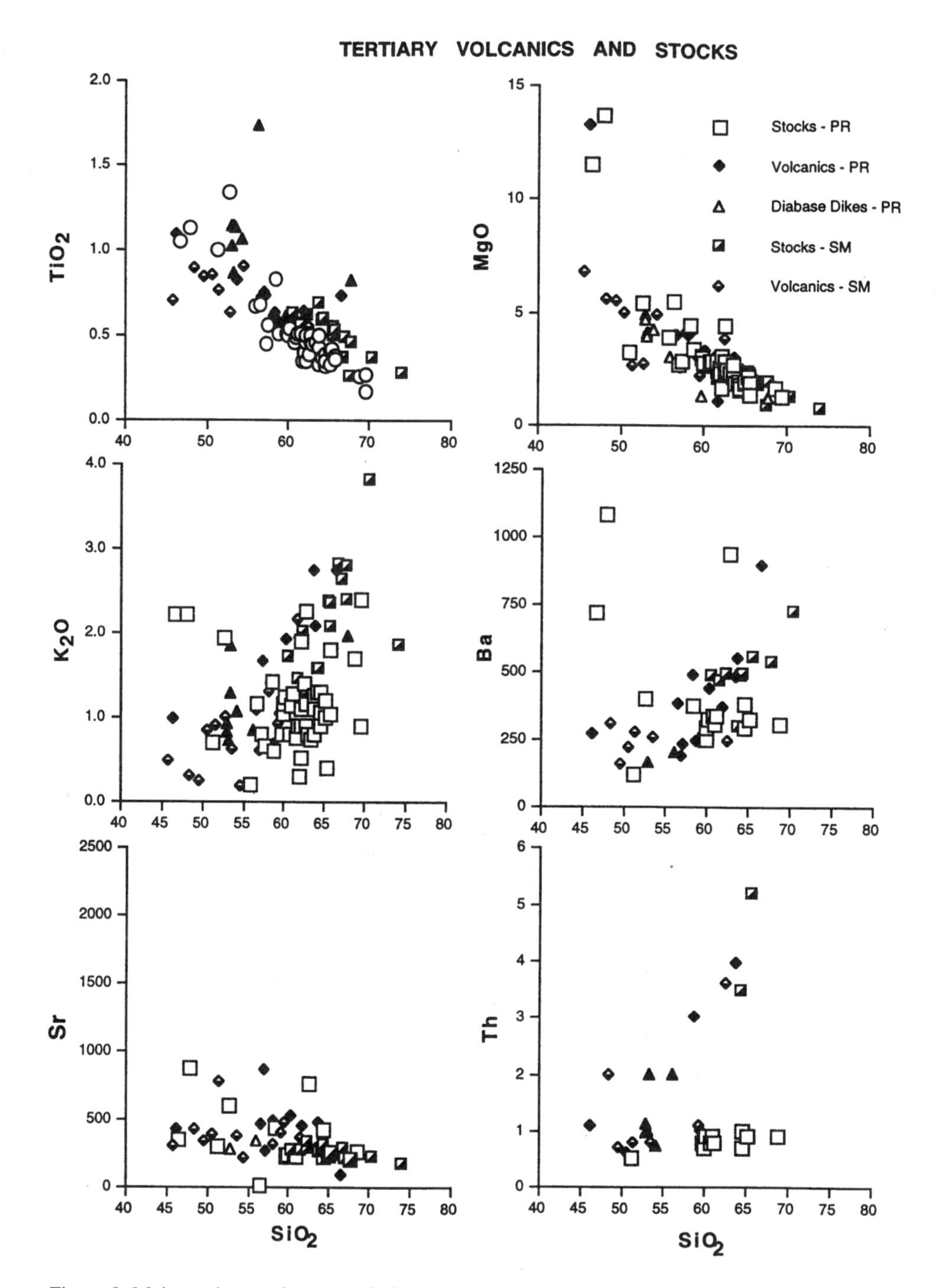

Figure 8. Major and trace element variations compared with SiO_2 for Tertiary stocks and associated volcanic rocks. Major elements in weight percent, trace elements in parts per million. (Data sources: Table 4; Davidson et al., 1993: T. W. Donnelly, unpublished data; W. T. Jolly, unpublished data; Kesler and Sutter, 1979; Schellekens, 1993).

active subduction zone, and on the southside was the rigid slab of the old subduction system (Fig. 14). Such a situation is thought to have caused a downbuckling of the island arc crust, which must have already been thickened by underplating from previous igneous activity. Evidence suggests that throughout the Upper Cretaceous and Lower Tertiary Puerto Rico had a relatively high geothermal gradient (Jolly, 1970; Cho, 1991; Larue, 1991; Smith et al., 1991), so that downbuckling of the island arc crust must have caused partial melting of the lower crust to produce dioritic-granodioritic melts (Beard and Lofgren, 1991). The lower crust beneath the Greater Antilles island arc would probably be composed of metamorphosed oceanic crust and products of the initial island arc.

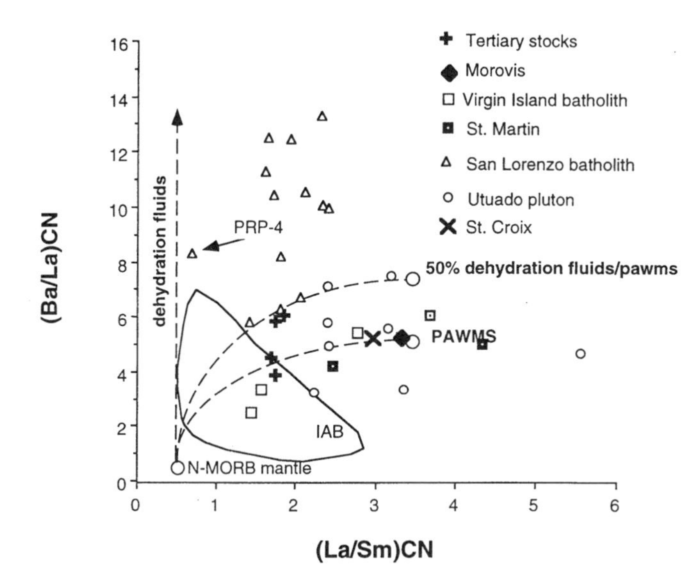

Figure 9. Chondrite-normalized Ba/La versus La/Sm data for stocks and batholiths from the northeast Caribbean. Field of IAB (Island Arc Basalt) after Arculus and Powell (1986). PAWMS (Pacific Authigenic Weighted Mean Sediment) after Hole et al. (1984). Mixing curves between N-MORB mantle and PAWMS, N-MORB mantle and 50% mixing of dehydration component and PAWMS, and N-MORB mantle and dehydration products from subducted slab after Hole et al. (1984) and Defant et al. (1991).

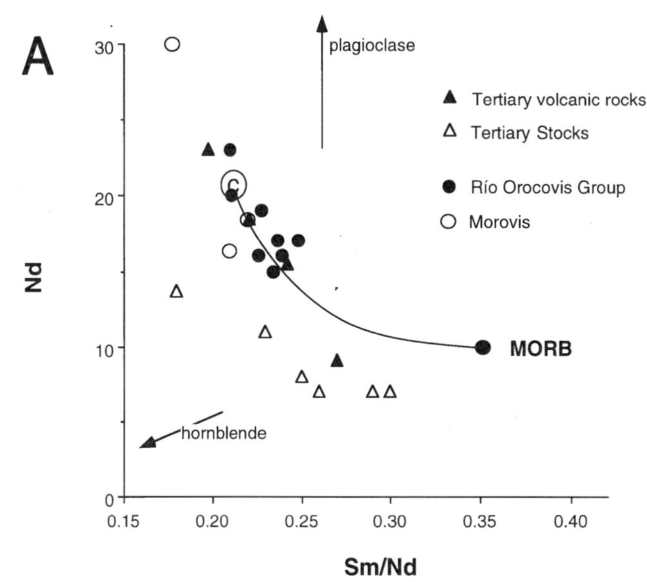

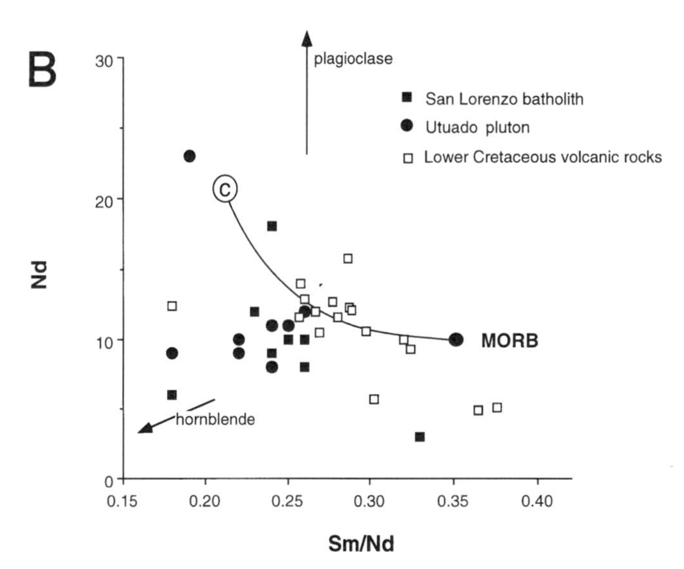

Figure 10. Nd against Sm/Nd for plutonic rocks from the NE Caribbean. Vectors are shown for directions of fractional crystallization of plagioclase and hornblende. Curve between MORB and C (crust) is for 50% addition of crust to a parental MORB source. Adapted from Davidson (1987). *A*, Cretaceous and Tertiary stocks and their associated volcanic rocks. *B*, San Lorenzo and Utuado batholiths and Lower Cretaceous volcanic rocks from Puerto Rico.

For Puerto Rico these early island arc products would probably have a composition similar to that shown by the Lower Cretaceous volcanics. As has been suggested from Figure 10*B* partial melting of such a composition could generate the magmas of an appropriate composition to form the San Lorenzo and Utuado batholiths. In addition, magma generated by partial melting of the mantle above the new subduction zone would not be able to penetrate this partially molten zone and would be ponded in the lower crust. This situation would generate further melting that would also produce magmas of generally intermediate composition (Huppert and Sparks, 1988). These magmas could then be intruded into the upper crust probably along shear zones produced by the downbuckling of the arc (Hutton and Reavy, 1992) as the San Lorenzo and Utuado batholiths. Evidence for shallow emplacement of the batholiths can be seen in the emplacement depths (8 to 10 km) calculated from their amphibole geobarometry (Lidiak, 1991). Similar depths of emplacement are also indicated for the Cretaceous and Tertiary stocks of Puerto Rico (Lidiak, 1991). Contemporaneously with these intrusions the upper crustal rocks were significantly folded and faulted, and the central part of Puerto Rico was uplifted (Mattson, 1966; Glover, 1971; Jolly et al., Chapter 1, this volume) to produce during the Maastrichtian a second major tectonic break (Fig. 2) (Jolly et al., Chapter 1, this volume).

By the Eocene, Puerto Rico was no longer in a transpressive regime as the old slab had been absorbed by the asthenosphere and magma generation now only occurred in the mantle wedge above the southward-dipping subduction zone (Fig. 15). Volcanic centers associated with this subduction are now preserved as domes and stocks, with their associated volcanic rocks in a zone across north-central Puerto Rico. Ar-Ar dates (Table 1) indicate that the initial intrusion of the Virgin Islands batholith also occurred at this time.

The continued northward migration of the Greater Antilles island arc caused the collision of the Cuban part of the arc with the Bahamas during the Paleocene-Eocene (Pindell and Barrett, 1990), and Hispaniola during the latest Eocene–earliest Oligocene (Joyce, 1991). This latter collision is thought to have caused

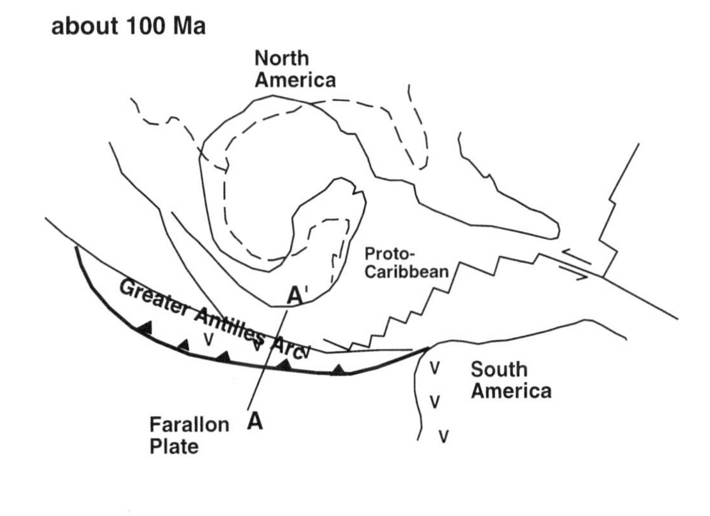

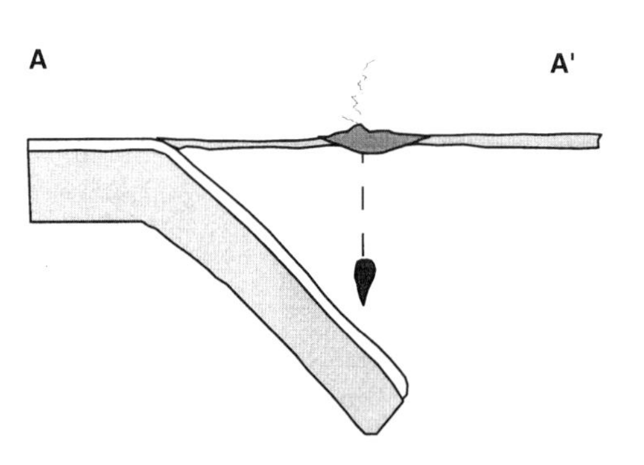

Figure 11. Schematic tectonic reconstruction of the Caribbean at about 100 Ma B.P. (after Pindell and Barrett, 1990). Cross section A–A′ across Early Cretaceous volcanic arc in Puerto Rico.

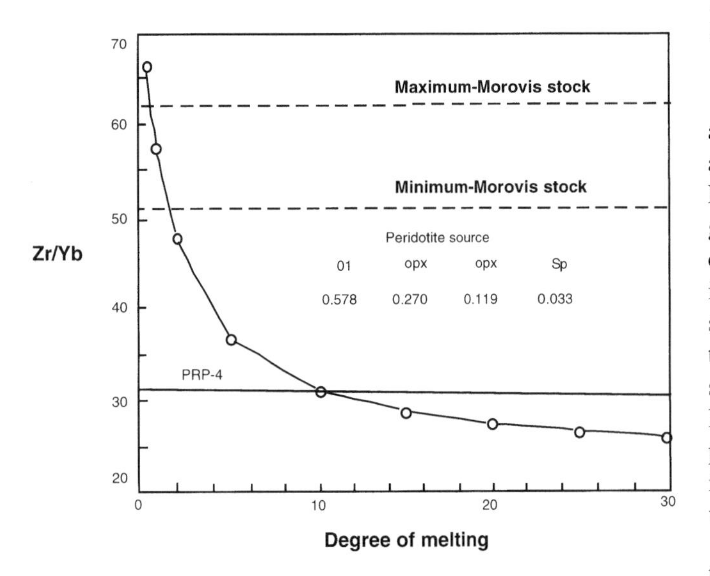

Figure 12. Relative degrees of melting for PRP-4 and Morovis stock calculated using Zr/Yb ratios for spinel peridotite. Original calculations by Jolly, written communication, 1995.

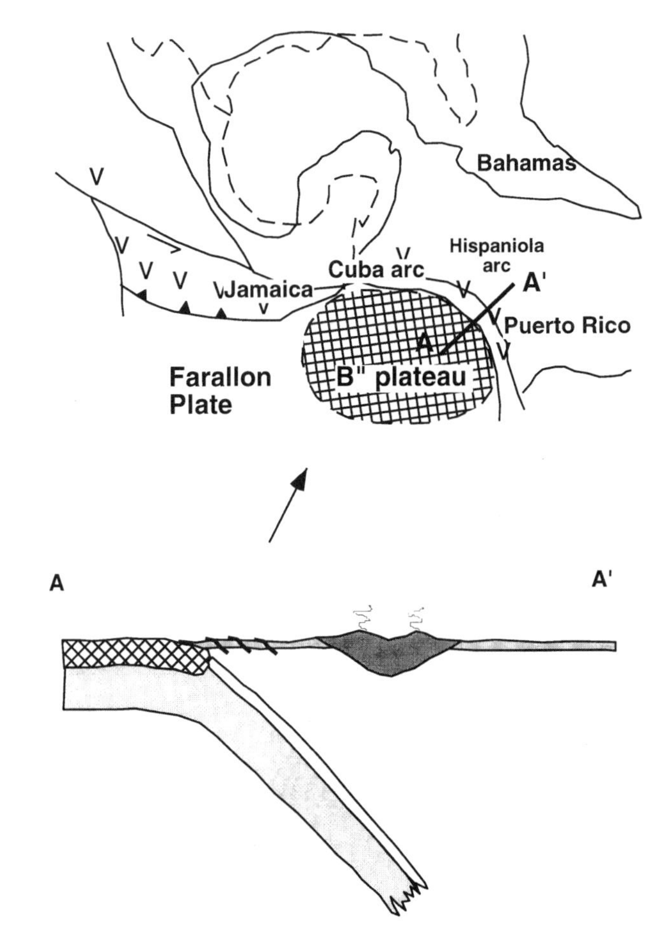

Figure 13. Schematic tectonic reconstruction of the Caribbean at about 85 Ma B.P. (after Pindell and Barrett, 1990). Cross section A–A′ across Santonian volcanic arc in Puerto Rico.

a shift in the direction of subduction from essentially north-south, as it had been during the latest Cretaceous and most of the Eocene, to east-west. Such a shift would have caused the convergence under the Puerto Rico–Virgin Islands segment of the arc to change from perpendicular to oblique, thus creating space for the intrusion of a large body of magma (Glazner, 1991) now represented by the Virgin Islands batholith. As has been already noted, the main phase of the Virgin Islands batholith is geochemically similar in composition to the Eocene igneous rocks of Puerto Rico, suggesting that both were probably formed by a similar process. The different modes of emplacement of these two suites is therefore thought to be solely related to the change in the convergence direction from perpendicular to oblique.

With this change in convergence direction, subduction became east-verging and the main locus of magma generation shifted from the Greater Antilles arc to the Lesser Antilles arc (Fig. 16). Tertiary igneous activity along this subduction zone pro-

about 73 - 58 Ma

Bahamas
Cayman Trough
A'
A
B" Plateau

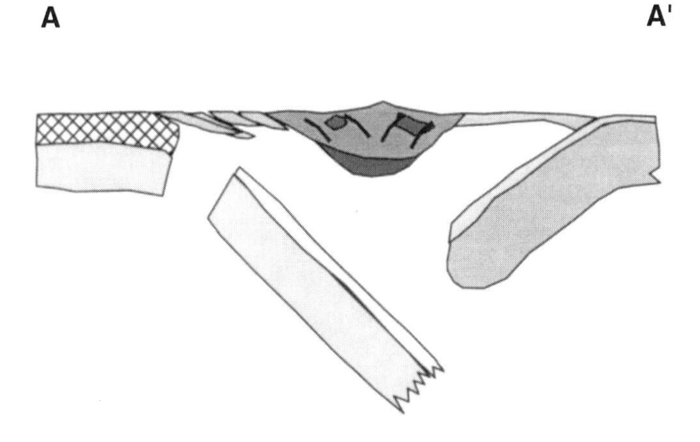

Figure 14. Schematic tectonic reconstruction of the Caribbean from about 73 to 58 Ma B.P. (after Pindell and Barrett, 1990). Cross section A–A′ across Puerto Rico.

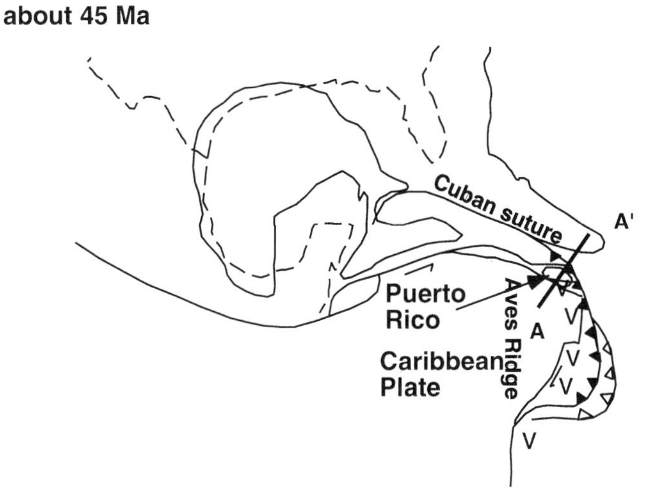

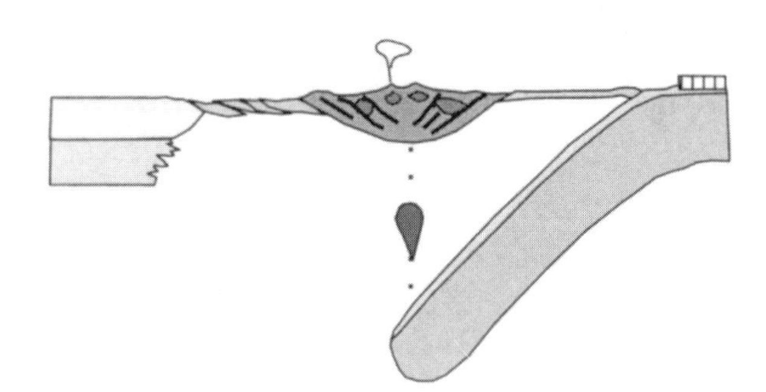

Figure 15. Schematic tectonic reconstruction of the Caribbean at about 45 Ma B.P. (after Pindell and Barrett, 1990). Cross section A–A′ across Eocene volcanic arc in Puerto Rico.

duced arcs of Eo-Oligocene and Miocene age (Wadge, 1986), which are now exposed on the islands of St. Martin, St. Barthélémy, and Antigua, which form part of the Limestone Caribbees. Small intrusions also occurred in the northern Virgin Islands during the Miocene (Kesler and Sutter, 1979). If this latter activity is associated with Lesser Antillean magmatism, then the northern Virgin Islands could represent the northern extension of the Limestone Caribbee arc. Currently the two areas are separated by a major strike-slip fault, the Anegada fault (Masson and Scanlon, 1991). Reconstruction of the Miocene Lesser Antilles arc by moving the Limestone Caribbees back along this fault also causes the St. Croix terrane to fall at the south end of the belt containing the Upper Cretaceous Yauco Formation. A comparison of the stratigraphy and lithology of these Late Cretaceous rocks from both St. Croix and Puerto Rico suggests that they may be related (J. Joyce, personal communication, 1996). This suggestion is supported by a similarity in the composition of the Fountain stock (Table 5) and the volcanic rocks of the Yauco Formation (Schellekens, 1993, this volume). Based on these data it is suggested that the St. Croix terrane could represent an extension of the Yauco basin that has subsequently been tectonically displaced.

Choking of the subduction zone of the Limestone Caribbees during the early Miocene by the attempted subduction of a buoyant aseismic ridge, and the subsequent migration of the zone of magma generation to the west has been suggested as an explanation for the formation of the currently active northern Volcanic Caribbees (Bouysse and Westercamp, 1990).

SUMMARY

The occurrence of volcanism, intrusion of small stocks, and the emplacement of large batholiths in the northeastern Caribbean island arc systems can be correlated with local tectonic conditions governing subduction and magma generation. During the first stage of south-facing island arcs during most of the Cre-

about 27 Ma

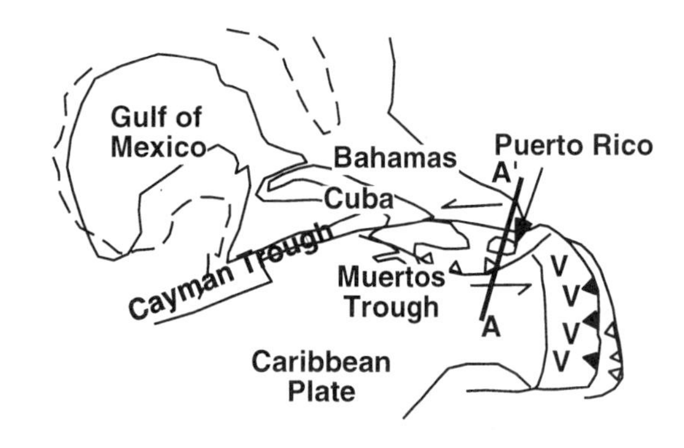

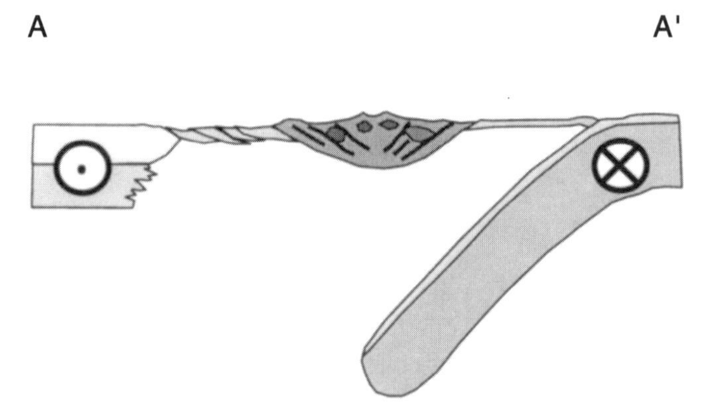

Figure 16. Schematic tectonic reconstruction of the Caribbean at about 27 Ma B.P. (after Pindell and Barrett, 1990).

taceous, volcanism with intrusion of spatially and geochemically associated plutons prevailed. Collision of the oceanic plateau of the Caribbean Cretaceous Basalt Province decelerated and stopped the northward-dipping subduction and associated volcanism, and caused the subduction direction to flip. The resulting vice-like position of the arc caused the island arc crust, already thickened by underplating, to be downwarped, resulting in large-scale melting of the lower crust, which prevented the rise of subduction generated magmas, the ponding of which produced further melting. Flower structures in the upper crust created space for the emplacement of large batholiths. Continued subduction in the lower Tertiary under a north-facing arc again produced island arc magmas, resulting in volcanism with associated small plutons. Collision of this arc with the Bahamas platform changed the vergence of this arc toward the east. Resulting left-lateral strike-slip faulting in the eastern end of the arc created space for the emplacement of the Virgin Islands batholith. Continuing westward, subduction produced volcanic rocks and associated small stocks of the Limestone Caribbee arcs. Attempted subduction of an aseismic ridge in the Miocene terminated magmatism in the Limestone Caribbees and caused a shift of the magmatic arc westward to form the Volcanic Caribbees.

ACKNOWLEDGMENTS

This research was supported by Grants EAR 77–17064, RII 88–02961, and HRD 93–53549 from the National Science Foundation, the University of Puerto Rico, and the Puerto Rico Electrical Power Authority. Thanks are extended to B. Gunn and M. J. Roobol for cooperation with some of the field work, and G. Mattioli for many useful suggestions.

REFERENCES CITED

Andreieff, P., Westercamp, D., Garrabé, F., Bonneton, J. R., and Dagain, J., 1988, Stratigraphie de l'île de Saint-Martin: Geologie de la France, n. 2–3, p. 71–88.

Arculus, R. J., and Powell, R., 1986, Source component mixing in the regions of arc magma generation: Journal of Geophysical Research, v. 91, p. 5913–5926.

Barabas, A. H., 1982, Potassium-argon dating of magmatic events and hydrothermal activity associated with porphyry copper mineralization in west central Puerto Rico: Economic Geology, v. 77 p. 109–126.

Beard, J. S., and Lofgren, G. E., 1991, Dehydration melting and water-saturated melting of basaltic and andesitic greenstones and amphibolites: Journal of Petrology, v. 32, p. 365–401.

Berryhill, H. L., Jr., 1965, Geology of the Ciales quadrangle, Puerto Rico: U.S. Geological Survey Bulletin 1184, 116 p.

Berryhill, H. L., Jr., and Glover, L., 3rd, 1960, Geology of the Cayey quadrangle, Puerto Rico: U.S. Geological Survey Miscellaneous Geologic Investigations Map I–319, scale 1:20,000.

Bouysse, P., and Westercamp, D., 1990, Subduction of Atlantic aseismic ridges and late Cenozoic evolution of the Lesser Antilles island arc: Tectonophysics, v. 175, p. 349–380.

Bouysse, P., Andreieff, P. and Westercamp, D., 1980, Evolution of the Lesser Antilles island arc; new data from the submarine geology: Transactions 9th Caribbean Geological Conference, p. 75–88.

Briggs, R. P., and Gelabert, P. A., 1962, Preliminary report of the geology of the Barranquitas quadrangle, Puerto Rico: U.S. Geological Survey Miscellaneous Geologic Investigations Map I-336, scale 1:20,000.

Broedel, C. H., 1961, Preliminary geologic map showing iron and copper prospects in the Juncos quadrangle, Puerto Rico: U.S. Geological Survey Miscellaneous Geologic Investigations Map I-326, scale 1:20,000.

Burke, K., 1988, Tectonic evolution of the Caribbean: Annual Reviews of Earth and Planetary Sciences, v. 16, p. 201–230.

Burke, K., Fox, P. J., and Sengör, A. M. C., 1978, Buoyant ocean floor and the evolution of the Caribbean: Journal of Geophysical Research, v. 83, p. 3949–3954.

Byrne, D. B., Suarez, G., and McCann, W. R., 1985, Muertos Trough subduction—Microplate tectonics in the northern Caribbean: Nature, v. 317, p. 420–421.

Chen, J. C., 1967, Petrological and chemical studies of Utuado pluton, Puerto Rico: Acta Geologica Taiwanica, v. 13, p. 21–41.

Cho, M., 1991, Zeolite to prehnite-pumpellyite facies metamorphism in the Toa Baja drill hole, Puerto Rico: Geophysical Research Letters, v. 18, p. 525–528.

Christman, R. A., 1953, Geology of St. Bartholemew, St. Martin, and Anguilla, Lesser Antilles: Geological Society of America Bulletin, v. 64, p. 65–96.

Cox, D. P., 1985, Geology of the Tanamá and Helecho Porphyry copper deposits and vicinity, Puerto Rico: U.S. Geological Survey Professional Paper 1327, 59 p.

Cox, D. P., Marvin, R. F., M'Gonigle, J. W., McIntyre, D. H., and Rogers, C. L., 1977, Potassium-argon geochronology of some metamorphic, igneous, and hydrothermal events in Puerto Rico and the Virgin Islands: U.S. Geological Survey Journal of Research, v. 5, p. 689–703.

Dagain, J., Andreieff, P., Westercamp, D., Bouysse, P., and Garrabé, F., 1989, Saint Martin–Carte Géologique a 1/50,000 et notice explicative: Bureau de Recherches Géologiques et Minieres, 1 sheet and 59 p.

Davidson, J. P., 1987, Isotopic and trace element constraints on the petrogenesis of subduction-related lavas from Martinique, Lesser Antilles: Journal of Geophysical Research, v. 91, 5943–5962.

Davidson, J. P., Boghossian, N. D., and Wilson, M., 1993, The geochemistry of the igneous rock suite of St. Martin, northern Lesser Antilles: Journal of Petrology, v. 34, p. 839–866.

Defant, M. J., Maury, R. C., Ripley, E. M., Feigenson, M. D., and Jacques, D., 1991, An example of island-arc petrogenesis: Geochemistry and petrology of the southern Luzon arc, Philippines: Journal of Petrology, v. 32, p. 455–500.

Dengo, G., and Case, J. E., 1990, The Caribbean region: Boulder, Colorado, Geological Society of America, The Geology of North America, v. H, 528 p.

Donnelly, T. W., 1966, Geology of St. Thomas and St. John, U.S. Virgin Islands, *in* Hess, H. H., ed., Caribbean geological investigations: Geological Society of America Memoir 98, p. 85-176.

Donnelly, T. W., and Rogers, J. J. W., 1980, Igneous series in island arcs: the northeastern Caribbean compared with worldwide island-arc assemblages: Bulletin Volcanologique, v. 43, p. 347–382.

Donnelly, T. W., and 10 others, 1990, History and tectonic setting of Caribbean magmatism, *in* Dengo, G., and Case, J. E., eds., The Caribbean region: Boulder, Colorado, Geological Society of America, The Geology of North America, v. H, p. 339–374.

Duncan R. A., and Donnelly, T. W., 1994, The Caribbean Basalt Province: an oceanic LIP: Eos (Transactions, American Geophysical Union) v. 75, p. 594.

Ghosh, N., Hall, S. A., Casey, J. F. and Burke, K., 1994, Magnetic stripes of the Caribbean ocean floor: formation at the Farallon-Phoenix-Pacific triple junction: Eos (Transactions, American Geophysical Union), v. 75, p. 594.

Glazner, A. F., 1991, Plutonism, oblique subduction, and continental growth: an example from the Mesozoic of California: Geology, v. 19, p. 784–786.

Glover, L., 3rd, 1971, Geology of the Coamo area, Puerto Rico and its relation to the volcanic arc-trench association: U.S. Geological Survey Professional Paper 636, 102 p.

Hanson, G. N., 1980, Rare earth elements in petrogenetic studies of igneous systems: Annual Reviews of Earth and Planetary Sciences, v. 8, p. 371–406.

Helsley, C. E., 1971, Summary of the geology of the British Virgin Islands: Transactions 5th Caribbean Geological Conference, p. 69–73.

Hole, M. J., Saunders, A. D., Marriner, G. F., and Tarney, J., 1984, Subduction of pelagic sediments: implications for the origin of Ce anomalous basalts from the Mariana Island Arc: Journal of the Geological Society of London, v. 141, p. 453–472.

Huppert, H. E. , and Sparks, R. S. J., 1988, The generation of granitic magmas by intrusion of basalt into continental crust: Journal of Petrology, v. 29, p. 599–624.

Hutton, D. H. W., and Reavy, R. J., 1992, Strike-slip tectonics and granite petrogenesis: Tectonics, v. 11, p. 960–967.

Ila, P., and Frey, F., 1984, Utilization of neutron activation analysis in the study of geologic material, *in* Harling, O., ed., Use in development of low and medium flux research reactors: Atomkern Energie Kerntechnik, v. 44 suppl., p.710–716.

Jolly, W. T., 1970, Zeolite and prehenite-pumpellyite facies in south central Puerto Rico: Contributions to Mineralogy and Petrology, v. 27, p. 204–224.

Joyce, J., 1991, Blueschist metamorphism and deformation on the Samana Peninsula—A record of subduction and collision in the Greater Antilles, *in* Mann, P., Draper, G., and Lewis, J. F., eds., Geologic and tectonic development of the North America–Caribbean plate boundary in Hispaniola: Geological Society of America Special Paper 262, p. 47–76.

Joyce, J., and Aronson, J., 1987, K-Ar ages for blueschist metamorphism on the Samana Peninsula, Dominican Republic: Transactions, 10th Caribbean Geological Conference, p. 454–458.

Kay, R. W., 1980, Volcanic arc magmas: implications of melting-mixing model for element recycling in the crust-upper mantle system: Journal of Geology , v. 88, p. 497–522.

Kesler, S. E., 1978, Evolution of porphyry copper mineralization in an oceanic island arc: Panama—A discussion: Economic Geology, v. 73, p. 982–985.

Kesler, S. E. and Sutter, J. F., 1979, Compositional evolution of intrusive rocks in the eastern Greater Antilles island arc: Geology, v. 7, p. 197–200.

Krushensky, R. D. and Curet, A. F., 1984, Geologic map of the Monte Guilarte quadrangle, Puerto Rico: U.S. Geologic Survey Miscellaneous Geologic Investigations Map I–1556, scale 1:20,000.

Krushensky, R. D., and Monroe, W. H., 1975, Geologic map of the Ponce quadrangle, Puerto Rico: U.S. Geological Survey Miscellaneous Geologic Investigations Map I–863, scale 1:20,000.

Krushensky, R. D., and Monroe, W. H., 1978, Geologic map of the Peñuelas and Punta Cucharra quadrangles, Puerto Rico: U.S. Geological Survey Miscellaneous Geologic Investigations Map I–1142, scale 1:20,000.

Krushensky, R. D., and Monroe, W. H., 1979, Geologic map of the Yauco and Punta Verraco quadrangles, Puerto Rico: U.S. Geological Survey Miscellaneous Geologic Investigations Map I–1147, scale 1:20,000.

Larue, D. K., 1991, The Toa Baja drilling project and current studies in Puerto Rican geology: introduction and summary: Geophysical Research Letters, v. 18, p. 493–496.

Lidiak, E. G., 1991, Depth of emplacement of granitoid plutonic rocks in the eastern Greater Antilles Island arc: Transactions, 12th Caribbean Geological Conference, p. 259–267.

Longshore, J. D., 1965, Chemical and mineralogical variations in the Virgin Island Batholith and its associated wall rocks [Ph.D. thesis]: Houston, Texas, Rice University, 94 p.

Masson, D. G., and Scanlon, K. M., 1991, The neotectonic setting of Puerto Rico: Geological Society of America Bulletin, v. 103, p. 144–154.

Mattson, P. H., 1960, Geology of the Mayaguez area, Puerto Rico: Geological Society of America Bulletin, v. 71, p. 319–362.

Mattson, P. H., 1966, Geological characteristics of Puerto Rico, *in* Poole, W. H., ed., Continental margins and island arcs, Canada Geological Survey Paper, v. 66–15, p. 49–54.

Mattson, P. H., 1968a, Geologic map of the Adjuntas quadrangle, Puerto Rico: U.S. Geological Survey Miscellaneous Geologic Investigations Map I–519, scale 1:20,000.

Mattson, P. H., 1968b, Geologic map of the Jayuya quadrangle, Puerto Rico: U.S. Geological Survey Miscellaneous Geologic Investigations Map I–520, scale 1:20,000.

Mattson, P. H., 1973, Middle Cretaceous nappe structures in Puerto Rican ophiolites and their relation to the tectonic history of the Greater Antilles: Geological Society of America Bulletin, v. 84, p. 21–38.

M'Gonigle, J. W., 1978, Geologic map of the Humacao quadrangle, Puerto Rico: U.S. Geological Survey Miscellaneous Geologic Investigations Map I–1070, scale 1:20,000.

Montgomery, H. M., Pessagno, E. A., Jr., Lewis, J. F., and Schellekens, J. H., 1994, Paleogeography of Jurassic fragments in the Caribbean: Tectonics, v. 13, p. 725–732.

Nagle, F., Stipp, J. J., and Fisher, D. E., 1976, K-Ar geochronology of the limestone Caribbees and Martinique, Lesser Antilles, West Indies: Earth and Planetary Science Letters, v. 29, p. 401–412.

Nelson, A. E., 1967, Geologic map of the Utuado quadrangle, Puerto Rico: U.S. Geological Survey Miscellaneous Geologic Investigations Map I–480, scale 1:20,000.

Nelson, A. E. , 1968, Intrusive rocks of north-central Puerto Rico: U.S. Geological Survey Professional Paper 600–B, p. B16–B20.

Nelson, A. E., and Tobisch, O. T., 1968, Geologic map of the Bayaney quadrangle, Puerto Rico: U.S. Geological Survey Miscellaneous Geologic Investigations Map I–525, scale 1:20,000.

Pessagno, E. A., Jr., 1976, Middle Cretaceous biostratigraphy of the Antillean-Caribbean and eastern Mexico region: Musée Histoire Naturelle de Nice, v. 4, p. 176–182.

Pindell, J. L., and Barrett, S. F., 1990, Geological evolution of the Caribbean region: a plate tectonic perspective, *in* Dengo, G. and Case, J. E., eds., The Caribbean region: Boulder, Colorado, Geological Society of America, The Geology of North America, v. H, p. 405–432.

Rogers, C. L., 1977, Geologic map of the Punta Guayanés quadrangle, southeastern Puerto Rico: U.S. Geological Survey Miscellaneous Geologic Investigations Map I–998, scale 1:20,000.

Rogers, C. L., 1979, Geologic map of the Caguas quadrangle: U.S. Geological Survey Miscellaneous Geologic Investigations Map I–1152, scale 1:20,000.

Rogers, C. L., Cram, C. M., Pease, M. H., Jr., and Tischler, M. S., 1979, Geologic map of the Yabuacoa and Punta Tuna quadrangles, Puerto Rico: U.S. Geological Survey Miscellaneous Geologic Investigations Map I–1086, scale 1:20,000.

Roobol, M. J. and Smith, A. L., 1989, Volcanic and associated hazards in the Lesser Antilles: IAVCEI Proceedings in Volcanology, v. 1, p. 57–85.

Rose, W. I., Jr., Bornhorst, T. J., and Sivonen, S. J., 1986, Rapid, high quality major and trace element analysis of powdered rock by x-ray fluorescence spectrometry: X-Ray Spectrometry, v. 15, p. 55–60.

Schellekens, J. H., 1991, Late Jurassic to Eocene geochemical evolution of volcanic rocks of Puerto Rico: Geophysical Research Letters, v. 18, p. 553–556.

Schellekens, J. H. 1993, Geochemical evolution of volcanic rocks in Puerto Rico [Ph.D. thesis]: Syracuse, New York, Syracuse University, 289 p.

Schellekens, J. H., Montgomery, H., Joyce, J., and Smith, A. L., 1991, Late Jurassic to Late Cretaceous development of island arc crust in southwestern Puerto Rico: Transactions, 12th Caribbean Geological Conference, p. 268–281.

Seiders, V. M., 1971, Geologic map of the El Yunque quadrangle, Puerto Rico: U.S. Geological Survey Miscellaneous Geologic Investigations Map I–658, scale 1:20,000.

Sinton, C. W., and Duncan, R. A., 1992, Temporal evolution of the Caribbean Cretaceous Basalt Province: results of ^{40}Ar-^{39}Ar dating: Eos (Transactions, American Geophysical Union), v. 73, p. 532.

Smith, A. L., Severin, K., and Larue, D. K., 1991, Stratigraphy, geochemistry, and mineralogy of Eocene rocks from the Toa Baja drillhole: Geophysical Research Letters, v. 18, p. 521–524.

Speed, R., 1989, Tectonic evolution of St. Croix: implications for tectonics of the northeastern Caribbean, *in* Hubbard, D. K., ed., Terrestrial and marine geology of St. Croix, U.S. Virgin Islands, Special Publication, n. 8, West Indies Laboratory, Teague Bay, St. Croix, U.S.Virgin Islands, p. 9–22.

Speed, R., and Joyce, J., 1989, Depositional and structural evolution of Cretaceous strata, St. Croix, *in* Hubbard, D. K., ed., Terrestrial and marine geology of St. Croix, U.S. Virgin Islands, Special Publication, no. 8, West Indies Laboratory, Teague Bay, St. Croix, U.S.Virgin Islands, p. 23–36.

Speed, R. C., Gerhard, L. C., and McKee, E. H., 1979, Ages of deposition, deformation, and intrusion of Cretaceous rocks, eastern St. Croix, Virgin Islands: Geological Society of America Bulletin, v. 90, p. 629–632.

Volckmann, R. P., 1984a, Geologic map of the Cabo Rojo and Parguera quadrangles, southwest Puerto Rico: U.S. Geological Survey Miscellaneous Geologic Investigations Map I–1557, scale 1:20,000.

Volckmann, R. P., 1984b, Geologic map of the San German quadrangle, southwest Puerto Rico: U.S. Geological Survey Miscellaneous Geologic Investigations Map I-1558, scale 1:20,000.

Wadge, G., 1986, The dykes and structural setting of the volcanic front in the Lesser Antilles Island Arc: Bulletin of Volcanology, v. 48, p. 349–372.

Weaver, J. D., 1958, Utuado pluton, Puerto Rico: Geological Society America Bulletin v. 69, p. 1125–1142.

Whetten, J. T., 1966, Geology of St. Croix, Virgin Islands, *in* Hess, H. H., ed., Caribbean geological investigations: Geological Society of America Memoir 98, p. 173–298.

Whetten, J. T., 1974, Field guide to the geology of St. Croix, *in* Multer, H. G., and Gerhard, L. C. , eds., Guidebook to the geology and ecology of some marine and terrestrial environments, St. Croix, U.S. Virgin Islands, West Indies Laboratory Special Publication 5, p. 129–144.

Manuscript Accepted by the Society June 20, 1997

Printed in U.S.A.

Geological Society of America
Special Paper 322
1998

Nd, Sr, and Pb isotopic characterization of Cretaceous and Paleogene volcanic and plutonic island arc rocks from Puerto Rico

Carol D. Frost
Department of Geology and Geophysics, University of Wyoming, Laramie, Wyoming 82071-3006
Johannes H. Schellekens and Alan L. Smith
Department of Geology, University of Puerto Rico, Mayagüez, Puerto Rico 00681-5000

ABSTRACT

Nd, Sr, and Pb isotopic data have been obtained for Cretaceous and Paleogene volcanic, plutonic and volcaniclastic rocks from Puerto Rico, along with data for two plutonic samples from the Virgin Islands and St. Martin. Two samples of Aptian-Albian age belong to the Primitive Island Arc (PIA) association; the remainder, of Late Cretaceous to Paleogene age, belong to the calc-alkaline (CA) island arc association. The PIA association samples have the most radiogenic initial Nd isotope compositions of the suite, confirming other geochemical evidence of their oceanic arc origin. Their Pb isotopic compositions are intermediate between time-correlative rocks on Hispaniola to the west and the Virgin Islands to the east, and suggest that the amount of seafloor sediment incorporated into PIA magmas decreases from west to east.

CA association rocks of Puerto Rico have Nd, Sr, and Pb isotopic characteristics similar to those of the northern Lesser Antilles. Eocene and Oligocene CA association rocks have similar isotopic characteristics to the Cretaceous CA samples, with the exception of volcanic and volcaniclastic rocks from southwestern Puerto Rico, which have Nd and Sr isotopic compositions consistent with the incorporation of a greater amount of continental material into the arc magmas.

The island arc rocks from Puerto Rico analyzed in this study exhibit no dramatic change in isotopic character with age that could be attributed to a change in magma sources related to a reversal in subduction direction. It remains possible that such a reversal took place between the emplacement of the PIA and CA suites in mid-Cretaceous time, but in this case the approach of the Caribbean Cretaceous Basalt Province to the arc cannot have caused the change in subduction polarity.

INTRODUCTION

Puerto Rico, the easternmost of the four largest islands that comprise the Greater Antilles, is an arc terrane that preserves a record of much of the geologic history of the northern Caribbean. This region is tectonically complex, the product of formation and fragmentation of island arcs. The oldest of these were built in an oceanic setting in the Pacific Ocean, and younger segments formed as the arc migrated into the Atlantic Ocean between North and South America. The island arc rocks, which range in age from Early Cretaceous to Eocene, presumably reflect in their geochemical and isotopic compositions the magma sources available at different times during the evolution of this arc terrane. The present study is an Nd, Sr, and Pb isotopic investigation of volcanic and plutonic island arc rocks from Puerto Rico. The isotopic compositions of these rocks are of interest because it is during this time

Frost, C. D., Schellekens, J. H., and Smith, A. L., 1998, Nd, Sr, and Pb isotopic characterization of Cretaceous and Paleogene volcanic and plutonic island arc rocks from Puerto Rico, *in* Lidiak, E. G., and Larue, D. K., eds., Tectonics and Geochemistry of the Northeastern Caribbean: Boulder, Colorado, Geological Society of America Special Paper 322.

period that subduction of Pacific seafloor may have ceased, and the Atlantic Ocean floor began to be consumed. Such a significant tectonic development is expected to result in changes in the relative proportions of mantle and crustal materials incorporated into island arc magmas, which in turn may be recorded by changes in the isotopic compositions of the rocks.

GEOLOGIC BACKGROUND

Island arc rocks of Puerto Rico represent a portion of an island arc system that extends from Cuba eastward to the Virgin Islands, southward along the volcanically active Lesser Antilles, and westward along the northern coast of South America. This island arc complex, referred to by Burke (1988) as the "Great Arc of the Caribbean" was initiated in Early Cretaceous time in the eastern Pacific Ocean and migrated into the Caribbean region in the Late Cretaceous.

Most tectonic interpretations suggest that the Pacific Ocean plate was subducted eastward beneath the early arc (i.e., Mattson, 1979; Pindell and Dewey, 1982; Burke, 1988). Today the active portion of Burke's Great Arc, the Lesser Antilles, is located above a west-facing subduction zone. Evidently, subduction polarity reversed, although the time at which this reversal occurred is the subject of continuing debate (see Jolly et al., Chapter 1, this volume, for a review). Mattson (1979) suggested that the change of subduction polarity coincided with a change in arc magma compositions from tholeiitic to calc-alkaline in mid-Cretaceous time. Jolly et al., (Chapter 3, this volume) found no isotopic or geochemical evidence consistent with a change of subduction polarity in Upper Aptian to Oligocene volanic rocks from Puerto Rico, concluding that a reversal, if it occurred at all, must predate Upper Aptian time. Smith et al., (this volume) have suggested that the reversal may have taken place as late as Maastrictian time, based on a change in style of pluton emplacement that took place in Puerto Rico between Cretaceous and Tertiary periods.

The cause of the hypothesized reversal in subduction polarity has been linked by Mattson (1979) and others (Burke, 1988; Pindell and Barrett, 1990) to a collision between the early Caribbean island arc and an oceanic plateau that developed in the Pacific basin. According to this model, the arc could no longer subduct the buoyant, thickened oceanic floor, and a new subduction zone was initiated on the opposite side of the arc. The oceanic plateau, known as Caribbean Cretaceous Basalt Province, has recently been dated at 88 to 90 Ma (Sinton et al., 1993; Duncan et al., 1994). If this model is correct, then the reversal of subduction polarity must postdate the formation of the plateau.

Donnelly and Rogers (1978) and Donnelly et al. (1990) have recognized a number of tectono-magmatic associations in which they relate the geochemistry of igneous rocks to stages in the evolution of the Caribbean region. The first is a Jurassic-Cretaceous basalt association, which resembles mid–ocean ridge basalt (MORB) and ophiolitic rocks in chemical composition. In Puerto Rico this association is represented by Late Jurassic cherts and amphibolites of the Bermeja Complex, which are interpreted as Pacific ocean floor fragments. Essentially coeval with this MORB association is the Primitive Island Arc (PIA) association, a group of tholeiitic island arc rocks characterized by low incompatible element concentrations, and low rare earth element (REE) abundances with flat patterns (Donnelly et al., 1990; Jolly et al., Chapter 3, this volume; Schellekens, this volume; Smith et al., this volume). The pre-Robles formations of central and eastern Puerto Rico belong to this association, as do the nearby Los Ranchos Formation in the Dominican Republic and Water Island Formation of the Virgin Islands. Donnelly et al. (1990) have speculated that the PIA association represents island arc activity in an entirely oceanic environment, in which subducted altered oceanic crust, perhaps accompanied by a minor amount of sediment, is involved in the formation of parental island arc magmas.

Calc-alkaline magmatism of Late Cretaceous age and younger is found throughout the Caribbean region. Donnelly et al. (1990) subdivided calc-alkaline igneous rocks into pre-Oligocene and post-Oligocene groups in recognition of the changing geographic position of magmatic activity. Calc-alkaline eruptive and intrusive units of Late Cretaceous through Eocene age are found in the Greater Antilles, northern South America, and central America. From Oligocene time to the present, magmatic activity is focused in the Lesser Antilles and central America. The dominant rock types of the calc-alkaline (CA) association are andesite and basalt, with minor rhyolite. Shoshonitic volcanic rocks are common, but low-K units occur as well.

Compared to the PIA series, the calc-alkaline association rocks are enriched in large ion lithophile elements and light REE. The CA rocks have more radiogenic Sr and Pb isotopic compositions than the older PIA series (Donnelly et al., 1971; Cumming and Kesler, 1987; Davidson, 1986, 1987; Davidson et al., 1993; Lebrón and Perfit, 1994). In Puerto Rico, the CA association is well represented and includes intrusive and extrusive units that range in age from Albian to Eocene. Schellekens (1991) identified the geochemical characteristics of the volcanic CA rocks in Puerto Rico as typical of mature arcs, in which considerable amounts of slab-derived material and/or differentiated arc crust are incorporated into arc magmas.

GEOLOGIC SETTING AND SAMPLE SELECTION

Island-wide lithostratigraphic correlations within the volcanic rocks of Puerto Rico are complicated because individual units appear to have had limited original extent and because they have been disrupted by subsequent faulting. Accordingly, the island is divided into three igneous provinces: the southwestern igneous province (SIP), the central igneous province (CIP), and the northeastern igneous province (NIP), based upon differences in stratigraphy, petrology, and geochemistry (Schellekens, 1991). The boundaries of these provinces are marked by major fault zones (Fig. 1).

The SIP contains the Bermeja Complex, the lowermost units of which have been interpreted as Pacific ocean floor fragments belonging to the MORB-like basalt association of Donnelly et al.

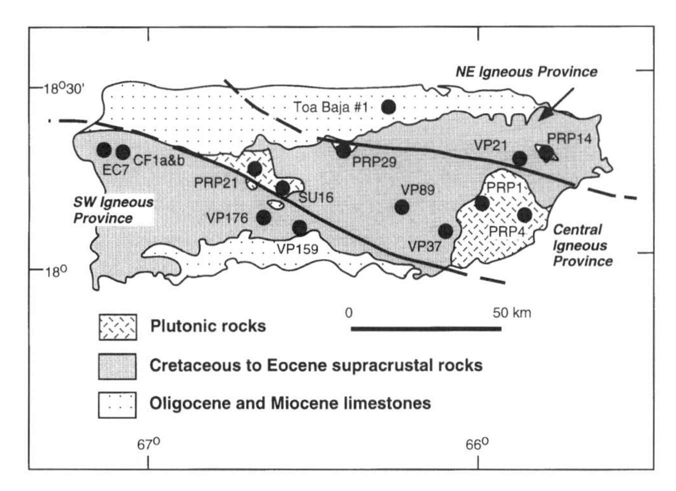

Figure 1. Generalized geologic map of Puerto Rico, showing sample locations, including the site of the Toa Baja drillhole from which samples 2134, 2149, and 3115 were collected.

(1990). Upper parts of the Bermeja Complex represent early island arc products. No samples of this serpentinized and metamorphosed complex are included in this study. Post–Bermeja Complex rocks include volcanic, volcaniclastic, and calcareous rocks, locally intruded by small plutons of Late Cretacous to Eocene age. The youngest rocks in this province are Eocene volcanic rocks, which crop out in a band from the northwest coast to the southcentral part of the island, and which form the boundary with the CIP. Samples from the SIP analyzed as part of this study are all Eocene in age. They include a dacite and an andesite from the Anón Formation (VP159 and VP176, respectively) and a basalt from the Mal Paso Formation (EC7). Also analyzed were two volcaniclastic samples from the Río Culebrinas Formation, which immediately overlies the Mal Paso Formation. CF1a is a fine-grained sandstone and CF1b is a coarse-grained sandstone from a single turbidite Bouma sequence.

The CIP is characterized by extensive exposures of Late Cretaceous plutonic rocks that have intruded a series of Cretaceous volcanic and sedimentary rocks. The oldest of these are the "pre-Robles" formations of volcanic flows, breccias, volcaniclastic sedimentary rocks and minor limestones. Pre-Robles volcanism, which belongs to the Primitive Island Arc (PIA) association of Donnelly et al. (1990), was predominantly submarine, but the younger portions of the association are interbedded with limestones suggesting that these rocks were extruded into increasingly shallow water. The pre-Robles sample in this study, VP 37, is from Formation A. Small tonalite and diorite stocks enclosed by the younger San Lorenzo batholith in the CIP also appear to belong the PIA association. Two of these stocks and enclaves were dated at 109 ± 9 and 100 ± 16 Ma by Cox et al. (1977) using the K-Ar method. A third petrographically similar sample, PRP4, is included in this study. It is geochemically similar to the pre-Robles formations and is interpreted as a plutonic member of the PIA association (Smith et al., this volume).

Overlying the pre-Robles formations are a series of volcanic flows and volcaniclastic rocks known as the Robles–Río Orocovis volcano-stratigraphic association (Schellekens, 1991), composed of submarine volcanic and volcaniclastic rocks and interbedded limestones. This association includes a number of high potassium units. One of these, the Lapa lava, was sampled as part of this study (VP89) and by Lebrón and Perfit (1994) (TD17). The Robles–Río Orocovis sequence is in turn overlain by marine and subaerial volcanic rocks of Santonian to Maastrichtian age.

The two largest plutonic complexes in the CIP, and indeed in Puerto Rico as a whole, are the San Lorenzo batholith in the southeastern corner of the island and the Utuado pluton in west-central Puerto Rico. The San Lorenzo batholith is composed mainly of granodiorite, 73 Ma in age (Cox et al., 1977), and quartz diorites that average 66 Ma in age (Cox et al., 1977). Sample PRP1 is from the granodiorite unit. The Utuado pluton was emplaced at approximately 75 Ma (Smith et al., this volume; Cox et al., 1977). The pluton is dominated by granodiorite (sample PRP21). One of the small bodies of gabbro that are found near the margin of the pluton was also sampled for this study (SU16). The much smaller, 18 km^2, Morovis stock intruded CIP volcanic rocks at 86 Ma (Smith et al., this volume; Cox et al., 1977). Sample PRP29 is a granodiorite sample from this stock.

Igneous and sedimentary rocks of the NIP range in age from Early Cretaceous to Early Tertiary. Sample VP21 is a basalt from the Martín Gonzáles Formation, which is Campanian in age. The Toa Baja drillhole yielded Eocene age samples of lava and volcaniclastic sediments. Analyzed for this study were a zeolite-facies mafic flow recovered from a depth of 949 m (3115 ft), and two volcaniclastic samples from depths of 650 and 655 m (2134 and 2149 ft), respectively, in the drillhole. The Río Blanco stock (sample PRP14) was emplaced into Albian-Cenomanian supracrustal rocks in the NIP at approximately 48 Ma (Cox et al., 1977).

Also included in this study is a 33-Ma granodiorite sample from the Virgin Islands batholith (DL3) on Virgin Gorda and a sample of a 27-Ma quartz diorite stock from St. Martin (SM11), both dated by Smith et al., (this volume).

ANALYTIC METHODS

Sr and Nd isotopic ratios, as well as Rb, Sr, Sm, and Nd concentrations, were determined by thermal ionization mass spectrometry at the University of Wyoming using a VG Sector multiple-collector mass spectrometer. Approximately 75 mg of whole rock powder was dissolved, and the elements of interest extracted using standard ion exchange chromatographic techniques. Normalizing values are $^{86}Sr/^{88}Sr = 0.1194$ and $^{146}Nd/^{142}Nd = 0.7219$. Standard values are $^{87}Sr/^{86}Sr = 0.710246 \pm 0.000023$ (2 standard deviations) for NBS 987 and $^{143}Nd/^{144}Nd = 0.511845 \pm 0.000012$ for La Jolla Nd. Procedural blanks are negligible at less than 100 pg for Nd and Sm, and less than 1 ng for Sr and Rb.

Pb isotopic ratios for plutonic samples were performed at Massachusetts Institute of Technology through Krueger Geochron Laboratories. Pb isotopic ratios for the volcanic rocks were determined at the University of Wyoming (UW). The measured Pb isotopic ratios obtained at UW were corrected by a mass fractionation factor of 0.1% per amu as determined by runs of NBS 981. Errors for all Pb data do not exceed 0.10% on the $^{206}Pb/^{204}Pb$ ratio, 0.15% on the $^{207}Pb/^{204}Pb$ ratio, and 0.19% on the $^{208}Pb/^{204}Pb$ ratio, all sources of error included. Procedural blanks do not exceed 30 pg, and were negligible compared to the typical sample size (>20 ng).

ISOTOPIC RESULTS

Sr, Nd, and Pb isotopic results have been obtained for seven volcanic rock samples, eight plutonic rock samples, and four volcaniclastic sediments (Tables 1 and 2). Included in this compilation are Sr and Nd isotopic data for six samples previously reported in Frost and Schellekens (1991). One of these samples, EC-7, had a comparatively high initial Sr ratio, which was explained by the presence of calcite-filled amygdules. A second whole rock powder of this sample was prepared from rock chips that did not contain amygdules, and the Sr isotopic ratio was reanalyzed. Sr and Rb concentrations were obtained on the amygdule-free powder by x-ray fluorescence, and these results along with the recalculated initial ratio are given in Table 1. Although the Sr concentration and initial Sr isotopic ratio of the amygdule-free powder are lower than the original value (433 ppm and 0.70466 versus 537 ppm and 0.70571), it is still higher than other Eocene lavas, and may indicate that most, but not all, secondary calcite was avoided.

Rb-Sr and Sm-Nd isotopic data

Rb contents of volcanic rocks vary from 2 to 49 ppm, and are highest in rocks with highest SiO_2 and K_2O contents. Sr ranges from 240 to 780 ppm, and Rb/Sr ratios are less than 0.14. Rb contents of plutonic rocks extend to higher concentrations, 2 to 115 ppm, as do Sr concentrations (192 to 1023 ppm). The Rb/Sr ratios of the plutonic samples are between 0.01 and 0.28 and are highest in the most silica-rich samples. Volcaniclastic samples generally have similar Rb and Sr contents to volcanic and plutonic rock samples, although CF1b, a coarse-grained volcaniclastic turbiditic sandstone, has a higher Sr content that may reflect its high plagioclase content. All the rocks analyzed in this study are somewhat altered, as indicated petrographically by sericitized feldspars and chloritized biotite and hornblende, and Rb and Sr concentrations may have been affected by alteration and metamorphism.

Sm and Nd contents vary from 1.38 to 7.61 ppm for Sm and from 3.6 to 30.5 ppm for Nd. $^{147}Sm/^{144}Nd$ ratios range from 0.1147 to 0.1699 with one exception: Early Cretaceous sample PRP4 has a higher ratio of 0.2317. This higher ratio is typical of MORB and oceanic island arc rocks, whereas the bulk of the samples have Sm/Nd ratios typical of most island arcs, values intermediate between average continental crust and MORB.

Initial Sr and Nd isotope ratios (Table 1) are plotted in Figure 2, along with fields for present-day MORB (White et al., 1987), seafloor sediment from the Barbados Ridge and Demerara Plain east of the Lesser Antilles (White et al., 1985), and Lesser Antilles Eocene to Recent volcanic rocks (White and Dupré, 1986; Davidson, 1986, 1987; Davidson et al., 1993). Also shown are initial Nd and Sr for Cretaceous Loma la Vega volcanic rocks from Hispaniola (Lebrón and Perfit, 1994). Initial ratios for all samples are displaced from MORB, indicating the incorporation of some isotopically evolved material, either subducted sediment or arc crust. The Puerto Rico samples fall close to the trend defined by Lesser Antilles volcanic rocks, although none have the very radiogenic Sr and unradiogenic Nd values measured from the southern Lesser Antilles.

The Puerto Rican samples may be divided into three groups based on age and tectono-magmatic association. The Aptian-Albian rocks of the PIA association have the most radiogenic initial ε_{Nd} of any samples, consistent with their oceanic arc environment. The intrusive and extrusive rocks of the second group, those of Donnelly's CA association of pre-Eocene age have less radiogenic initial ε_{Nd} of 6.0 to 7.4. The third group, CA association rocks of Eocene to Oligocene age, have initial ε_{Nd} that overlap the older CA rocks, but extend to less radiogenic values as low as 3.0. The Eocene volcaniclastic rocks include the least radiogenic Nd isotopic compositions of the suite, with ε_{Nd} of 6.5 to –0.5. Initial Sr ratios for both the PIA and CA association volcanic and plutonic rocks fall between 0.7034 and 0.7042, except for sample EC-7, which, as described above, may contain calcite with more radiogenic Sr. With the exception of sample EC-7, the range in initial Sr ratios is identical to that documented by Jolly et al. (Chapter 3, this volume).

Pb isotopic results

Present-day Pb isotopic ratios, obtained on the same samples as were analyzed for Sr and Nd isotope compositions, are shown in Figure 3A, B. The data from Puerto Rico and adjacent islands are compared with data from the Lesser Antilles (Davidson, 1986, 1987; White and Dupré, 1986); Atlantic seafloor sediment (White et al., 1985); MORB (White et al., 1987); the Water Island Formation of the Virgin Islands (Donnelly et al., 1971); and the Los Ranchos Formation (Cumming and Kesler, 1987) and Loma la Vega volcanic rocks (Lebrón and Perfit, 1994) of Hispaniola. Both on diagrams of $^{208}Pb/^{204}Pb$ versus $^{206}Pb/^{204}Pb$ and $^{207}Pb/^{204}Pb$ versus $^{206}Pb/^{204}Pb$, the Puerto Rican data are intermediate between the field for Water Island PIA and the central and southern Lesser Antilles, and overlap the Los Ranchos and northern Lesser Antilles fields.

More detailed interpretation of the present-day Pb isotope data requires consideration of radiogenic growth subsequent to crystallization or deposition. U, Th, and Pb concentrations are available for very few of the samples included in Figures 3A, B, and thus it is not possible to correct many data points to their initial compositions. However, we can calculate the slope of the line defined by radiogenic growth between the time of formation and the present day. Both present-day and initial values lie on

TABLE 1. Rb–Sr AND Sm–Nd ISOTOPIC DATA FOR VOLCANIC, VOLCANICLASTIC, AND PLUTONIC ROCKS OF PUERTO RICO AND ADJACENT ISLANDS

Sample	Description	Age (Ma)	SiO_2	Rb (ppm)	Sr (ppm)	$^{87}Rb/^{86}Sr$	$^{87}Sr/^{86}Sr$	I_{Sr}	Sm (ppm)	Nd (ppm)	$^{147}Sm/^{144}Nd$	$^{143}Nd/^{144}Nd$	I_{Nd}	$\varepsilon_{Nd}^{Initial}$
Eocene volcaniclastic rocks														
2134*	Toa Baja core	50	nd	27.67	219.4	0.3648	0.70580	0.70554	2.4	8.638	0.16802	0.512737	0.512682	2.11
2149*	Toa Baja core	50	52.89	27.53	174.5	0.4563	0.70604	0.70571	2.285	8.283	0.16682	0.512606	0.512551	-0.45
CF1a	Río Culebrinas Fm	50	52.89	12.39	348.5	0.1028	0.70474	0.70467	3.434	14.39	0.14434	0.512954	0.512907	6.5
CF1b	Río Culebrinas Fm	50	58.64	13.92	1,290	0.0315	0.70524	0.70522	3.293	13.64	0.14604	0.512957	0.512909	6.54
CA association volcanic and plutonic rocks														
SM11	St. Martin stock	27	67.8	56.52	208.5	0.7838	0.70429	0.70399	2.666	10.69	0.15089	0.512978	0.512952	6.8
DL3	Virgin I. batholith	33	68.86	58.36	205.9	0.8196	0.70443	0.70405	4.86	21.36	0.13761	0.513001	0.512972	7.34
PRP14	Río Blanco stock	48	60.07	21.28	242.8	0.2534	0.70409	0.70392	1.863	6.999	0.16101	0.512999	0.512948	7.25
3115*	Toa Baja basalt	50	55.38	2.716	242.5	0.0324	0.70400	0.70398	7.447	27.86	0.16166	0.512987	0.512934	7.02
EC7*	Mal Paso Fm	50	45.81	8	433	0.053	0.70470	0.70466	3.316	13.05	0.15367	0.512953	0.512903	6.42
VP159*	Anón Fm	50	63.63	37.89	537.1	0.204	0.70401	0.70387	4.539	23.94	0.11466	0.512877	0.512838	5.17
VP176*	Anón Fm	50	58.36	14.9	426.1	0.1011	0.70403	0.70396	3.781	17.48	0.13081	0.512769	0.512726	2.97
PRP1	S. Lorenzo batholith	73	64.84	36.11	427.1	0.2445	0.70372	0.70346	2.481	10.81	0.13882	0.513008	0.512942	7.76
SU16	Utuado pluton	75	49.46	30.31	1,023	0.0856	0.70350	0.70342	7.612	30.51	0.15087	0.512962	0.512888	6.76
PRP21	Utuado pluton	75	64.61	26.57	752.1	0.1021	0.70367	0.70356	2.661	12.49	0.12888	0.512984	0.512921	7.41
VP21	Martín Gonzalez Fm	85	54.13	30.37	782	0.1123	0.70358	0.70344	3.764	16.04	0.14195	0.512971	0.512892	7.09
PRP29	Morovis stock	86	62.78	114.9	725.9	0.4577	0.70415	0.70358	4.164	20.43	0.12328	0.512906	0.512837	6.03
VP89	Robles Fm	105	52.69	48.72	353.6	0.3985	0.70432	0.70373	3.027	12.72	0.14391	0.512929	0.512830	6.39
PIA association volcanic and plutonic rocks														
PRP4	E. Cretaceous stock	105	53.94	1.951	192.4	0.0293	0.70368	0.70364	1.386	3.619	0.23172	0.513161	0.513002	9.74
VP37	Formation A	115	48.46	2.373	332.3	0.0207	0.70422	0.70419	2.967	10.56	0.16991	0.513054	0.512926	8.51

*Analyses previously published in Frost and Schellenkens, 1991. Errors are 0.2% on the $^{147}Sm/^{144}Nd$ ration, and 1% on the $^{87}Rb/^{86}Sr$ ratio. I_{Sr} and I_{Nd} calculated for the crystallization age. Present-day bulk earth values used in calculating initial ε_{Nd} are $^{143}Nd/^{144}Nd = 0.512638$ and $^{147}Sm/^{144}Nd = 0.19676$.

TABLE 2. Pb ISOTOPE DATA

Sample	Description	Age (Ma)	$^{206}Pb/^{204}Pb$	$^{207}Pb/^{204}Pb$	$^{208}Pb/^{204}Pb$
Eocene volcaniclastic rocks					
2134	Toa Baja core	50	18.672	15.628	38.408
2149	Toa Baja core	50	18.680	15.629	38.420
CF1a	Río Culebrines Fm	50	18.778	15.625	38.468
CF1b	Río Culebrines Fm	50	18.758	15.623	38.483
CA association volcanic and plutonic rocks					
SM11	St. Martin stock	27	18.866	15.638	38.608
DL3	Virgin I. batholith	33	19.220	15.655	38.640
PRP14	Río Blanco stock	48	18.866	15.629	38.586
3115	Toa Baja core	50	18.788	15.576	38.346
EC7	Mal Paso Fm	50	18.913	15.638	38.609
VP159	Anón Fm	50	18.800	15.609	38.486
VP176	Anón Fm	50	18.849	15.643	38.624
PRP1	San Lorenzo batholith	73	18.675	15.540	38.149
SU16	Utuado pluton	75	18.768	15.575	38.374
PRP21	Utuado pluton	75	18.707	15.601	38.353
VP21	Martín Gonzalez Fm	85	18.939	15.581	38.581
PRP29	Morovis stock	86	19.226	15.586	38.773
VP89	Robles Fm	105	19.988	15.725	39.269
PIA association volcanic and plutonic rocks					
PRP4	E. Cretaceous stock	105	18.683	15.579	38.322
VP37	Formation A	115	19.366	15.645	38.757

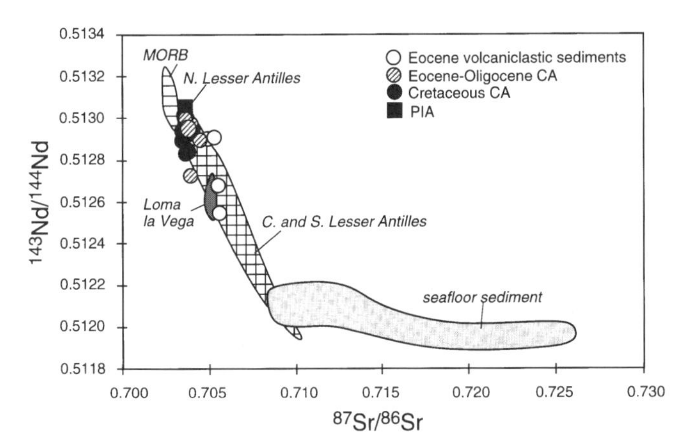

Figure 2. Initial Nd isotope ratios plotted against initial Sr isotope ratios for the data presented in this study. Also shown are fields for MORB, Barbados Ridge–Demerara Plain seafloor sediment, the Lesser Antilles, and initial ratios for Cretaceous Loma la Vega volcanic rocks from Hispaniola. Data from White et al. (1985), White and Dupré (1986), Davidson (1986, 1987), Davidson et al., (1993), and Lebrón and Perfit (1994). The isotopic data for Puerto Rico, Hispaniola, and Lesser Antilles arc rocks fall along mixing curves constructed by White and Dupré (1986, Fig. 9) between depleted mantle and Atlantic seafloor sediment.

this line, and the exact position of the initial values depends on the U/Pb ratio of the sample. Growth lines for samples VP89 (Lapa Lava), VP37 (Fm A), and PRP29 (Morovis) are shown in Figure 3. The shallow slope of these growth lines reflects the relatively low abundance of ^{235}U and the modest increases in the $^{207}Pb/^{204}Pb$ ratio that occur in short time intervals on the order of 100 Ma or less. For example, using a reasonable estimate of $^{238}U/^{204}Pb$ ratio of 16, 100 Ma of radiogenic Pb growth increases the $^{206}Pb/^{204}Pb$ ratio by 0.3, and the $^{207}Pb/^{204}Pb$ ratio by only 0.01. Very little of the variation in $^{207}Pb/^{204}Pb$ exhibited by the samples from Puerto Rico can be accounted for by radiogenic Pb growth, and instead must reflect differences in initial Pb isotopic compositions.

There is no simple relationship between age and Pb isotopic compositions. Among the least radiogenic $^{207}Pb/^{204}Pb$ compositions are samples from the San Lorenzo and Morovis plutons and the Utuado diorite and lava samples VP21 and 3115. These analyses overlap with the $^{207}Pb/^{204}Pb$ ratios from the Water Island Formation, the most mantle-like of the arc rocks of the Greater and Lesser Antilles. The volcaniclastic sediments are among the samples with the highest $^{207}Pb/^{204}Pb$ ratios, which also display comparatively unradiogenic Nd isotope compositions. Other samples with high $^{207}Pb/^{204}Pb$ ratios include VP89, the Lapa lava, the Eocene and Oligocene plutons of St. Martin, the Virgin Islands, and Rio Blanco, and Eocene volcanics EC7 and VP176. These relatively radiogenic compositions are consistent with the incorporation of a isotopically evolved component, such as seafloor sediment.

DISCUSSION

Primitive island arc association

The Primitive Island Arc association probably formed in the eastern Pacific Ocean above a northward- or eastward-dipping subduction zone (Burke, 1988; Pindell and Barrett, 1990; Smith et al., this volume). The chemically and isotopically primitive nature of this association was first identified in the Water Island Formation in the Virgin Islands (Donnelly et al., 1971). Cumming and Kesler (1987) studied Pb isotopic composition of the correlative Los Ranchos Formation in the Dominican Republic. As observed by Cumming and Kesler (1987), the Pb isotopic composition of the PIA association varies from unradiogenic, almost purely MORB-like isotope ratios in the Water Island Formation to more radiogenic Pb isotope ratios that are best explained by incorporation of pelagic sediments. In Los Ranchos, this sedimentary component was well homogenized with the unradiogenic components of the arc lavas, yielding a limited range in $^{207}Pb/^{204}Pb$ ratios for rocks from this formation (Cumming and Kesler, 1987).

On Puerto Rico, correlative PIA rocks include the pre-Robles and Daguayo-Figuera volcano-stratigraphic associations of Aptian-Albian or older age, and the Early Cretaceous diorite and tonalite enclaves within the San Lorenzo batholith (Schellekens, 1991, this volume; Smith et al., this volume). The oceanic character of Puerto Rican PIA rocks is supported by their radiogenic Nd isotope ratios, which are the highest of the sample set (Table 1). Of these two PIA samples, one has a Pb isotopic composition similar to those of the Los Ranchos Formation, and one is intermediate between the Water Island and Los Ranchos arrays (Table 2; Fig.

3A, B). The Formation A volcanic sample, VP37, has a similar $^{207}Pb/^{204}Pb$ ratio to the Los Ranchos samples from Hispaniola, and therefore presumably a similar proportion of sediment component. Its higher $^{206}Pb/^{204}Pb$ suggests it may have a higher U/Pb ratio than Los Ranchos Formation rocks. The Early Cretaceous plutonic sample, PRP4, has a somewhat lower $^{207}Pb/^{204}Pb$ ratio consistent with a sediment component intermediate between the small amount present in the Water Island Formation, Virgin Islands (Donnelly et al., 1971), and the larger amount proposed for the Los Ranchos Formation (Cumming and Kesler, 1987). Thus it appears that the amount of sediment incorporated into PIA magmas decreases rather uniformly between Hispaniola to the west and the Virgin Islands to the east.

Calc-alkaline association

Cretaceous group. Cretaceous CA rocks record a fairly small range of initial Nd and Sr isotopic ratios, which do not correlate with crystallization age (Table 1). Most of the Cretaceous rocks have only slightly less primitive initial Nd isotope compositions than the PIA, although they are LREE-enriched compared to the PIA rocks. Two Cretaceous samples have distinctly less radiogenic initial Nd isotope compositions: PRP29, from the 86-Ma Morovis stock, and VP 89, the Lapa lava member of the Robles Formation. Lapa lava sample T-17 (M. Perfit, unpublished data, 1992) also has less radiogenic Nd and more radiogenic Sr isotope ratios than other Cretaceous Puerto Rico samples. Consistent with these Nd and Sr characteristics is the high $^{207}Pb/^{204}Pb$ ratio of the Lapa lava (Table 2; Fig. 3). The correlative high-potassium Loma la Vega volcanic rocks of Hispaniola appear to have similar Pb isotope characteristics, although none of the available analyses is as radiogenic as Lapa lava sample VP89 (Fig. 3A, B) (Lebrón and Perfit, 1994). Lebrón and Perfit (1994) have suggested that subduction of seafloor sediment is required in the petrogenesis of the Loma la Vega volcanics, a conclusion that is also compatible with the geochemical and isotopic characteristics of the Lapa lava.

Eocene-Oligocene group. The Eocene and Oligocene age rocks of Puerto Rico, the Virgin Islands, and St. Martin have similar Pb isotope characteristics, but less radiogenic present-day Nd isotope ratios, compared to modern volcanic rocks from St. Kitts, Statia, Montserrat, and Redonda, the most northerly of the Lesser Antilles (Figs. 2 and 3A, B) (Davidson, 1987; Davidson et al., 1993). The Pb, Sr, and Nd isotopic characteristics of the Lesser Antilles lavas have been interpreted to reflect the incorporation of a lesser quantity of subducted terrigeneous sediment and arc crust into the arc magmas in the northern part of the arc than in the central and southern segments (Davidson, 1987; Thirlwall and Graham, 1984; White and Dupré, 1986). The isotope data from Eocene-Oligocene lavas of Puerto Rico suggest that the amount of terrigeneous material involved in the genesis of the Puerto Rican suite was similar to or only slightly greater than the amount involved in the genesis of the northern Lesser Antilles volcanic rocks.

The Eocene and Oligocene rocks may be subdivided on the basis of geographic location. The first group are volcanic and plutonic rocks from the northeast igneous province (NIP), St. Martin, and the Virgin Islands. They have initial Nd, Sr, and Pb isotope compositions that are identical to the isotopic composition of the Cretaceous arc crust on Puerto Rico in Eocene time (Figs. 4 and 5). The magma sources supplying the Cretaceous arc apparently continued to produce arc magmas of the same isotopic character into Paleogene time in these areas.

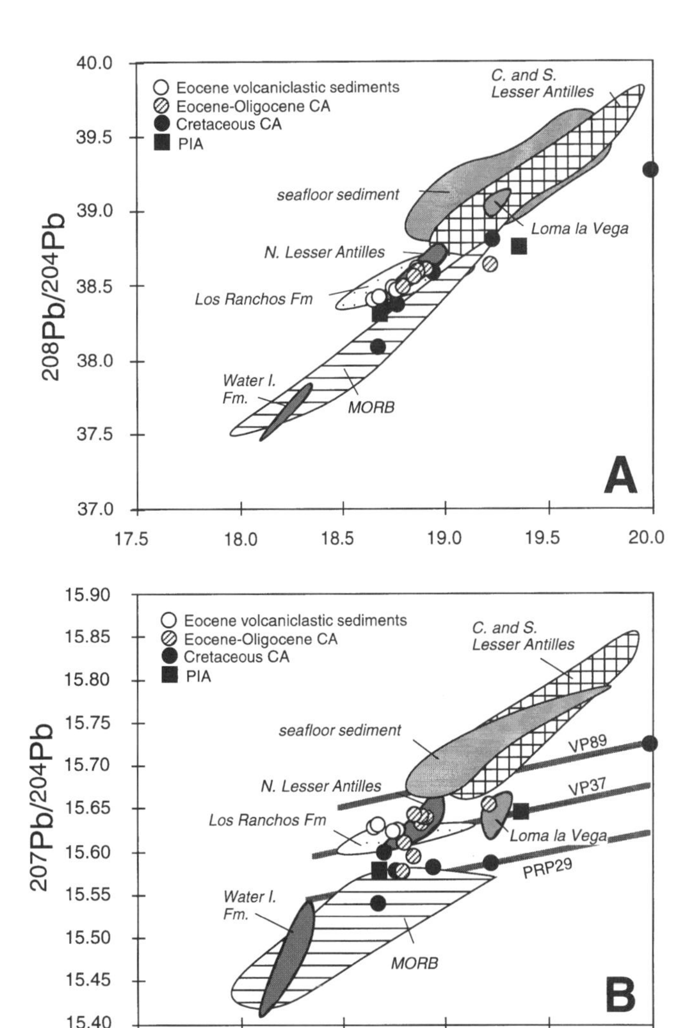

Figure 3. A and B. Present-day Pb isotope ratios of samples analyzed in this study. Shaded bands in B give the slopes along which radiogenic growth took place between the time of crystallization and the present day for three samples with radiogenic $^{206}Pb/^{204}Pb$ ratios: VP89, VP37, and PRP29. The initial lead compositions of these samples will plot at lower Pb isotope ratios along these lines, the exact position depending on the U/Pb ratio of the sample. Also shown are fields for present-day Pb isotopic composition of MORB, Barbados Ridge–Demerara Plain seafloor sediment, the Lesser Antilles, the Water Island Formation of the Virgin Islands, and the Los Ranchos Formation and Loma la Vega volcanic rocks from Hispaniola. Data from Cumming and Kesler (1987), Donnelly et al. (1971), Lebrón and Perfit (1994), Davidson (1986, 1987), Davidson et al. (1993), White and Dupré (1986), and White et al. (1985).

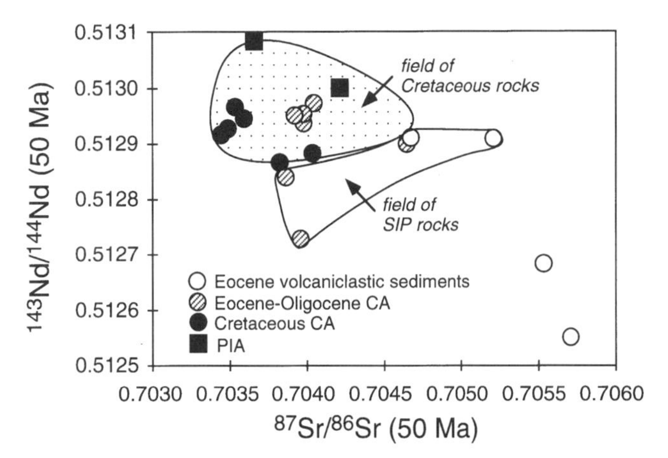

Figure 4. Nd and Sr isotope data from Puerto Rico, calculated to 50 Ma. Also plotted are initial ratios for two Oligocene plutonic samples from St. Martin and the Virgin Islands. The field for Cretaceous rock encompasses those from this study (plotted as solid symbols) and unpublished data (from M. Perfit), presented graphically in Lebrón and Perfit (1994). The Nd and Sr data for Eocene igneous rocks from the northeast igneous province of Puerto Rico, and the Oligocene St. Martin and Virgin Islands plutonic samples plot within the Cretaceous field. Volcanic and volcaniclastic samples from the southwestern igneous province have less radiogenic Nd and more radiogenic Sr isotope ratios than do the Cretaceous samples at 50 Ma.

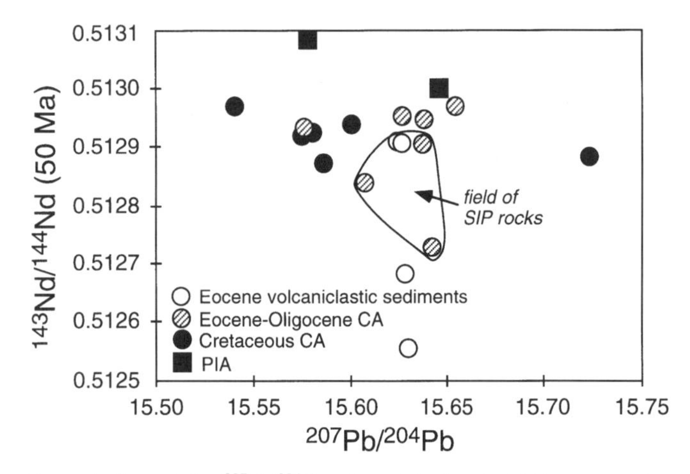

Figure 5. Present-day $^{207}Pb/^{204}Pb$ ratios plotted against Nd isotope ratios at 50 Ma for data presented in this study. The Pb and Nd data from the Eocene rocks of the northeast igneous province and the Oligocene plutonic samples from St. Martin and the Virgin Islands fall within the field for Cretaceous arc rocks of Puerto Rico. Although the Nd isotope ratios of the southwestern igneous province samples are less radiogenic than the other samples, their $^{207}Pb/^{204}Pb$ isotope ratios are indistinguishable.

The second group is the Eocene magmatism in the southwest igneous province (SIP). These flows and sediments have less radiogenic Nd and more radiogenic Sr isotopic compositions than the Cretaceous arc rocks of this study, although their Pb isotopic compositions are similar (Figs. 4 and 5). The Nd and Sr isotopic compositions of these samples indicate that these magmas incorporated more isotopically evolved material than the lavas and plutonic rocks to the north and east. Pindell and Barrett (1990) have suggested that the SIP province was situated westward of the CIP and NIP; thus, it is possible that the proportions of subducted sediment may have been different. Alternatively, the arc crust in the SIP, which includes the Bermeja Complex—the oldest rocks on Puerto Rico—may include rocks (not sampled here) that had evolved to radiogenic compositions by 50 Ma and are isotopically suitable contaminants to Eocene SIP magmas.

The volcaniclastic samples from the SIP also exhibit evidence for incorporation of isotopically evolved material in amounts similar to that present in the SIP lavas. Initial Nd isotopic compositions of the volcaniclastic sandstones from the Río Culebrinas Formation (CF1a, fine; CF1b, coarse) and the underlying basalt of the Mal Paso Formation (EC7) are identical (Table 1; Fig. 4). If the basalt has a higher U/Pb ratio than the volcaniclastic sediments, then the initial Pb compositions of the sediments and basalts may also have been very similar (Table 2; Fig. 5). Only the initial Sr isotopic compositions are different, and the more radiogenic $^{87}Sr/^{86}Sr$ ratios of the sediments may reflect seawater alteration. These volcaniclastic sediments appear to be composed entirely of locally derived arc debris.

In contrast, the other volcaniclastic sediments, 2134 and 2149 from the Toa Baja drillhole in the NIP, have isotopic compositions that contrast with underlying basalt (3115) (Figs. 4 and 5). Compared to the basalt they overlie, Sr and Pb isotopic compositions of the sediments are more radiogenic, and their Nd isotopic compositions are less radiogenic. It is possible that authigenic components, such as ferromanganese precipitates, are responsible for the shift in Nd, Sr, and Pb compositions away from those of the lava. Alternatively, continent-derived detritus must have been incorporated at the site where the volcanogenic sediment was deposited. In either case, these volcaniclastic sedimentary rocks acquired their more evolved isotopic signatures at the site of deposition, not during magma generation or ascent through the older arc edifice.

Isotopic constraints on subduction zone orientation

The isotopic compositions of the Cretaceous and Tertiary rocks of Puerto Rico are important because it is during this time period that subduction polarity may have reversed, such that subduction of the Pacific seafloor ceased and the Atlantic Ocean floor began to be consumed. Hypotheses range from no reversal, to reversal occurring at different proposed times in the interval 105 to 55 Ma (Jolly et al., Chapter 1, this volume).

The samples analyzed in this study exhibit a restricted range in isotopic compositions: except for volcaniclastic sediments, all samples have $\varepsilon_{Nd}^{initial}$ more radiogenic than bulk earth values, ranging from +9.74 to +2.97. Likewise, again excepting the volcaniclastic sedimentary rocks and calcite-rich basalt EC7, initial $^{87}Sr/^{86}Sr$ ratios are consistently unradiogenic (0.7034–0.7042). $^{207}Pb/^{204}Pb$ ratios vary from 15.54 to 15.73. These isotopic characteristics are typical of mantle-derived rocks that have incorporated only minor amounts of isotopically evolved components, such as subducted sediment or differentiated arc crust. Despite their broad isotopic similarities, three subgroups can be identified: the PIA samples, distinguished by radiogenic initial Nd ratios and low incompatible element abundances (Jolly et al., Chapter 3, this volume; Schellekens, this volume); the Eocene samples from the southwest igneous province, characterized by less radiogenic Nd isotope ratios and more radiogenic Sr isotope ratios than other plutonic and volcanic samples; and the CA samples other than the Eocene SIP rocks, which have intermediate initial Nd isotope ratios. It is possible that the transition from tholeiitic PIA magma compositions with radiogenic initial Nd isotope ratios to calc-alkaline rocks with less radiogenic Nd isotope compositions marks the time at which the subduction of Pacific ocean floor ceased, and consumption of the Atlantic seafloor began, as previously hypothesized by Mattson (1979) and Lebrón and Perfit (1994). However, Jolly et al. (Chapter 3, this volume) point out that geochemically and isotopically primitive arc magmas may not be compatible with the subduction of an old, sediment-laden Pacific plate unless very little pelagic sediment was subducted. Moreover, a reversal in subduction polarity at this time cannot be related to the impingement of the Caribbean Cretaceous Basalt Province because that oceanic plateau was not formed until 88 to 90 Ma (Duncan et al., 1994). The significance of the PIA to CA transition observed on Puerto Rico and elsewhere remains unclear.

If the subduction direction reversed subsequent to the formation of the Caribbean Cretaceous Basalt Province, no change in the character of the arc rocks is identifiable isotopically. The chemically and isotopically distinctive Lapa lava apparently predates the formation of the oceanic plateau (Jolly et al., Chapter 1, this volume), and hence the apparently abrupt appearance of high-K calc-alkaline lavas is probably not related to this event. Other volcanic and plutonic rocks emplaced over the time interval 88 to 55 Ma do not exhibit any identifiable change in isotopic composition with crystallization age. Apparently, if the subduction direction changed during this time, it did not lead to the incorporation into arc magmas of isotopically distinctive sources or detectably different proportions of the same magma sources.

Finally, the difference in isotopic character of the Eocene samples from the southwest igneous province compared to coeval igneous rocks elsewhere in Puerto Rico, St. Martin, and the Virgin Islands must be related to differences in relative geographic position along the Greater Antilles arc, such that the amount of subducted sediment varied along the arc, or that the magmas ascended through arc crust that had evolved geochemically to different degrees. If relatively subtle changes geographically along a short segment of a single arc produce identifiable shifts in isotopic composition, it is surprising that such a major tectonic event as a reversal in subduction direction has not been recorded in the isotopic composition of arc magmas.

CONCLUSIONS

1. The radiogenic Nd isotopic composition of samples belonging to the Primitive Island Arc association (PIA) on Puerto Rico confirms other geochemical evidence of their oceanic arc origin. The Pb isotopic composition of Puerto Rico PIA is intermediate between time-correlative rocks on Hispaniola and the Virgin Islands, suggesting that the amount of seafloor sediment incorporated into PIA magmas decreases uniformly from west to east.

2. The Cretaceous and Paleogene calc-alkaline lavas and plutonic rocks of Puerto Rico have isotopic compositions similar to those from the northern Lesser Antilles, suggesting that these Puerto Rican island arc magmas have incorporated a similar, minor amount of isotopically evolved material.

3. Island arc rocks from Puerto Rico exhibit no systematic change in isotopic character with age, despite the fact that many tectonic models hypothesize a reversal in the polarity of subduction during this time interval. If the reversal is unrelated to the Caribbean Cretaceous Basalt Province, formed at 88 to 90 Ma (Duncan et al., 1994), then it may have occurred in mid-Cretaceous time when arc magmas changed from tholeiitic to calc-alkaline in character, and when on Puerto Rico a modest shift toward less radiogenic Nd isotope ratios is recorded in the arc rocks. However, a more pronounced difference in isotopic composition would be predicted for such a significant tectonic event.

4. Eocene and Oligocene volcanic and plutonic rocks from the northeast igneous province, St. Martin, and the Virgin Islands are similar isotopically to older Cretaceous calc-alkaline association rocks of Puerto Rico. In contrast, the Eocene lavas and volcaniclastic sediments from the southwest igneous province have less radiogenic Nd and more radiogenic Sr isotope compositions than the other calc-alkaline association rocks, suggesting that magmas emplaced into this geographic province incorporated more isotopically evolved material than did magmas elsewhere, either by introduction of subducted sediment at the site of magma generation, or during ascent through arc crust of Late Jurassic and Cretaceous age.

ACKNOWLEDGMENTS

This project was funded by Puerto Rico EPSCoR National Science Foundation Grant RII–85–13533, and by the Toa Baja Drilling Project sponsored by the Puerto Rico Electric Power Authority. We thank M. R. Perfit for permission to include his unpublished data in Figure 4, and K. R. Chamberlain for his assistance with the lead isotope data.

REFERENCES CITED

Burke, K., 1988, Tectonic evolution of the Caribbean: Annual Reviews of Earth and Planetary Science, v. 16, p. 201–230.

Cox, D. P., Marvin, R. F., M'Gonigle, J. W., McIntyre, D. H., and Rogers, C. L., 1977, Potassium-argon geochronology of some metamorphic, igneous, and hydrothermal events in Puerto Rico and the Virgin Islands: Journal of Research of the U.S. Geological Survey, v. 5, p. 689–703.

Cumming, G. L., and Kesler, S. E., 1987, Lead isotopic composition of the oldest volcanic rocks of the eastern Greater Antilles island arc: Chemical Geology, v. 65, p. 15–23.

Davidson, J. P., 1986, Isotopic and trace element constraints on the petrogenesis of subduction-related lavas from Martinique, Lesser Antilles: Journal of Geophysical Research, v. 91, p. 5943–5962.

Davidson, J. P., 1987, Crustal contamination versus subduction zone enrichment:

examples from the Lesser Antilles and implications for mantle source compositions of island arc volcanic rocks: Geochimica et Cosmochimica Acta, v. 51, p. 2185–2198.

Davidson, J. P., Boghossian, N. D., and Wilson, M., 1993, The geochemistry of the igneous rock suite of St. Martin, northern Lesser Antilles: Journal of Petrology, v. 34, p. 839–866.

Donnelly, T. W., and Rogers, J. J. W., 1978, The distribution of igneous rock suites throughout the Caribbean: Geologie en Mijnbouw, v. 57, p. 151–162.

Donnelly, T. W., Rogers, J. J. W., Pushkar, P., and Armstrong, R. L., 1971, Chemical evolution of the igneous rocks of the eastern West Indies: an investigation of thorium, uranium and potassium distributions, and lead and strontium isotopic ratios: Geological Society of America Memoir 130, p. 181–224.

Donnelly, T. W., and 10 others, 1990, History and tectonic setting of Caribbean magmatism, *in* Dengo, G., and Case, J. E., eds., The Caribbean region: Boulder, Colorado, Geological Society of America, The Geology of North America, v. H, p. 339–374.

Duncan, R. A., Sinton, C. W., and Donnelly, T. W., 1994, The Caribbean Cretaceous Basalt Province and ocean LIP: EOS, (Transactions of American Geophysical Union) v. 75, p. 594.

Frost, C. D., and Schellekens, J. H., 1991, Rb-Sr and Sm-Nd isotopic characterization of Eocene volcanic and volcaniclastic rocks from Puerto Rico: Geophysical Research Letters, v. 18, p. 545–548.

Lebrón, M. C., and Perfit, M. R., 1994, Petrochemistry and tectonic significance of Cretaceous island-arc rocks, Cordillera Oriental, Dominican Republic: Tectonophysics, v. 229, p. 69–100.

Mattson, P. H., 1979, Subduction, buoyant braking, flipping and strike-slip faulting in the northern Caribbean: Journal of Geology, v. 87, p. 293–304.

Pindell, J. L., and Barrett, S. F., 1990, Geological evolution of the Caribbean region: a plate-tectonic perspective, *in* Dengo, G., and Case, J. E., eds., The Caribbean region: Boulder, Colorado, Geological Society of America, The Geology of North America, v. H, p. 405–432.

Pindell, J., and Dewey, J. F., 1982, Permo-Triassic reconstruction of western Pangea and the evolution of the Gulf of Mexico/Caribbean region: Tectonics, v. 1, p. 179–211.

Schellekens, J. H., 1991, Late Jurassic to Eocene geochemical evolution of volcanic rocks in Puerto Rico: Geophysical Research Letters, v. 18, p. 553–556.

Sinton, C. W., Duncan, R. A., and Storey, M., 1993, ^{40}Ar-^{39}Ar ages from Gorgona Island, Colombia and the Nicoya Penninsula, Costa Rica: EOS, (Transactions, American Geophysical Union) v. 74, p. 553.

Thirlwall, M. F., and Graham, A. M., 1984, Evolution of high Ca, high Sr C-series basalt from Grenada, Lesser Antilles: the effects of intra-crustal contamination: Journal of the Geological Society of London, v. 141, p. 427–445.

White, W. M., and Dupré, B., 1986, Sediment subduction and magma genesis in the Lesser Antilles: isotopic and trace element constraints: Journal of Geophysical Research, v. 91, p. 5927–5941.

White, W. M., Dupré, B., and Vidal, P., 1985, Isotope and trace element geochemistry of sediments from Barbados Ridge–Demerara Plain region, Atlantic Ocean: Geochimica et Cosmochimica Acta, v. 49, p. 1875–1886.

White, W. M., Hofmann, A. W., and Puchelt, H., 1987, Isotope geochemistry of Pacific mid-ocean ridge basalt: Journal of Geophysical Research, v. 92, p. 4881–4893.

Manuscript Accepted by the Society June 20, 1997

Printed in U.S.A.

Geological Society of America
Special Paper 322
1998

Geochemistry of intrusive igneous rocks, St. Croix, U.S. Virgin Islands

Edward G. Lidiak
Department of Geology and Planetary Science, University of Pittsburgh, Pittsburgh, Pennsylvania 15260
Wayne T. Jolly
Department of Earth Sciences, Brock University, St. Catherines, Ontario L2S 3A1, Canada

ABSTRACT

Igneous rocks of Late Cretaceous age on St. Croix occur as plutons, sills, and dikes that are intrusive into a thick Cretaceous turbidite sequence. Plutons are composed of layered gabbro and massive diorite. The gabbro is a cumulate rock that contains plagioclase, augite, and hypersthene, along with accessory hornblende and biotite. The diorite consists mainly of plagioclase, hornblende, and minor augite. Sills and less abundant dikes are divisible on the basis of petrography and geochemistry into four main compositional types, which, in order of decreasing abundance, are augite-hornblende diabase, hornblende diabase, pyroxene porphyry, and dacite. The pyroxene porphyry is basaltic and contains at least two generations of clinopyroxenes (partially resorbed megacrysts and microphenocrysts), resorbed hornblende, and pseudomorphs after olivine. Augite-hornblende diabase varies from basalt to andesite and is characterized by plagioclase, augite, and hornblende. Hornblende diabase is basaltic andesite to andesite and contains plagioclase and hornblende. Dacite contains phenocrysts of plagioclase and pseudomorphs of hornblende or mica and is the most evolved of the rocks studied.

The intrusives have geochemical signatures typical of island arc igneous rocks. As a group, they are strongly enriched in large ion lithophile elements, display moderate enrichment in light and moderate rare earth elements, are slightly depleted in heavy rare earth elements, and strongly depleted in high field strength elements compared to normal mid–ocean ridge basalts (N-MORB). All rocks of the St. Croix igneous suite display flat HREE on N-MORB distribution diagrams and limited ranges in Ta/Yb and Hf/Yb ratios. These features are consistent with derivation from a spinel peridotite source region where only minor variation in the degree of melting occurred. Trace element ratios also suggest that hydrous fluxes in the mantle wedge source region were dominated by aqueous fluids derived from the subducted slab and that sediment contributions were of minor importance in the generation of St. Croix magmas. Petrographic and geochemical evidence indicate that the dikes and sills record subvolcanic gabbroic fractionation characterized by the removal of plagioclase and clinopyroxene.

The St. Croix intrusives have incompatible element concentrations and elemental ratios that are closely comparable to volcanic rocks of similar Campanian age in Puerto Rico. This similarity suggests the possibility that the thick volcanogenic strata on St. Croix are correlative with similar volcanogenic strata in Puerto Rico and that the two regions may have been part of a developing and continuous island arc sequence during Campanian time.

Lidiak, E. G., and Jolly, W. T., 1998, Geochemistry of intrusive igneous rocks, St. Croix, U.S. Virgin Islands, *in* Lidiak, E. G., and Larue, D. K., eds., Tectonics and Geochemistry of the Northeastern Caribbean: Boulder, Colorado, Geological Society of America Special Paper 322.

INTRODUCTION

The island of St. Croix is located in the northeastern Caribbean and is separated from the Puerto Rico–Virgin Islands platform by the Anegada Trough (Fig. 1 in Preface, this volume). Although the island is nominally part of the Lesser Antilles, it has geologic affinities with the eastern Greater Antilles and is generally regarded as part of that complex arc system. The island is part of a partially submerged ridge that represents a normal fault block in the southeastern Greater Antilles (Speed and Joyce, 1991). Outcrops on St. Croix (Fig. 1) reveal a thick sequence of folded Upper Cretaceous sedimentary rocks, intruded by two mafic igneous plutons and a series of sills, dikes, and diatremes. These units are unconformably overlain by Miocene limestone that crops out in a central graben and by younger cover rocks (Whetten, 1966; Speed et al., 1979; Lidz, 1988; Speed and Joyce, 1989, 1991). The Cretaceous sedimentary rocks consist mainly of turbidites and contourites that are principally of volcanogenic origin (Speed and Joyce, 1989; Stanley, 1989). These volcaniclastic sediments were derived from contemporaneous volcanoes and represent accumulations in an arc tectonic setting. Whetten (1966) mapped four Cretaceous stratigraphic units and recognized two generations of folds and a series of normal faults. An alternate interpretation of these rocks was reached by Speed and Joyce (1989, 1991), who mapped the Cretaceous sequence as a complex assemblage of tectonic sheets (K1 through K6 in Fig. 1), each bounded by shallowly dipping thrust faults. The relations between the thrust sheets and exposed Cretaceous rocks are shown in Figure 1.

Intrusive igneous rocks are of minor volume compared to the Cretaceous sedimentary cover rocks and have not been studied in detail. They are, however, of considerable importance in deciphering the evolutionary development of St. Croix. Whetten (1966) described the two plutons and several of the dikes, and Speed et al. (1979) reported five K-Ar dates from these rocks. The intrusives apparently were emplaced mainly in late Cretaceous time. K–Ar dates on hornblende separates yield an average date of 69.3 Ma on the sills and dikes and 66 to 71 Ma (Maaastrichtian) on the plutons (Speed et al., 1979; Lidz, 1988). An older date of 75.2 Ma (Campanian) was obtained on an igneous clast in a boulder bed. Igneous activity may thus span an interval from Campanian to Maastrichtian time.

This chapter presents the first study of the geochemical, mineralogic, and petrographic characteristics of these intrusive rocks. It focuses primarily on the mineral chemistry, major and trace element chemistry, fractionation processes that may have produced the variety of igneous rocks, and the possible role that the underlying mantle wedge and subducted oceanic crust had in the generation of the St. Croix magmas.

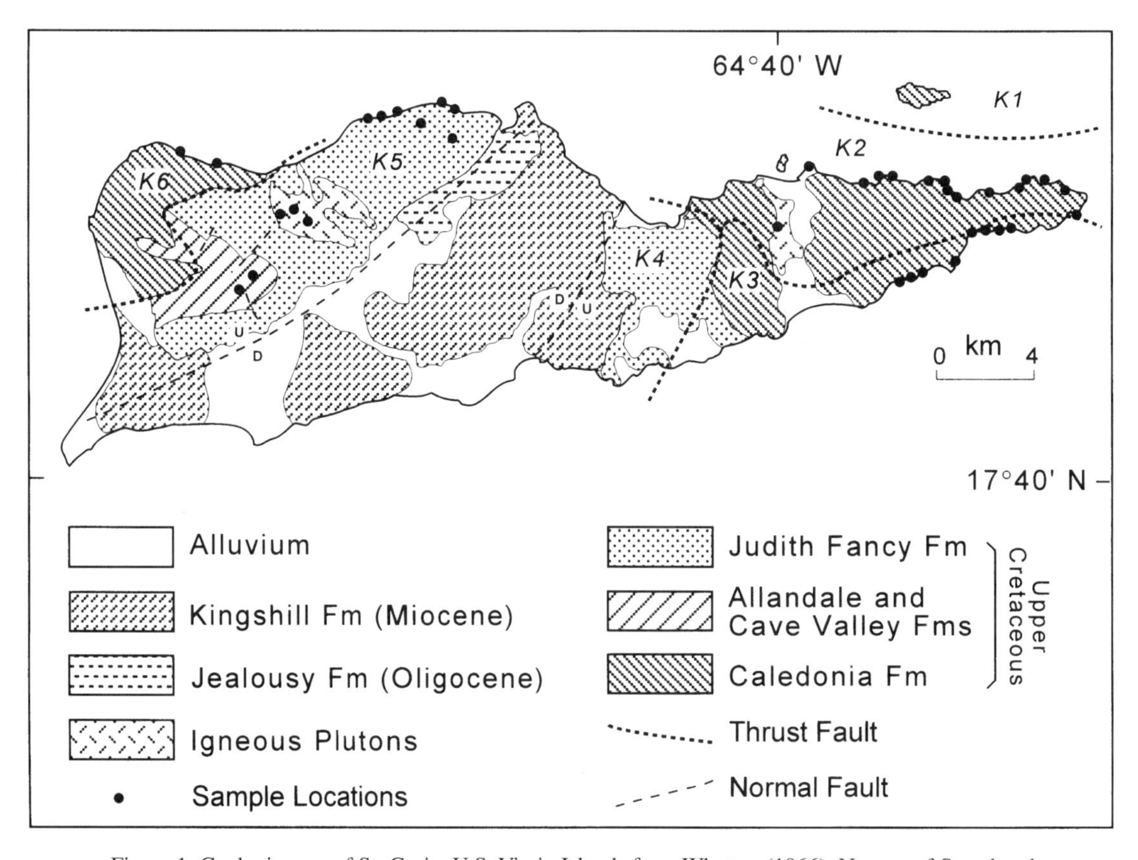

Figure 1. Geologic map of St. Croix, U.S. Virgin Islands from Whetten (1966). Nappes of Speed and Joyce (1989) are shown by dotted line and labels K1 through K6.

CLEAVAGE IN THE INTRUSIVES

Penetrative slaty cleavage is ubiquitous in all of the Cretaceous sedimentary rocks except the thick lithic–rich layers of the Judith Fancy Formation (Speed et al., 1979). Imbrication and accompanying folding and cleaving of the Cretaceous strata were regarded as pre-dating emplacement of the igneous intrusions (Speed and Joyce, 1989). However, Draper and Bartel (1991) observed that cleavage is present in a sill and a diatreme dike in the East End Range of St. Croix. They concluded that at least some of the magmatism predates or is synchronous with tectonism on the island.

Among 21 dikes and sills studied in the present investigation, six display cleavage. These occur at the following localities: Carden Point, east side of Pow Point at Solitude Bay, Tague Point, west side of Knight's Bay, Point Cudejarre, and Grapetree Point (Table 1). The first four of these outcrops are within nappe K-2; the remaining two are in nappe K-3 (Fig. 1). Not all of the dikes and sills in these two nappes are deformed; the other dikes and sills show no evidence of cleavage. Furthermore, there is no apparent relation between the presence or absence of cleavage and petrographic rock type. Cleavage was not observed in either of the two plutons or in the dikes and sills of the other nappes.

TABLE 1. SAMPLE LOCATIONS OF ST. CROIX IGNEOUS ROCKS

Sample	Rock	Location	Grid Reference Coordinates (EW/NS)*
SX-1	Southgate Diorite	Southgate Baptist Church, Route 62	2345/6349
SC-2	Fountain Gabbro	Road Excavation, Route 78	0697/6439
SX-3	Fountain Layered Gabbro	Road Excavation, Route 78	0704/6440
SX-4	Fountain Anorthositic Gabbro	Road Excavation, Route 78	0710/6437
SC-5	Turbidite of Caledonia Fm.	Northshore Drive, Route 80	1229/6683
SC-6	Hornblende Diabase Sill	Northshore Drive, Route 80	1192/6700
SX-7	Augite Hornblende Diabase Sill	St. George Quarry (south)	0590/6156
SX-8	Augite Hornblende Diabase Sill	St. George Quarry (north)	3208/6454
SX-9	Plagioclase Diacite Sill	Cramer Park	3208/6454
SX-10	Pyroxene Porphyry	Cottongarden Point	3211/6466
SC-11	Pyroxene Porphyry	Cottongarden Point	3217/6462
SC-12	Southgate Diorite	Pull Point	2450/6512
SC-13	Hornblende Diabase Sill	East of Carden at Carden Point	2639/6450
SC-14	Pyroxene Porphyry Sill	West side of Pow Point, Solitude Bay	2705/6458
SC-15	Plagioclase Dacite Sill	East side of Pow Point, Solitude Bay	2703/6458
SC-16	Hb Diabase Boulder in Caledonia Fm.	West of Tague Point	2878/6459
SC-17	Augite Hornblende Diabase Sill	Tague Point	2905/6458
SC-18	Pyroxene Porphyry Sill	Tague Point	2914/6440
SC-19	Augite Hornblende Diabase Sill	Tague Point	2919/6425
SC-20	Augite Hornblende Diabase Sill	Lamb Point	3308/6451
SC-21	Augite Hornblende (?) Diabase Dike	West of Knight Bay	3083/6410
SC-22	Pyroxene Porphyry Dike	Point Cudejane	3371/6352
SC-23	Augite Hornblende Diabase Sill	Grapetree Point	3036/6282
SC-24	Hornblende Diabase Sill	Grapetree Point	3020/6287
SC-25	Hornblende Diabase Sill	Robin Bay	2785/6129
SC-26	Hb Diabase Boulder in Caledonia Fm.	Robin Bay	2785/6129
SC-27	Hb Diabase Boulder in Caledonia Fm.	Robin Bay	2785/6129
SC-28	Augite Hornblende Diabase Sill	North of Grass Point	2932/6177
SC-29	Basalt Boulder in Judith Fancy Fm.	Sea Cliff West of Greig Hill	1227/6691
SC-30	Hb Diabase Boulder in Judith Fancy Fm.	Sea Cliff West of Greig Hill	1219/6693
SC-31	Basalt Boulder in Judith Fancy Fm.	Sea Cliff at Baron Bluff	1089/6718
SC-32	Hb Diabase Boulder in Judith Fancy Fm.	Sea Cliff at Baron Bluff	1098/6722
SC-33	Augite Hornblende Diabase Sill	Sea Cliff at Baron Bluff	1106/6727
SC-34	Diorite Boulder in Caledonia Fm.	Grapetree Point	3036/6282
SC-35	Basalt Boulder in Caledonia Fm.	Grapetree Point	3036/6282
SC-36	Hb Diabase Boulder in Caledonia Fm.	East of Hams Bluff	0171/6582
SC-37	Augite Hornblende Diabase Sill	East of Maroon Hole	1234/6547

*Coordinate system from Christiansten, Frederiksted, and East Point, St. Croix, 7.5-minute Quadrangle Maps of the U.S. Geological Survey.

PETROGRAPHY

Igneous bodies on St. Croix include the Fountain Gabbro, the Southgate Diorite, and a series of dikes and sills. Of the 21 dikes and sills sampled and studied in this investigation, 18 are sills, 2 are dikes, and 1 is a dike/sill ramp intrusion. Dikes and sills are divisible on the basis of petrography and geochemistry into four main lithologic and compositional types: pyroxene porphyry, augite-hornblende diabase, hornblende diabase, and dacite. Draper and Bartel (1991) reported rhyolite clasts in a diatreme dike, but this dike was not sampled in the present study.

Fountain gabbro

The Fountain Gabbro occurs as a discordant pluton in the Northside Range (Fig. 1). It is a crudely layered two-pyroxene gabbro that contains accessory hornblende, biotite, Fe-Ti oxides, and apatite (Table 2). All samples studied have cumulate texture, the most common being a mesocumulate in which pyroxene and accessory minerals occur interstitially to subhedral plagioclase laths. Both augite and hypersthene occur as discrete grains. Some augite is partly replaced by prismatic blue-green to light green hornblende. Biotite occurs as both fresh and partly chloritized crystals. Fresh biotite has orange-brown to light brown pleochrism and is partly replaced at crystal rims and along individual cleavage flakes by light green chlorite. Patches of calcite and chlorite occur sporadically throughout the rock. Rock types include layered gabbro, massive gabbro, and anorthositic gabbro.

Southgate diorite

The Southgate Diorite is a discordant, massive pluton that is exposed along the East End Range in the vicinity of Southgate and along the coastline at Pull Point. The diorite consists of hornblende and plagioclase and accessory augite, Fe-Ti oxides, and apatite (Table 2). The texture is hypidiomorphic-poikilitic, in which subhedral to anhedral hornblende enclose small plagioclase laths and the various accessory minerals; plagioclase occurs as anhedral laths and aggregates.

Pyroxene porphyry

Pyroxene porphyry, characterized by 1 to 5-mm diopsidic augite megacrysts, is a distinctly porphyritic intrusive that occurs

TABLE 2. PETROGRAPHIC SUMMARY OF ST. CROIX INTRUSIVE IGNEOUS ROCKS

Rock Type	Texture	Essential Minerals	Accessory Minerals	Secondary Minerals
		Plutons		
Fountain Gabbro	Mesocumulate	Plagioclase ($An_{70–60}$) Augite Hypersthene	Hornblende Biotite Fe-Ti Oxides Apatite	Chlorite
Southgate Diorite	Hypidiomorphic- Poikilitic	Plagioclase (An_{35}) Hornblende	Augite Fe–Ti Oxides Apatite	Chlorite Epidote Prehnite
Rock Type	**Texture**	**Phenocryst**	**Groundmass**	**Secondary Minerals**
		Dikes and Sills		
Pyroxene Porphyry	Panidiomorphic- Mesocratic	Augite ($Ca_{44}Mg_{45}Fe_{11}$) Plagioclase Pseudomorphs Hornblende (resorbed) Olivine Pseudomorphs	Augite Plagioclase (An_{65}) Fe–Ti Oxides	Actinolite, Calcite Chlorite, Epidote Prehnite Pumpellyite
Augite-Hornblende Diabase	Intergranular- Subophitic and Intergranular	Plagioclase ($An_{78–50}$) Augite ($Ca_{37}Mg_{46}Fe_{17}$) Hornblende Olivine Pseudomorphs (±)	Plagioclase Augite Fe–Ti Oxides Sphene	Calcite Chlorite Epidote Serpentine
Hornblende Diabase	Pilotaxic- Orthophyric	Plagioclase ($An_{57–50}$) Hornblende Fe–Ti Oxides Quartz Xenocrysts Dacitic Xenoliths	Plagioclase Hornblende Fe–Ti Oxides Quartz Apatite	Calcite Chlorite Epidote Prehnite Pumpellyite
Dacite	Felsophyric	Plagioclase (An_{8}) Pseudomorphs (Hornblende or Mica)	Feldspar Quartz Fe–Ti Oxides	Calcite, Chlorite Epidote Prehnite

entirely as sills. Pyroxene in the sills are composed of at least two generations of crystals. The larger of these are partially resorbed megacrysts with both embayed and euhedral rims. Also present are smaller microphenocrysts of generally euhedral augite. The texture is typically panidiomorphic (Fig. 2*A*) with euhedral and resorbed augite (30%), subhedral plagioclase pseudomorphs (10%), and resorbed hornblende (<5%) set in a fine-grained mesocratic groundmass of augite, plagioclase, and Fe-Ti oxides (Table 2). Olivine pseudomorphs are present in several of the sills. Secondary minerals, present as ovoids and patches in the groundmass, typically include chlorite, calcite, epidote, prehnite, actinolite, and pumpellyite (±). Actinolite partly mantles some of the augite megacrysts in the more altered sills.

Some of these rocks have previously been referred to as lamprophyres (Whetten, 1966). They are petrographically similar to calc-alkaline lamprophyres such as kersantites and spessartites (Rock, 1991); however, critical differences are the absence of phlogopitic biotite as an essential phenocryst, the presence of resorbed hornblende (xenocrysts?), and the presumed presence of essential plagioclase phenocrysts. Furthermore, compared to average calc-alkaline lamprophyre (Rock, 1991), the porphyry is geochemically depleted in large ion lithophile elements (LILE), light rare earths (LREE), and high field strength elements (HFSE) and thus differs from typical lamprophyre. The combined petrographic and geochemical characteristics distinguish these sills that are referred to herein by the descriptive term "porphyry."

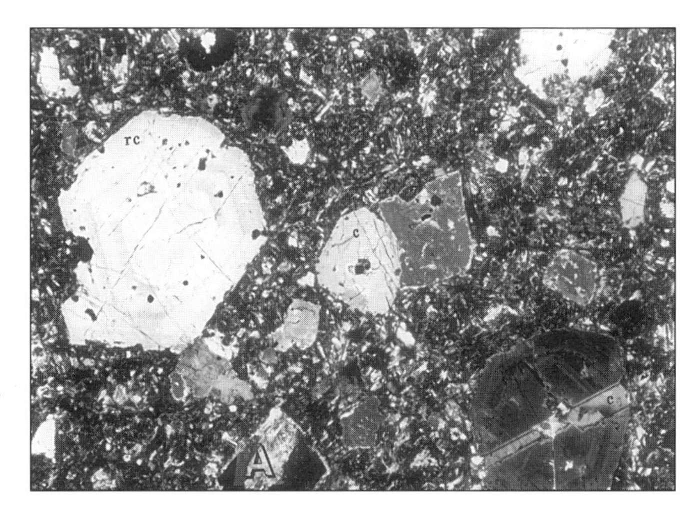

Figure 2. Photomicrograph of St. Croix sills. *A*, Panidiomorphic texture in pyroxene porphyry sill. *B*, Intergranular to subophitic texture in augite hornblende diabase. Field of view is 3.75 mm across. c, clinopyroxene; rc, partly resorbed clinopyroxene; p, plagioclase.

Augite-hornblende diabase

Dikes and sills of augite-hornblende diabase are the most common type of tabular intrusion on St. Croix. Two main textural types (Table 2) are present: equigranular, subophitic to intergranular rock (Fig. 2*B*) and porphyritic, intergranular rock. Both are characterized by augite and greenish brown hornblende. The equigranular diabase contains plagioclase (55%), augite (35%), hornblende (5%), and Fe-Ti oxides (5%), and olivine pseudomorphs and patches of secondary minerals (5%). Hornblende is commonly resorbed and may be partly replaced by augite. Olivine pseudomorphs are filled with serpentine; typical secondary minerals are chlorite, calcite, and epidote. Microprobe analyses indicate that diabasic pyroxene is compositionally distinct in wollastonite component from pyroxene in the porphyry (Table 2).

The porphyritic diabase contains phenocrysts (1 to 3 mm) of plagioclase (15%), augite (12%), hornblende (10%), and Fe-Ti oxides (3%) in a fine-grained intergranular groundmass (60%) of plagioclase, augite, Fe-Ti oxides, and sphene. Chlorite, calcite, and epidote may occur as small patches in the groundmass.

Hornblende diabase

Hornblende diabase occurs as sills. They are porphyritic rocks containing phenocrysts (0.5 to 3.0 mm) of plagioclase (18%), greenish brown hornblende (15%), and Fe-Ti oxides (2%) in a pilotaxic to orthophyric groundmass (65%) of plagioclase, hornblende, Fe-Ti oxides, quartz, and apatite (Table 2). Small, angular quartz fragments and quartz–bearing dacitic xenoliths (up to 10%) are present is some of the sills; small, basaltic xenoliths may also be present. Secondary chlorite, calcite, epidote, prehnite, and pumpellyite (±) occur as patches in the groundmass or as small ovoids.

Dacite

Porphyritic dacite forms two sills. The rocks contain phenocrysts (0.1 to 1.0 mm) of plagioclase (25%), and pseudomorphs (10%) of either hornblende(?) or mica(?) set in fine-grained felsophyric matrix of feldspar, quartz, and Fe-Ti oxides (Table 2). Secondary chlorite, calcite, epidote, and prehnite occur sporadically in the matrix.

TABLE 3. REPRESENTATIVE MICROPROBE ANALYSES AND STRUCTURAL FORMULA UNITS OF CLINOPYROXENE

Sample	SX-3	SX-8	SX-8	SX-24	SX-24	SX-11	SX-11
Rock	Gabbro	Diabase	Diabase	Diabase	Diabase	Porphyry	Porphyry
Mineral	Random	Rim	Core	Rim	Core	Microphen	Megacryst
(Wt. %)							
SiO_2	49.91	51.64	51.62	51.06	50.58	48.15	48.13
TiO_2	0.27	0.37	0.35	0.45	0.46	0.58	0.47
Al_2O_3	1.88	2.38	2.36	2.52	3.05	4.27	4.27
FeO	10.59	11.01	10.73	11.46	11.00	7.79	7.58
MgO	13.90	16.52	16.34	15.96	16.01	14.67	14.66
CaO	21.22	17.92	18.36	17.84	17.95	22.37	22.78
Na_2O	0.17	0.30	0.29	0.28	0.27	0.26	0.21
K_2O	0.00	0.00	0.01	0.01	0.00	0.00	0.02
MnO	0.27	0.29	0.29	0.31	0.29	0.19	0.22
NiO	0.01	0.01	0.01	0.02	0.04	0.05	0.01
Cr_2O_3	0.04	0.10	0.11	0.09	0.16	0.01	0.03
Total	98.28	100.51	100.49	99.98	99.81	98.33	98.35
Cations (O = 6)							
Si	1.916	1.916	1.916	1.910	1.894	1.834	1.834
Al	0.085	0.104	0.104	0.111	0.134	0.192	0.192
Fe_2	0.340	0.342	0.333	0.359	0.344	0.248	0.242
Mg	0.795	0.914	0.904	0.890	0.894	0.833	0.833
Ca	0.873	0.712	0.730	0.715	0.720	0.913	0.930
Na	0.013	0.022	0.021	0.020	0.020	0.020	0.016
K	0.000	0.000	0.000	0.000	0.000	0.000	0.001
Ti	0.008	0.010	0.010	0.013	0.013	0.017	0.013
Mn	0.009	0.009	0.009	0.10	0.009	0.007	0.007
Cr	0.001	0.003	0.003	0.003	0.005	0.000	0.001
Ni	0.001	0.000	0.000	0.001	0.001	0.001	0.000
Mg#	69.98	72.77	73.08	71.30	72.18	77.04	77.53
Total Cat	4.040	4.031	4.031	4.031	4.034	4.064	4.066
Wollastonite	43.47	36.20	37.11	36.41	36.77	45.78	46.41
Enstatite	39.57	46.43	45.96	45.33	45.64	41.76	41.54
Ferrosillite	16.96	17.37	16.93	18.26	17.59	12.46	12.04

MINERALOGY

Quantitative mineral analyses were determined at the Department of Earth and Atmospheric Sciences, Purdue University, West Lafayette, Indiana, using a CAMECA SX50 electron microprobe equipped with four wavelength dispersive x-ray crystal spectrometers having two crystals for each spectrometer. A 20-nA beam current with a 20-kV accelerating potential were used in all analyses. The beam size was set at 1 μm for analyses of amphibole, biotite, and clinopyroxene, and at 5 μm for analyses of plagioclase. Data were acquired for 40s for all elements and were corrected using Bence and Albee (1968) procedures. The reported analyses are averages of three to six points on each of three to five crystals per thin section.

Clinopyroxene

Pyroxenes from the St. Croix intrusives are all Na-poor and compositionally are augite or diopside (Table 3) according to the classification of Morimoto (1989). Three main compositional groupings may be distinguished mainly on the basis of their wollastonite component (Fig. 3). Zoning is minimal. Pyroxene from the Fountain Gabbro is intermediate between the Ca-rich pyroxene of the pyroxene porphyry and the Ca-poor pyroxene of the diabase. All contain moderate amounts of Al and display enrichment in the Ca-Fe^{3+}-Tschermak's component (Kushiro, 1962; Cebriá Gómez, 1990), with the pyroxenes from the pyroxene porphyry, the diabase, and the gabbro containing, 15 to 16%, 7 to 8%, and 7% of this $CaFe^{3+}Al^{iv}SiO_6$ molecule, respectively. Pyroxenes are further characterized by low Ti content that is typical of pyroxene from island arc igneous rocks (Basaltic Volcanism Study Project, 1981; Leterrier et al., 1982). Of additional petrogenetic significance is the composition of microphenocrysts and megacrysts in the pyroxene porphyry. Although these pyroxenes are petrographically distinct, they have closely similar compositions (Table 3), suggesting that they equilibrated during magmatic crystallization.

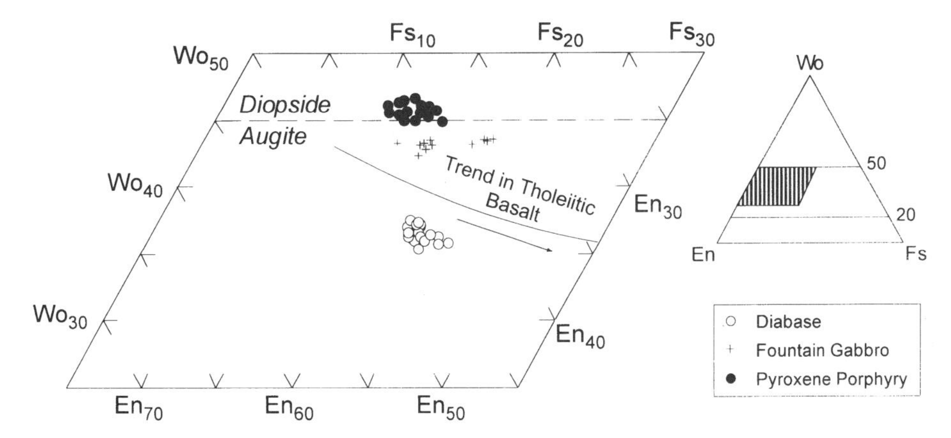

Figure 3. Clinopyroxene compositional variation in St. Croix intrusive rocks. Diopside/augite field boundary and fields in Wo-En-Fs inset are from Morimoto (1989).

Amphibole

Analyses of representative amphibole crystals are listed in Table 4 and the range in compositions is shown in Figure 4. Allocation of cations and amphibole nomenclature is according to Leake (1978). Two main compositional variants are present, both of which belong to the calcic group. Amphibole from the Fountain Gabbro is characterized by $(Na + K)_A < 0.5$ and compositional variations that range from ferro-hornblende to ferro-actinolitic hornblende. Amphibole from hornblende diabase and augite-hornblende diabase is compositionally distinct, having $(Na + K)_A > 0.5$, lower Si, and higher Mg number than amphibole in the gabbro. They are high-Mg ferroan pargasitic hornblende and ferroan pargasite (Fig. 4).

Biotite

Two analyses of biotite from the Fountain Gabbro are summarized in Table 4, a fresh orange-brown biotite and a biotite that is almost totally altered to light green chlorite and that contains only sporadic patches of the original biotite. The altered biotite is enriched in Al, Fe, Mg, and Ca, and depleted in Si, Al, Cr, and especially K. Individual spot analyses of both types are rather variable in composition. On a plot of Mg number versus Al^{iv} (Speer, 1984) (not shown), the fresh biotite is enriched in the eastonite and siderophyllite components. In terms of Mg, Al, and Fe + Mn, the fresh biotite lies within the field of biotite from orogenic andesites (Ewart, 1982).

Plagioclase

Representative microprobe analyses of plagioclase are reported in Table 5. Plagioclase compositions were also estimated by the extinction angle method using a four-axis universal stage. Compositional variations in the various intrusives are summarized in Tables 2 and 5.

TABLE 4. REPRESENTATIVE MICROPROBE ANALYSES AND STRUCTURAL FORMULA UNITS OF AMPHIBOLE AND BIOTITE

Sample	SX-3	SX-3	SX-3	SX-4	SX-6	SX-33
Rock	Gabbro	Gabbro	Gabbro	Gabbro	Diabase	Diabase
Mineral	Biotite	Biotite (altered)	Amphibole	Amphibole	Amphibole	Amphibole
(Wt. %)						
SiO_2	33.48	27.87	47.87	47.13	39.15	41.27
TiO_2	4.67	3.69	0.32	0.32	1.97	1.90
Al_2O_3	14.14	15.17	5.01	5.09	13.38	11.09
FeO	22.29	26.20	22.23	20.32	11.28	12.34
MgO	10.22	12.77	9.33	10.22	14.24	14.13
CaO	0.12	0.95	11.56	11.75	12.04	11.69
Na_2O	0.08	0.04	0.63	0.63	2.09	2.05
K_2O	8.31	1.43	0.49	0.47	0.79	0.51
MnO	0.13	0.16	0.41	0.31	0.20	0.37
NiO	0.02	0.07	0.02	0.02	0.01	0.05
Cr_2O_3	0.31	0.18	0.01	0.02	0.01	0.00
Total	93.77	88.53	97.88	96.28	95.16	95.40
Cations						
Si	5.304	4.665	7.279	7.238	5.959	6.262
Al (total)	2.640	2.993	0.897	0.921	2.398	1.982
Al(iv)			0.721	0.762	2.044	1.738
Al(vi)			0.176	0.159	0.354	0.244
Fe_2	2.953	3.668	2.826	2.61	1.435	1.566
Mg	2.414	3.187	2.115	2.341	3.229	3.195
Ca	0.020	0.170	1.884	1.933	1.962	1.901
Na	0.025	0.013	0.186	0.187	0.615	0.603
K	1.680	0.305	0.095	0.091	0.153	0.100
Ti	0.556	0.464	0.037	0.037	0.225	0.217
Mn	0.017	0.023	0.052	0.04	0.026	0.048
Cr	0.039	0.024	0.002	0.002	0.002	0.000
Ni	0.003	0.009	0.003	0.002	0.002	0.006
Mg#	44.97	46.49	42.80	47.28	69.23	67.11
Total Cat	15.652	15.521	15.376	15.402	16.003	15.880
Ox Equiv	22	22	23	23	23	23

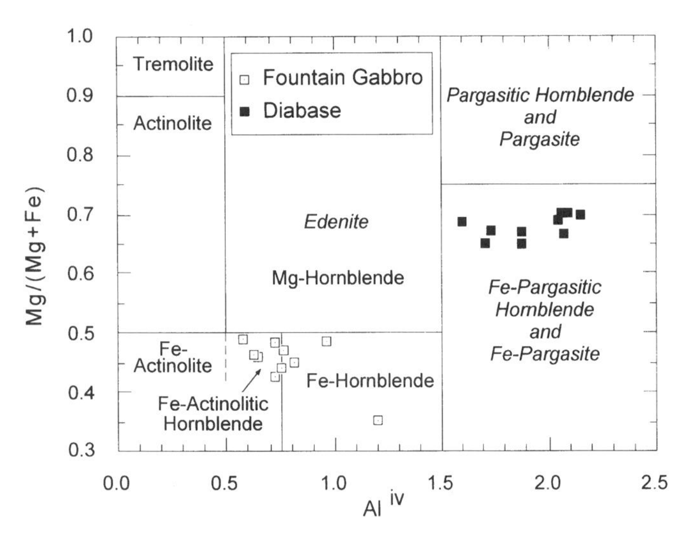

Figure 4. Compositional variation in amphibole from St. Croix intrusive rocks. Field boundaries are from Leake (1978) and Hammarstrom and Zen (1986).

GEOCHEMISTRY

Analytical methods

Major and trace element analyses of 16 igneous rocks from the island of St. Croix are presented in Table 6. Samples with the SX prefix were analyzed at the Centre for Earth Resources Research, Department of Earth Sciences, Memorial University of Newfoundland. Major elements, Sc, V, and Cr were analyzed by x-ray fluorescence (XRF) using fused lithium metaborate/lithium tetraborate glass beads. Trace elements were analyzed by inductively coupled plasma–mass spectrometry (ICP-MS) (Jenner et al., 1990; Longerich et al., 1990). Samples having the SC prefix were analyzed by Xral Activation Services, Ann Arbor, Michigan, where major elements, Ba, Nb, Rb, Sr, Y, and Cr were determined by XRF. Analyses of the other trace elements were carried out by instrumental neutron activation analysis (INAA). The greater precision of the ICP-MS analyses is readily evident in Table 6.

Effects of low temperature alteration

Because the igneous rocks of St. Croix contain minor to trace amounts of secondary minerals (noted previously), the effects of low-temperature alteration on the primary mineralogy need to be considered. The degree of alteration can be evaluated by comparing the distribution of the soluble large-ion lithophile elements (LILE: Rb, Ba, K) with the more stable (Pearce, 1983) light rare earth elements (LREE: La, Ce) that have similar degrees of incompatibility to LILE. The values for Rb are highly scattered if plotted against La (Fig. 5*A*), indicating significant redistribution of Rb during incipient burial metamorphism. These results can be compared, for example, to a similar plot (Fig. 5*B*) for a suite of lavas from the Lesser Antilles that show a positive linear array of incompatible elements. In contrast to the Rb distribution in St. Croixian rocks, both Ce versus Ba (Fig. 5*C*) and La versus K_2O (Fig. 5*E*) form linear arrays that are approximately parallel to 1:1 enrichment vectors as might be expected from magmatic variation in a suite of co-genetic rocks. Furthermore, the degree of variation of Ba and K_2O in the St. Croix rocks, reflected in the standard deviation from least-square trends (Fig. 5*C*, *E*) are comparable to those displayed by recent lavas from the Lesser Antilles (Fig. 5*D*, *F*) and from lavas of the Mariana arc (Fig. 5*F*); hence, the coherent patterns of St. Croix Ba and K_2O are indicative of essentially primary distribution of these two elements.

Major and trace elements

St. Croix igneous rocks are mainly CIPW quartz- or hypersthene-olivine normative (Table 6). The only exceptions are the nepheline-normative Southgate Diorite (SX-1, high alkali content) and a basalt boulder (SC-31, low SiO_2).

The compositional variation of SiO_2 and K_2O of St. Croix rocks is shown on Figure 6. Using the chemical classification scheme of Peccerillo and Taylor (1976), the pyroxene porphyry, a mafic boulder, the hornblende diabase, and the dacite all plot in the calc-alkaline field; the augite-hornblende diabase and Fountain Gabbro plot in both the calc-alkaline and high-K calc-alkaline fields; and Southgate Diorite plots in the high-K calc-alkaline field. On an AFM diagram (not shown), all samples lie within the calc-alkaline (or hypersthenic) field of Kuno (1968). With the exception of Fountain Gabbro, the samples form an elongate array toward the alkali apex. The gabbros are displaced toward the MgO corner. Similarly, a plot of FeO^T/MgO ratio versus SiO_2 (also not shown) shows that St. Croix rocks lack iron enrichment but lie along the tholeiite/calc-alkaline boundary line of Miyashiro (1974). In this regard, they are similar to other Caribbean igneous rocks in having slightly elevated FeO^T/MgO ratios (Brown et al., 1977; Walker, 1989).

Petrographic and geochemical evidence indicate that the dikes and sills have undergone a degree of low-pressure fractionation and do not record primary magmatic compositions. This evidence includes (1) the general presence of the phenocryst assemblage plagioclase + augite + hornblende ± olivine (Table 2); (2) low Mg numbers of 43 to 53 (Table 6); and (3) low Ni (<120 ppm) and Cr (<280 ppm) contents; all of which suggest that the dikes and sills have undergone fractionation. Also of note are samples of the Fountain gabbro that have high Mg numbers, but which are cumulate rocks, as evidenced by their texture and high Eu content (Eu/Eu* = 1.1 to 1.4), (Table 6); these gabbros probably do not represent magmatic compositions.

The effects of gabbroic-type fractionation are also recorded by the distribution of compatible elements. Plots of both SiO_2 versus MgO (Fig. 7*A*) and Mg number versus Ni (Fig. 7*B*) reveal linear arrays, both within and among rock groups. These varia-

TABLE 5. REPRESENTATIVE MICROPROBE ANALYSES AND STRUCTURAL FORMULA UNITS OF PLAGIOCLASE

Sample	SX-3	SX-3	SX-7	SX-7	SX-8	SX-8	SX-9
Rock	Gabbro	Gabbro	Diabase	Diabase	Diabase	Diabase	Dacite
Mineral	Rim	Core	Rim	Core	Rim	Core	Random
(Wt. %)							
SiO_2	46.47	45.66	53.13	45.54	53.56	51.54	66.73
TiO_2	0.00	0.00	0.04	0.64	0.04	0.02	0.00
Al_2O_3	33.75	33.94	27.87	23.78	27.68	28.94	22.31
FeO	0.25	0.21	0.75	8.71	0.87	1.06	0.04
MgO	0.00	0.00	0.08	2.31	0.10	0.16	0.01
CaO	17.25	17.60	11.21	13.49	11.27	12.98	1.49
Na_2O	1.81	1.50	5.11	1.97	4.78	3.93	9.22
K_2O	0.04	0.04	0.51	0.27	0.47	0.36	0.08
MnO	0.00	0.01	0.01	0.18	0.03	0.01	0.01
NiO	0.03	0.00	0.02	0.00	0.00	0.02	0.01
Cr_2O_3	0.01	0.03	0.01	0.04	0.02	0.01	0.01
Total	99.60	98.97	98.72	96.90	98.83	99.03	99.91
Cations (O = 8)							
Si	2.148	2.125	2.447	2.259	2.461	2.378	2.908
Al	1.838	1.862	1.514	1.369	1.500	1.574	1.146
Fe_2	0.010	0.008	0.029	0.379	0.034	0.041	0.001
Mg	0.000	0.000	0.006	0.179	0.007	0.011	0.001
Ca	0.854	0.878	0.554	0.711	0.556	0.642	0.070
Na	0.163	0.135	0.456	0.188	0.425	0.352	0.779
K	0.002	0.003	0.030	0.018	0.027	0.021	0.005
Ti	0.000	0.000	0.002	0.025	0.001	0.001	0.000
Mn	0.000	0.001	0.000	0.008	0.001	0.001	0.000
Cr	0.000	0.001	0.000	0.001	0.001	0.001	0.000
Ni	0.001	0.000	0.001	0.000	0.000	0.001	0.000
Total Cat	5.015	5.012	5.038	5.134	5.014	5.021	4.910
Albite	15.94	13.29	43.89	20.38	42.19	34.66	91.26
Anorthite	83.85	86.47	53.25	77.62	55.09	63.26	8.18
Orthoclase	0.21	0.24	2.86	2.00	2.72	2.08	0.56

tions are consistent with general low-pressure fractionation of mainly plagioclase and pyroxene and probably olivine.

The distribution of incompatible elements is also consistent with subvolcanic gabbroic fractionation. Figure 8 shows the effects of fractionation on the main element groups (LILE-K_2O, LREE-La, HREE-Yb, HFSE-Hf, and Th). Most of the diabase samples lie along or between fractionation vectors for plagioclase and clinopyroxene. The chemical trends in the diabases also coincide approximately with 1:1 enrichment vectors, which are further consistent with gabbroic fractionation. Some of the scatter in the data may be attributable to variations in the degree of partial melting or to minor differences in the composition of a related series of source melts. The main elemental distribution, however, is dominated by the effects of fractionation. In addition, incompatible element pairs such as Ce/Ba (Fig. 5*C*), La/K_2O (Fig. 5*E*), Hf/Th, Hf/ La, and Hf/Yb also form linear arrays with broadly parallel 1:1 enrichment vectors. These relations are consistent with the fractional crystallization of gabbroic phases that are typically depleted in incompatible elements.

The above conclusions are further supported by least-squares calculations (Bryan et al., 1969; Wright and Doherty, 1970). Table 7 shows the results of the calculation made utilizing pyroxene hornblende diabase (SX-8: Table 6) as the fractionated or derivative rock and a representative island arc calc-alkaline basalt (Perfit et al., 1980) as the hypothetical parent. The model calculation demonstrates that the diabase can be derived from the basalt by subtraction of olivine (7.5%) + plagioclase (17.7%) + clinopyroxene (19.8%) + titanomagnetite (2.3%). This typical phenocrystic assemblage, together with the generally low residual of the best-fit composition, is not unreasonable and suggests that the diabase may have been derived from a fairly typical calc-alkaline basalt parent. With respect to variations within the St. Croix dike suite, a further calculation (Table 7) shows that hornblende diabase (SC-30: Table 6) can be differentiated from less evolved augite hornblende diabase (SX-8) by fractionation of olivine (3.0%), plagioclase (6.6%), clinopyroxene (20.5%), hornblende (3.8%), and magnetite (4.6%). The low residual (0.098) of this calculation along with the petrography of the two rocks are consistent with a fractional crystallization relationship.

TABLE 6. MAJOR AND TRACE ELEMENT DATA FOR ST. CROIX INTRUSIVE ROCKS

Sample	SX-1	SC-2	SX-3	SC-4	SC-6	SX-7	SX-8	SX-9	SX-10	SC-11	SC-17
Rock	Diorite	Gabbro	Gabbro	Gabbro	Hb Diabase	Px Hb Diabase	Px Hb Diabase	Dacite	Porphyry	Porphyry	Px Hb Diabase
Intrusive	Pluton	Pluton	Pluton	Pluton	Sill	Sill	Sill	Sill	Sill	Sill	Sill
SiO_2	52.50	50.60	48.10	49.10	54.30	52.50	50.60	63.00	45.90	45.80	56.20
TiO_2	0.93	0.24	0.32	0.39	0.77	0.94	0.86	0.50	1.09	1.09	0.64
Al_2O_3	16.10	16.10	21.60	21.90	17.80	16.10	13.60	16.70	14.00	14.10	14.20
Fe_2O_3	9.02	5.62	5.75	4.57	8.30	11.50	12.30	5.12	14.20	14.40	6.90
MnO	0.17	0.17	0.11	0.10	0.28	0.18	0.21	0.15	0.19	0.20	0.16
MgO	4.25	7.27	4.48	4.59	3.46	4.60	6.93	1.95	7.46	7.84	3.36
CaO	7.75	17.30	15.10	13.20	7.71	8.91	9.45	2.97	11.90	12.50	7.72
Na_2O	4.79	1.53	1.83	2.36	3.47	2.65	2.10	6.27	0.90	0.94	3.46
K_2O	1.94	0.63	0.88	1.48	1.09	1.54	1.17	1.22	0.82	0.64	1.67
P_2O_5	0.42	0.08	0.10	0.05	0.28	0.29	0.24	0.20	0.13	0.13	0.26
LOI	2.47	1.00	1.77	2.54	3.08	0.93	1.47	2.16	2.70	3.08	4.20
Total	100.34	100.54	100.04	100.28	100.54	100.14	;98.93	100.24	99.29	100.72	96.77
Mg#	48.28	71.93	60.68	66.55	45.23	44.21	52.74	43.00	51.00	51.89	49.10
Q	0.00	0.18	0.00	0.00	7.34	3.94	2.48	12.02	0.00	0.00	11.00
Ne	1.41	0.00	0.00	0.27	0.00	0.00	0.00	0.00	0.00	0.00	0.00
Di	16.23	40.35	21.57	16.62	5.80	12.54	18.07	0.00	22.87	24.61	16.02
Hy	0.00	3.97	1.50	0.00	13.62	17.33	22.96	7.99	24.00	19.67	6.75
Ol	7.91	0.00	3.09	4.51	0.00	0.00	0.00	0.00	0.41	3.67	0.00
Li	2.52		5.58			7.27	11.59	17.03	20.64		
Cs	0.15	0.6	0.46	1	0.9	0.25	0.29	0.18	1.88	2	1
Rb	33.75	20	30.57	30	20	19.47	14.88	18.84	16.23	20	30
Sr	622.2	670	851.3	900	680	436.9	346.0	804.3	514.9	450	770
Ba	881.2	210	204.6	300	360	642.6	483.6	942.0	419.2	390	900
Th	2.24	1.4	3.01	1.7	1.5	1.28	0.97	1.36	0.42	0.3	1.7
U	0.61	1.3	1.58	1.2	0.7	0.67	0.59	0.68	0.24	0.2	0.6
Nb	4.32	5	3.29	3	4	2.54	2.13	11.15	1.53	2	5
Ta	0.26	0.3	0.23	0.3	0.2	0.17	0.15	0.66	0.10	0.2	0.6
Zr	24.01	30	30.16	20	60	63.62	55.18	36.03	19.52	20	25
Hf	1.29	1.4	1.52	1.4	2	2.09	1.70	1.36	0.74	0.9	1.8
Pb	8.57	4	4.76	4	4	4.22	3.66	6.53	1.67	2	9
La	19.39	6.7	8.86	7.5	10.6	9.22	7.79	16.48	3.61	3.7	13.3
Ce	42.18	15	18.19	16	23	20.63	17.58	33.17	8.68	9	27
Pr	5.63		2.36			2.96	2.55	4.18	1.37		
Nd	24.49	9	9.73	8	13	13.36	11.87	15.89	7.12	6	10
Sm	5.87	2.15	2.29	1.69	3.14	3.51	3.13	3.20	2.32	1.73	2.49
Eu	1.63	1	0.79	0.95	1.28	1.15	1.02	1.07	0.86	0.74	0.84
Gd	6.02		2.27			3.80	3.51	2.89	2.92		
Tb	0.85	0.3	0.32	0.3	0.5	0.61	0.52	0.38	0.44	0.4	0.3
Dy	5.26		2.14			3.85	3.53	2.32	3.01		
Hb	1.05		0.42			0.81	0.71	0.45	0.63		
Er	3.00		1.25			2.42	2.13	1.20	1.67		
Tm	0.43		0.18			0.33	0.31	0.17	0.25		
Yb	2.69	1.35	1.13	1.01	2.03	2.31	2.06	1.18	1.60	1.54	1.41
Lu	0.41	0.21	0.17	0.15	0.31	0.34	0.30	0.17	0.23	0.23	0.21
Y	26.67	10	9.47	10	10	18.87	17.95	11.23	15.11	10	10
Sc	28.3	37.5	29.4	22	26.2	31.9	41.5	13.6	88.3	84.3	18.8
V	260	150	210	130	180	370	360	130	560	560	170
Cr	99	150	130	150	73	110	250	60	280	250	30
Co	27	24	30	20	19	35	46	13	47	47	16
Ni	40	140	53	130	20	62	120	23	87	74	36

TABLE 6. MAJOR AND TRACE ELEMENT DATA FOR ST. CROIX INTRUSIVE ROCKS (continued – page 2)

Sample	SC-24	SC-28	SC-30	SC-31	SC-33
Rock	Hb Diabase	Px Hb Diabase	Hb Diabase	Basalt	Px Hb Diabase
Type	Sill	Sill	Boulder	Boulder	Sill
SiO_2	56.10	53.20	56.40	44.70	55.00
TiO_2	0.66	0.71	0.69	1.18	0.69
Al_2O_3	17.00	16.90	17.20	10.10	18.00
Fe_2O_3	7.62	9.75	7.82	16.30	7.14
MnO	0.17	0.22	0.18	0.22	0.21
MgO	3.70	4.57	2.85	8.48	2.82
CaO	8.00	5.74	7.33	12.70	7.68
Na_2O	2.86	5.39	3.21	2.28	3.36
K_2O	1.07	1.10	1.56	0.42	1.76
P_2O_5	0.20	0.21	0.23	0.14	0.29
LOI	1.55	3.00	2.40	2.90	2.40
Total	98.93	99.79	99.87	99.42	99.35
Mg#	49.03	48.15	41.93	50.75	43.90
Q	12.42	0.00	11.22	0.00	8.15
Ne	0.00	0.00	0.00	3.29	0.00
Di	6.86	7.27	6.05	39.92	6.44
Hy	12.84	4.41	11.24	0.00	9.95
Ol	0.00	10.20	0.00	16.31	0.00
Li					
Cs	0.3	0.2	0.4	0.3	1
Rb	30	20	20	20	10
Sr	610	450	410	150	510
Ba	550	600	530	130	420
Th	1.2	0.8	0.8	0.4	1.8
U	0.5	0.5	0.4	0.1	0.8
Nb	5	5	8	4	10
Ta	0.5	0.5	0.7	0.6	0.3
Zr	25	30	30	20	25
Hf	1.8	1.3	2.1	0.6	2.2
Pb	14	6	30	13	5
La	9	7.2	8.9	3.7	13.1
Ce	19	17	20	9	28
Pr					
Nd	10	9	11	6	15
Sm	2.37	2.18	2.53	1.65	3.55
Eu	0.73	0.86	0.85	0.58	0.96
Gd					
Tb	0.3	0.4	0.4	0.3	0.5
Dy					
Ho					
Er					
Tm					
Yb	1.67	1.62	1.57	1.15	2.22
Lu	0.27	0.24	0.24	0.19	0.35
Y	10	20	20	10	30
Sc	25.7	35.6	23.6	83.7	17.2
V	200	290	180	660	110
Cr	30	50	10	270	10
Co	17	23	15	46	13
Ni	29	35	9	54	8

Characteristics of incompatible trace elements

The igneous rocks on St. Croix have trace element affinities of island arc volcanic rocks. They are characterized by moderately high LILE/LREE ratios such as Ba/La (Fig. 9), which are typical of island arc volcanic rocks (Hawkesworth and Powell, 1980; Kay, 1980; Perfit et al., 1980; White and Patchett, 1984; Arculus and Powell, 1986). Furthermore, these ratios serve as useful discriminants for distinguishing subduction-related igneous rocks from oceanic basalts in nonconvergent tectonic settings. As shown in Figure 9, the St. Croix rocks have higher Ba/La ratio than most typical mid-ocean ridge basalt (N-MORB and E-MORB) and ocean island basalt (OIB) samples. In contrast, the Th/Ta ratio (Fig. 9), previously used by Wood et al. (1979b) to distinguish magma series of converging plate margins from other oceanic environments, show considerable overlap between St. Croix instrusives and E-MORB and OIB. Only the more geochemically evolved St. Croix rocks have higher Th/Ta ratio.

Their subduction zone character is further demonstrated on N-MORB–normalized elemental distribution diagrams in which the St. Croix intrusives (Fig. 10) uniformly display the following features typical of island arc associations: (1) sharp positive spikes for LILE (as discussed previously for Ba but also including Rb, K, Pb, and Sr), representing strong overenrichment in these elements ranging from about 150 to 5 times N-MORB; (2) moderate enrichment in LREE of about two to eight times N-MORB; (3) strong negative anomalies for HFSE (Nb, Ta, Zr, Hf, and Ti); and (4) depleted heavy rare earth element (HREE) abundances, ranging from about 0.4 to 0.9 times N-MORB. All these characteristics are similar to patterns displayed by equivalent Campanian-age island arc lavas from northeastern and central Puerto Rico (Jolly et al., Chapter 3, this volume, Table 2, unpublished data).

Additional evidence of the chemical character of St. Croix rocks is the abundance of U and Th. These two elements have been used as primary discriminants of Greater Antilles igneous rock series (Donnelly et al., 1971; Donnelly and Rogers, 1978, 1980). In these early studies, the calc-alkaline series has been characterized by higher U and Th content than island arc tholeiite (primitive island arc series of Donnelly) or basalt of the Caribbean plateau province (Donnelly et al., 1973). The St. Croix intrusives have U and Th concentrations that are similar to the Greater Antilles calc-alkaline igneous suites, containing Th contents >1.0 ppm and U contents >0.5 ppm (Table 6). The only exceptions are the pyroxene porphyries and basalt boulder (Table 6), which have lower U and Th content. These lower abundances are attributed to clinopyroxene accumulation, which has the effect of diluting the magmatic U and Th component. Consistent with this interpretation is the fact that similar depletions in the other incompatible elements are also recorded in these rocks (Table 6; Fig. 10).

Although St. Croix igneous rocks have a distinct subduction zone and calc-alkaline signature, there are also differences in trace element concentrations among the individual rock types. These

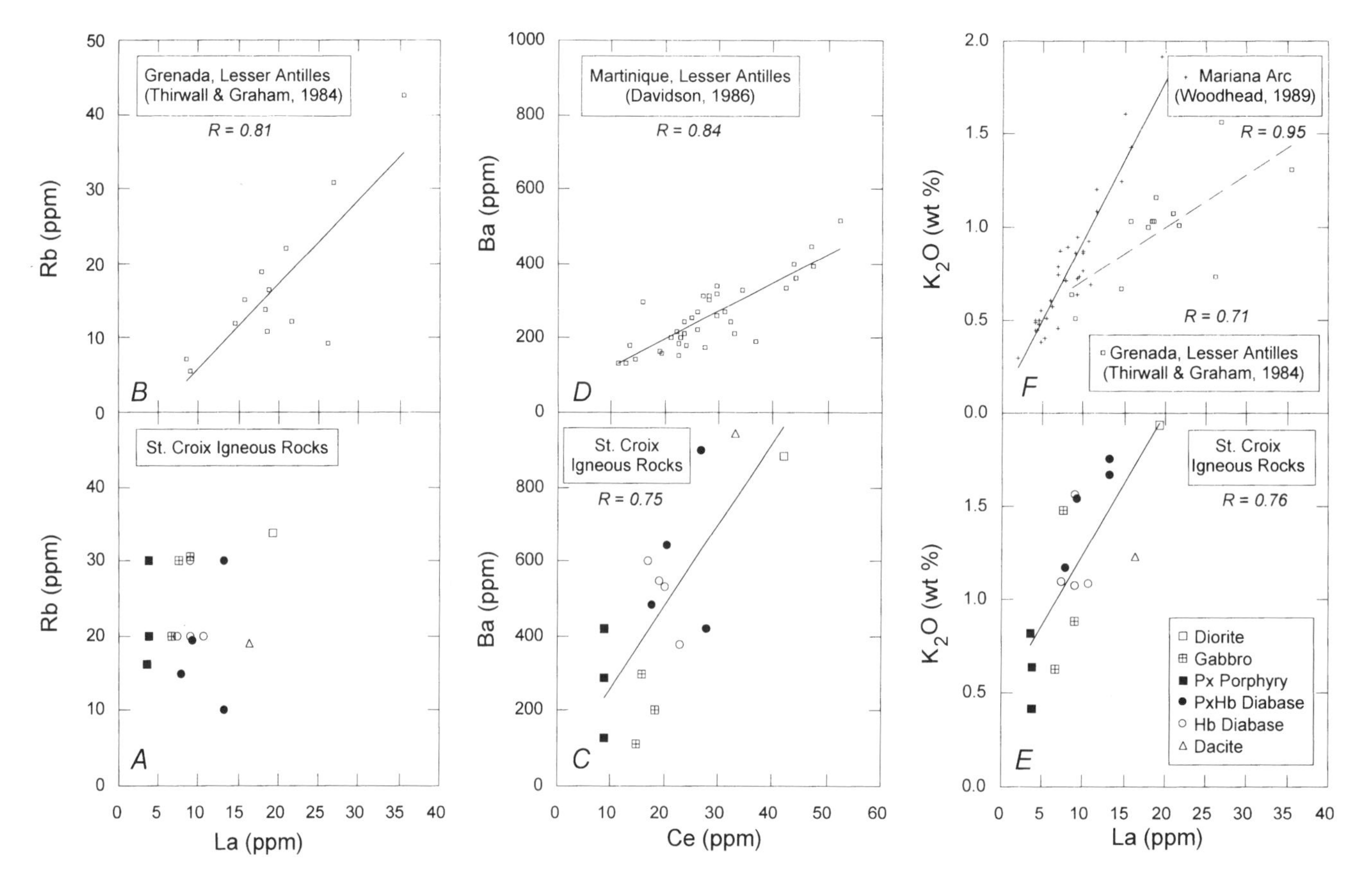

Figure 5. Interelement comparison of soluble LILE (Rb, Ba, K_2O) and insoluble LREE (La, Ce) in St. Croix igneous rocks. *A* and *B*, La versus Rb; *C* and *D*, Ce versus Ba; *E* and *F*, La versus K_2O. St. Croix data (*A*, *C*, *E*) are compared to recent lavas from Grenada (*B*, *F*) (Thirlwall and Graham, 1984), Martinique (*D*) (Davidson, 1986), and the Marianas (*F*) (Woodhead, 1989).

differences are evident, for example, in REE abundances (Fig. 11). St. Croix plutons (Fig. 11*A*) have slightly elevated LREE patterns (Ce_N/Yb_N ~3 to 5), with the Southgate Diorite having higher levels of total REE enrichment than the Fountain Gabbro. The positive Eu anomalies of the gabbro reflects its cumulative character. The essentially flat REE patterns of the pyroxene porphyrys and the basalt boulder are also distinct (Fig. 11*B*). These rocks have LREE concentrations of about 15 times those of chondrites and $(Ce/Yb)_N$ ratios of 1.5 to 2.0. Their abundances are consistent with the presence of excess clinopyroxene (and to a lesser extent, amphibole, in the porphyry). The more voluminous pyroxene hornblende diabase and hornblende diabase sills and dikes are more enriched in LREE (Fig. 11*C*, *D*). The former have $(Ce/Yb)_N$ ratios of 2 to 7 and the latter, 3 to 4. The dacite (Fig. 11*D*) is the most LREE-enriched of the dikes and sills and comparable to the Southgate Diorite in LREE content.

Comparison to other arcs

The overall trace element REE enrichment patterns of St. Croix igneous rocks are similar to the late Cretaceous calc-alkaline sequence of Puerto Rico (Donnelly and Rogers, 1980). The calc-alkaline character of the St. Croix rocks is consistent with relatively late emplacement into a thick sequence of turbidites and related rocks. The calc-alkaline series in the Greater Antilles is typically developed following the initial stages of arc development and during the more mature stages as the island arc platform began to emerge (Donnelly and Rogers, 1980; Donnelly, 1989; Larue et al., 1991b; Donnelly, 1994). Furthermore, the close similarity in trace element concentration between the St. Croix intrusives and contemporaneous volcanics in Puerto Rico (Fig. 10) suggests that a broad island arc platform extending through these two regions was in existence by Campanian time. These relationships suggest further that the thick volcanogenic strata of St. Croix (Whetten, 1966; Speed and Joyce, 1989) and volcanogenic rocks of similar age in Puerto Rico (Jolly et al., Chapter 1, this volume), such as the Guaynabo Formation (Pease, 1968) in northeastern Puerto Rico and the Yauco Formation (Kruskensky and Monroe, 1978; Larue et al., 1991a) of western Puerto Rico, may have accumulated in a similar tectonic environment.

An intriguing aspect of modern island arcs is their geochemical diversity. Figure 12, a plot of $(La/Sm)_N$ against $(La/Sr)_N$, compares St. Croix intrusives to the volcanics of other intraoceanic arcs. Significantly, the intrusives exhibit consis-

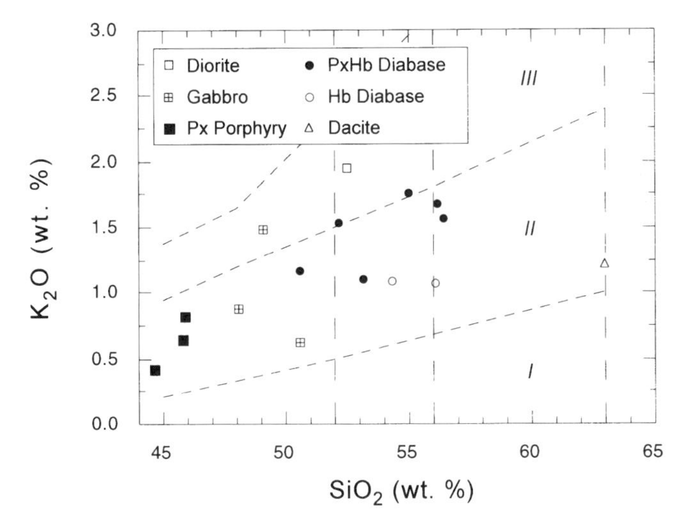

Figure 6. Variation of K_2O versus SiO_2 of St. Croix intrusive igneous rocks. I, Island arc tholeiite series; II, calc-alkaline series; III, high-K calc-alkaline series. Compositional boundary lines are from Peccerillo and Taylor (1976), as modified by Rickwood (1989).

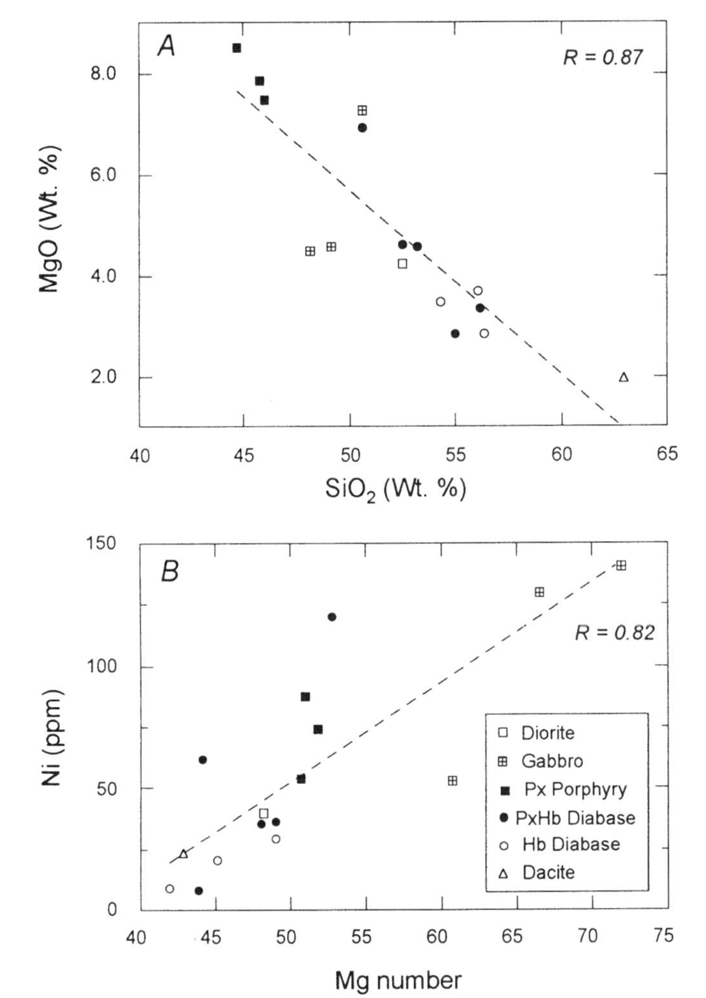

Figure 7. Variation of selected compatible elements in St. Croix intrusive igneous rocks. *A*, SiO_2 versus MgO; *B*, Mg number versus Ni. Dashed lines are least squares-regression lines of the total suite.

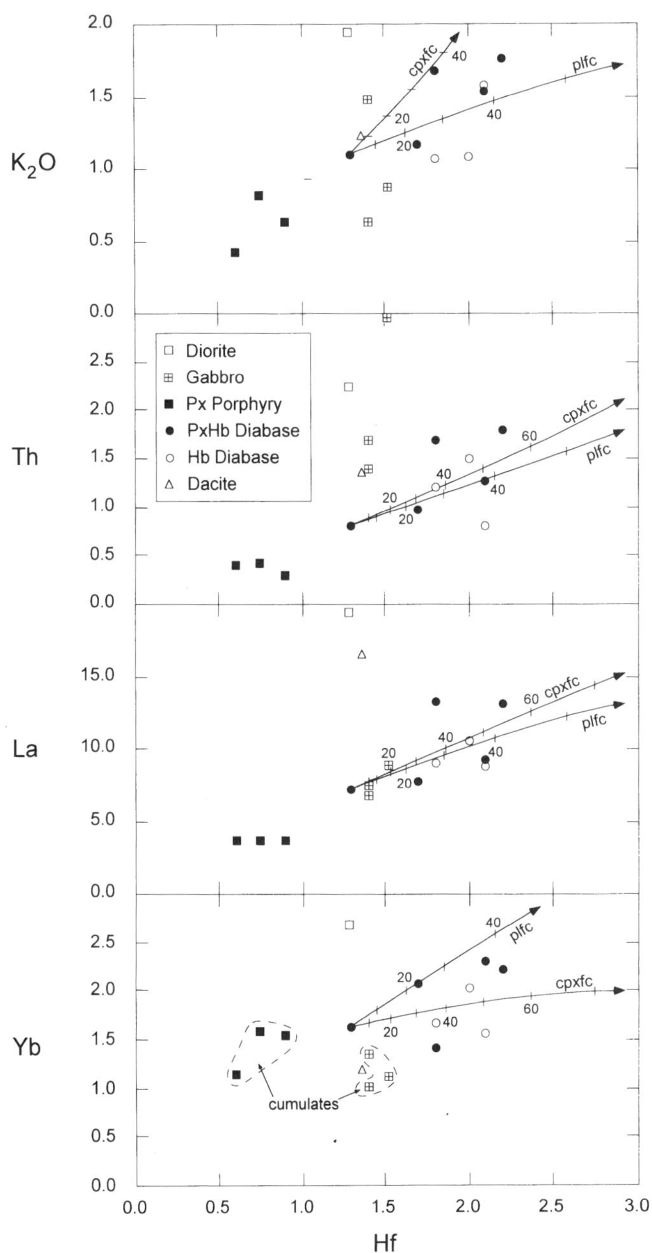

Figure 8. Distribution of incompatible elements plotted against Hf abundances in St. Croix igneous rocks. Partition coefficients used to construct fractionation vectors of plagioclase (plfc) and clinopyroxene (cpxfc) are from Jolly et al., Chapter 3, this volume, Table 6).

tently lower ratios in these elemental pairs (Fig. 12) than modern island arc basalts (IAB) analyzed by White and Patchett (1984) in their survey of some representative intraoceanic arcs, including the Marianas, Aleutians, and Lesser Antilles. Instead, relatively high Sr abundances resemble patterns in the New Britain (Woodhead and Johnson, 1993) and Tonga-Kermadec (Ewart et al., 1977; Ewart and Hawkesworth, 1987) arc, both of which reflect subduction of a young, sediment-poor slab. They are, however, distinct from most Tonga-Kermadec volcanics

TABLE 7. LEAST-SQUARES MODELING CALCULATIONS OF ST. CROIX DIABASES

Sample	Island Arc Calc-Alkaline Basalt*			Pyroxene-Hornblende Diabase (SX-8)†		
	Observed	Calculated	Residual	Observed	Calculated	Residual
SiO_2	49.40	49.44	-0.043	50.60	50.60	-0.001
TiO_2	0.70	0.82	-0.121	0.86	0.89	-0.025
Al_2O_3	13.29	13.31	-0.016	13.60	13.57	0.032
FeO	10.15	10.13	0.024	11.07	11.07	-0.000
MnO	0.20	0.11	0.088	0.21	0.20	0.014
MgO	10.44	10.41	0.031	6.93	6.93	0.001
CaO	12.22	12.15	0.072	6.45	9.45	0.002
Na_2O	2.16	1.73	0.434	2.10	2.34	-0.241
K_2O	1.06	0.71	0.347	1.17	1.00	0.168
P_2O_5	0.20	0.13	0.072	0.24	0.14	0.100
		SSR = 0.345			SSR = 0.098	
	Component	Percent		Component	Percent	
	SX-8	52.7		SC-30	61.5	
	Ol	7.5		Ol	3.0	
	Plag	17.7		Plag	6.6	
	Cpx	19.8		Cpx	20.5	
	Mt	2.3		Hbld	3.8	
				Mt	4.6	

*Mass-balance calculation of an island arc calc-alkaline basalt (Perfit et al., 1980) as a hypothetical parent magma that differentiates to pyroxene hornblende diabase (SX-8) by fractionation of stoichiometric olivine (Fo_{85}), plagioclase (An_{70}), augite ($Wo_{45}En_{45}Fs_{10}$), and titano-magnetite ($Mt_{55}Ulv_{45}$).
†Derivation of hornblende diabase (SC-30) from pyroxene hornblende diabase (SX-8) by fractionation of olivine, plagioclase, augite, hornblende, and magnetite. Minerals used in the modeling are as follows: olivine and Fe-Ti oxide from Lewis, 1973; clinopyroxene (Table 2, core crystals from SX-8); hornblende (Table 3, SC-6); and plagioclase (Table 4, core crystals from SX-8).

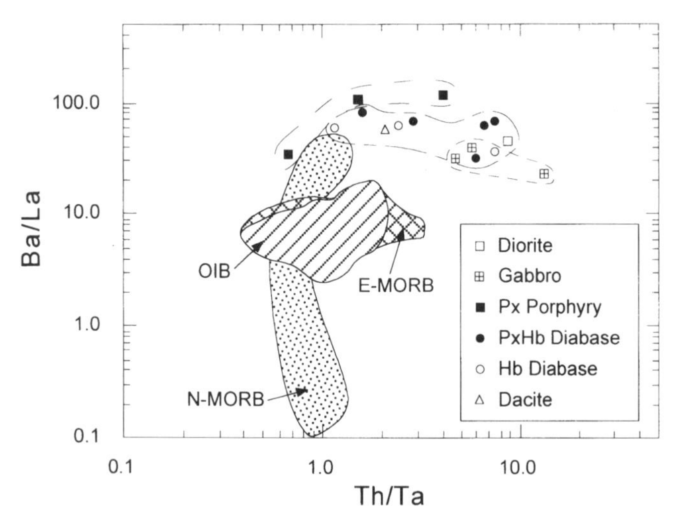

Figure 9. Th/Ta versus Ba/La ratios in St. Croix intrusive igneous rocks compared to oceanic basalts from nonconvergent tectonic settings. Data sources: N-MORB (Wood et al., 1979a; Bougault et al., 1984; Schiano et al., 1993); E-MORB (Wood et al., 1979a,c); ocean island basalt, OIB (Roden et al., 1984; Chen and Frey, 1985; Palacz and Saunders, 1986; Gautier et al., 1990; Frey et al., 1994).

and from the less-evolved segments of the New Britain arc in their greater enrichment in LREE. In this enrichment, they closely resemble Campanian-age volcanic rocks in Puerto Rico (Fig. 12).

PETROGENESIS OF ST. CROIX INTRUSIVES

Composition of the mantle wedge source

The presence of subduction-related calc-alkaline igneous rocks on St. Croix leads to considerations of the composition and characteristics of the mantle wedge beneath the island and to the possible role that a subduction-related component may have had in generating these rocks. The composition of the mantle wedge beneath St. Croix is unknown, so that the presence of a depleted N-MORB–type component in the wedge as opposed to an enriched E-MORB–type component cannot be precluded by the available data. However, in nearby Puerto Rico, LREE-depleted basement tholeiitic basalt associated with partly serpentinized peridotite, amphibolite, and siliceous radiolarian sedimentary rock of the Sierra Bermeja complex are thought to represent the pre-arc oceanic crust (Donnelly et al., 1971; Montgomery et al., 1994a,b), which is consistent with depleted mantle beneath at least a portion of the Caribbean plate. Moreover, relatively non-radiogenic, N-MORB–like Sr and Nd isotopic ratios throughout the Puerto Rican lava sequence (Jolly et al., Chapter 3, this volume), are consistent with minimal involvement of enriched mantle. In contrast to the depleted character of early Puerto Rican crust, early crust to the west in the Dominican Republic, now preserved as the Duarte complex (Lewis and Jiménez G., 1991) is enriched in trace elements. For example, normalized average ratios of La/Sm and La/Nb are 1.7 and 1.9, respectively. These and other trace element ratios in Duarte rocks are more similar to E-MORB or T-MORB (transitional) than to N-MORB (Lewis and Jiménez G., 1991).

The mantle wedge beneath St. Croix may also have contained an E-MORB–type component. Samples of augite hornblende diabase and hornblende diabase with the highest Mg numbers (Table 6), for example, have normalized average La/Sm and La/Nb ratios of 2.4 (Fig. 12) and 2.5, respectively. These high ratios suggest that the diabases may have been derived from an enriched source. Furthermore, rare earth abundances of the St. Croix intrusives are more closely similar to E-MORB than to N-MORB. Concentrations of LREE and HREE are, respectively, 0.6 to 2.0 and 0.5 to 1.0 times E-MORB, compared, for example, to values of 1.5 to 8 and 0.3 to 0.8 for N-MORB.

High field strength element (HFSE) anomalies

One of the most characteristic features of island arc igneous rocks is the presence of prominent negative normalized HFSE anomalies (McCulloch and Gamble, 1991; Hawkesworth et al., 1993a). This phenomena may be the result, in part, of very low solubility of HFSE in aqueous fluids (Pearce, 1983; Tatsumi et

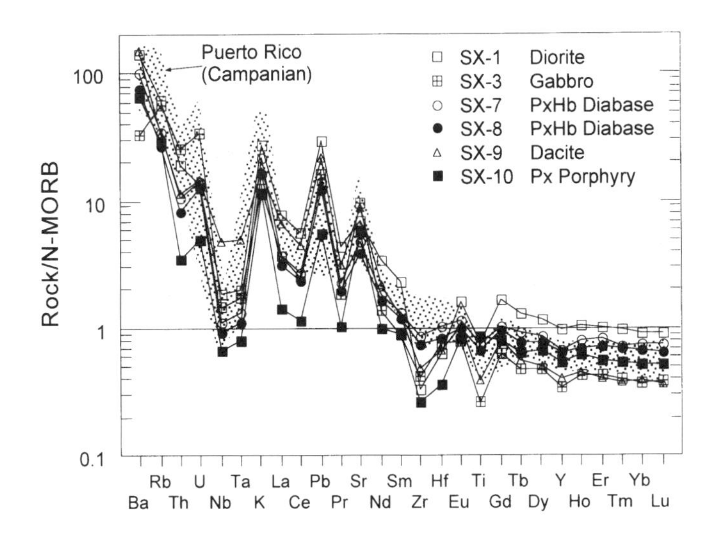

Figure 10. Representative N-MORB–normalized incompatible element patterns of St. Croix intrusive rocks. Elemental sequence and normalization factors from Sun and McDonough (1989). Stippled pattern, volcanic strata (15 samples) of Campanian age in central and northeastern Puerto Rico (Jolly et al., Chapter 3, this volume, Table 2; unpublished data).

al., 1986) and of low abundances of these elements in subducted pelagic sediments. The main cause of the low abundances of HFSE in arc magmas, however, is presumably attributable to partial melting in the mantle wedge.

The question of the incompatibility of HFSE in arc magmas has been controversial, and Ringwood (1990) suggested that residual titanate may play a significant role. However, a number of researchers (McCulloch and Gamble, 1991; Woodhead et al., 1993; Thirlwall et al., 1994) have recently demonstrated that ratios of the incompatible elements such as Zr/Nb in island arc basalts are very similar to primitive MORB, regardless of HFSE concentrations, and that specific Nb-bearing residual phases such as rutile must be postulated to be absent from the arc source region. They further concluded that HFSE behave incompatibly during arc melting, and that the solid/melt distribution coefficients (D) for HFSE in arc rocks are similar to those in MORB. A plot of Nb versus Hf/Nb (Fig. 13) shows that South Pacific island arc basalts (McCulloch and Gamble, 1991) and Puerto Rican island arc basalts (Jolly et al., Chapter 3, this volume) form linear arrays that overlap primitive MORB and have negative slopes, consistent with distribution coefficient patterns of $D_{Hf}>D_{Nb}$. The St. Croix igneous suite (Fig. 13) forms a similar negative linear array subparallel to the trend of primitive MORB data, but with generally lower Hf/Nb ratio. These relations suggest that the distribution coefficients of HFSE such as Hf in St. Croix rocks may be similar to those in N-MORB (Bougault et al., 1980; Hofmann, 1988) where $D_{Zr\sim Hf}>D_{Nb}$. Furthermore, the incompatible behavior of the HFSE and their low concentrations in olivine, plagioclase, clinopyroxene, and orthopyroxene are insensitive to gabbroic fractionation (Pearce, 1983). Thus, a range in Hf/Nb and Hf/Yb ratios may reflect variations in the degree of melting rather than fractionation processes.

Heavy rare earth element (HREE) patterns

The St. Croix igneous suite, like its calc-alkaline counterparts in Puerto Rico (Jolly et al., Chapter 3, this volume) and Hispaniola (Lebrón and Perfit, 1994), display uniformly flat normalized HREE patterns (Fig. 10). The abundance of HREE is typically lower than in N-MORB, even in moderately fractionated end-members. Flat HREE patterns in MORB-normalized elemental distribution diagrams, together with different concentrations levels in the HREE (Fig. 10), reflect a range in the degree of fusion of the source area. These relations are inconsistent with partial fusion of garnet peridotite. They are consistent, however, with partial melt generation from spinel peridotite (i.e., low-angle subduction zone), where bulk partition coefficients are controlled by clinopyroxene rather than by garnet, and where

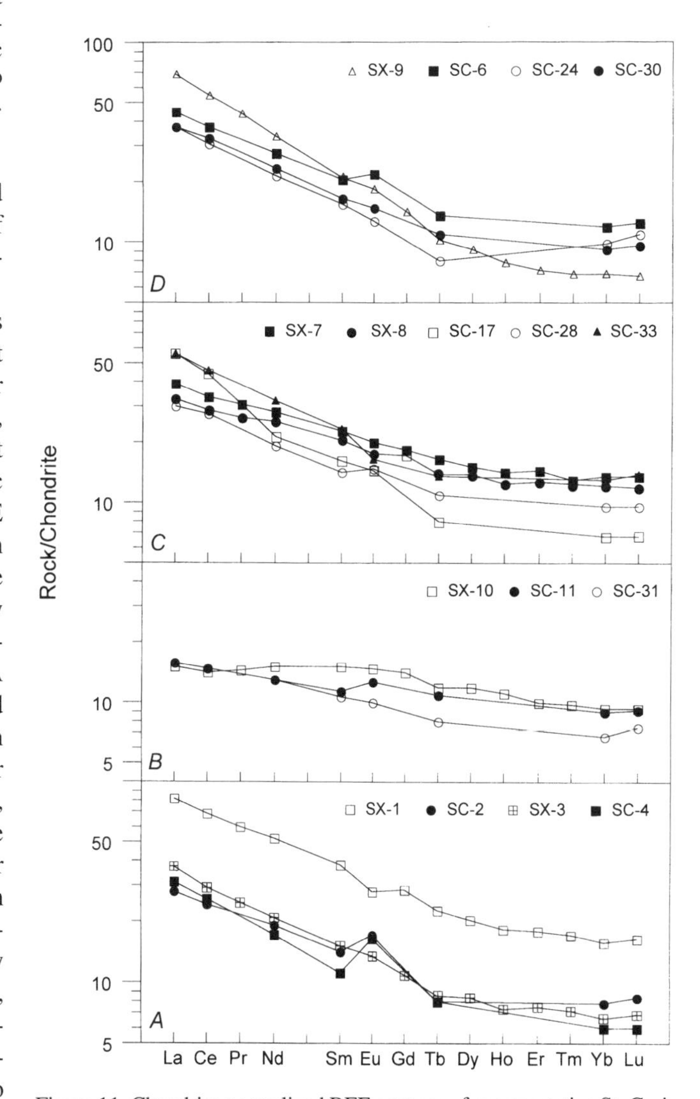

Figure 11. Chondrite-normalized REE patterns of representative St. Croix intrusive igneous rocks. *A*, Gabbro and diorite; *B*, pyroxene porphyry and basalt boulder; *C*, augite-hornblende diabase; *D*, hornblende diabase and dacite. Normalizing factors from Sun and McDonough (1989).

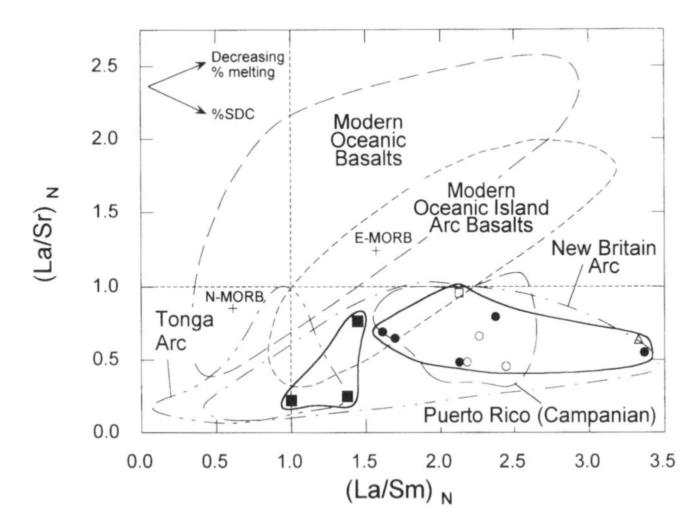

Figure 12. Chondrite-normalized La/Sr versus La/Sm ratios in St. Croix igneous suite (symbols keyed to Fig. 5), compared to modern oceanic basalts (Hawkesworth and Powell, 1980), modern intra-oceanic island arcs (White and Patchett, 1984), island arc lavas from New Britain (Woodhead and Johnson, 1993), and Tonga–Kermadec–New Zealand arc lavas (Ewart et al., 1977; Ewart and Hawkesworth, 1987); Campanian-age lavas of Puerto Rico from Jolly et al. (Chapter 3, this volume, Table 2; unpublished data). Vector representing decreasing degree of melting is equivalent to increasing degree of E-MORB-type mantle enrichment. Chondrite normalizing factors and MORB values from Sun and McDonough (1989).

different degrees of fusion produce melts with relatively flat HREE patterns.

Composition of the subduction-related component

In island arc tectonic settings, subduction-related fluids are generated in the descending slab (Pearce, 1983; Wyllie, 1983; Hawkesworth et al., 1985; Peacock, 1990; Stolper and Newman, 1994). The fluids, derived from altered oceanic basalt and accompanying sediments (Tatsumi et al., 1986; Nichols et al., 1994) and scavenged from the slab itself (Hawkesworth and Ellam, 1989; McDermott et al., 1993), migrate into the overlying mantle wedge. There they modify the peridotite and add incompatible elements to the wedge source of arc magmas. Although aqueous fluids are several orders of magnitude less efficient as transporters of incompatible elements than magmas (Hawkesworth et al., 1993b), they are abundant in arc environments due to dehydration reactions in the subducted oceanic crust (Pearce, 1983; Wyllie, 1983; Tatsumi et al., 1986; Hawkesworth et al., 1993b). Thus they are likely sources of wedge contamination, and incompatible element mobility in aqueous fluids is of significance in understanding the generation of arc magmas.

Experimental studies of REE and other incompatible elements in hydrous fluids reveal that atom mobility is a function of ionic radius and that larger atoms have greater mobility (Tatsumi et al., 1986). Solid/aqueous fluid partition coefficients are less well known, but it is recognized that salts, such as carbonates, hydroxides, and chlorides (Eggler, 1987), which are in solution, promote formation of ionic complexes, thereby significantly enhancing the solubility of larger elements (Helgeson, 1969). Brennan and Watson (1991) have reported olivine/fluid partition coefficients for several representative incompatible elements in pure water and in concentrated chloride brines, which are typical of pore fluids from a variety of rocks, including those from modern island arc volcanic settings. Further evaluation of these results (Lidiak and Jolly, 1996) reveals that solubilities of LILE in chloride-rich fluids are increased by 1.5 to 3 orders of magnitude compared to those of REE, which remain similar to values obtained in pure H_2O.

An efficient measure of the mobility of an element in aqueous fluids is provided by the ionic potential (Z/r), or ratio of the ionic charge (Z) to the ionic radius of the element (Goldschmidt, 1937; Pearce, 1983). In general, elements with ionic potential less than about 2 are mobile, whereas those with intermediate to high values between 3 and 7 are immobile. REE and Th have intermediate ionic potentials between 3 and 4, indicating limited mobility, whereas LILE (including Ba, Rb, K, Pb, and Sr), with Z/r ratios between 0 and 2 are highly mobile, and HFSE (including Nb, Ta, Zr, Hf, and Ti) are highly immobile. The relations are illustrated in Figure 14*A*, in which selected incompatible elements are listed from left to right in order of decreasing normalized abundances in N-MORB (Sun and McDonough, 1989).

The ionic potential of selected incompatible elements correlates well with N-MORB–normalized data from St. Croix island arc intrusives (Fig. 14). The HFSE (Fig. 14*B*) have relatively low concentrations (high ionic potential of Fig. 14*A*) and are effectively stable in aqueous fluids. In contrast, LILE are enriched (low ionic potential) relative to MORB and are particularly

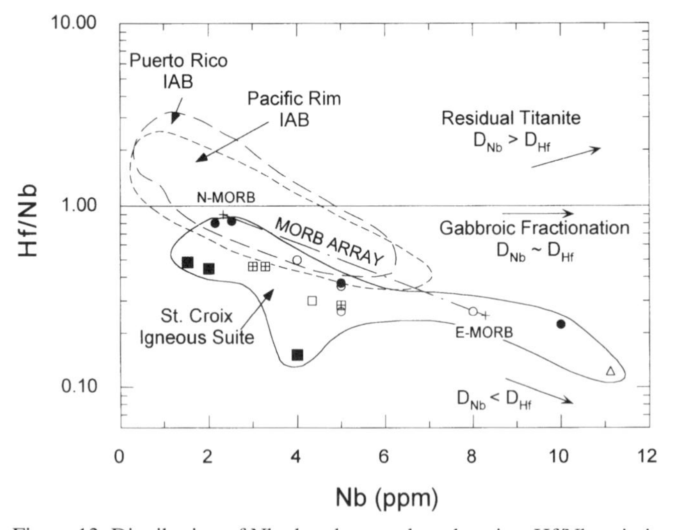

Figure 13. Distribution of Nb abundances plotted against Hf/Nb ratio in St. Croix igneous rocks. St. Croix intrusives follow the MORB trend, which is consistent with incompatible behavior of the HFSE. Pacific rim island arc basalt (IAB) field from McCulloch and Gamble (1991) using the factor Hf = Zr/36.2 (Sun and McDonough, 1989). Puerto Rico IAB from Jolly et al. (Chapter 3, this volume). MORB data from Sun and McDonough (1989).

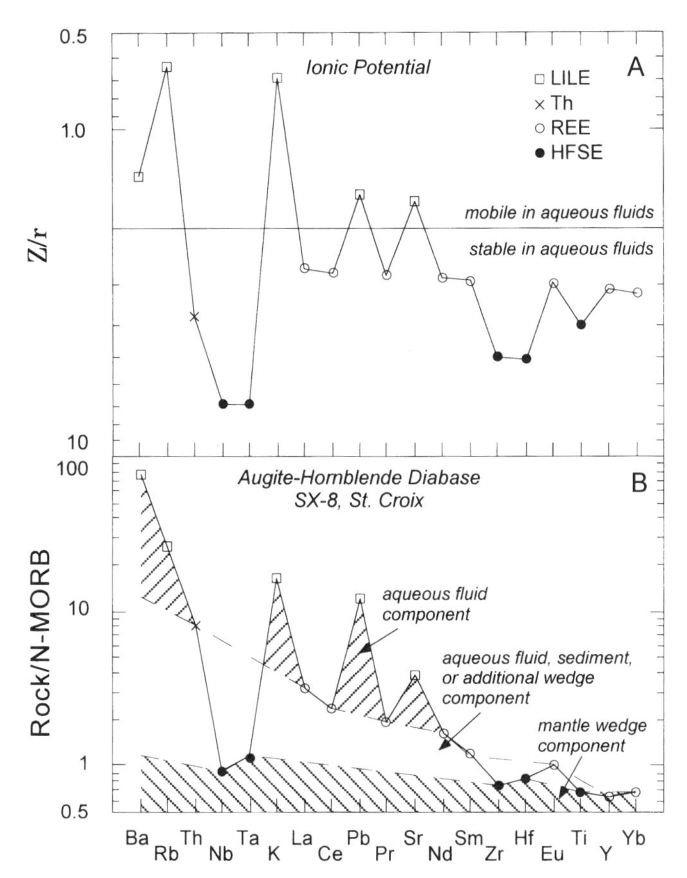

Figure 14. *A*, Ionic potential (Z/r) of selected incompatible elements, arranged from left to right in the order of decreasing incompatibility in N-MORB (Sun and McDonough, 1989). *B*, N-MORB–normalized island arc augite-hornblende diabase from St. Croix (sample SX-8), illustrating variations in abundance of selected incompatible elements in the aqueous fluid, mantle wedge, and sediment plus aqueous fluid components. Variations in the degree of fusion are reflected in the mantle wedge component.

mobile in aqueous fluids. The REE are intermediate between these two extremes, with LREE being slightly more enriched than HREE, and would be expected to have only limited mobility in aqueous fluids. The incompatible elements in St. Croix arc rocks can thus be subdivided into three components (Fig. 14*B*). The basic component, containing material derived from the mantle wedge source, consists of material below a line connecting the HFSE. The slope of this component increases with decreasing degree of melting and increasing degree of incompatible element enrichment of the wedge; part of this pattern may be due to an E-MORB component. A second component, consisting largely of LILE (Rb, Ba, K, Pb, and Sr) supplied by an aqueous fluid flux, is delineated by a line connecting the relatively immobile REE and Th. A third intermediate component, consists of additional LILE contributed by an aqueous fluid together with REE contributed by pelagic sediment (REE), or an additional mantle wedge component.

Because solubility of REE in chloride brines is several orders of magnitude lower than LILE, it is commonly suggested (Pearce, 1983; McDermott et al., 1993) that elevated REE abundances in island arc volcanics result from bulk addition of REE by a separate magma phase, generated by flux-related fusion of subducted sediments, rather than by the aqueous fluid. Consequently, in the following discussion, the total subduction-related component (SDC) is subdivided into two separate end-members representing the aqueous fluid and the sediment contributions.

Application of incompatible element solubility relations to St. Croix intrusives

The characteristics of subduction-related components in island arc volcanics may be evaluated by analysis of the ratios of trace elements having similar degrees of incompatibility. Such elemental pairs minimize effects of variable partial melting and subvolcanic gabbroic fractionation (Pearce and Peate, 1995) and may thus have important bearing on the subduction component and source characteristics during generation of St. Croix magmas. In this paper, four such ratios are used (Fig. 15). Behavior of highly incompatible elements is represented by La/Ta and K/La ratios, whereas that of moderately incompatible counterparts is represented by Sm/Hf and Sr/Nd ratios. Also shown are Ta/Yb and Hf/Yb ratios, which reflect the degree of melting and the magnitude of E-MORB-type enrichment beneath St. Croix.

Enrichment in LILE with respect to REE is shown by prominent positive anomalies in N-MORB normalized patterns (Fig. 10), which reveal that K and Sr are enriched in St. Croix intrusives, ranging from about 3 to at least 10 times N-MORB for both elements. This enrichment is reflected in high K/La and Sr/Nd values on element ratio diagrams (Fig. 15*A*, *C*). The enrichment is considerably greater than can be derived from the presence of pelagic sediments, which are less enriched in LILE than the intrusives themselves. Additionally, the St. Croix data fall outside the ranges of expected MORB values. The excess LILE is therefore inferred to have been supplied by an aqueous phase. Similarly, the degree of REE overenrichment is proportional to the magnitude of La/Ta and Sm/Hf ratios (Fig. 15*B*, *D*). The degree of enrichment in both La and Sm is minimal, however, averaging only about 1.5 to 4.0 times N-MORB (Fig. 10). The LILE enrichment thus exceeds that of REE by a factor of about 2 to 3, suggesting that aqueous fluids dominated the total SDC, and that sediments played only a minor role in the melting process.

The presumed source regions for the St. Croix intrusive suite was thus apparently dominated by the input of aqueous fluids rather than by additions of sedimentary material. These features are similar to the petrogenetic characteristics of the volcanic rocks in eastern Puerto Rico (Jolly et al., Chapter 3, this volume) where low Pb and Sr and high Nd isotope ratios are also indicative of minimal sediment input. It is significant that the only Puerto Rican volcanic rock with appreciable sediment content, as measured by elevated Pb isotope ratios, are the shoshonitic Perchas Lavas of Cenomanian age (75 to 85 Ma), which also display elevated La/Ta and Sm/Hf ratios compared to most St. Croix rocks (Fig. 15*B*, *D*). These results, therefore, like those in Puerto

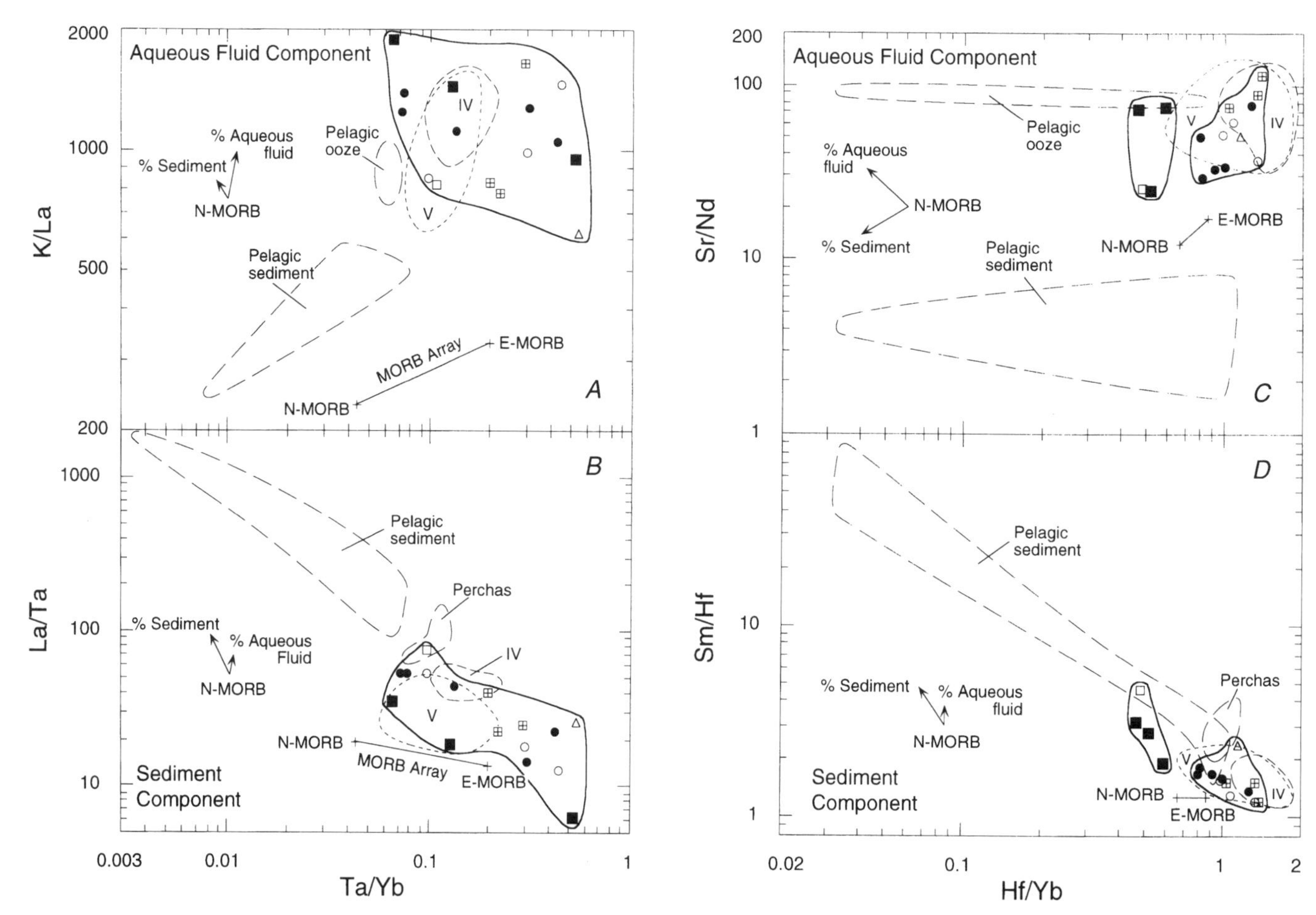

Figure 15. Variation diagrams illustrating aqueous fluid and sediment components of the St. Croix intrusive rock suite compared to Puerto Rican lavas. *A*, Aqueous fluid component as expressed by K/La ratio; *B*, sediment component as expressed by La/Ta ratio; *C*, aqueous fluid component as expressed by Sr/Nd ratio; *D*, sediment component as expressed by Sm/Hf ratio. Puerto Rican lava data: Perchas Lava, phase IV volcanics, and phase V volcanics (from Jolly et al., Chapter 3, this volume; unpublished data). Atlantic and Pacific pelagic sediment data from the following sources: Hole et al. (1984), White et al. (1985), and Ben-Othman et al. (1989). Vector lengths for aqueous fluid and sediment are not quantitative. Symbols for St. Croix rocks are keyed to Figure 5. The St. Croix porphyrys and basalt boulder are separated from the other intrusives by lower Hf/Yb ratio, perhaps because of diluting effects of crystal accumulation.

Rico (exclusive of the shoshonites), are consistent with generation of the igneous suite through subduction of the relatively young, sediment-poor Atlantic crust, rather than the sediment-rich crust (Montgomery et al., 1994a,b) that characterized the much older early Jurassic Pacific plate. Further research is under way to investigate additional aspects of the geochemical characteristics and possible genetic relationships among the arc rocks of St. Croix, Puerto Rico, and other magmatic centers in the eastern Greater Antilles.

CONCLUSIONS

Field study and geochemical, mineralogic, and petrographic data lead to the following conclusions:

1. Intrusive igneous rocks on St. Croix consist of the Southgate Diorite, Fountain Gabbro, and a series of sills and less abundant dikes. The sills and dikes consist of pyroxene porphyry (basalt), augite-hornblende diabase (basalt to andesite), hornblende diabase (basaltic andesite to andesite), and dacite.

2. Mineralogically, the main compositional variation among clinopyroxenes in the intrusives is in the wollastonite content, which is highest in the pyroxene porphyry, intermediate in the Fountain Gabbro, and lowest in the diabase. Hornblende varies from ferro-hornblende to ferro-actinolitic hornblende in the Fountain Gabbro and is ferroan pargasite in the diabase.

3. St. Croix intrusives are mainly quartz- or hypersthene-normative. They have major and trace element calc-alkaline chemical affinities. The distribution of both compatible and incompatible elements and mass balance calculations indicate that the main compositional variations are dominated by subvolcanic gabbroic fractionation of mainly plagioclase and clinopyroxene. Differences in the degree of melting and minor differences in a

family of source melt compositions may have contributed to some of the compositional variations.

4. Incompatible element variations and LILE/LREE ratios indicate that the St. Croix intrusives formed in a subduction-related tectonic setting. Their overall calc-alkaline signature (as opposed to an island arc tholeiitic signature) is consistent with the intrusives being emplaced during a relatively mature or evolved island arc stage rather than during an early stage of arc development. Furthermore, the closely similar incompatible element data between St. Croix intrusives and contemporaneous Campanian volcanic rocks in Puerto Rico suggests correlation between the rocks of these two regions. The thick volcanogenic strata on St. Croix and similar rocks in Puerto Rico may thus have accumulated above a broad island arc platform that extended through these two regions in Campanian time.

5. St. Croix igneous rocks are characterized by flat HREE segments in N-MORB–normalized REE distribution diagrams and limited ranges in Ta/Yb and Hf/Yb ratios. Together, these features are consistent with minor variations in source compositions and in degree of fusion at relatively low P_t, presumably within the spinel peridotite facies. The relations are indicative of a low-angle subduction zone as compared with most modern arcs, in which fusion occurs in garnet peridotite (Carr et al., 1990; McCulloch and Gamble, 1991; Hawkesworth et al., 1993a,b).

6. Trace element ratios suggest that the subduction-related component (SDC) introduced into the mantle wedge source beneath St. Croix dikes was derived from elemental fluxes that were dominated by aqueous fluids generated in the descending oceanic crust; sediment contributions were of minor significance. The relations, like those reported from volcanic rocks of the same general age in Puerto Rico, are consistent with subduction of a young, sediment-poor Atlantic crust.

ACKNOWLEDGMENTS

We acknowledge with appreciation the late Henry O. A. Meyer for kindly providing access to the electron microprobe facility at Purdue University; Carl Hager assisted in the microprobe analyses. We have benefited from the constructive reviews of Gerald E. Adams, Thomas H. Anderson, Mark D. Feigenson, David K. Larue, and especially James A. Walker. This research was supported by the Igneous Petrology Research Fund of the University of Pittsburgh.

REFERENCES CITED

Arculus, R. J., and Powell, R., 1986, Source component mixing in the regions of arc magma generation: Journal of Geophysical Research, v. 91, p. 5913–5926.

Basaltic Volcanism Study Project, 1981, Basaltic volcanism on the terrestrial planets: New York, Pergamon Press, 1286 p.

Ben-Othman, D., White, W. M., and Patchett, J., 1989, The geochemistry of marine sediments, island arc magma genesis, and crust–mantle recycling: Earth and Planetary Science Letters, v. 94, p. 1–21.

Bence, A. E., and Albee, A. L., 1968, Empirical correction factors for the electron microanalysis of silicates and oxides: Journal of Geology, v. 76, p. 382–403.

Bougault, H., Joron, J. L., and Treuil, M., 1980, The primordial chondritic nature and large-scale heterogeneities in the mantle: Evidence from high and low partition coefficient elements in oceanic basalts: Royal Society of London Philosophical Transactions A, v. 297, p. 203–213.

Bougault, H., Joron, J., Maury, R. C., Bohn, M., Tardy, M., and Biju-Duvan, B., 1984, Basalts from the Atlantic crust west of the Barbados Ridge (Site 543, Leg 78A); geochemistry and mineralogy, *in* Biju-Duval, B., et al., ed., Initial reports of the Deep Sea Drilling Project, 78A–78B: Washington, D.C., U.S. Government Printing Office, p. 401–408.

Brennan, J. M., and Watson, E. B., 1991, Partitioning of trace elements between olivine and aqueous fluids: Earth and Planetary Science Letters, v. 107, p. 672–688.

Brown, G. M., Holland, J. G., Sigurdsson, H., Tomblin, J. F., and Arculus, R. J., 1977, Geochemistry of the Lesser Antilles volcanic island arc: Geochimica et Cosmochimica Acta, v. 41, p. 785–802.

Bryan, W. B., Finger, L. W., and Chayes, F., 1969, Estimating proportions in petrographic mixing equations by least squares approximation: Science, v. 163, p. 926–927.

Carr, M. J., Feigenson, M. D., and Bennett, E. A., 1990, Incompatible element and isotopic evidence for tectonic control of source mixing and melt extraction along the Central American arc: Contributions to Mineralogy and Petrology, v. 105, p. 369–380.

Cebriá Gómez, J. M., 1990, PX: A program for pyroxene classification and calculation of end-members: American Mineralogist, v. 75, p. 1426–1427.

Chen, C.-Y., and Frey, F. A., 1985, Trace element and isotopic geochemistry of lavas from Haleakala volcano, east Maui, Hawaii: implications for the origin of Hawaiian basalts: Journal of Geophysical Research, v. 90, p. 8743–9768.

Davidson, J. P., 1986, Isotopic and trace element constraints on the petrogenesis of subduction-related lavas from Martinique, Lesser Antilles: Journal of Geophysical Research, v. 91, p. 5943–5962.

Donnelly, T. W., 1989, Geologic history of the Caribbean and Central America, *in* Bally, A. W., and Palmer, A. R., eds., The Geology of North America—An overview: Boulder, Colorado, Geological Society of America, The Geology of North America, v. A, p. 299–321.

Donnelly, T. W., 1994, The Caribbean Cretaceous basalt association: A vast igneous province that includes the Nicoya complex of Costa Rica, *in* Seyfried, H., and Hellman, W., eds., Geology of an evolving island arc: the isthmus of southern Nicaragua, Costa Rica, and western Panama: Stuttgart, Germany, Profile (Band 7), Institut fur Geologie und Palaontologie, p. 17–45.

Donnelly, T. W., and Rogers, J. J. W., 1978, The distribution of igneous rocks throughout the Caribbean: Geologie en Mijnbouw, v. 57, p. 151–162.

Donnelly, T. W., and Rogers, J. J. W., 1980, Igneous series in island arcs: the northeastern Caribbean compared with worldwide island-arc assemblages: Bulletin Volcanologique, v. 43-2, p. 347–382.

Donnelly, T. W., Rogers, J. J. W., Pushkar, P., and Armstrong, R. L., 1971, Chemical evolution of the igneous rocks of the eastern West Indies: An investigation of thorium, uranium, and potassium distributions, and lead and strontium isotopic ratios, *in* Donnelly, T. W., ed., Caribbean geophysical, tectonic, and petrologic investigations: Boulder, Colorado, Geological Society of America Memoir 130, p. 181–224.

Donnelly, T. W., Melson, W., Kay, R., and Rogers, J. J. W., 1973, Basalts and dolerites of late Cretaceous age from the central Caribbean: Initial reports of the Deep Sea Drilling Project, Volume 15: Washington, D.C., Government Printing Office, p. 989–1012.

Draper, G., and Bartel, J. M., 1991, A note of the relative timing of cleavage formation and magmatism in the Cretaceous rocks of St. Croix, U.S. Virgin Islands, *in* Larue, D. K., and Draper, G., eds., Transactions; 12th Caribbean Geological Conference, St. Croix: Coral Gables, Florida, Miami Geological Society, p. 314–318.

Eggler, D. H., 1987, Solubility of major and trace elements in mantle metasomatic fluids: experimental constraints, *in* Menzies, M. A., and Hawkesworth,

C. J., eds., Mantle metasomatism: London, Academic Press, p. 21–41.
Ewart, A., 1982, The mineralogy and petrology of Tertiary-Recent orogenic volcanic rocks: with special reference to the andesitic-basaltic compositional range, *in* Thorpe, R. S., ed., Andesites: orogenic andesites and related rocks: Chichester, United Kingdom, John Wiley & Sons, p. 25–95.
Ewart, A. W., and Hawkesworth, C. J., 1987, The Pleistocene to Recent Tonga-Kermadec arc lavas: Interpretation of new isotope and rare earth element data in terms of a depleted mantle source model: Journal of Petrology, v. 28, p. 495–530.
Ewart, A. W., Brothers, R. N., and Mateen, A., 1977, An outline of the geology and geochemistry, and the possible petrogenetic evolution of the volcanic rocks of the Tonga–Kermadec–New Zealand island arc: Journal of Volcanology and Geothermal Research, v. 2, p. 205–250.
Frey, F. A., Garcia, M. O., and Roden, M. F., 1994, Geochemical characteristics of Koolau volcano: implications of intershield geochemical differences among Hawaiian volcanoes: Geochimica et Cosmochimica Acta, v. 58, p. 1441–1462.
Gautier, I., Weis, D., Mennessier, J. P., Vidal, P., Giret, A., and Loubet, M., 1990, Petrology and geochemistry of the Kerguelen Archipelago basalts (south Indian Ocean): Evolution of the mantle sources from ridge to intraplate position: Earth and Planetary Science Letters, v. 100, p. 59–76.
Goldschmidt, V. M., 1937, The principles of distribution of chemical elements in minerals and rocks: Journal of the Chemical Society, v. 140, p. 655–673.
Hammarstrom, J. M., and Zen, E.-a., 1986, Aluminum in hornblende: An empirical igneous geobarometer: American Mineralogist, v. 71, p. 1297–1313.
Hawkesworth, C. J., and Ellam, R. M., 1989, Chemical fluxes and wedge replenishment rates along recent destructive plate margins: Geology, v. 17, p. 46–49.
Hawkesworth, C. J., and Powell, M., 1980, Magma genesis in the Lesser Antilles island arc: Earth and Planetary Science Letters, v. 51, p. 297–308.
Hawkesworth, C. J., Rogers, N. W., van Calsteren, P., and Menzies, M. A., 1985, Mantle enrichment processes: Nature, v. 311, p. 331–335.
Hawkesworth, C. J., Gallagher, K., Hergt, J. M., and McDermott, F., 1993a, Mantle and slab contributions in arc magmas: Annual Reviews of Earth and Planetary Sciences, v. 21, p. 175–207.
Hawkesworth, C. J., Gallagher, K., Hergt, J. M., and McDermott, F., 1993b, Trace element fractionation processes in the generation of island arc basalts: Philosophical Transactions of the Royal Society of London A, v. 342, p. 179–191.
Helgeson, H. C., 1969, Thermodynamics of hydrothermal systems at elevated temperatures and pressures: American Journal of Science, v. 267, p. 729–804.
Hofmann, A. W., 1988, Chemical differentiation of the Earth: The relationship between mantle, continental crust, and oceanic crust: Earth and Planetary Science Letters, v. 90, p. 297–314.
Hole, M. J., Saunders, A. D., Marriner, G. F., and Tarney, J., 1984, Subduction of pelagic sediments: implications for the origin of Ce-anomalous basalts from the Mariana Islands: Geological Society of London Journal, v. 141, p. 453–472.
Jenner, G. A., Longreich, H. P., Jackson, S. E., and Fryer, R. D., 1990, ICP-MS; a powerful tool for high-precision trace-element analyses in earth sciences; evidence from analysis of selected U.S.G.S. reference samples: Chemical Geology, v. 83, p. 133–148.
Kay, R. W., 1980, Volcanic arc magmas: Implications for a melting-mixing model for element recycling in the crust–upper mantle system: Journal of Geology, v. 88, p. 497–522.
Kruskensky, R. D., and Monroe, W. H., 1978, Geologic map of the Yauco and Punta Verraco quadrangles, Puerto Rico: U.S. Geological Survey Miscellaneous Investigations Map, I–1147, scale 1:20,000.
Kuno, H., 1968, Differentiation of basalt magmas, *in* Hess, H. H., and Poldervaart, A., eds., The Poldervaart treatise on rocks of basaltic composition: New York, Interscience, v. 2, p. 623–688.
Kushiro, I., 1962, Clinopyroxene solid solutions. Part 1. The $CaAl_2SiO_6$ component: Japanese Journal of Geology and Geography, v. 33, p. 213–220.
Larue, D. K., Pierce, P., and Erikson, J., 1991a, Cretaceous intra-arc summit basin on Puerto Rico, *in* Gillezeau, K. A., ed., Transactions, 2nd Geological Conference of the Geological Society of Trinidad and Tobago: Port-of-Spain, Trinidad, April 3–8, 1990, p. 184–190.
Larue, D. K., Smith, A. L., and Schellekens, J. H., 1991b, Ocean island arc stratigraphy in the Caribbean region: Don't take it for granite: Sedimentary Geology, v. 74, p. 289–308.
Leake, B. E., 1978, Nomenclature of amphiboles: Mineralogical Magazine, v. 42, p. 533–563.
Lebrón, M. C., and Perfit, M. R., 1994, Petrochemistry and tectonic significance of Cretaceous island-arc rocks, Cordillera Oriental, Dominican Republic: Tectonophysics, v. 229, p. 69–100.
Leterrier, J., Maury, R. C., Thonon, P., Girard, D., and Marchal, M., 1982, Clinopyroxene composition as a method of identification of the magmatic affinities of paleo-volcanic series: Earth and Planetary Science Letters, v. 59, p. 139–154.
Lewis, J. F., 1973, Petrology of the ejected plutonic blocks of the Soufriere volcano, St. Vincent, West Indies: Journal of Petrology, v. 14, p. 81–112.
Lewis, J. F., and Jiménez G., J. G., 1991, Duarte complex in the La Vega–Jarabacoa–Janico area, central Hispaniola; geologic and geochemical features of the sea floor during the early stages of arc evolution, *in* Mann, P., Draper, G., and Lewis, J. F., eds., Geologic and tectonic development of the North American–Caribbean plate boundary in Hispaniola: Boulder, Colorado, Geological Society of America Special Paper 262, p. 115–141.
Lidiak, E. G., and Jolly, W. T., 1996, Rare earth elements in the geological sciences, *in* Evans, C. H., ed., Episodes from the history of the rare earth elements: Dordrecht, Netherlands, Kluwer Academic Publishers, Chemists and Chemistry, v. 15, p. 149–187.
Lidz, B., 1988, Upper Cretaceous (Campanian) and Cenozoic stratigraphic sequences, northeastern Caribbean (St. Croix, USVI): Geological Society of America Bulletin, v. 100, p. 282–298.
Longerich, H. P., Jenner, G. A., Fryer, B. J., and Jackson, S. E., 1990, Inductively coupled plasma-mass spectrometric analysis of geological samples: a critical evaluation based on case studies: Chemical Geology, v. 83, p. 105–118.
McCulloch, M. T., and Gamble, J. A., 1991, Geochemical and geodynamical constraints on subduction zone magmatism: Earth and Planetary Science Letters, v. 102, p. 358–374.
McDermott, F., Defant, M. J., Hawkesworth, C. J., Maury, R. C., and Joron, J. L., 1993, Isotope and trace element evidence for three component mixing in the genesis of the North Luzon arc lavas (Philippines): Contributions to Mineralogy and Petrology, v. 113, p. 9–23.
Miyashiro, A., 1974, Volcanic rock series in island arcs and active continental margins: American Journal of Science, v. 274, p. 321–355.
Montgomery, H., Pessagno, E. A., Jr., Lewis, J. F., and Schellekens, J. H., 1994a, Paleogeography of Jurassic fragments in the Caribbean: Tectonics, v. 13, p. 725–732.
Montgomery, H., Pessagno, E. A., Jr., and Pindell, J. L., 1994b, A 195 Ma terrane in a 165 Ma sea: Pacific origin of the Caribbean plate: GSA Today, v. 4, p. 1–6.
Morimoto, N., 1989, Nomenclature of pyroxenes: Canadian Mineralogist, v. 27, p. 143–156.
Nichols, G. T., Wyllie, P. J., and Stern, C. R., 1994, Subduction zone-melting of pelagic sediments constrained by melting experiments: Nature, v. 371, p. 785–788.
Palacz, Z. A., and Saunders, A. D., 1986, Coupled trace element and isotope enrichment in the Cook-Austral-Samoa Islands, southwest Pacific: Earth and Planetary Science Letters, v. 79, p. 270–280.
Peacock, S. M., 1990, Fluid processes in subduction zones: Science, v. 248, p. 329–337.
Pearce, J. A., 1983, Role of the sub-continental lithosphere in magma genesis at active continental margins, *in* Hawkesworth, C. J., and Norry, M. J., eds., Continental basalts and mantle xenoliths: Cheshire, United Kingdom, Shiva Publishing, p. 230–249.
Pearce, J. A., and Peate, D. W., 1995, Tectonic implications of the composition of volcanic arc magmas: Annual Review of Earth and Planetary Sciences, v. 23, p. 251–285.

Pease, M. H., Jr., 1968, Cretaceous and lower Tertiary stratigraphy of the Naranjito and Aguas Buenas quadrangles and adjacent areas: U.S. Geological Survey Bulletin 1253, 57 p.

Peccerillo, A., and Taylor, S. R., 1976, Geochemistry of Eocene calc-alkaline volcanic rocks from the Kastamonu area, northern Turkey: Contributions to Mineralogy and Petrology, v. 58, p. 63–91.

Perfit, M. R., Gust, D. A., Bence, A. E., Arculus, R. J., and Taylor, S. R., 1980, Chemical characteristics of island-arc basalts: implications for mantle sources: Chemical Geology, v. 30, p. 227–256.

Rickwood, P. C., 1989, Boundary lines within petrologic diagrams which use major and minor elements: Lithos, v. 22, p. 247–263.

Ringwood, A. E., 1990, Slab-mantle interactions; 3, Petrogenesis of intraplate magmas and the structure of the upper mantle: Chemical Geology, v. 82, p. 187–207.

Rock, N. M. S., 1991, Lamprophyres: Glasgow, United Kingdom, Blackie, 285 p.

Roden, M. F., Frey, F. A., and Clague, D. A., 1984, Geochemistry of tholeiitic and alkalic lavas from the Koolau Range, Oahu, Hawaii: Implications for Hawaiian volcanism: Earth and Planetary Science Letters, v. 69, p. 141–158.

Schiano, P., Allègre, C. J., Dupré, B., Lewin, E., and Joron, J.-L., 1993, Variability of trace elements in basaltic suites: Earth and Planetary Science Letters, v. 119, p. 37–51.

Speed, R., and Joyce, J., 1989, Depositional and structural evolution of Cretaceous strata, St. Croix, *in* Hubbard, D. K., ed., Terrestrial and marine geology of St. Croix, U.S. Virgin Islands: St. Croix, West Indies Laboratory, Special Publication No. 8, p. 23–35.

Speed, R., and Joyce, J., 1991, Cretaceous tectonic complex, St. Croix, *in* Larue, D. K., and Draper, G., eds., Transactions; 12th Caribbean Geological Conference, St. Croix: Coral Gables, Florida: Miami Geological Society, p. 301–313.

Speed, R. C., Gerhard, L. C., and McKee, E. H., 1979, Ages of deposition, deformation, and intrusion of Cretaceous rocks, eastern St. Croix, Virgin Islands: Geological Society of America Bulletin, v. 90, p. I, p. 629–632.

Speer, J. A., 1984, Micas in igneous rocks, *in* Bailey, S. W., ed., Micas, reviews in mineralogy: Washington, D.C., Mineralogical Society of America, v. 13, p. 299–356.

Stanley, D. J., 1989, Sedimentology and paleogeography of Upper Cretaceous rocks, St. Croix, U.S. Virgin Islands: new interpretations, *in* Hubbard, D. K., ed., Terrestrial and marine geology of St. Croix, U.S. Virgin Islands: St. Croix, West Indies Laboratory, Special Publication No. 8, p. 37–47.

Stolper, E., and Newman, S., 1994, The role of water in the petrogenesis of Marianas trough magmas: Earth and Planetary Science Letters, v. 121, p. 293–325.

Sun, S., and McDonough, W. F., 1989, Chemical and isotopic systematics of oceanic basalts: Implications for mantle composition and processes, *in* Saunders, A. D., and Norry, M. J., eds., Magmatism in the ocean basins: Oxford, United Kingdom, Geological Society Special Publication No. 42, Blackwell Scientific Publications, p. 313–345.

Tatsumi, Y., Hamilton, D. L., and Nesbitt, R. W., 1986, Chemical characteristics of fluid phase released from a subducted lithosphere and origin of arc magmas: Evidence from high-pressure experiments and natural rocks: Journal of Volcanology and Geothermal Research, v. 29, p. 293–309.

Thirlwall, M. F., and Graham, A. M., 1984, Evolution of high-Ca, high Sr C-series basalts from Grenada, Lesser Antilles: The effects of intra-crustal contamination: Geological Society of London Journal, v. 141, p. 427–445.

Thirlwall, M. F., Smith, T. E., Graham, A. M., Theodorou, N., Hollings, P., Davidson, J. P., and Arculus, R. J., 1994, High field strength element anomalies in arc lavas: source or process?: Journal of Petrology, v. 35, p. 819–838.

Walker, J. A., 1989, Caribbean arc tholeiites: Journal of Geophysical Research, v. 94, p. 10539–10548.

Whetten, J. T., 1966, Geology of St. Croix, U.S. Virgin Islands, *in* Hess, H. H., ed., Caribbean Geological Investigations: Boulder, Colorado, Geological Society of America Memoir 98, p. 177–239.

White, W. M., and Patchett, J., 1984, Hf-Nd-Sr isotopes and incompatible element abundances in island arcs: implications for magma origins and crust-mantle evolution: Earth and Planetary Science Letters, v. 67, p. 167–186.

White, W. M., Dupré, B., and Vidal, P., 1985, Isotope and trace element geochemistry of sediments from the Barbados ridge–Demerara plain region, Atlantic Ocean: Geochimica et Cosmochimica Acta, v. 49, p. 1875–1886.

Wood, D. A., Joron, J., Treuil, M., Norry, M., and Tarney, J., 1979a, Elemental and Sr isotope variations in basic lavas from Iceland and the surrounding ocean floor: Contributions to Mineralogy and Petrology, v. 70, p. 319–339.

Wood, D. A., Joron, J. L., and Treuil, M., 1979b, A reappraisal of the use of trace elements to classify and discriminate between magma series erupted in different tectonic settings: Earth and Planetary Science Letters, v. 45, p. 326–336.

Wood, D. A., Tarney, J., Varet, J., Saunders, A. D., Bougault, H., Joron, J., Treuil, M., and Cann, J. R., 1979c, Geochemistry of basalts drilled in the North Atlantic by IPOD Leg 49: implications from mantle heterogeneity: Earth and Planetary Science Letters, v. 42, p. 77–97.

Woodhead, J. D., 1989, Geochemistry of the Mariana arc (western Pacific): source composition and processes: Chemical Geology, v. 76, p. 1–24.

Woodhead, J. D., and Johnson, R. W., 1993, Isotopic and trace-element profiles across the New Britain island arc, Papua New Guinea: Contributions to Mineralogy and Petrology, v. 113, p. 479–491.

Woodhead, J. D., Eggins, S., and Gamble, J., 1993, High field strength and transition element systematics in island arc and back-arc basin basalts: Evidence for multi-phase extraction and a depleted mantle wedge: Earth and Planetary Science Letters, v. 114, p. 491–504.

Wright, T. L., and Doherty, P. C., 1970, A linear programming and least squares computer method for solving petrologic mixing problems: Geological Society of America Bulletin, v. 81, p. 1995–2008.

Wyllie, P. J., 1983, Experimental and thermal constraints on the deep-seated parentage of some granitoid magmas in subduction zones, *in* Atherton, M. P., and Gribble, C. D., eds., Migmatites, melting and metamorphism: Nantwich, United Kingdom, Shiva Publishing, p. 37–51.

MANUSCRIPT ACCEPTED BY THE SOCIETY JUNE 20, 1997

Printed in U.S.A.

Geological Society of America
Special Paper 322
1998

North Coast Tertiary basin of Puerto Rico: From arc basin to carbonate platform to arc-massif slope

D. K. Larue,* R. Torrini, Jr.,* A. L. Smith, and J. Joyce
Department of Geology, University of Puerto Rico, Mayagüez, Puerto Rico 00681-5000

ABSTRACT

Several thousand kilometers of offshore and onshore multichannel seismic reflection data, logs from two boreholes, 4 CPR and Toa Baja # 1, and outcrop information were integrated to construct an evolutionary history of the North Coast basin of Puerto Rico. This basin contains strata that span the age of a significant late Eocene to middle Oligocene tectonic event that occurred on Puerto Rico and elsewhere in the Greater Antilles magmatic arc. Key seismic reflection horizons were mapped by Western Geophysical, Inc., and by us to develop a series of isotime maps of the basin and its margins. Horizon III is a key seismic reflection horizon that separates a lower basinal succession from an upper platformal succession. The lower succession is deformed onshore and unconformably underlies Horizon III discordantly, whereas offshore, the lower succession is in apparent concordant contact with the overlying upper succession. The change from an discordant to concordant contact between the lower succession and Horizon III is thought to be due to a structural front that occurs approximately at the present-day shoreline of Puerto Rico.

The purpose of this study is to: (1) review what is known about the Tertiary evolution of Puerto Rico and to incorporate recently published information derived from the Toa Baja borehole; (2) present new seismic reflection and structural data that have bearing on the evolution of Puerto Rico; and (3) synthesize the evolution of Puerto Rico and the northeastern Caribbean in general.

The North Coast basin of Puerto Rico witnessed four stages of evolution. Early Tertiary basin subsidence within a magmatic arc formed an intra-arc basin by extensional deformation. Late Eocene to middle Oligocene deformation along the basin's south margin uplifted basinal strata and formed a structural front within the basin. North of the structural front, basinal strata are essentially undeformed and exhibit progressive northward onlap on pre-basinal arc basement. Strata above Horizon III lie with angular unconformity onshore and with apparent conformity offshore and represent a middle Oligocene to Miocene carbonate bank succession. Seismic reflection profiles show these strata contain clinoforms indicative of a deep embayment offshore. During a late Miocene to Pliocene flexural event, the northern margin of the basin subsided to water depths locally in excess of 4 km. This flexure may have been associated with tectonic erosion in the Puerto Rico Trench region, or associated with listric normal faulting in the trench region.

---

*Present address: Larue, Chevron Petroleum Technology Co., P.O. Box 446, La Habra, California 90633-0446; Torrini, Woodward-Clyde International, 2318 Millpark Drive, Maryland Heights, Maryland 63043.

Larue, D. K., Torrini, R., Jr., Smith, A. L., and Joyce, J., 1998, North Coast Tertiary basin of Puerto Rico: From arc basin to carbonate platform to arc-massif slope, *in* Lidiak, E. G., and Larue, D. K., eds., Tectonics and Geochemistry of the Northeastern Caribbean: Boulder, Colorado, Geological Society of America Special Paper 322.

INTRODUCTION

The North Coast Tertiary basin of Puerto Rico is situated on the Puerto Rico–Virgin Islands platform in the boundary zone between the North American and Caribbean plates (Fig. 1). Eocene to Pliocene strata fill the basin and present a historical evolutionary record of the northern Caribbean plate's margin.

This study reviews what is known about the Tertiary evolution of Puerto Rico and incorporates recently published information derived from the Toa Baja borehole; presents new seismic reflection and structural data that have bearing on the evolution of Puerto Rico; and synthesizes the evolution of Puerto Rico and the northeastern Caribbean in general. This Chapter represents a synthesis of information described in the volume edited by Larue (1991), with considerable amounts of new data and reprocessed seismic reflection profiles.

We will develop a four-stage evolutionary history for the basin constrained by extensive multichannel seismic reflection coverage, outcrop information, and information provided by two intermediate depth boreholes, 4 CPR and Toa Baja # 1.

REGIONAL GEOLOGY

Puerto Rico and the northern Virgin Islands are subaerial portions of the Puerto Rico–Virgin Islands platform and represent the eastern edge of the ancestral Greater Antilles island arc (Fig. 1). Arc volcanism in the eastern Greater Antilles commenced in the Cretaceous, and continued to the Eocene, extending into the Oligocene in the northern Virgin Islands (Cox et al., 1977; Pindell and Barrett, 1990). Cessation of arc volcanism in the late Eocene was accompanied by orogenesis, including folding and faulting and uplift on the order of several kilometers (Monroe, 1980; Larue et al., 1991a). Termination of arc volcanism was related to the collision of the western (Cuban) part of the Greater Antilles arc with the Bahamas Bank (Pindell and Barrett, 1990), subduction of the Bahamas Bank beneath the Puerto Rican part of the arc (Erikson et al., 1990) or associated with subduction of buoyant oceanic crust (Larue et al., 1991b). On Puerto Rico, this early Tertiary orogenic event is dated by a late Eocene to middle Oligocene angular unconformity (Cox et al., 1977). In the northern Virgin Islands, the unconformity is poorly dated as post–early Oligocene and pre–late Miocene to Recent (Cox et al., 1977).

Oligocene to Recent carbonate sediments and sediments derived from weathering of the island arc massif were deposited in the Puerto Rico region (Seiglie and Moussa, 1984). Complicated tectonism from the middle Miocene to the Recent in Puerto Rico and the Virgin Islands is associated with easterly transtensional motion of the Caribbean plate relative to North America (Jordan, 1975; DeMets et al., 1990) and 25° counterclockwise rotation of the Puerto Rico and northern Virgin Islands platform (Reid et al., 1991).

A south-dipping slab of oceanic crust extends from the vicinity of the Puerto Rico trench to depths on the order of 150 km (McCann and Sykes, 1984); focal mechanisms are extremely

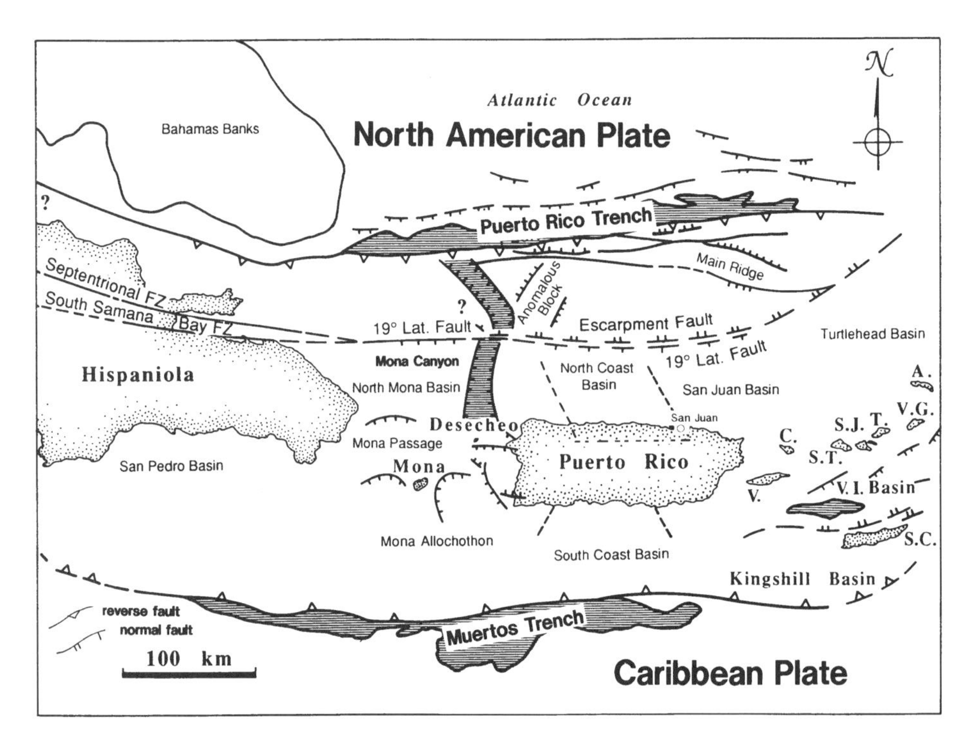

Figure 1. Regional tectonic setting of Puerto Rico in the Caribbean–North American Plate Boundary zone. C., Culebra; V., Vieques; S.T., St. Thomas; S.J., St. John; T., Tortola; A., Anegada; S.C., St. Croix. Hatchured lines, normal faults. Barbed lines, thrust faults. Horizontal shading, bathymetric deeps. Dashed lines used to define basins described in text (North Coast basin, San Juan basin).

oblique (Molnar and Sykes, 1969; Speed and Larue, 1991). On the south, the Muertos Trench is a zone of northward underthrusting, and the north-dipping slab extends to depths of about 30 km (Byrne et al., 1985). On the east is the Virgin Island basin, a zone of complicated extension (Houlgatte, 1983; Lepinay et al., 1987). The Mona Canyon is found in the northern part of the Mona Passage, which separates Puerto Rico and Hispaniola (Gardner et al., 1980; Larue and Ryan, 1991). South of the Mona Canyon is the Mona extensional allochthon, which is moving south (Larue and Ryan, 1991). The crustal thickness beneath Puerto Rico is about 25 km (Talwani et al., 1959).

Puerto Rico and northern Virgin Islands represent a composite arc terrane, not cut by any large-offset active faults. Surrounding the arc terrane are zones of complex tectonic activity, including the Puerto Rico and Muertos Trenches (and associated subbasins), where oceanic plates are being underthrust, and extensional basins separating the Puerto Rico–northern Virgin Islands composite arc terrane from adjacent arc terranes in Hispaniola (Mona Canyon) and the northern Lesser Antilles (Virgin Islands basin).

PREVIOUS STUDIES OF THE NORTH COAST TERTIARY BASIN

The history of the North Coast basin has been described by several workers (Monroe, 1980; Meyerhoff et al., 1983; Birch, 1986; Larue and Berrong, 1991) and there are fundamental differences in interpretation. It was originally thought that Oligocene and younger strata on Puerto Rico could be divided into two basinal groups—those occurring off the north coast and those occurring off the south coast (North and South Coast Basins); (Fig. 1). Based on outcrop projections, single-channel seismic reflection data, and a well drilled in 1960, 4 CPR (total depth 1.9 km) that intersected Eocene or older volcaniclastic strata at 1.7 km (Briggs, 1961), the North Coast basin was thought to contain a relatively thin (<2 km) succession of carbonates and arc-derived clastics of Oligocene to Pliocene age unconformably overlying deformed Eocene and older strata. This Oligocene and younger succession onlaps arc basement to the south on the northern flank of the Central Mountains of Puerto Rico.

The North Coast Oligocene and younger basinal succession extends about 50 km north of the present coastline of Puerto Rico, based on dredge haul recoveries of shallow water carbonates of Oligocene and Miocene age along the Puerto Rican Escarpment (Schneidermann et al., 1972; Perfit et al., 1980) on the inner wall of the Puerto Rico Trench (Escarpment fault in Fig. 1). These shallow water carbonates subsided to water depths of greater than 4 km in the middle Miocene to Pliocene (Perfit et al., 1980; Larue et al., 1991b) associated with normal motion on the 19° Latitude fault. Dredge hauls also recovered Eocene to Cretaceous age arc volcanic rocks beneath the shallow water carbonates at the Puerto Rico Escarpment, indicating that the entire North Coast basin is underlain by arc basement. However, several kilometers farther to the north and topographically down the Puerto Rico Escarpment, dredge hauls recovered metamorphic rocks, indicating a terrane boundary approximately coincides with the Puerto Rico Escarpment (Perfit et al., 1980; Speed and Larue, 1991) that truncates the northern margin of the North Coast basin. This terrane boundary may be an older structure reactivated by Miocene to Recent tectonism (Speed and Larue, 1991).

In the early 1970s, Western Geophysical, Inc. (supported by the Puerto Rico Water Resources Authority) collected approximately 5,000 km of onland and offshore multichannel seismic data for a nuclear power plant safety study (Fig. 2), much of it centered on the north coast of Puerto Rico (Western Geophysical, 1974: these data are now owned by the University of Puerto Rico). This study defined a deeper North Coast basinal succession, with flat-lying to gently tilted reflectors with cumulative thicknesses up to 3 sec (two-way travel time), or about 6 km. The basinal succession also contained a number of amplitude anomalies that excited Puerto Rican government officials about the petroleum potential of the basin.

Because these deep basinal reflectors are essentially undeformed, they were interpreted to be of late Eocene or younger age (Meyerhoff et al., 1983; Moussa et al., 1987). Birch (1986) recognized three phases of basinal evolution—an early extensional phase (late Eocene to middle Oligocene), accompanied by normal faulting, followed by a period of cooling and sediment loading in the middle Oligocene into Pliocene, and followed by a period of flexure resulting in the flooding of the northern part of the basin to water depths locally in excess of 4 km.

In 1986, additional multichannel seismic reflection data (Fig. 2) were collected by Western Geophysical for the Puerto Rico Electric Power Authority (PREPA). These data were collected in order to define an area for a test well. A structural high on Line 2 was chosen as the area for testing by drilling, and the Toa Baja borehole was drilled in 1989 to a total depth of 2.7 km (Larue, 1990). Because Eocene volcaniclastic strata were encountered at about 575 m, Larue and Berrong (1991) concluded that the deeper part of the North Coast Basin was filled with early Tertiary volcaniclastic and associated strata and that a deformation gradient exists between deformed early Tertiary rocks in the northern flank of the Central Mountains of Puerto Rico and the Toa Baja borehole, and the offshore flat-lying deep basinal reflectors.

EARLY TERTIARY ROCKS IN THE NORTHERN FLANK OF THE CENTRAL MOUNTAINS OF PUERTO RICO

Cretaceous rocks make up most of the exposed bedrock underlying the central mountains of Puerto Rico; such ages are largely based on biostratigraphic and physical stratigraphic studies, because radiometric studies are relatively rare. Three structural blocks defined by Garrison et al. (1972) were more recently redefined as four structural blocks (Larue et al., 1991c): the southwest, south-central, central, and northeast. Each is characterized by a unique stratigraphy, although all are characteristic of

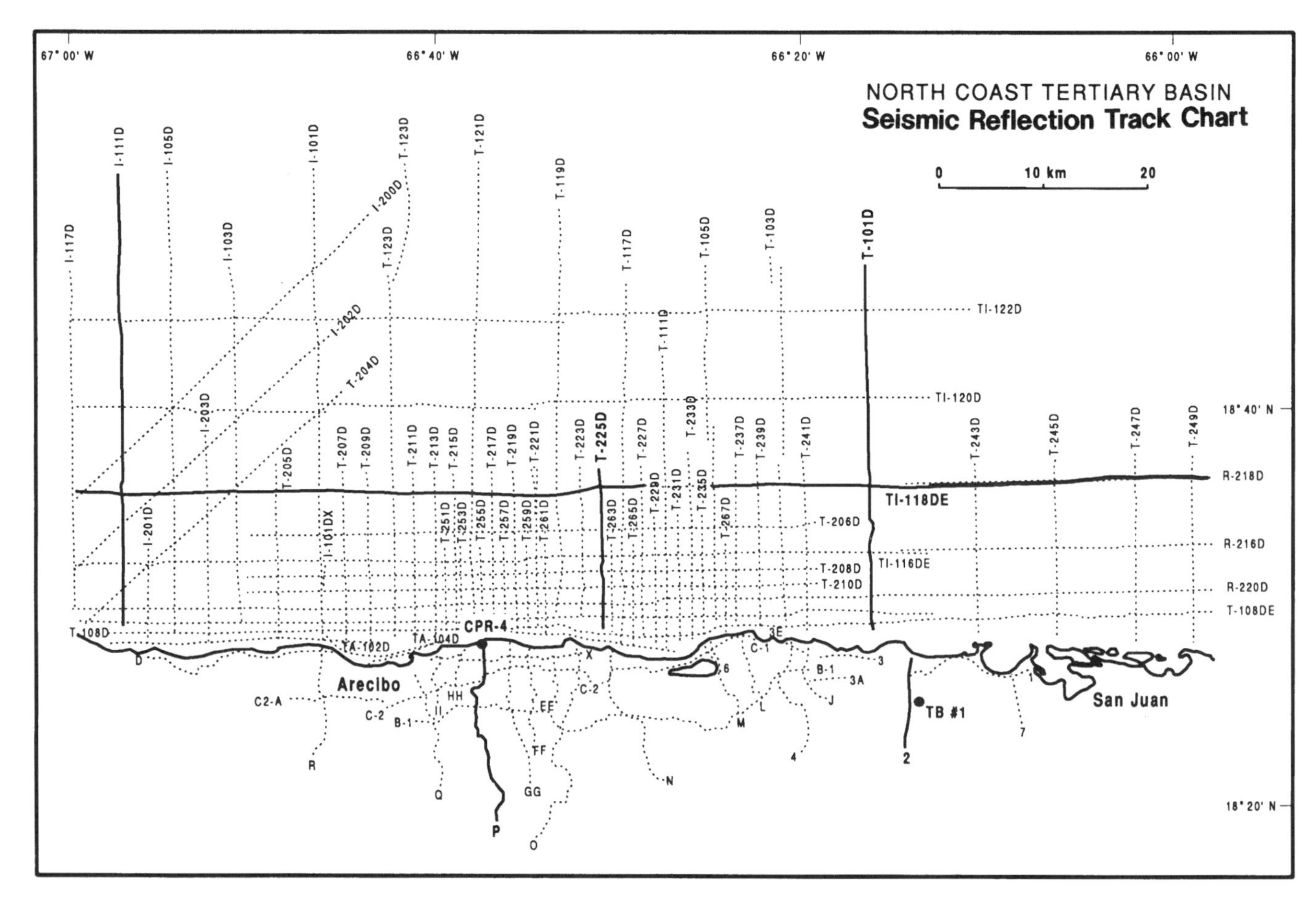

Figure 2. North Coast basin region of Puerto Rico, showing location of available data, including seismic reflection tracks, and boreholes. All offshore seismic lines were collected in the early 1970s by Western Geophysical for the Puerto Rico Water Authority, and are 24 channel. Onshore seismic lines labeled with letters were collected in the early 1970s using Vibroseis, are 24 channel and of poor quality. Numbered lines onshore were collected in 1986, and are 120 channel and better quality.

island arcs. Early Tertiary strata are dominantly found between fault blocks: the Eocene belt occurs between the south-central and central block, and the northern early Tertiary belt (Figs. 3 and 4) is a diffuse association of early Tertiary strata present in the complicated fault zone between the central and northeast blocks and between the central block and onlapping Oligocene and younger cover. It is believed that these early Tertiary strata (Table 1), onlapped by Oligocene and younger cover, probably extend to the north and represent at least part of the North Coast basin strata (Larue and Berrong, 1991).

The nature of the Cretaceous-Tertiary boundary in Puerto Rico is not well documented, but it may be conformable (or approximately so) in the northern flank of the Central Mountains in that fossils of both Late Cretaceous and early Tertiary age occur in the Trujillo Alto Limestone Member of the Monacillo Formation (Pease, 1968a-c). The Monacillo Formation (Table 1) is apparently, at least locally, conformably overlain by the upper Paleocene to lower Eocene Guaracanal Andesite, a turbiditic volcaniclastic unit (Pease, 1968a-c).

Lower Tertiary rock types are mostly volcaniclastic sandstones and mudstones and marly limestones of Paleocene and Eocene age (Table 1) (Kaye, 1959; Briggs and Pease, 1961; Monroe and Pease, 1962; Berryhill, 1965; Nelson and Monroe, 1966; Nelson, 1967a,b; Seiders, 1971; Monroe, 1977). Apparently, deposition mostly occurred in a deep water environment, although some poorly understood and poorly dated units may represent coastal plain or fluvial deposits (for example, Naranjito Formation, Paleocene?). Units such as the Guaracanal Andesite and Rio Piedras Formation represent relatively thick (200 to 700 m) (Monroe, 1977) accumulations of volcaniclastic and marly strata, apparently deposited in deep water conditions.

Cretaceous shallow water limestone deposits are present both below (Trujillo Alto Limestone) and in fault contact (that is, nonstratigraphic) with deep water early Tertiary strata described here, indicating a basinal deepening event sometime in the Paleocene. This basin-forming event was also apparently associated approximately in time with unroofing of plutons, as indicated by granodiorite clasts in the poorly dated Cibuco Formation (of Latest Cretaceous to Paleocene age) (Nelson, 1967a). We therefore speculate that the age of formation of the North Coast basin is Paleocene.

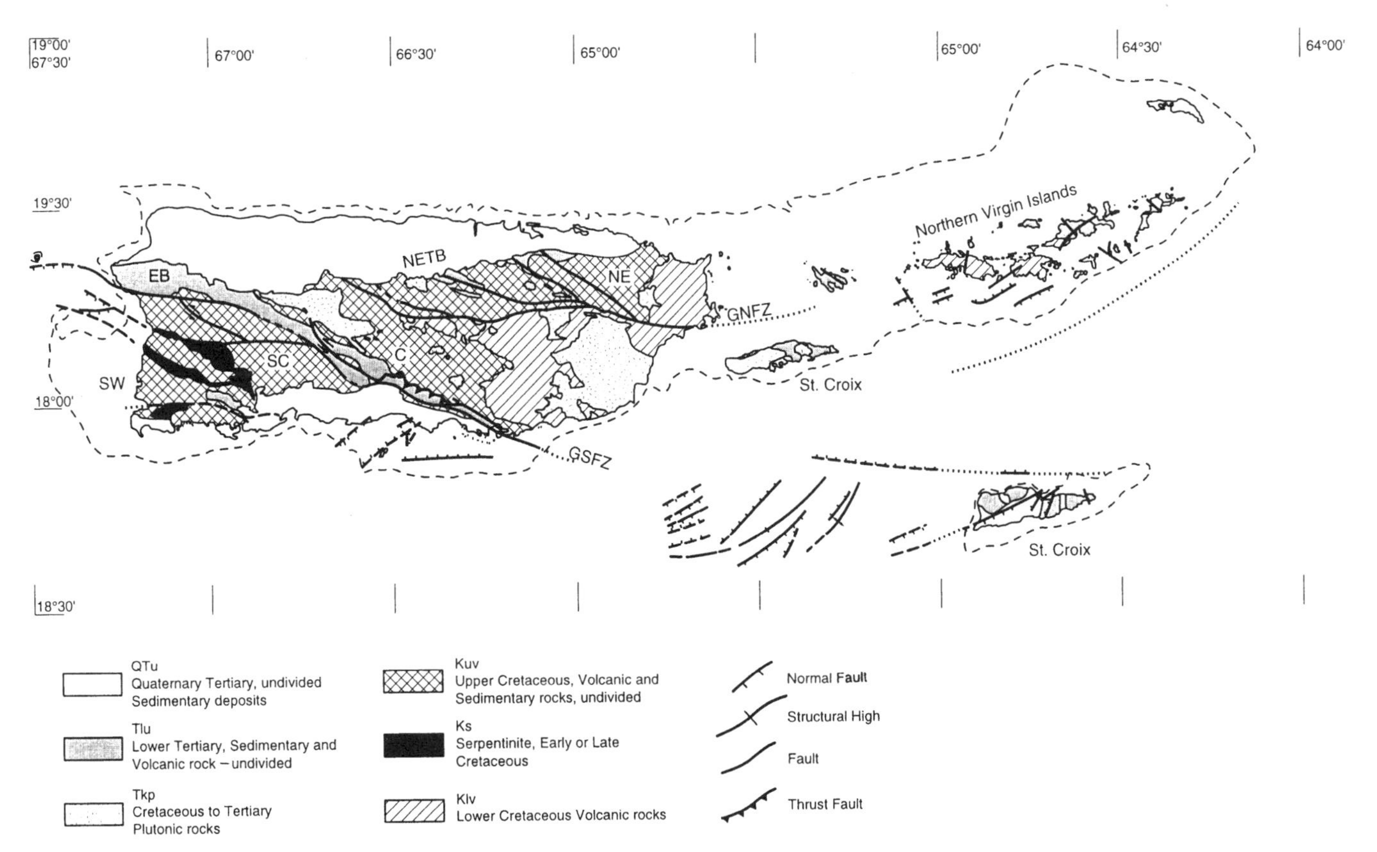

Figure 3. Simplified geologic map of Puerto Rico (from Garrison et al., 1972). SW, southwest block; occurs southwest of last exposure to northeast of serpentinite. SC, south-central block; occurs between SW block and central (C) block, separated from C by Eocene belt (EB) and Great Southern Fault Zone (GSFZ). NE (northeast) block, separated from central by Great Northern Fault Zone (GNFZ). NETB, northern early Tertiary belt, which may extend north and form lower succession of North Coast basin.

VOLCANISM AND PLUTONISM IN THE EARLY TERTIARY

Based on biostratigraphic and petrographic studies described above, volcanism in Puerto Rico extended into the Eocene, and was characterized by basalts, andesites, and basaltic andesites (see Jolly et al., Chapter 3, this volume). Ar laser-fusion studies of hornblendes from epiclastic sandstones in the Toa Baja borehole give an age of about 48 ± 2 my for depths from 2781 to 2787 m including two recycled hornblendes (67.6 and 72.2 Ma) (Table 2) (M. Heizler and T. M. Harrison, personal communication, 1992).

Associated with the Eocene volcaniclastic sedimentation was volcanism as indicated by lava flows and dikes that cut Eocene age strata. Several Eocene lava flows or dikes were penetrated in the Toa Baja borehole, and Smith et al. (1991) were able to show the chemical similarity between the volcanic and volcaniclastic rocks and inferred similar provenance. Eocene dikes have a strong west- to northwest-trend across northern Puerto Rico, probably associated with north to northeast extension and normal faulting along the southern margin of the North Coast basin.

Plutonic rocks on Puerto Rico range in age from the Cretaceous into the Eocene, with the youngest ages around 45 Ma, and are characterized by dioritic, quartz dioritic, and granodioritic compositions. This contrasts with the northern Virgin Islands (Virgin Gorda, Tortola, St. John) (Fig. 1), where some plutons are as young as 35 m.y. This trend of diminishing age of plutons extends to the south, to the islands of St. Martin and St. Bartholemy, where Oligocene to lowermost Miocene (minimum age, 23.5 m.y.) plutons are present (Nagle et al., 1976).

DEFORMATION OF EARLY TERTIARY ROCKS IN THE NORTHERN FLANK OF THE CENTRAL MOUNTAINS OF PUERTO RICO

Early Tertiary stratified rocks are exposed in the northern flank of the Central Mountains of Puerto Rico in north- and south-dipping homoclines, and broad-faulted folds with west-trending axes (Fig. 4: note spread of orientations from west-southwest in net II–IV to west-northwest in net V). Small wavelength folds are found rarely in fault zones that cut the homoclinal packages and also have west-trending axes. Figure 4 shows poles to homoclinal bedding planes in these early Tertiary rocks (from U.S. Geological Survey [USGS] maps: see Fig. 4 caption for references), and together the poles to bedding define a

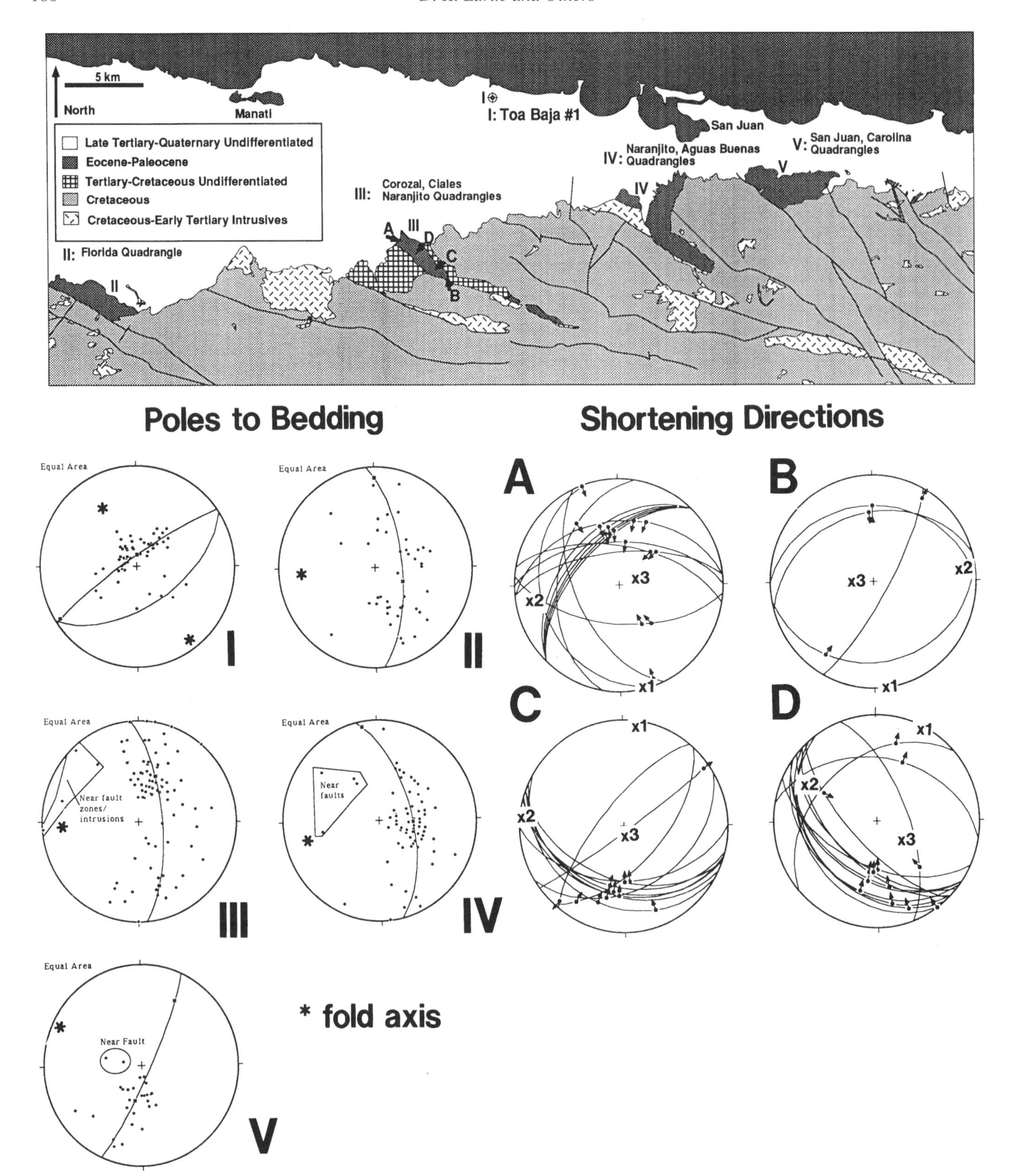

Figure 4. Parts 1 and 2, Map of Early Tertiary formations in northern Puerto Rico (after Kaye, 1959; Monroe and Pease, 1962; Berryhill, 1965; Nelson and Monroe, 1966; Nelson, 1967a,b; Seiders, 1971; Monroe, 1977). Lower hemisphere stereonets for structural data collected in early Tertiary rocks of the northern flank of the Central Mountains of Puerto Rico. Dipmeter data from the Toa Baja No. 1 borehole are also shown. Poles to bedding (dots) in stereonets I–V (see map for location) define rotation axes shown as stars. Shortening directions are shown in stereonets A–D, where the direction of shortening is the 1–3 plane, and the intermediate axis is shown as a 2. Calculated from fault planes, shown as great circles with motion direction given as an arrow.

TABLE 1. SUMMARY OF EARLY TERTIARY ROCKS EXPOSED IN THE NORTHERN FOOTHILLS OF PUERTO RICO*

Formation	Description	Age
Río Piedras Siltstone (Río Piedras, Carolina, Bayamon, Aguas Buenas Quads)	Volc siltstone, f gr ss, turbidites, pelagic forams, rare radiolarite. Includes impure ls member. Deep marine	Upper Paleocene–Eocene Underlain by Guaracanal Andesite
Nararjito Fm. (Naranjito Quad)	Volcaniclastic ss, sh, cgl. Fluvial/nonmarine?	Paleocene? (similar in appearance to Guaracanal). Fault-bound
Guaracanal Andesite (San Juan, Río Piedras, Carolina, Naranjito, Gurabo, Aguas Buenas Quads)	Coarse-grained volcaniclastic ss and cgl, sediment gravity flows. Local resedimented shallow water ls. Deep marine	Upper Paleocene–Lower Eocene. Overlain by Río Piedras Siltstone. Conformable(?) on Monacillo Fm.
Ortiz Fm. (Corozal Quad)	Volc. sh, ss, local impure ls member. Deep marine	Paleocene/Eocene
Corozal Limestone (Corozal Quad)	Limestone breccia, bedded ls. Shallow water, resed. in deep marine?	Paleocene/Eocene
Palmarejo Fm. (Naranjito, Corozal Quad)	Volcaniclastic sh, siltst. Deep marine (pelagic forams., rare turbidite beds)	Paleocene? Looks like Río Piedras Fm., may be same age
Yunes/Jobos Fms.	Volc ss and sh with ls lens	Upper Paleocene/Mid Eocene
(Florida Quad) Cibuco Fm. (Corozal Quad)	Deep marine. Volc. ss, cgl containing granodiorite clasts. Deep marine?	Cretaceous/Tertiary?
Carreras Siltstone (Corozal, Ciales Quads)	Thin-bd siltst, sh, ss. Locally limey. Deep marine	Cretaceous/Paleocene (uncertain)
Trujillo Alto Ls Member, Monacillo Fm. (Gurabo, Carolina, San Juan, Aguas Buenas Quads)	Coralgal ls, echinoids, millolid forams. Shallow marine	Late Cretaceous/Tertiary (Paleocene)

*References: Berryhill, 1965; Nelson, 1967a,b,c; Pease, 1968a,b,c; Seiders, 1971; Monroe, 1977, 1980; Monroe and Pease, 1962; Seiders, 1971.

crude girdle with a west-trending axis. Circled poles in stereonets III, IV, and V are those that are not contained within the girdle; such aberrant bed orientations are associated with faults and intrusions and probably reflect local heterogeneous strain.

Populations of small-offset faults were studied in fault zones where sense of displacement and slickenside striations were known and visible; these data were used to calculate stress tensors using a program written at Cornell University by R. Almendinger (Fig. 4: stereonets A, B, C, D). Directions of shortening from these data (shown by principal axis 1 on stereonets A–D, Fig. 4) are north-south, and range from north-northeast to north-northwest. These shortening directions are also inferred to have formed the folds of regional homoclinal bedding shown in Figure 4.

OLIGOCENE THROUGH PLIOCENE STRATA OF THE NORTH COAST

Lying with pronounced angular unconformity over Cretaceous through Eocene rocks is the middle Oligocene and younger succession (Monroe, 1980; Montgomery et al., 1991, this volume). Where the succession is complete, it consists of a basal siliciclastic formation, the San Sebastian Formation, overlain respectively by the Lares Limestone (late Oligocene to early Miocene), Cibao Formation (early Miocene to middle(?) Miocene), Los Puertos Limestone (middle Miocene), and Aymamon Limestone (Middle Miocene) (Sieglie and Moussa, 1984). Unconformably above the Aymamon Limestone is the Quebradillas Limestone of late Miocene to Pliocene age. All formations represent coastal (San Sebastian Formation) or shallow water shelf deposits except the Quebradillas formation, which contains both shallow water and bathyal fauna (Moussa et al., 1987). This succession is locally modified; for example, in some parts of northern Puerto Rico, no San Sebastian Formation or Lares Limestone is present, and mappable quartzose lenticular bodies are locally present (see Fig. 4 caption for USGS references).

Sieglie and Moussa (1984) were able to show a strong correlation between changes in sedimentation and eustatic sea-level

TABLE 2. SINGLE CRYSTAL LASER FUSION HORNBLENDE AGES FROM 2,780 TO 2,787 M IN TOA BAJA NO. 1*

Sample	Age (Ma)	Error (Ma)	Textural Interpretation
a	48.1	3.4	Primary
b	72.2	1.2	Recycled
c	48.0	2.2	Primary
e	45.9	1.8	Primary
f	67.6	3.9	Recycled
g	46.2	2.3	Primary
h	51.8	1.7	Primary
Summary	48.0	2.25	Primary only

*M. Heizler and T. M. Harrison, personal communication, 1992.

fluctuations, except for the Quebradillas Limestone. Bathyal conditions indicated by Quebradillas Limestone deposition and later emergence were attributed to local Miocene-Pliocene tectonism by Seiglie and Moussa (1984) and Moussa et al. (1987). As shown by paleomagnetic studies of the middle Tertiary section, Puerto Rico rotated 25° during the Mio-Pliocene, apparently during Quebradillas Limestone deposition (Reid et al., 1991).

TEST WELL 4 CPR AND THE TOA BAJA # 1 BOREHOLE

Kewanee Interamerican Oil Company test well 4 CPR was drilled in 1960 on the north coast of Puerto Rico near Arecibo (Figs. 2 and 5). At the time it was drilled, it was the first deep well to test the post-Eocene strata of the north coast of Puerto Rico (Briggs, 1961). The well was dry, with no traces of oil or gas encountered, and reached a total depth of 1961 m, having penetrated nearly 1706 m of middle Tertiary rocks (San Sebastian through Quebradillas Formations) and underlying strata of probable Eocene age (Briggs, 1961) (Fig. 5). Figure 5 shows the correlation between units penetrated and an onshore to offshore seismic line collected in the early 1970s (Western Geophysical, 1974). The middle Tertiary strata can be traced laterally as a northward-thickening wedge, whereas the Eocene rocks are poorly imaged. Birch (1986) modeled deposition of the middle Tertiary strata of the 4 CPR well and concluded that tectonic subsidence was driven by thermal cooling from the Oligocene to the Miocene, and flexure from the late Miocene to the Holocene.

The Toa Baja borehole (Fig. 6) was selected to test a structure characterized by two-way closure in Line 2 (Figs. 2 and 7). Line 2 also shows high-amplitude reflectors similar to reflectors offshore, which had generated considerable speculation about their hydrocarbon potential. The Toa Baja # 1 well penetrated 579 m of middle Tertiary rocks (San Sebastian, Cibao, Aymamon Formations) unconformably underlain by Eocene volcaniclastic and volcanic rocks to a total depth of 2704 m. Middle Tertiary rocks penetrated by the well were deposited in shallow water conditions (Montgomery et al., 1991), whereas underlying Eocene rocks represent basinal deposits (Smith et al., 1991). Eocene strata are mostly volcaniclastic, both epiclastic and minor pyroclastic (Smith et al., 1991) sandstones and mudstones, locally volcaniclastic marlstones, and volcanic rocks including lava flows and/or intrusive rocks. Eocene strata penetrated in the well are therefore similar to those exposed in the northern flank of the Central Mountains of Puerto Rico (for example, Rio Piedras Formation, Ortiz Formation) (Table 1).

Based on biostratigraphic studies, the oldest middle Tertiary rocks in Toa Baja # 1 were deposited about 30 Ma (Montgomery et al., 1991), whereas Eocene rocks have been dated at a depth of 2584 m as 48 ± 2 Ma using Ar laser fusion dating of single hornblende crystals (M. Heisler and T. M. Harrison, written communication, 1991) in addition to biostratigraphic studies (Montgomery et al., 1991) (Fig. 6A). The profound angular unconformity at 579 m, imaged on seismic line 2, therefore represents a lacuna of around 16 m.y.

Dipmeter logs (Fig. 6B) were used to infer the presence of approximately eight faults in Eocene strata (Anderson, 1991). Orientations of Eocene beds in the Toa Baja borehole based on dipmeter data define a girdle on a stereonet with axis trending northwest (Fig. 4: stereonet I), which is oblique to the west-trending axis defined by homoclinal layers in Eocene rocks in the northern flank of the Central Mountains of Puerto Rico.

Gamma ray data (Fig. 6B) show that the Eocene rocks are deficient in radioactive components (typical shales are 100 to 200 API units). Porosity logs indicate no evidence of free gas in the borehole (Anderson, 1991; Larue et al., 1991a).

A synthetic seismogram (Fig. 6C) generated from density and sonic log information (Anderson, 1991) can be used to correlate depth in the borehole to two way travel time. The angular unconformity between the middle Tertiary and Eocene strata occurs at 0.5 sec (two-way travel time), based on correlation of the synthetic seismogram with seismic Line 2 (Fig. 7). Larue et al. (1991a) compared in detail reflections in Line 2 with rock properties from geophysical logs, drill cuttings, and core. They concluded that the uppermost of the high amplitude reflectors at the base of Line 2 (1.4 sec or 2.533-km depth) were perhaps related to a fault at that depth, or volcanic flows or dikes, and that little hydrocarbon potential existed for the high-amplitude reflectors.

Paleothermometric studies of rocks penetrated by the Toa Baja borehole include studies of low-temperature mineral assemblages (Cho, 1991; Tribble, 1991) and oxygen isotopes of bulk carbonates (Gonzalez, 1991). All three studies indicate that the middle Tertiary strata have not been significantly heated, and that the Eocene strata were characterized by a paleogeothermal gradient of 40° to 60°C/km. This steep geothermal gradient is in stark contrast to the present gradient of about 13°C/km, and heat flow of 23 to 35mW/m^2 (Anderson and Larue, 1991). The higher geothermal gradient was apparently associated with deposition of the Eocene strata in a volcanic arc environment, and effects of local intrusive heating. The paleogeothermal gradient were used to calculate that 1 to 2 km of section were eroded in the late Eocene to middle Oligocene.

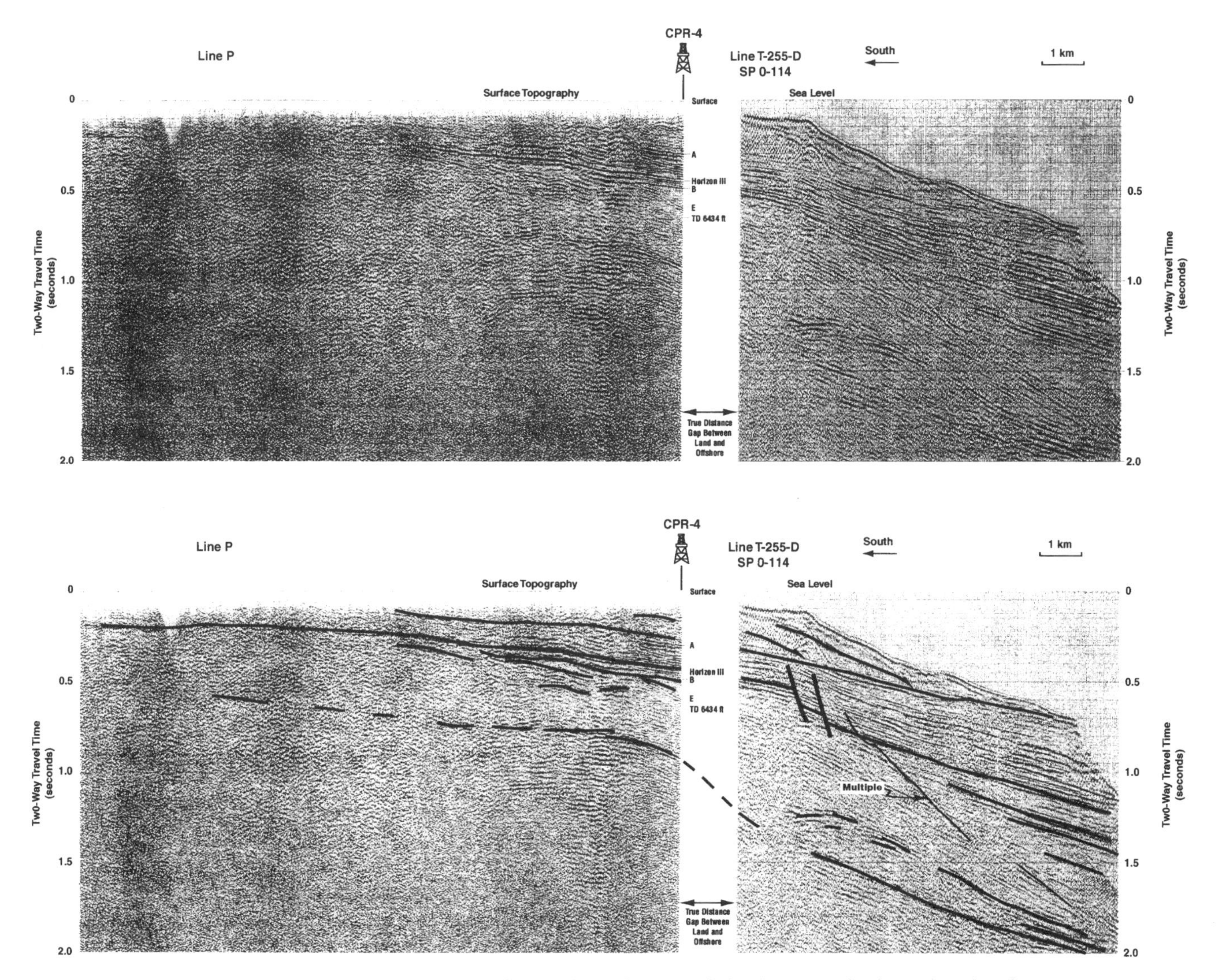

Figure 5. Modified original Western Geophysical (1974) correlation between seismic stratigraphy of north-south seismic reflection profiles Line P (onshore) and T-255D (offshore), and position of the borehole CPR-4. Point A, a marker horizon in the Miocene section; Horizon III, a prominent reflector that has been traced throughout the region; B, the top of the San Sebastian Formation; E, the top of the Eocene section. Location of seismic profiles shown in Figure 2. Upper figure shows data, lower shows interpretation. From the interpretation, the San Sebastian Formation (B) represents valley-fill deposits discordantly lying above Eocene strata (E) and concordantly onlapped by younger strata. See text for discussion.

NORTH COAST TERTIARY BASIN: INTRODUCTION TO SEISMIC REFLECTION STUDIES

The North Coast basin (Fig. 8) is an east-trending basin with east-west length of ~70 km and north-south width of 40 to 50 km. The basin is bounded on the south by exposed Cretaceous "basement" (pre-basinal: may include some early Tertiary strata) rocks of the Cordillera Central of Puerto Rico and on the east and west by shallow basement rocks of the San Juan and Guajataca Highs, respectively, as imaged using seismic reflection (Figs. 8 and 9). The basin's northern flank, according to seismic reflection profiles, lies some 40 to 50 km north of the present-day north coast of Puerto Rico. The basin contains a few large, second order subbasins and several smaller, third order subbasins (Fig. 8).

Seismic reflection analysis

The objectives of our seismic reflection analysis were to develop an understanding of the structure of the North Coast basin, and characterize the basin's stratigraphic and structural evolution. In order to meet these objectives, we developed the following steps for our study: (1) pick distinctive reflectors that could be correlated between seismic reflection profiles on a basin-wide basis; (2) determine the kinematic significance of structures that deform reflectors; (3) interpret the age of distinctive reflectors

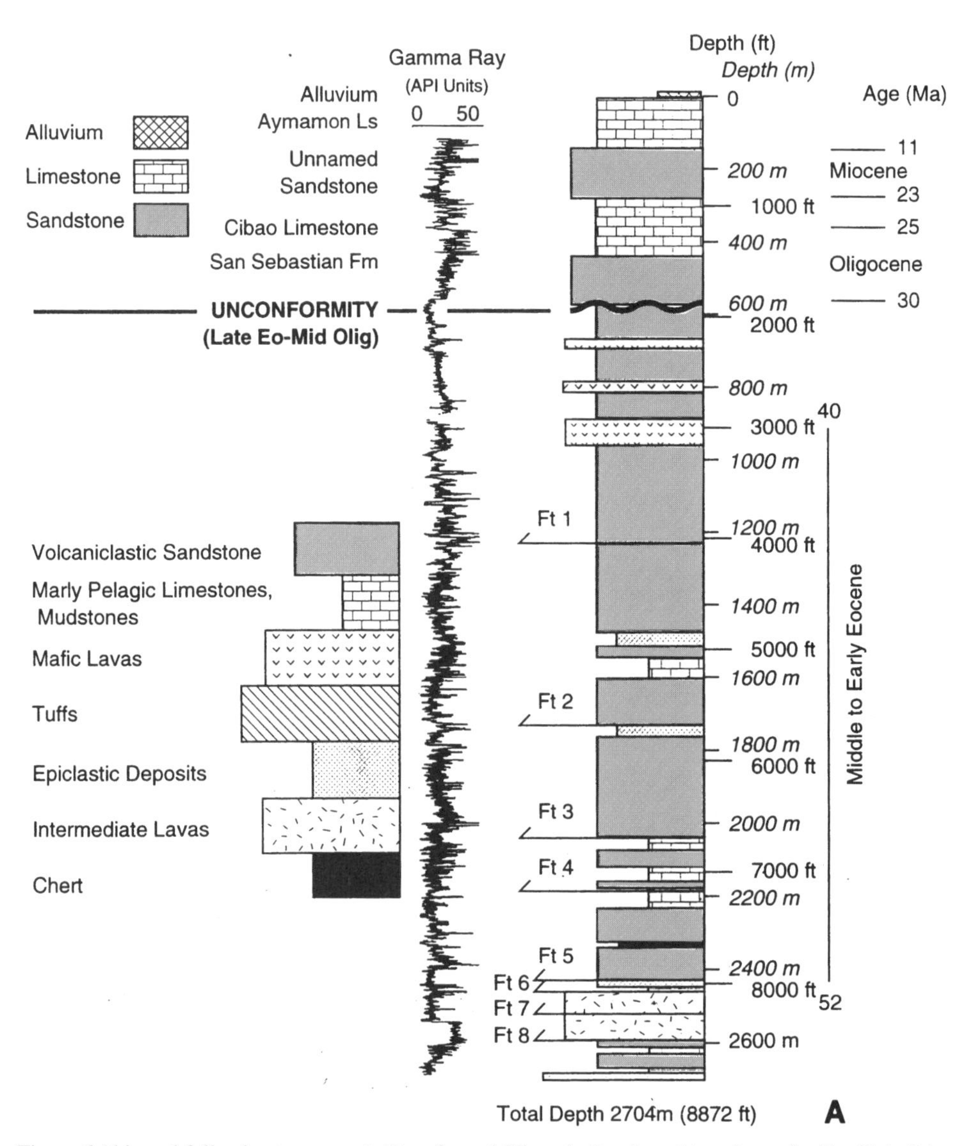

Figure 6 (this and following two pages). Data from drilling. A, Stratigraphic column for Toa Baja # 1. B, Summary of geophysical logging results, including dipmeter (from Anderson, 1991). C, Synthetic seismogram for Toa Baja # 1 (Anderson, 1991).

based on correlation with the outcrop geology of Puerto Rico and the logs of the north coast wells, 4 CPR and Toa Baja No. 1; (4) construct isotime maps indicating the total sediment thickness and thickness of individual successions in units of two-way time; and (5) divide the seismic stratigraphy into successions defined by seismic reflection characteristics (parallelism or divergence, amplitude, frequency, and lateral continuity of reflectors) that can be used to interpret sedimentary facies. Seismic reflection profile tracks are shown in Figure 2.

Basement reflector. The boundary between basinal reflectors and pre-basinal basement is typically abrupt and marked on several profiles by a prominent set of high-amplitude, low-frequency reflections (Figs. 7, 10, and 14). On a few profiles, there is no clear demarcation of the basement-basinal boundary. By correlation with the outcrop and borehole (No. 4 CPR, Toa Baja # 1) geology, the basement is inferred to represent weakly metamorphosed and deformed, Cretaceous to early Tertiary arc-related rocks. The set of strong reflectors above pre-basinal basement may represent limestone, volcanic flows, or dikes (such as were observed in Toa Baja # 1), or basal clastic beds deposited atop volcanic and volcaniclastic basement. Offshore, evidence of downlap onto the basal reflectors is observed (Fig. 14).

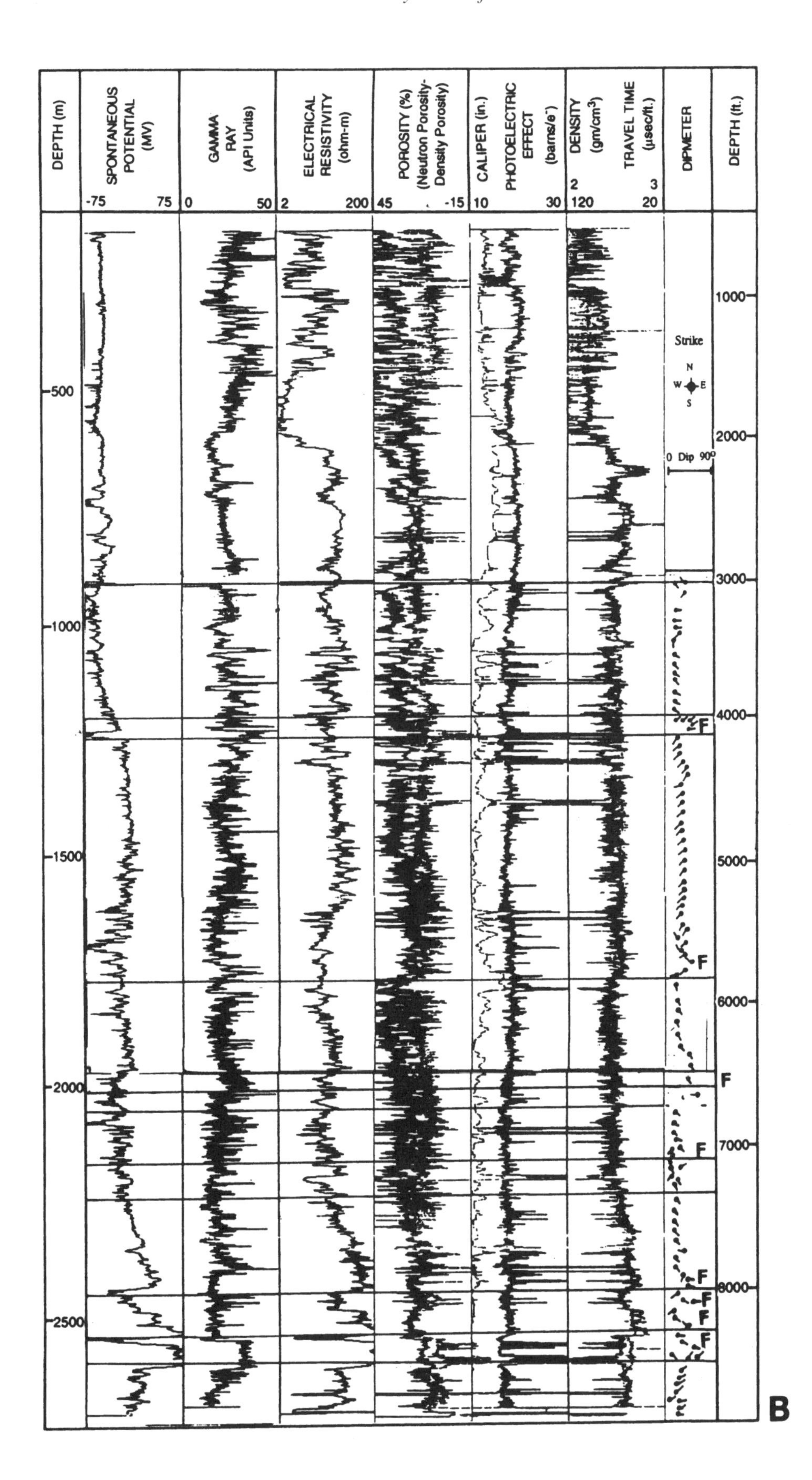
DEPTH (m)
SPONTANEOUS POTENTIAL (MV)
-75 75
GAMMA RAY (API Units)
0 50
ELECTRICAL RESISTIVITY (ohm-m)
2 200
POROSITY (%) (Neutron Porosity-Density Porosity)
45 -15
CALIPER (in.)
10
PHOTOELECTRIC EFFECT (barns/e⁻)
30
DENSITY (gm/cm³)
2 3
TRAVEL TIME (µsec/ft.)
120 20
DIPMETER
DEPTH (ft.)
500
1000
1500
2000
2500
1000
2000
3000
4000
5000
6000
7000
8000
Strike
N
W
E
S
0 Dip 90°
F
B

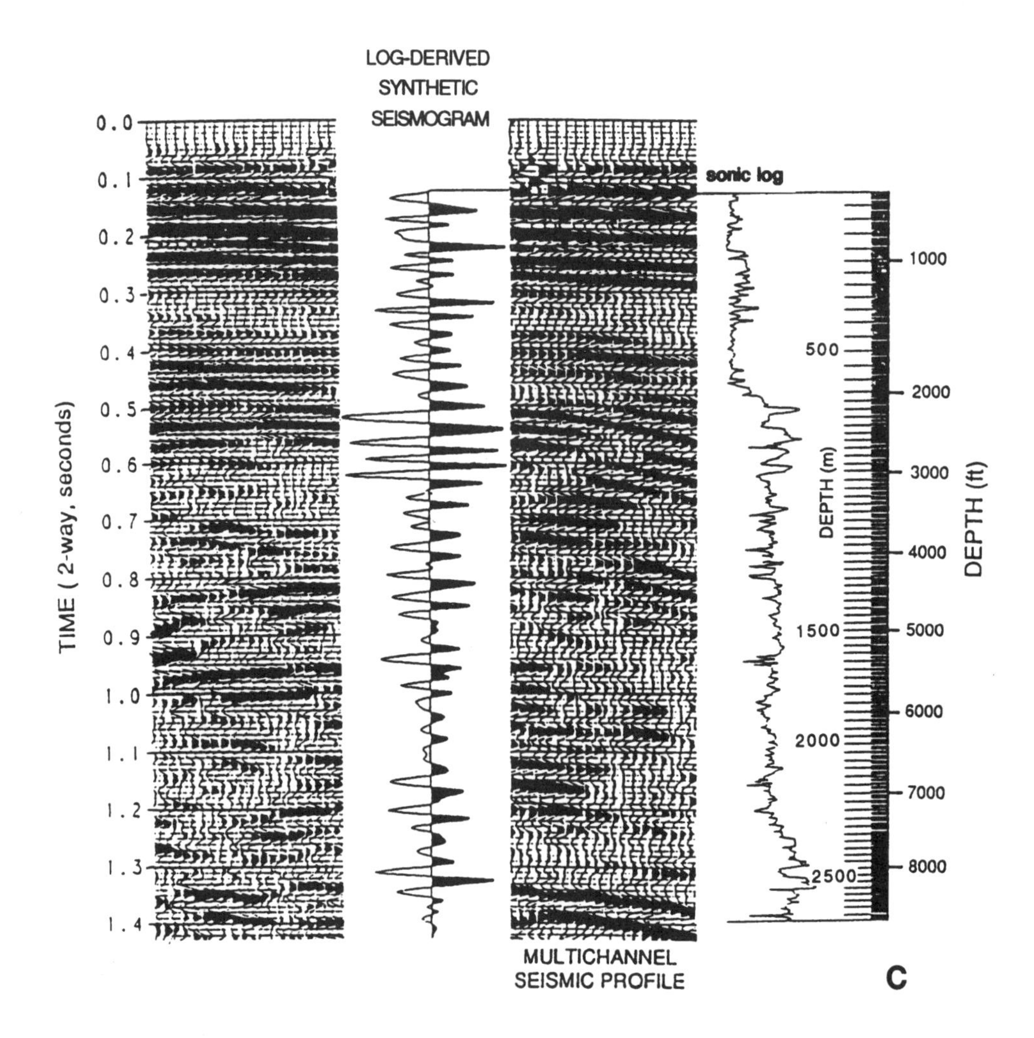

Horizon III. In addition to the prominent basement reflectors, Western Geophysical (1974) chose a distinctive stratigraphic reflector traceable on both onland and offshore seismic reflection profiles for the purpose of regional (basin-wide) mapping. They called this reflector Horizon III (Figs. 5, 9, and 10). We agree with Western Geophysical's choice, as Horizon III is distinguished from other stratal reflectors by its generally high amplitude and can generally be easily correlated from one reflection profile to another. Figure 5 shows Western Geophysical's correlation of Horizon III with the log of the 4 CPR well and with the Tertiary stratigraphy of the overlap succession. Horizon III is regarded as the approximate base of the mid-Tertiary section.

Sedimentary successions and isotime maps

In this section we describe reflection characteristics of the upper and lower successions of the North Coast basin that are separated by Horizon III and interpret isotime contour maps of the total and partial sedimentary successions. In order to evaluate the total sediment thickness and thicknesses of successions above and below Horizon III, we have constructed isotime maps rather than isopach (thickness) maps. The isotime maps can be converted to isopach maps if the velocity of the succession is known (Fig. 14). Isotime maps were constructed for the total sedimentary succession (sea bottom—acoustic basement) (Fig. 11), Horizon III—acoustic basement (Fig. 12), and sea bottom—Horizon III (Fig. 13). The maps employ both onshore and offshore seismic reflection data.

Total sedimentary succession. The isotime map of the total sedimentary succession (sea bottom—acoustic basement) (Fig. 11) indicates the existence of several regional (second order) basement highs and lows within the North Coast basin, together with local (third order) high frequency undulations. The Manati-

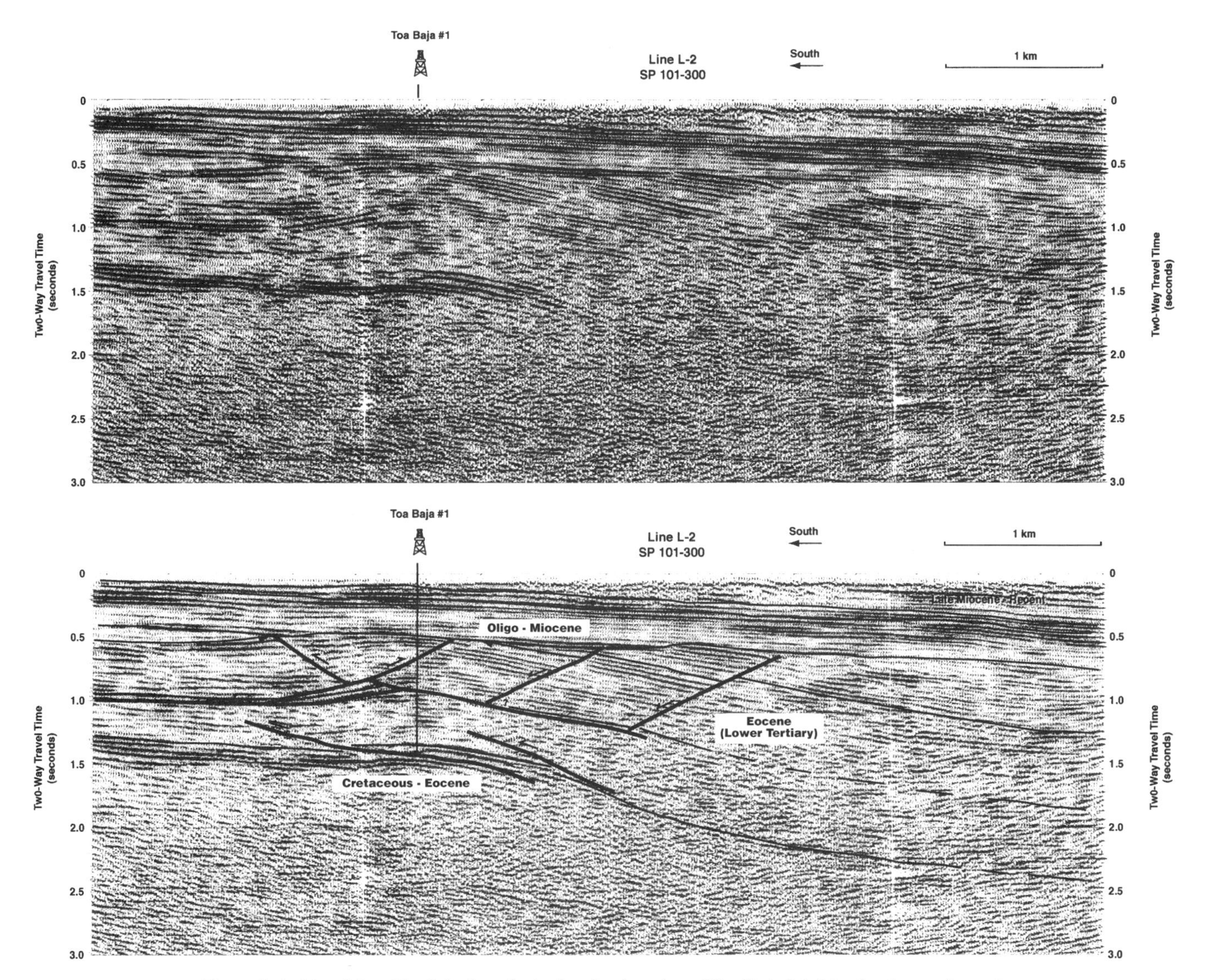

Figure 7. A, Line 2 (see Fig. 2 for location), showing location of Toa Baja # 1. Line has been migrated and has radial predictive filter (Western Geophysical, 1987). B, Interpretation of Line 2. Note local angular relationship between lower deformed basinal succession (Eocene to perhaps as old as Paleocene) and upper homoclinal north-dipping succession (middle Oligocene and younger). Several faults were interpreted beneath the prominent Eocene-Oligocene angular unconformity: These faults were corroborated with borehole information. The strong reflectors imaged near the base of the Toa Baja #1 borehole define the top of an older succession, which may include Cretaceous strata. Two unconformable successions are shown by onlap in the upper part of the middle to upper Tertiary succession.

Bayamon regional low (Fig. 8) extends onshore, as do several of the local (third order) lows (Figs. 8 and 11). The regional basement highs and lows shown in map view in Figures 8 and 11 can also be seen in seismic sections in Figures 7, 9, and 14.

Lower sedimentary succession. The succession below Horizon III is of probable Paleocene/Eocene to middle Oligocene age and includes strata that yield a variety of reflection characteristics. On onshore profiles (e.g., Fig. 7), the lower succession includes laterally continuous reflectors of moderate amplitude and frequency, which are generally unconformable with respect to overlying strata above Horizon III.

On offshore profiles (Fig. 9), the angular discordance below Horizon III becomes less obvious, and is apparently conformable or paraconformable, although evidence locally is observed for truncation beneath the surface (Fig. 14). Over a large area in the center of the North Coast basin, the lower succession contains "transparent" areas between Horizon III and acoustic basement that are characterized by weak, poorly defined, laterally discontinuous, low-amplitude, parallel to slightly divergent reflectors that onlap acoustic basement highs (Fig. 10). Such characteristics indicate an absence of marked impedance contrast.

The isotime map of the lower succession (Fig. 12) shows

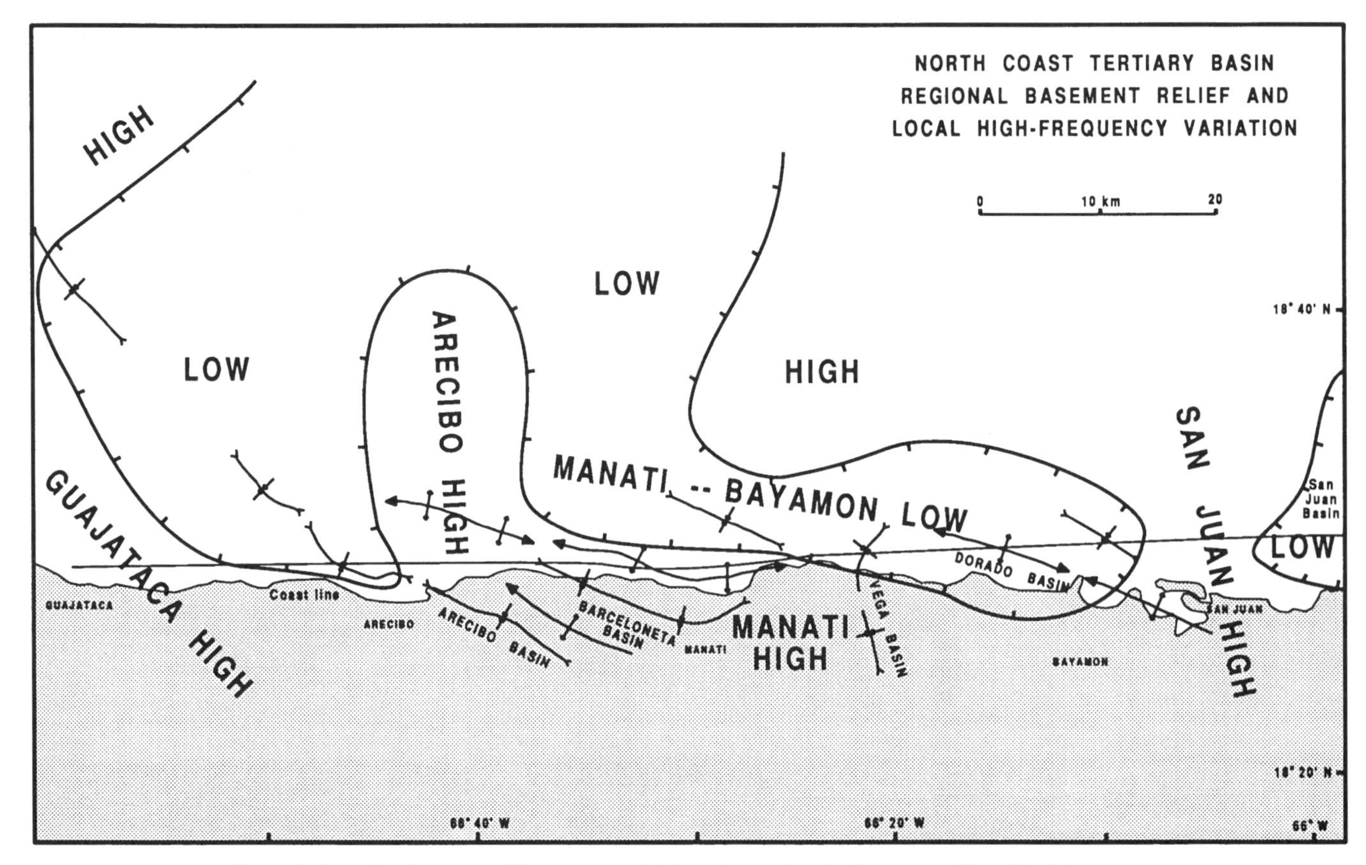

Figure 8. Map showing regional basement undulations (second-order features) and local high-frequency undulations (third-order features) of the North Coast basin, representing basinal thicks and thins. Map is based on seismic reflection isotime maps, and on magnetic and gravity anomaly maps.

regional and local basement undulations and depositional patterns similar to those of the total sedimentary succession isotime map (Fig. 11). It differs, however, by the more easterly trend of long, continuous contours in the northern half of the study area. The difference is due to the fact that the thickness of the uppermost succession (sea bottom—Horizon III) (Fig. 13) is nonuniform and increases northward. The isotime contours of the lower sedimentary succession (Fig. 12) are the difference between the total sedimentary succession (Fig. 11) and the nonuniformly thick upper succession (Fig. 13) and give the most accurate indication of the relief and trend of basement structures in the North Coast basin.

Upper sedimentary succession. The upper sedimentary succession above Horizon III is of probable middle Oligocene to Recent age. It has an average seismic velocity of about 2.57 km/sec according to calculations by Western Geophysical (1974). The succession generally consists of alternately high and low amplitude, continuous to discontinuous, high-frequency reflectors of parallel and clinoform geometry (Figs. 5, 9, and 10), but includes local transparent intervals that pass laterally into clinoform reflectors (Fig. 10). The clinoforms and other reflection characteristics indicate that the upper succession consists of shelf, slope, and local basinal facies. The thickness of clinoform reflectors (Fig. 10) suggests bathymetric relief of 200 to 600 m between the shelf and basin and local basin depths as great as 800 m (upper bathyal). The upper succession is interpreted to form a broad shelf with local lower neritic to upper bathyal embayments; this conclusion is supported by evidence from dredge hauls that recovered Tertiary shallow water and upper bathyal limestones from submarine fault scarp exposures of the upper succession (Schneidermann et al., 1972; Perfit et al., 1980). As stated earlier, the profound present-day depths north of Puerto Rico are related to late Miocene to Pliocene northward tilting and subsidence of the former aerially extensive shelf. The tilting and deepening are not obviously recorded by the seismic stratigraphy of the upper succession except for the presence of thin-skinned slump sheets and scars near the sea bottom (Fig. 8).

The upper succession (sea bottom—Horizon III) (Fig. 13) thickens northward but depositional patterns conform to regional basement features of the North Coast basin (Fig. 8). The similarity suggests regional subsidence and "sag" during deposition of the upper succession. Such subsidence was apparently accommodated by reactivated basement faults and by broad flexure of overlying sediments. The upper succession also includes high frequency, low-amplitude thickness variations (not shown in Fig. 13) due to downcutting submarine canyons and submarine

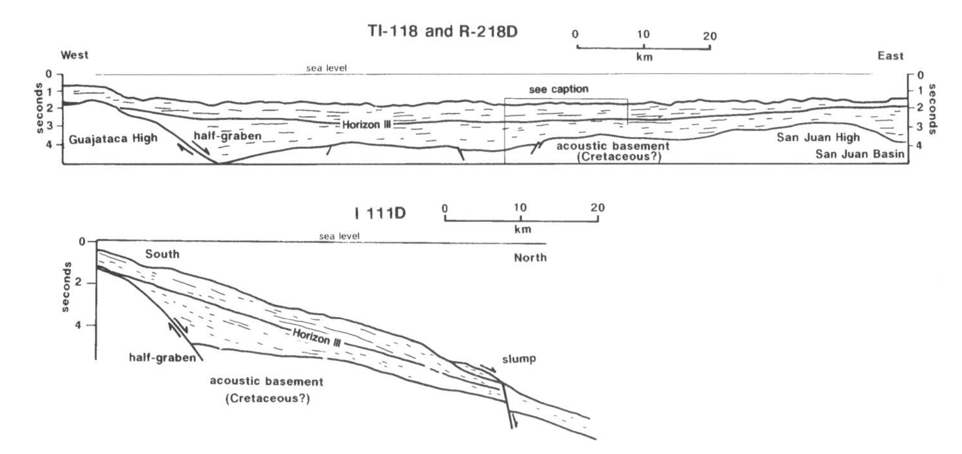

Figure 9. Line drawings of seismic reflection profiles across the North Coast Basin. A, East-west profiles showing principal highs and lows of acoustic basement. Box shows location of detailed segment shown in Figure 10. B, North-south profile showing present-day northward deepening of sea bottom that resulted from northward tilting and subsidence in the late Miocene to early Pliocene. Location of profiles shown in Figure 2.

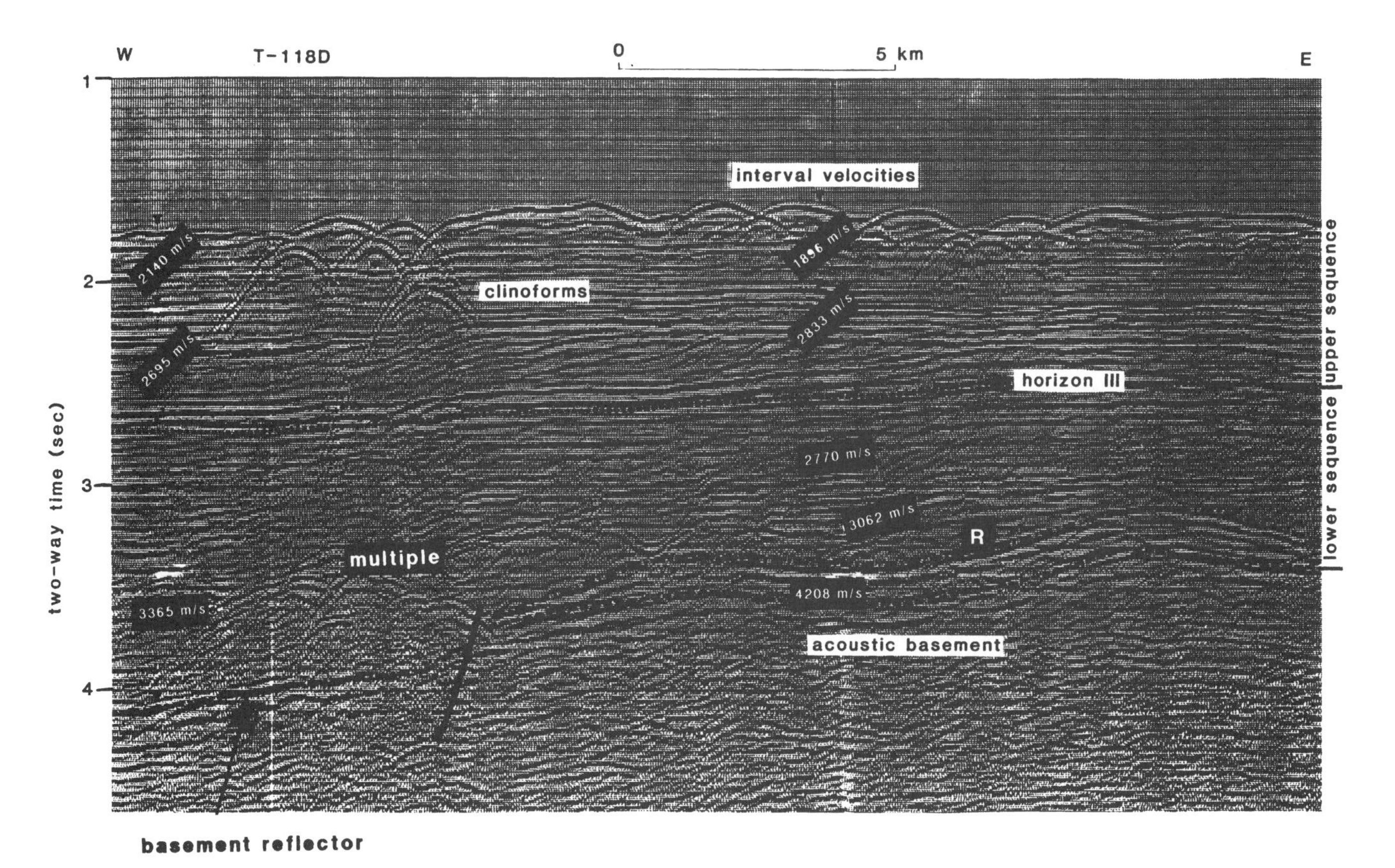

Figure 10. Detailed segment of east-west–trending offshore seismic reflection profile T-118D, showing Horizon III, acoustic basement reflector R, upper succession clinoforms prograding westward from local high, and interval velocities of upper and lower successions. Location of profile shown in Figure 2.

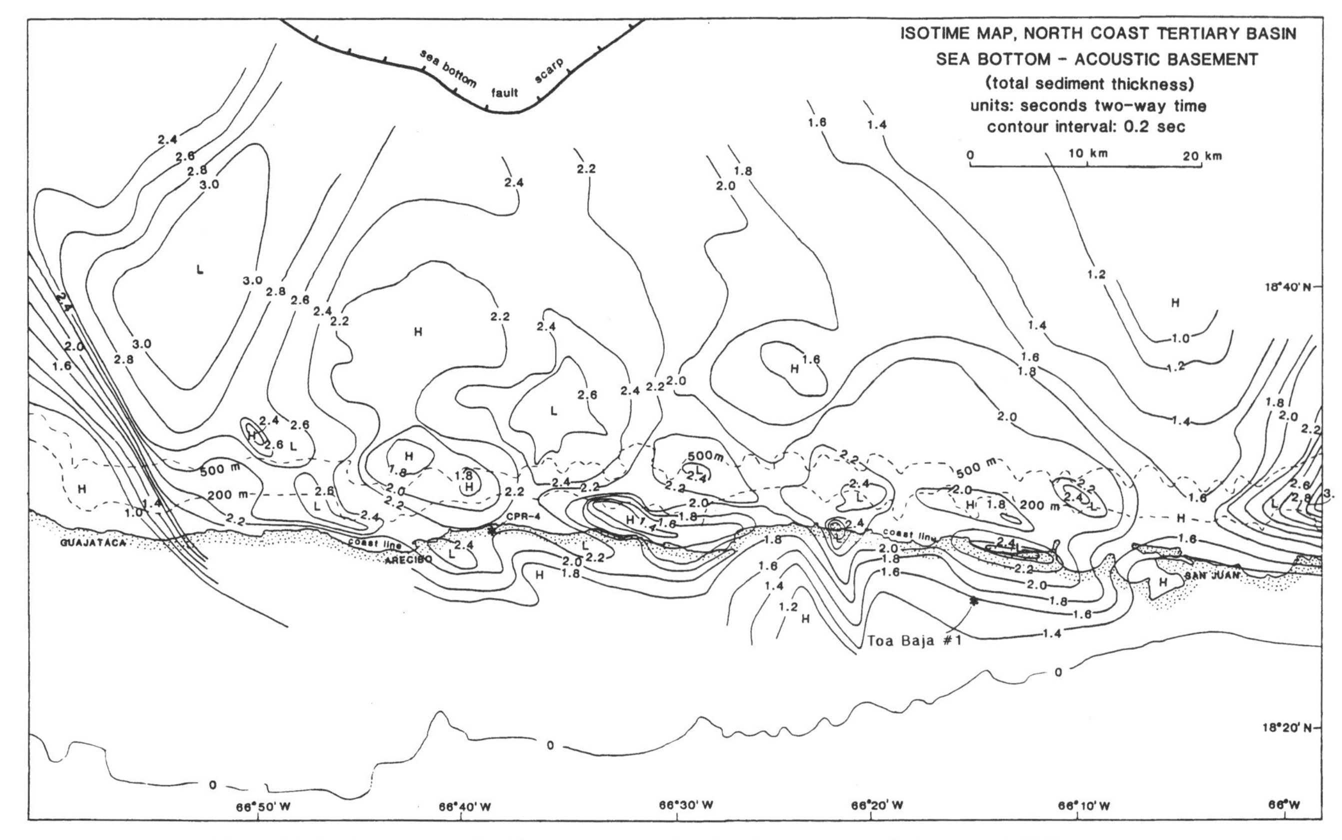

Figure 11. Isotime map, total sedimentary succession (sea bottom–acoustic basement); H, basement high; L, basement low. Dashed lines mark 200- and 500-bathymetric contours. Note sites of CPR-4 and Toa Baja # 1.

slumps. The northward thickening of the upper succession is related to northstepping, southward offlap that may be related to progressive eustatic sea level fall in Middle to late Miocene time (Sieglie and Moussa, 1984).

Paleofacies map

Figure 15 shows a paleofacies map for late Oligocene through Miocene time based on the seismic stratigraphy of the upper succession above Horizon III. The map shows a broad carbonate shelf, as discussed earlier, that extends some 40 to 50 km northward from the present-day coast line and includes local lower neritic to upper bathyal embayments that appear to correspond crudely to regional second order basement lows (Fig. 8) and to thus be related to late subbasin subsidence (sag). The seismic reflection characteristics of the shelf, slope, and basin facies are described in Figure 15 and shown graphically in Figure 10. As earlier stated, the paleofacies interpretation of a broad carbonate shelf with local embayments is substantiated by the dredge haul recovery, north of Puerto Rico, of Tertiary shallow water and upper bathyal limestones from submarine fault scarp exposures of the upper succession (Perfit et al., 1980).

Basement structure

Figure 9 shows line drawings of regional marine seismic reflection profiles across the North Coast basin, and Figure 10 shows a local seismic reflection segment in detail. The structural relief of the basement during early basin formation is best interpreted from the isotime map of the basinal succession because, as earlier stated, the true trends of basement structures are obscured on the total sediment isotime map (Fig. 11) by the additive effect of the upper succession (Fig. 13). The Horizon III—acoustic basement isotime map (Fig. 12) indicates that the early North Coast basin had prominent northwest-trending northeast and southwest flanks, an east-west–trending southern flank, and a northeast-trending northwestern flank.

Reflections are poorly defined and laterally discontinuous below the basement reflector (Figs. 9 and 10). However, the basement reflector itself is locally cut by faults with a normal component of displacement (Figs. 9 and 10), and a large basin adjacent to the Guajataca High (Fig. 9) has a distinctly asymmetric geometry suggesting it is a half-graben. The inferred fault marking the Guajataca half-graben strikes northwest, and other faults with smaller normal components of displacement strike between west-northwest and northwest. It is uncertain whether

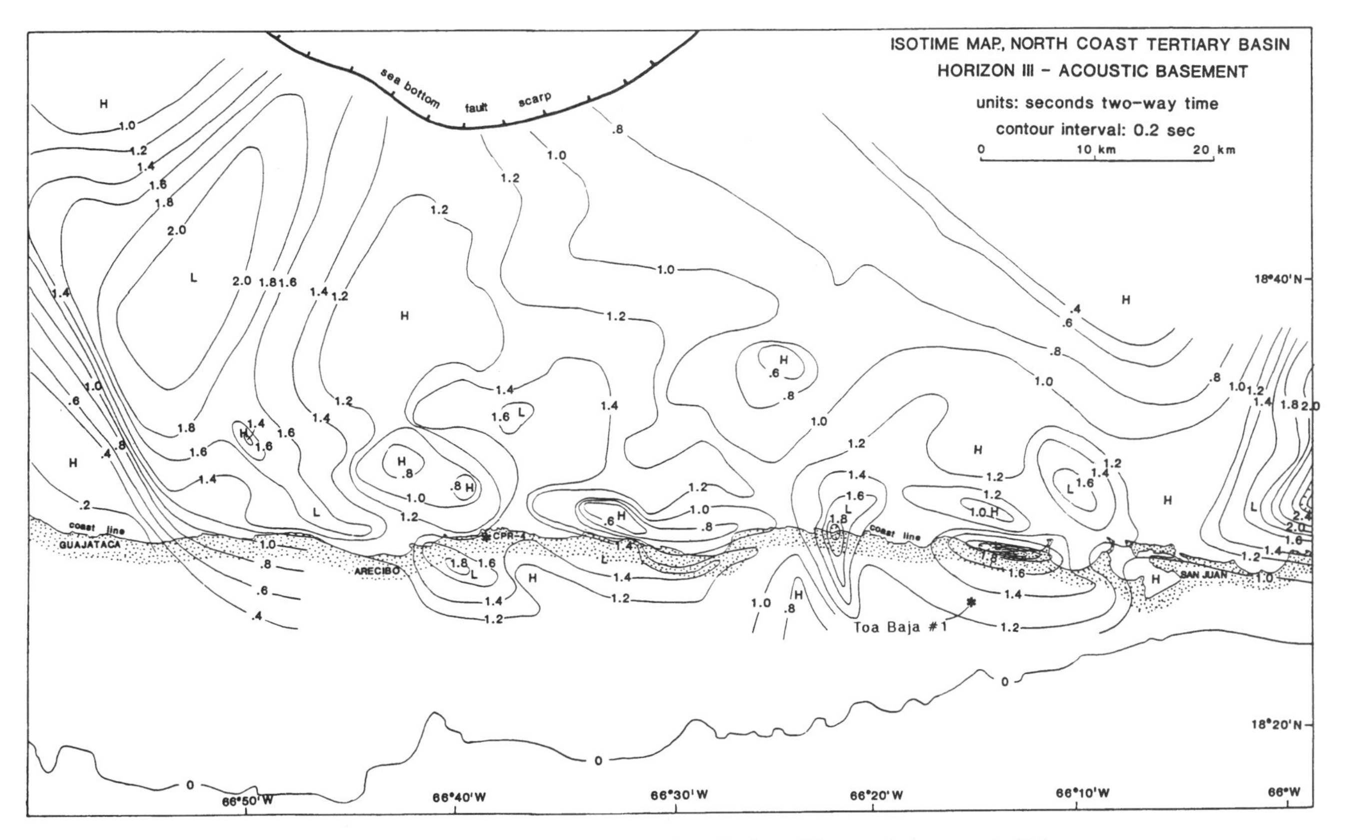

Figure 12. Isotime map, lower sedimentary succession (Horizon III–acoustic basement); H, basement high; L, basement low.

such faults were newly formed or reactivated equivalents of older, northwest-striking faults in the basement of Puerto Rico. If the basement faults have only normal components of displacement, then their west-northwest to northwest strikes indicate formation by northeast- to north-northwest–trending tectonic extension. If the basement faults included a strike-slip component of displacement, however, then the direction of tectonic extension can only be constrained to between north and east-southeast. The tectonic significance of an extension direction in the northeast quadrant is discussed in a later section.

Deformation of the lower succession below Horizon III

The contact between the lower succession and upper succession in much of the offshore region is concordant, whereas onshore there is locally a strong unconformable contact between the two successions (Figs. 5 and 7). The structural high penetrated by Toa Baja # 1 (Fig. 7) is a thrust-faulted anticline that was overlain with angular unconformity by middle Oligocene and younger strata. This same angular unconformity is noted on other onland seismic profiles, and evidence of compressional deformation is also observed beneath the unconformity. Regional dip beneath the angular unconformity is northward, indicating that the offshore lower succession probably contains younger strata beneath the contact between the two successions than the lower succession onshore. Two scenarios are presented to explain the discrepancy between the onshore angular discordance above thrust-faulted rocks and the offshore concordant contact. First, Larue and Berrong (1991) suggested that a structural front existed between the offshore and onshore transition, and that the offshore rocks represented undeformed equivalents to the onshore rocks. While this is probably at least in part true, it is also possible that the source of some of the offshore lower succession strata was uplifted onshore lower succession strata. Therefore, while the age of the strata penetrated by Toa Baja # 1 is clearly Eocene, the offshore strata may be as young as Eocene to middle Oligocene in age immediately below the contact between the two successions. Unfortunately, separating the merits of the two arguments is not simple without additional wellbore information or more detailed seismic stratigraphic mapping.

CONCLUSIONS

The North Coast basin of Puerto Rico evolved in four stages (Fig. 16). The earliest history involved extension on an arc platform and development of an intra-arc basin. This basin deepened

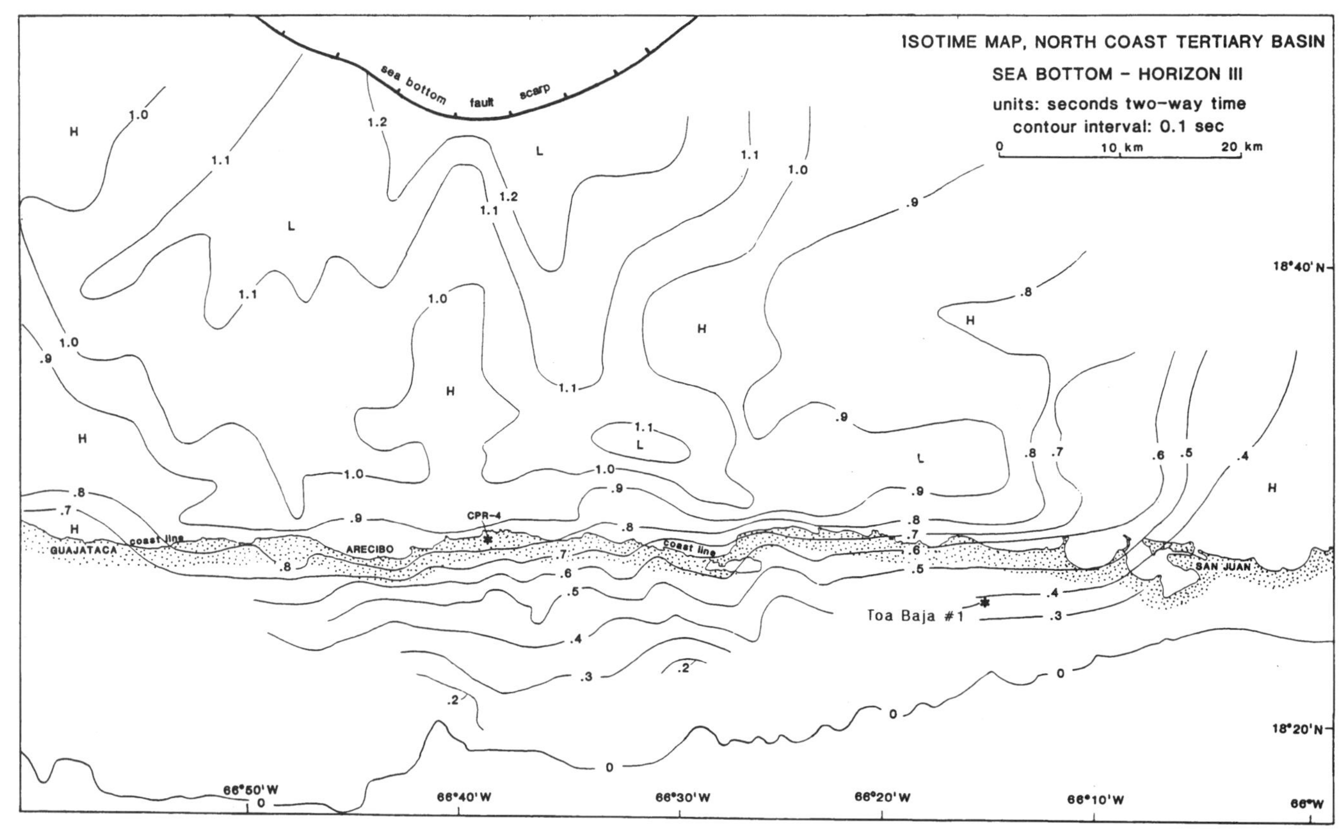

Figure 13. Isotime map (sea bottom—Horizon III); H, high characterized by low sediment accumulation or preservation; L, depositional low characterized by high sediment accumulation and preservation.

toward the south, as indicated by onlap relations on the north and the presence of turbidites in the northern flank of the central mountains of Puerto Rico. The mechanism of basin subsidence was probably normal faulting such as those that are observed to offset the basement reflector in the offshore region. The transition from the Guajataca High into the North Coast basin may be associated with a large half graben (Fig. 9). Extension was probably in a north to northeast direction based on mapped fault relations from seismic studies and dike orientations in outcrop, although this is uncertain. We believe that the central block of Puerto Rico was the principal source area of the Paleocene-Eocene volcaniclastic strata (see also Montgomery, this volume). The onlap on the north side of the North Coast basin may represent the toes of the north-prograding clinoforms (Fig. 16).

In the late Eocene to middle Oligocene, the southern part of the basin underwent compressive, possibly transpressive, deformation, resulting in the uplift of the region. The northern part of the basin (now the offshore region) was largely unaffected by this deformation. It is likely that basin inversion or uplift resulted from motion on same faults that lead to initial subsidence. It is not clear whether large amounts of eroded materials derived from the uplift in the south were transported to the north into the basin; that is, the age of the offshore part of the North Coast basin fill below Horizon III can only be constrained as Eocene to middle Oligocene.

Horizon III and younger strata, middle Oligocene through Miocene siliciclastics and carbonates, were deposited as a sheet across the pre–Horizon III lower succession. Based on dredge haul information and interpretation of seismic stratigraphy, shallow water sedimentation on a carbonate bank prevailed to distances of 50 km north of the present shoreline. Mapping of clinoforms in this upper succession reveals the presence of an embayment in the carbonate platform, with basinal water depths in excess of 200 to 600m.

In the late Miocene to Pliocene, flexural subsidence of the northern part of the basin occurred, resulting in the submergence of the carbonate platform to water depths locally in excess of 4 km.

In summary, the initiation of basin subsidence occurrence during extension of an arc platform. This basin was later modified on its southern margin by compressional deformation, which applied an additional load resulting in continued basinal subsidence toward the north. In the third stage of basin development, a carbonate bank extended across the North Coast basin. Studies of subsidence during this interval indicate evidence of thermal cooling and sediment loading. Finally, an intense flexural event occurred at the most recent phase of basinal evolution. Birch (1986) suggested that this flexure may have been the result of tectonic erosion in the trench to the north. Speed and Larue (1991) indicated that the flexure may have been associated with listric normal faulting in the Puerto Rico Trench region, either associated with rotation of the Puerto Rico–Virgin Islands platform

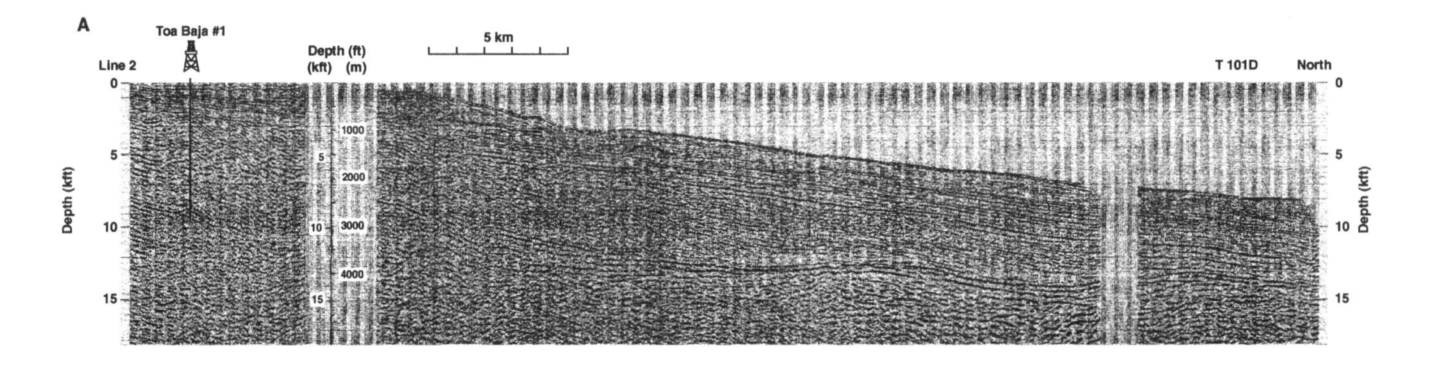

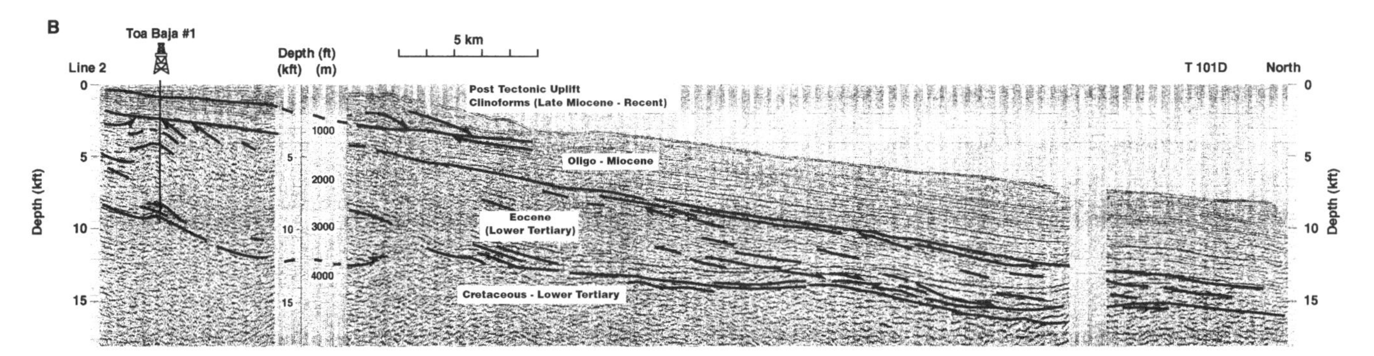

Figure 14. A, Depth migrated seismic reflection profile through the Toa Baja # 1 drill site, including Line 2 onshore and Line T-101D offshore (in kilofeet, thousands of feet). Processed by Berrong Enterprises, Ltd. Location in Fig. 2. B, Interpretation of A. Four stratal packages are defined: (1) a basal Cretaceous–Lower Tertiary (Paleocene) "basement" complex; onlapped by (2) Eocene to Paleocene (lower Tertiary) strata; in pronounced discordant contact with (3) Oligo-Miocene strata, which are truncated locally by another prominent angular unconformity and overlain by (4) late Miocene to Recent strata. The apparent downlap of Eocene and Paleocene strata onto older "basement" strata is in fact onlap if the present-day seafloor is used as a datum surface. This onlap defines the northern edge of the North Coast basin. Note that the pronounced angular unconformity observed near Toa Baja #1 separating the Eocene and Oligocene strata is not present in the offshore region, and the angular unconformity becomes progressively more conformable. The uppermost angular unconformity at the base of the late Miocene section is inferred to be related to a tilting event that lead to the subsidence of the present-day Puerto Rico shelf region.

(Larue et al., 1991c) or regional transtension between the Caribbean and North American plates.

ACKNOWLEDGMENTS

These studies were supported by the Puerto Rico Electric Power Authority; we gratefully acknowledge the continued assistance of PREPA staff, especially Ings. Orlando Anglero and Fernando Perez Bracetti. In addition, the project was also supported by EPSCoR and MRCE grants from the National Science Foundation.

REFERENCES CITED

Anderson, R. N., 1991, Geophysical logs from the Toa Baja scientific drill hole, Puerto Rico: Geophysical Research Letters, v. 18, p. 497–501.

Anderson, R. N., and Larue, D. K., 1991, Wellbore heat flow from the Toa Baja scientific drill hole, Puerto Rico: Geophysical Research Letters, v. 18, p. 537–540.

Berryhill, H. L., Jr., 1965, Geology of the Ciales quadrangle, Puerto Rico: U.S. Geological Survey Bulletin 1184, 84 p.

Birch, F. S., 1986, Isostatic, thermal and flexural models of the subsidence of the north coast of Puerto Rico: Geology, v. 14, p. 427–429.

Briggs, R. P., 1961, Geology of Kewanee Interamerican Oil Company test well number 4CPR, northern Puerto Rico, *in* Oil and gas possibilities of northern Puerto Rico: San Juan, Puerto Rico, Puerto Rico Mining Commission, 1–23 p.

Briggs, R. P., and Pease, M. H., 1961, Compressional graben and horst structures in east-central Puerto Rico: U.S. Geological Survey Research Short Papers, p. B365–366.

Byrne, D. B., Suarez, G., and McCann, W. R., 1985, Muertos Trough subduction-microplate tectonics in the northern Caribbean: Nature, v. 317, p. 420–421.

Cho, M., 1991, Zeolite to prehnite-pumpellyite facies metamorphism in the Toa Baja drill hole, Puerto Rico: Geophysical Research Letters, v. 18, p. 525–528.

Cox, D. P., Marvin, F. R., M'Gonigle, J. W., McIntyre, D. H., and Rogers, C.,

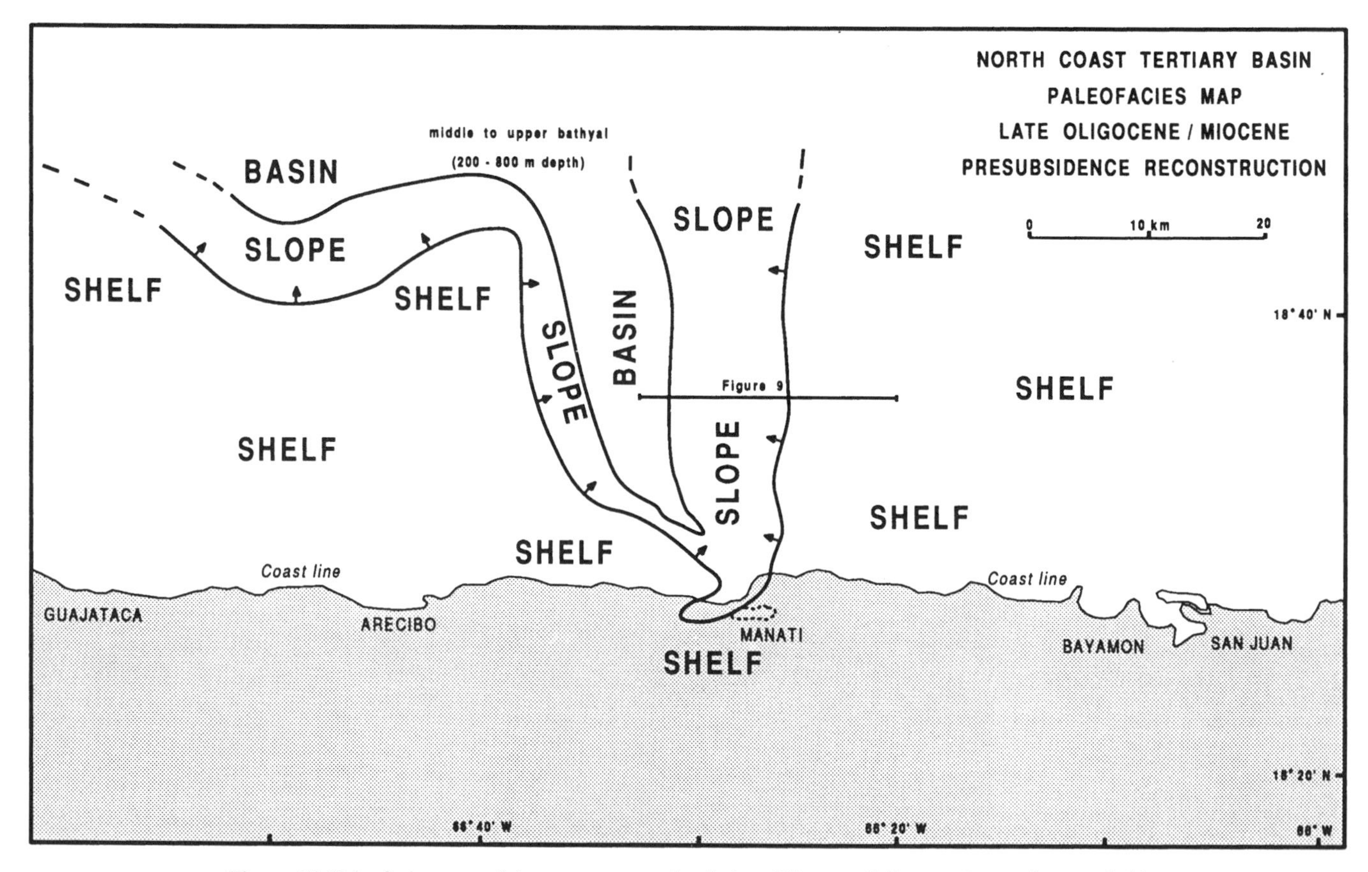

Figure 15. Paleofacies map of the upper succession in late Oligocene/Miocene time, prior to subsidence of the broad offshore shelf. Arrows on shelf/slope boundary denote direction of clinoform dip and depositional progradation. Map shows trends and outlines of gross features observed during study of seismic reflection profiles.

1977, Potassium-argon geochronology of some metamorphic, igneous and hydrothermal events in Puerto Rico and the Virgin Islands: U.S. Geological Survey Journal of Research, v. 5, p. 689–703.

DeMets, C. R., Gordon, D., Argus, and Stein, S., 1990, Current plate motions: Geophysical Journal International, v. 101, p. 425–478.

Erickson, J. P., Pindell, J. L., and Larue, D. K., 1990, Mid-Eocene–Early Oligocene sinistral transcurrent faulting in Puerto Rico associated with formation of the northern Caribbean plate boundary zone: Journal of Geology, v. 98, p. 365–384.

Gardner, W. D., Glover, L. K., and Hollister, C. D., 1980, Canyons off northwest Puerto Rico: studies of their origin and maintenance with the nuclear research submarine NR-1: Marine Geology, v. 37, p. 41–70.

Garrison, L. E., Martin, R. G., Berryhill, H. R., Beuli, M. W., Ensminger, H. R., and Perry, R. K., 1972, Preliminary tectonic map of the eastern Greater Antilles region: U.S. Geological Survey Miscellaneous Geologic Investigations Map I–732, scale 1:500,000.

Gonzalez, L. A., 1991, Carbon and oxygen stable isotopes in the Toa Baja well, Puerto Rico: implications for burial diagenesis and hydrocarbon generation: Geophysical Research Letters, v. 18, p. 533–536.

Houlgatte, E., 1983, Etude d'une partie de la frontiere nord-est de las plaque caraibe [Ph.D. thesis]: Universite de Bretagne Occidentale, 69 p.

Jordan, T. H., 1975, The present day motions of the Caribbean plate: Journal of Geophysical Research, v. 80, p. 4433–4440.

Kaye, C. A., 1959, Geology of the San Juan metropolitan area, Puerto Rico: U.S. Geological Survey Professional Paper 317–A, 48 p.

Larue, D. K., 1990, Toa Baja drilling project, Puerto Rico: EOS (Transactions, American Geophysical Union), v. 71, p. 233–234.

Larue, D. K., and Berrong, B., 1991, Cross section through the Toa Baja drill site: evidence for northward change in Late Eocene deformation intensity: Geophysical Research Letters, v. 18, 561–564.

Larue, D. K., and Ryan, H. F., 1991, Extensional tectonism in the Mona Passage, Puerto Rico and Hispaniola: A preliminary study, *in* Larue, D. K., and Draper, G., eds., Transactions, 12th Caribbean Geological Conference, St. Croix: Coral Gables, Florida, Miami Geological Society, p. 223–230.

Larue, D. K., Anderson, R. N., Goldberg, D., and Moos, D. N., 1991a, Origin of reflectors in seismic Line 2, Toa Baja, small gas horizons associated with enhanced reflector amplitudes, and recognizing leaky and sealing faults using gas chromatography data: Geophysical Research Letters, v. 18, p. 541–544.

Larue, D. K., Joyce, J., and Ryan, H. F., 1991b, Neotectonics of the Puerto Rico Trench: extensional tectonism and forearc subsidence, *in* Larue, D. K., and Draper, G., eds., Transactions, 12th Caribbean Geological Conference, St. Croix: Coral Gables, Florida, Miami Geological Survey, p. 231–247.

Larue, D. K., Pierce, P., and Erikson, J., 1991c, Cretaceous intra-arc summit basin on Puerto Rico, *in* Transactions, 2nd Geological Conference of the Geological Society of Trinidad and Tobago: Port-of-Spain, Trinidad, April 3–8 1990, p. 184–190.

Lepinay, B., Renard, D., and Stephan, F., 1987, Seabeam survey and wrench tectonics south of the Virgin Islands (northeastern Caribbean): Compte Rendu de l'Academie des Sciences, Paris, t. 304, Serie II, p. 527–532.

McCann, W. R., and Sykes, L. R., 1984, Subduction of aseismic ridges beneath the Caribbean plate: implications for the tectonics and seismic potential of the north eastern Caribbean: Journal of Geophysical Research, v. 89,

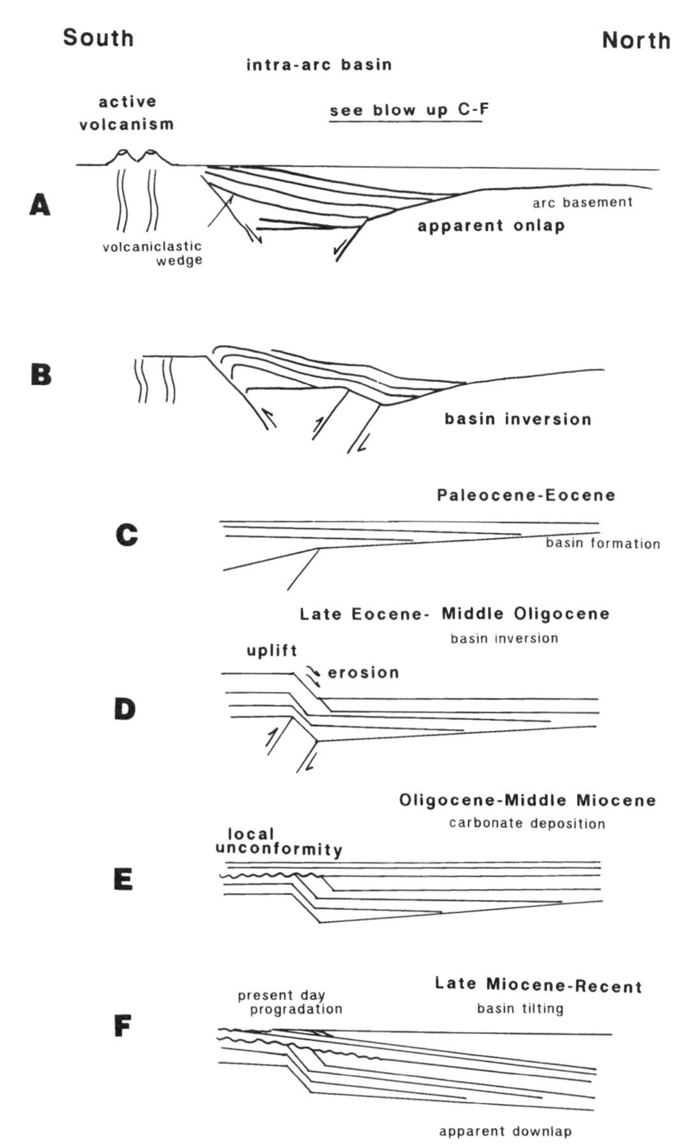

Figure 16. Summary of the geologic evolution of the North Coast Tertiary Basin. A, Intra-arc basin formation occurred in the earliest Tertiary (Paleocene?) and resulted in the formation of a basin in the arc platform environment. Volcanism was active during sedimentation. Volcaniclastic sediment was derived from the south, and downlapped to the north, and was likely deposited in a submarine slope and base of slope setting. B, Basin inversion associated with contraction occurred during the late Eocene to middle Oligocene, mostly shoreward of the present-day coastline of Puerto Rico. C, Paleocene-Eocene model of sedimentation in the North Coast basin. Volcaniclastic sediment was supplied from the south, downlapping toward the north. Deposition occurred in a submarine slope and base of slope setting. D, Basin inversion during the late Eocene–middle Oligocene resulted in uplift of the southern part of the basin, shedding sediment toward the north. It is not clear how much of this sediment is present beneath Horizon III in the offshore region. Further seismic stratigraphic studies are needed. E, Carbonate bank deposition occurred in the Oligocene through middle Miocene. Basin margins were similar to those of the earlier North Coast basin, although tectonism during sedimentation was marginal. F, Tilting of the island of Puerto Rico toward the north occurred in the late Miocene to Recent associated with the counterclockwise rotation of the arc massif. Tilting resulted in drowning of the northern part of the basin to water depth exceeding 4km.

p. 4493–4519.

Meyerhoff, A. A., Krieg, E. W., Cloos, J. D., and Taner, I., 1983, Petroleum possibilities of Puerto Rico: Oil and Gas Journal, v. 81, no. 51, p. 113–120.

Molnar, P., and Sykes, L. R., 1969, Tectonics of the Caribbean and Middle America regions from focal mechanisms and seismicity: Geological Society of America Bulletin, v. 59, p. 801–854.

Monroe, W. H., 1977, Geologic map of the Carolina quadrangle, Puerto Rico: U.S. Geological Survey Miscellaneous Geologic Investigations Map I–1054, scale 1:20,000.

Monroe, W. H., 1980, Geology of the middle Tertiary formations of Puerto Rico: U.S. Geological Survey Professional Paper, 954, 93 p.

Monroe, W. H., and Pease, M. H., Jr., 1962, Preliminary geologic map of the Bayamon quadrangle, Puerto Rico: U.S. Geological Survey Miscellaneous Investigations Map I–347, scale 1:20,000.

Montgomery, H., Robinson, E., Saunders, J., and Bold, W. Van den, 1991, Paleontology of the Toa Baja No. 1 well, Puerto Rico: Geophysical Research Letters, v. 18, p. 509–512.

Moussa, M. T., Seiglie, G. A., Meyerhoff, A. A., Taner, I., 1987, The Quebradillas Limestone (Miocene-Pliocene), northern Puerto Rico, and tectonics of the northeastern Caribbean margin: Geological Society of America Bulletin, v. 99, p. 427–439.

Nagle, F., Stipp, J. J., and Fisher, D. E., 1976, K-Ar geochronology of the Limestone Caribbees and Martinique, Lesser Antilles, West Indies: Earth and Planetary Science Letters, v. 29, p. 401–412.

Nelson, A. E., 1967a, Geologic map of the Corozal quadrangle, Puerto Rico: U.S. Geological Survey Miscellaneous Geologic Investigations Map I–473, scale 1:20,000.

Nelson, A. E., 1967b, Geologic map of the Utuado quadrangle, Puerto Rico: U.S. Geological Survey Miscellaneous Geologic Investigations Map I–480, scale 1:20,000.

Nelson, A. E., and Monroe, W. H., 1966, Geology of the Florida quadrangle, Puerto Rico: U.S. Geological Survey Bulletin 1221–C, p. C1–C22.

Pease, M. H., Jr., 1968a, Cretaceous and Lower Tertiary stratigraphy of the Naranjito and Aguas Buenas quadrangles and adjacent areas, Puerto Rico: U.S. Geological Survey Bulletin 1253, 57 p.

Pease, M. H., Jr., 1968b, Geologic map of the Aguas Buenas Quadrangle, Puerto Rico: U.S. Geological Survey Miscellaneous Geologic Investigations Map I–479, scale 1:20,000.

Pease, M. H., Jr., 1968c, Geologic map of the Naranjito quadrangle, Puerto Rico: U.S. Geological Survey Miscellaneous Geologic Investigations Map I–508, scale 1:20,000.

Perfit, M. R., Heezen, B. C., Rawson, M., and Donnelly, T. W., 1980, Chemistry, origin, and tectonic significance of metamorphic rocks from the Puerto Rico Trench: Marine Geology, v. 34, p. 125–156.

Pindell, J. L., and Barrett, S. F., 1990, Geological evolution of the Caribbean region: a plate-tectonic perspective, *in* Dengo, G., and Case, J. E., eds., The Caribbean region: Boulder, Colorado, Geological Society of America, The Geology of North America, v. H, p. 405–432.

Reid, J., Plumley, P., and Schellekens, J., 1991, Paleomagnetic evidence for Late Miocene counterclockwise rotation of north coast carbonate sequence, Puerto Rico: Geophysical Research Letters, v. 18, p. 565–568.

Schneidermann, N., Beckmann, J. C., and Heezen, B. C., 1972, Shallow water carbonates from the Puerto Rico Trench region, *in* Petzall, C., ed., Transactions; 6th Caribbean Geological Conference; Isla de Margarita, Venezuela, 1971: Caracas, Venezuela, Chromotip, p. 423–425.

Seiders, V. M., 1971, Geologic map of the Gurabo quadrangle, Puerto Rico: U.S. Geological Survey Miscellaneous Geologic Investigations Map I–657, scale 1:20,000.

Sieglie, G. A., and Moussa, M. T., 1984, Late Oligocene–Pliocene transgressive-regressive cycles of sedimentation in northwestern Puerto Rico, *in* Schlee, J. S., ed., Interregional unconformities and hydrocarbon accumulation: American Association of Petroleum Geologists Memoir 36, p. 89–96.

Smith, A. L., Severin, K., and Larue, D. K., 1991, Stratigraphy, geochemistry and mineralogy of Eocene rocks from the Toa Baja drill hole: Geophysical Research Letters, v. 18, p. 521–524.

Speed, R. C., and Larue, D. K., 1991, Extension and transtension in the plate boundary zone of the northeastern Caribbean: Geophysical Research Letters, v. 18, p. 573–576.

Talwani, M., Sutton, G. H., and Worzel, J. L., 1959, A crustal section across the Puerto Rico Trench: Journal of Geophysical Research, v. 64, p. 1545–1555.

Tribble, J. S., 1991, Clay mineral and zeolite diagenesis in the Toa Baja well, Puerto Rico: Geophysical Research Letters, v. 18, p. 529–532.

Western Geophysical, Inc., 1974, Offshore geophysical investigations for siting of a nuclear power station on Puerto Rico, for Puerto Rico Water Resources Authority, Preliminary Safety Analysis Report: U.S. Atomic Energy Commission, Docket No. 50–376, North Coast Nuclear Plant No. 1, v. III, 101 p.

MANUSCRIPT ACCEPTED BY THE SOCIETY JUNE 20, 1997

Printed in U.S.A.

Geological Society of America
Special Paper 322
1998

Paleogene stratigraphy and sedimentology of the North Coast, Puerto Rico

Homer Montgomery
Programs in Geosciences, University of Texas at Dallas, P.O. Box 830688, Richardson, Texas 75083, and Department of Geology, University of Puerto Rico, Mayagüez, Puerto Rico 00681

ABSTRACT

The Paleogene section of the North Coast of Puerto Rico is an exposed remnant of the North Coast Tertiary basin. Paleocene-Eocene sedimentary rocks were deposited unconformably on Paleocene volcanic basement. Although diminished in volume, volcanic eruptions persisted through the early Eocene as evidenced by primary volcanic strata intercalated with deep marine volcaniclastic sandstone. Paleocurrents suggest the primary source of sediment filling the Paleocene-Eocene basin in the San Juan area was from the northeast, probably from a local source. Farther to the west, Paleocene-Eocene breccia and sandstone composition is inconsistent with a southern source.

The poorly defined chronostratigraphy of the Paleocene-Eocene section of the North Coast Tertiary basin is improved by new planktic foraminiferal data. The base of the Corozal Limestone is upper lower Paleocene. The base of the overlying Ortiz Formation straddles the Paleocene-Eocene boundary. Planktic foraminifers from the upper part of the Río Piedras Siltstone are middle Eocene.

The Paleocene-Eocene section was uplifted and planed, producing a regional upper Eocene–lower Oligocene unconformity. Directly above the unconformity non-marine to marginal marine sandstone and shale are overlain by shallow water carbonates deposited on the broad shelf of a northward-deepening basin. Oligocene carbonates contain abundant shallow water fossils of open to slightly restricted marine environments. Extensive beds of broken, abraded, and sorted fossils are the product of reworking in a shallow marine setting. Punctuated inclusion of terrigenous sediments records diminishing river influx from the south.

INTRODUCTION

Puerto Rico is located along the northern margin of the Caribbean plate. The Caribbean plate originated in the Pacific and moved into the Jurassic spreading gap between North and South America (see Montgomery et al., 1994, for a review). As part of an extensive Cretaceous–early Paleogene island arc, the northern margin of the Caribbean plate underwent complicated oblique collision with the Bahama platform. Thick packages of mostly volcaniclastic sediments collected in numerous basins along the margin. Collision shut down volcanism, altered regional sedimentation, and redistributed terranes within a large-scale strike-slip fault regime.

The focus of this chapter is the North Coast Tertiary basin (NCTB) of Puerto Rico. The NCTB is located mostly offshore along the length of the island wedged between the Guajataca High east of Mona Canyon on the west end of the island and the San Juan High west of the San Juan Basin on the east end of the island (Fig. 1). Deposited on arc basement, the NCTB was uplifted approximately 2 km during the late Eocene to early Oligocene, producing a widespread unconformity. Late Paleogene shallow water deposition predominated on a broad shelf.

Montgomery, H., 1998, Paleogene stratigraphy and sedimentology of the North Coast, Puerto Rico, *in* Lidiak, E. G., and Larue, D. K., eds., Tectonics and Geochemistry of the Northeastern Caribbean: Boulder, Colorado, Geological Society of America Special Paper 322.

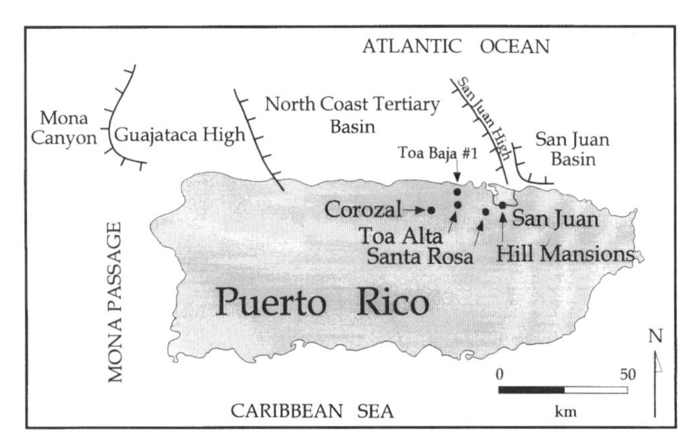

Figure 1. Location map of north coast basins and measured section localities of Puerto Rico.

Part of the basin crops out onshore along a shallow arc extending from the northwest part of the island to San Juan. Geologic investigations (especially geologic mapping by the U.S. Geological Survey) of Puerto Rico conducted before 1990 established the lithostratigraphy but only superficially defined the biostratigraphy, sedimentology, and tectonic evolution of the North Coast Tertiary section. Eocene and younger strata were drilled in the wildcat well Toa Baja #1 as the culminating step in a petroleum exploration project sponsored by the Puerto Rico Electric Power Authority (Larue, 1991). A stratigraphic section of 579 m of middle Oligocene through Miocene sandstone and limestone was drilled above the regional upper Eocene–lower Oligocene unconformity (Fig. 2). Below the unconformity, 2,119 m of Eocene volcaniclastic sandstone, primary volcanics, pelagic limestone, and chert were drilled without reaching arc basement. Scientific results from the well better defined the nature, age, and geologic evolution of the North Coast Paleogene section.

As a complementary study to the Toa Baja project, this investigation is directed at a better understanding of the North Coast Paleogene section, with special focus on biostratigraphy, sedimentology, and depositional environments of the Paleocene-Eocene interval. Although much of the Paleocene-Eocene section is nonfossiliferous, several intervals contain planktic foraminifers of biostratigraphic utility. Due to the shallow water nature of the Oligocene section and the long ranges of larger foraminifers, post-Eocene biostratigraphy was not further refined.

Most of the measured and sampled sections in this chapter are in close geographic proximity to the Toa Baja well site. Oligocene rocks were investigated in the Toa Alta area located 5 km south of the Toa Baja well. The Paleocene-Eocene sections are exposed farther to the east and west.

PALEOCENE-EOCENE SECTION

The Paleocene-Eocene section in Puerto Rico has been most thoroughly studied in the Cerrillos belt (informally known as the Eocene belt) extending in a band from the northwest part of the island to the south-center (Dolan et al., 1991). Deposited in linear troughs, epiclastic, volcaniclastic, and volcanic rocks of the Cerrillos belt were interpreted as intra-arc basin deposits. Shallow marine rocks of Oligocene age unconformably overlie the Cerrillos belt, which is no younger than middle Eocene.

Paleogene sedimentary rocks of the NCTB crop out in the hills south and west of San Juan. Near San Juan the Río Piedras Siltstone is at or near the base of the Paleocene sedimentary section. Underlying the Río Piedras in San Juan is the Guaracanal Andesite. In the Corozal area west of San Juan, the Palmarejo Formation, Corozal Limestone, and Ortiz Formation comprise most of the Paleocene-Eocene section. Whether the Palmarejo Formation is the base of the sedimentary Paleogene section remains unknown, as underlying volcaniclastic units have not been dated. Several samples were processed from the Palmarejo but none yielded fossils of biostratigraphic utility. Volcaniclastic sandstones of the NCTB are notoriously lacking biostratigraphic control. The Corozal Limestone was the lowest unit in this Paleocene-Eocene group yielding identifiable fossils.

Paleocene-Eocene formation ages have remained poorly constrained within a largely superpositional stratigraphic scheme bounded at the base by Cretaceous igneous and sedimentary rocks and at the top above the regional unconformity by the San Sebastián Formation, which is restricted to the middle(?) Oligocene. Based on thin section and isolated specimen identifications of planktic foraminifers, Montgomery et al., (1991) reported upper lower to middle Eocene volcaniclastic strata from the Toa Baja well between –2188 and –885 m. Biostratigraphic picks were supported by Ar/Ar ages (Larue et al., this volume). Planktic foraminifers of short range identified both in thin section and isolated from matrix provide new biostratigraphic constraints of the outcropping Paleocene-Eocene section. Planktic foraminiferal zonations of Tourmarkine and Luterbacher (1985) and Sartorio and Venturini (1988) are utilized herein. Thin sections were made of rock samples collected at an average of every 1.8 m through measured sections of the Paleocene-Oligocene interval. Because of the exposure of excellent sedimentary structures, paleocurrent data were collected and analyzed for the Río Piedras Siltstone.

Corozal Limestone

The Corozal Limestone crops out through the town of Corozal along a 4.5-km-long northwest-southeast–trend (Nelson, 1967). Beds strike northwest-southeast to north-south and dip generally 20º to 30º to the southwest. Alluvium crosses the outcrop trend in several places, giving the Corozal Limestone an appearance of discontinuous pods along the length of the trend. The Corozal is composed predominantly of thick beds of gray limestone breccia. Secondary breccia components are abundant volcanic and metamorphic rock fragments and rare sedimentary and plutonic rock fragments. Many limestone beds that appear in the field to be fairly homogeneous wackestone or packstone are composed of carbonate rock fragments.

Thin and discontinuous sandstone beds are variably composed of grains of plagioclase feldspar, chert, minor angular

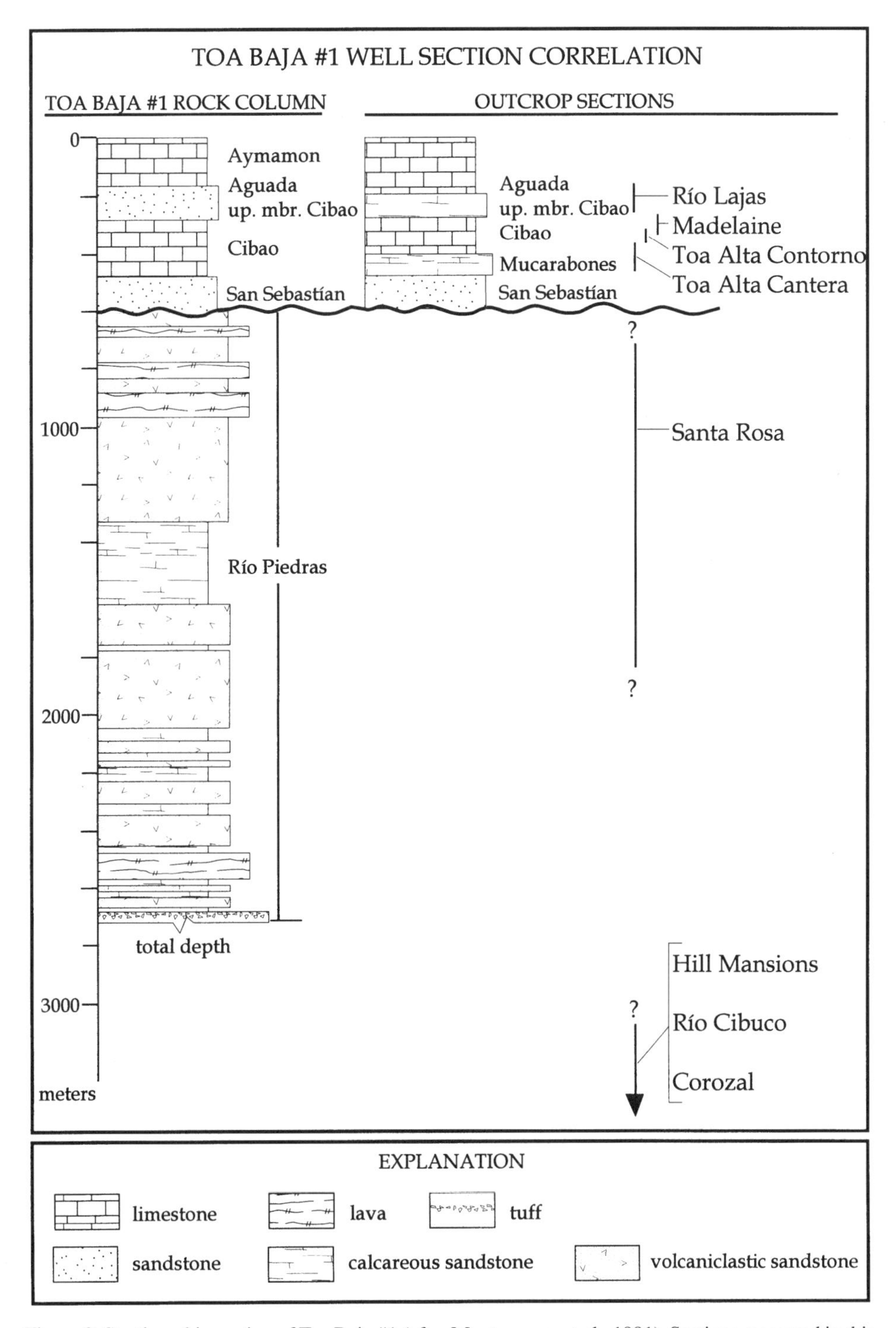

Figure 2. Stratigraphic section of Toa Baja #1 (after Montgomery et al., 1991). Sections measured in this report are compared at right.

quartz, volcanic rock fragments, articulated coralline algae, larger foraminifers, mollusks, echinoids, rare corals, and abundant limestone fragments containing mostly pellets and miliolid foraminifers. Biostratigraphically important beds of planktic foraminiferal grainstone-packstone interbedded with miliolid packstone are located at the southeast end of the outcrop trend.

At the base of the Corozal southeast section, blocks up to 55 cm across are "floating" in a carbonate mud matrix containing abundant 2- to 4-cm clasts. Numerous beds are composed of limestone fragments with little interstitial mud. Most of the breccia clasts are miliolid and algal packstone and wackestone of lagoonal origin. Normally graded beds of carbonate sand with subordinate volcanic clasts are present at several intervals in the section. Rare coarsening upward intervals of 5- to 15-cm clasts are present.

Determination of true thickness of the Corozal Limestone is complicated by faulting and by poor exposure at the Corozal southeast cantera (quarry) (Fig. 3). A complete exposure from underlying Palmarejo to overlying Ortiz is 45 m thick at the Corozal south section (Fig. 4). The Corozal may be up to 150 m thick (Nelson, 1966) at the quarry west of Corozal. The basal contact with the Palmarejo Formation is exposed in several places, being clearly identified as a shift in lithology from interbedded Palmarejo shale and volcaniclastic sandstone to the gray Corozal breccia.

Age. The Corozal Limestone has long been considered Paleocene or Eocene in age on the basis of fossils recovered in a quarry west of the town of Corozal (Kaye, 1956). A concerted effort to achieve higher resolution biostratigraphy proved successful. At the base of the Corozal southeast section are abun-

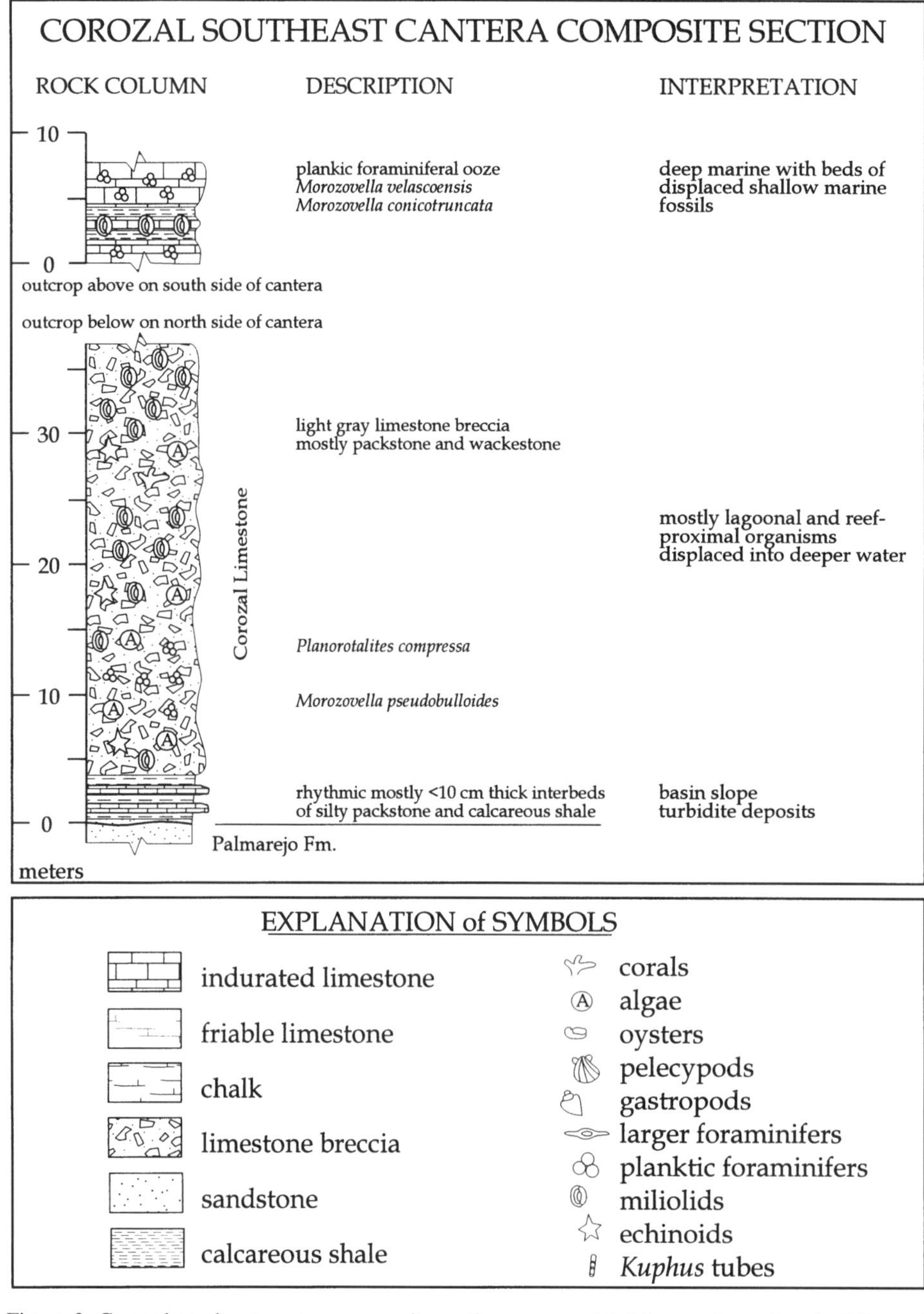

Figure 3. Corozal southeast cantera composite section measured 1.5 km south-southeast of Corozal town square, P.R. m grid: 54,150; 165,480 (Nelson, 1967).

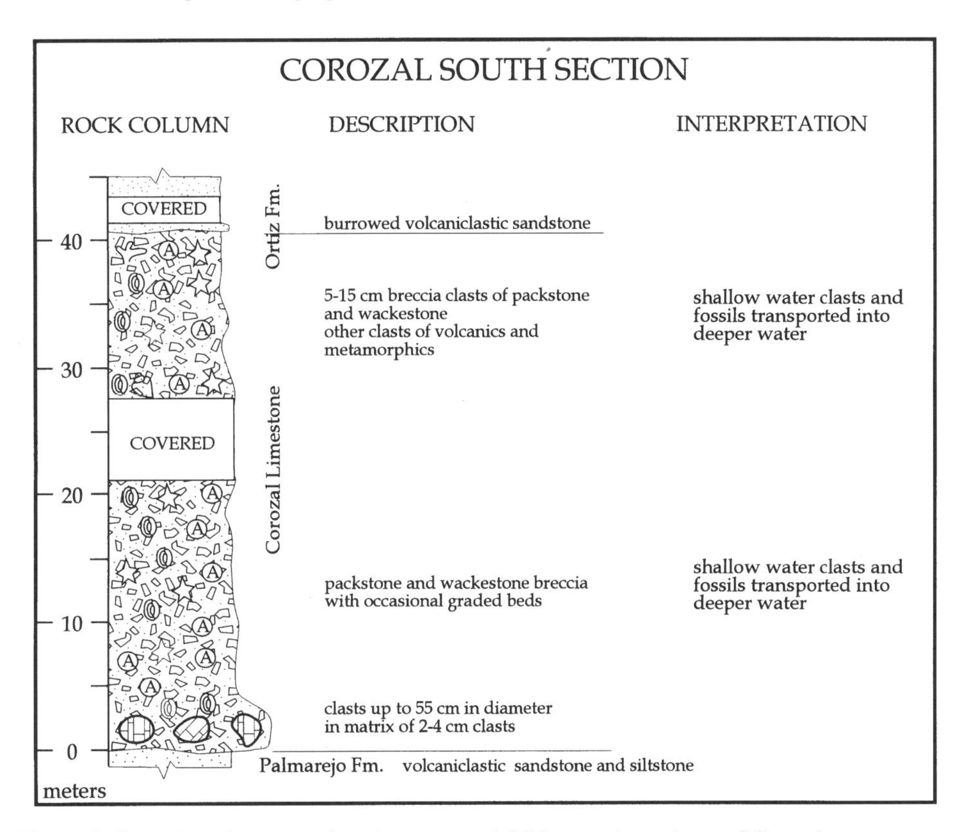

Figure 4. Corozal south measured section measured 0.5 km south-southeast of Corozal town square, P.R. m grid: 54,900; 164,820 (Nelson, 1967). Explanation as for Figure 3.

dant small, globular, and unornamented planktic foraminifers common to the Paleocene. *Planorotalites compressa* (middle lower to lower upper Paleocene) and *Morozovella pseudobulloides* (lower Paleocene) (Fig. 5A, B) are typical thin section components. Abundant planktic foraminifers are in spiculitic packstone with shallow water fossils including miliolids, articulated coralline algae, and larger foraminifers. Higher in the section, keeled and more highly ornamented forms characteristic of slightly younger faunas become abundant. *Morozovella conicotruncata* (middle to lower upper Paleocene) and *Morozovella velascoensis* (upper Paleocene) (Fig. 5C, D) are abundant constituents in foraminiferal grainstone sampled from a prominent ledge on the south side of the quarry. Displaced shallow water micro- and megafauna are present in various beds of the Corozal Limestone, but no other planktic foraminifers were found.

Depositional environment. Beds of *Globigerina* ooze in the Corozal are solid evidence of deposition in a deep marine setting. Planktic foraminifers comprise more than 90% of the microfauna. *Globigerina* ooze must have been deposited above the Atlantic Calcium Carbonate Compensation Depth (CCD), which for the Eocene was estimated at approximately 3,500 m (van Andel et al., 1975). Accumulation of planktic foraminifers comprising more than 75% of the microfauna is characteristic of waters of the lower slope (Boersma, 1978). The commonly utilized depth zone for the lower slope is approximately 1,000 to 2,000 m (Boersma, 1978). Thus, based on the presence of *Globigerina* ooze, it might be assumed that the Corozal ooze was deposited in water depths between approximately 1,000 and 3,500 m.

Complicating this depth analysis is the thick package of coarse-grained, angular limestone clasts of lagoonal origin. The shallow water clasts must have been transported into ooze at the base of the slope. Review of any of several sediment distribution maps reveals pelagic carbonates in narrow and relatively restricted marine basins. For example, the Mediterranean region generates pelagic carbonate sediments adjacent to deep-water terrigenous clastic deposits. The "floating" nature of larger blocks in muddy matrix containing abundant other smaller fragments suggests origin as a debris flow. Debris flows are common elements of the lower slope. The slope into the basin from the arc massif must have been steep to interbed *Globigerina* ooze and allochthonous lagoonal breccia and detritus.

Ortiz Formation

The Ortiz Formation is exposed in the hills south of Corozal along a northwest-southeast strike trend. Beds dip to the southwest. The best exposed contact is at the top of the Corozal south section (Fig. 4). The Ortiz Formation rests conformably on the Corozal Limestone with a transitional contact identified by a shift from limestone breccia to calcareous sandstone. The section is composed of mostly nonfossiliferous volcanic sandstone and siltstone with subordinate shale, conglomerate, and tuff, as

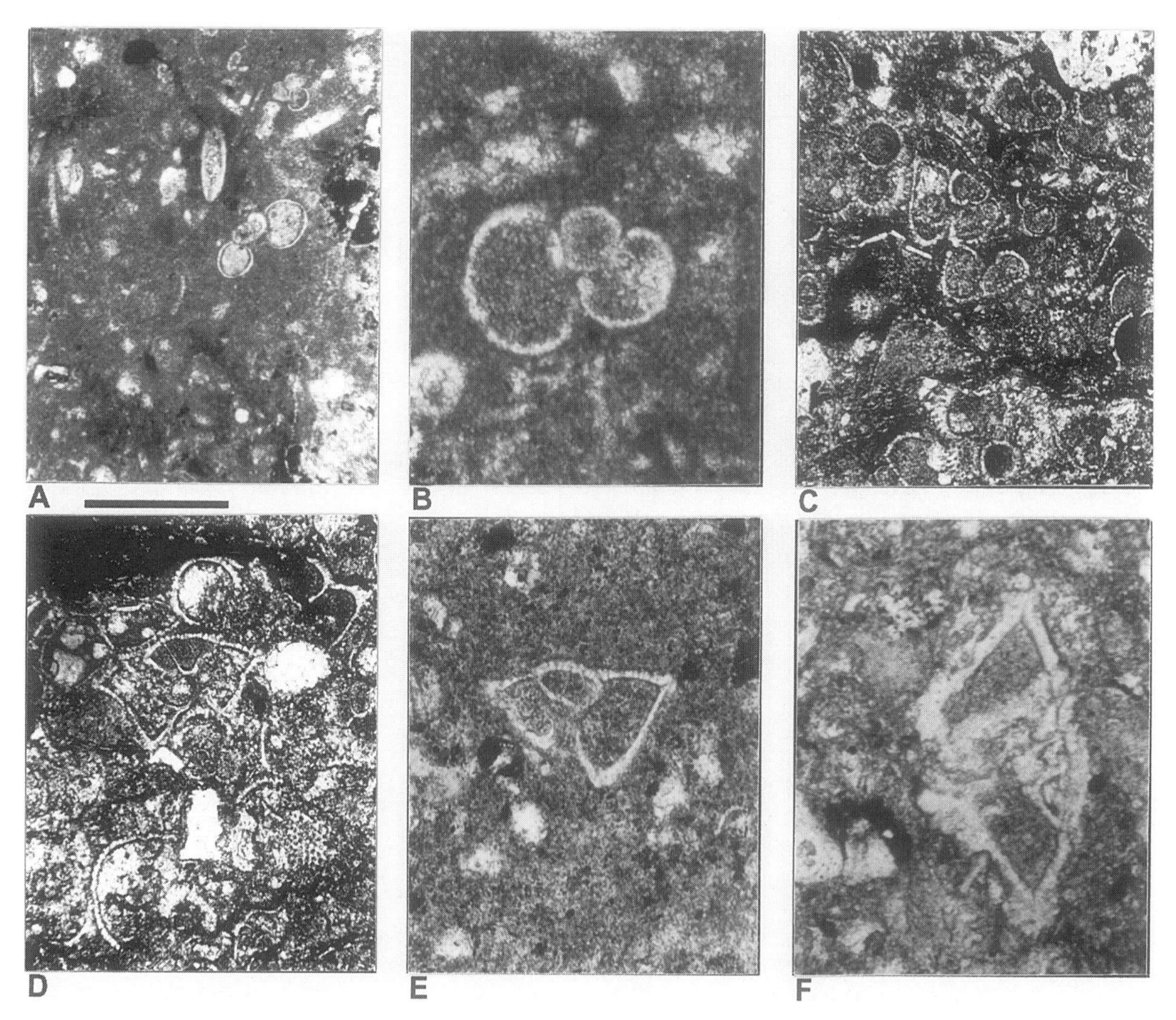

Figure 5. Planktic foraminifers from Paleocene and Eocene rocks, North Coast Tertiary basin, Puerto Rico: A, *Planorotalites compressa* (middle lower to lower upper Paleocene). B, *Morozovella pseudobulloides* (lower Paleocene) at base of Corozal Limestone. C, *Morozovella conicotruncata* (middle middle to lower upper Paleocene). D, *Morozovella velascoensis* (upper Paleocene) from *Globigerina* ooze, Corozal Limestone. E, *Morozovella aequa* (upper Paleocene–lowermost Eocene) at the base of the Ortiz Formation in the Río Cibuco. F, *Morozovella spinulosa* (upper Paleocene–lowermost Eocene) in the upper part of the Río Piedras at the Santa Rosa quarry. Bar = 0.25 mm for A–E; 0.13 mm for F.

well as minor limestone and chert. The top of the Ortiz Formation is not present. The formation has a maximum thickness of 600 m (Nelson, 1966).

Age. Planktic foraminifers are present in dark, well-bedded siltstone collected at the base of the Ortiz Formation from the bed of the Río Cibuco under the highway bridge 2.1 km west-northwest of the Corozal town square (Puerto Rico meter grid [P.R. m]: 56,350; 162,730). *Morozovella aequa* (upper Paleocene–lowermost Eocene) was identified in thin section (Fig. 5E). *M. aequa* is a common marker for the Paleocene-Eocene boundary (Sartorio and Venturini, 1988). Discontinuous bedded chert in the middle part of the Ortiz and a lens of limestone at the top yielded no fossils of biostratigraphic utility either in acid residue or in thin section.

Depositional environment. Rhythmically graded beds, products of turbidity currents, are prominent especially at the base of the Ortiz Formation. Clastic grains in the basal turbidites include mostly plagioclase feldspar and volcanic rock fragments. Planktic foraminifers are abundant constituents of the turbidity currents, especially prominent in hemipelagic layers. At least the basal part of the Ortiz Formation was deposited in a deep basin. In the middle of the Ortiz section radiolarians are abundant in a few thin chert and silicified limestone stringers. Radiolarians are open-ocean organisms with no known coastal forms. However, as illustrated by sediments in the Gulf of California, radiolarians can exist in deep water not far offshore as long as there is little coastal runoff. The radiolarians apparently accumulated in deep water during periods of little terrigenous influx. A small limestone body at the top of the formation is of unknown depositional environment. Recent bulldozing of the area has broken up much of the limestone body, making it difficult to study as a contiguous unit.

Río Piedras Siltstone

Cropping out south and southwest of San Juan, the Río Piedras Siltstone is composed largely of thin bedded volcaniclastic siltstone and sandstone with subordinate volcanic pebble conglomerate, mudstone, tuffaceous limestone, and tuff. Strata are well bedded and strike west-northwest–east-southeast and dip generally 25° north-northeast. The contact at the base of the Río Piedras Siltstone with the Paleocene Guaracanal Andesite is exposed in the Hill Mansions quarry (P.R. m grid: 60,550; 193,925).

Exposure of the Río Piedras in a quarry near Santa Rosa (P.R. m grid: 57,050; 185,500) is more extensive than at the Hill Mansions quarry. Beds of greenish tuffaceous siltstone and shale are prominent in the Santa Rosa section. The base of the Río Piedras is not exposed in the Santa Rosa quarry. The maximum thickness of the Río Piedras is unknown but is probably in excess of 1,000 m.

Age. Mudstone and siltstone at both quarries sampled for this report are punctuated by intervals of abundant planktic foraminifers and occasional radiolarians in thin parallel layers. Unfortunately, the radiolarians have been coarsely calcified. Only abundant siliceous spicules are present in hydrochloric acid residue.

Thin sections from the base of the Río Piedras at Hill Mansions contain numerous but rather poorly preserved planktic foraminifers. Radiolarians are unidentifiable. Planktic foraminifers are present free in matrix and reworked as constituents of rock fragments. This indication of reworking does not preclude a chronostratigraphic assignment as the foraminifers have overlapping age ranges. Specimens include possible to probable *Morozovella conicotruncata*, *M.* sp., *Planorotalites pusilla pusilla*, and *Chiloguembelina* sp. This assemblage produces an age range for the base of the Río Piedras at Hill Mansions that extends from upper lower to the lower upper Paleocene. Confidence in this biostratigraphic determination based on poorly preserved Hill Mansions specimens is corroborated by a report indicating small foraminifers at the base of the Río Piedras were "upper but not uppermost Paleocene" (Pease, 1968, p. 46). Cox et al. (1977) reported a K-Ar age of 60.4 ± 1.2 Ma (middle upper Paleocene with reference to the 1983 Decade of North American Geology chart) for the underlying Guaracanal. This paleontologic assignment for the Hill Mansions section is in close agreement with previous paleontologic and isotopic age determination, suggesting the nonconformable contact does not represent a great elapse of time between deposition of the two units.

Calcareous mudstone from the Santa Rosa Quarry yielded planktic foraminifers in hydrofluoric acid residue. The acid dissolved much of the rock matrix while fluoritizing and preserving foraminifers. Numerous specimens of *Pseudohastigerina wilcoxensis* suggest the Río Piedras Siltstone in the Santa Rosa quarry is early to middle middle Eocene in age. Well-preserved *Morozovella spinulosa* (middle Eocene) are present in thin section (Fig. 5*F*). Taken as an assemblage, planktic foraminifers from the Santa Rosa quarry are early middle to middle middle Eocene. Rocks of the Hill Mansions quarry are older than any drilled in the Toa Baja well, while rocks of the Santa Rosa Quarry are of roughly the same age as the rocks directly below the unconformity in the Toa Baja section.

Depositional environment. As noted above, the base of the clastic Paleogene North Coast section rests, in part, on Guaracanal Andesite. Interbedded with Guaracanal lava and turbidites are a few miliolid and algal limestone bodies (Pease, 1968). These limestones are composed of resedimented material. Resedimented coral heads are also present in the Guaracanal. Siltstone less than 1 m above the Guaracanal contains deep water planktic foraminifers and radiolarians. No shallow water fossils were observed in dissolved samples or thin sections at Hill Mansions.

The Río Piedras Siltstone at the Hill Mansions is mostly laminated siltstone with subordinate ripple-laminated sandstone and ripple-laminated tuff. A prominent bed of ungraded conglomerate is a maximum of a 1 m thick. Subrounded to rounded volcanic clasts up to 10 cm in diameter but averaging 1 to 3 cm fill a wide channel. The base of the conglomerate bed is deeply scoured into and overlain by ripple-laminated and parallel-laminated siltstone. Pebbles prominently protrude from the top of the muddy-pebbly flow. Pebbles are mostly composed of volcaniclastic sandstone, although a few pebbles of green tuffaceous mudstone and dark volcanic rock were collected. The conglomerate is interpreted as a debris flow possibly induced by flood conditions.

Volcanic rocks are present at several intervals at Hill Mansions in homogeneous beds and mixed with other components. Coarse volcaniclastic sandstone contains altered primary volcanic minerals. Fresh glass shards are present in thin sections of siltstone. Higher in the section are beds of tuffaceous siltstone and white, ripple-laminated, water-lain tuff.

Well-preserved *Cruziana-Zoophycos-Nereites*–facies trace fossils are present on bedding planes especially at the base of the section. Common fossil types include morphologies of *Crossopodia*, *Zoophycus*, and *Cosmoraphe*. Unfortunately, the paleobathymetric significance of ichnofossils is unclear. From a traditional view (i.e., Seilacher, 1967), burrow patterns are controlled by bathymetry. Recent research suggests trace-fossil associations are a function of oxygenation of bottom sediments (Ekdale and Mason, 1988) among other factors including turbulence, substrate type, sedimentation rate, and salinity. From the Seilacher viewpoint, the Hill Mansions ichnofossils are of deep water origin. Assuming an oxygen-controlled mechanism was operant, ichnofossils at Hill Mansions would be characteristic of aerobic or dysaerobic (poorly oxygenated) bottom water with dysaerobic interstitial water. This assumption may not be accurate as the presence of punctuated *Nerites* could be due to sedimentation effects on an oxygenated bottom. Dysaerobic bottom water is consistent, however, with the predominance of preserved planktic fossils.

Paleocurrents were measured predominantly from ripple laminations with subordinate information derived from imbricated pebbles, grooves, and channel axes at the Hill Mansions quarry and from ripple laminations at the Santa Rosa quarry. At the Hill Mansions section, ripple-laminated tuff, siltstone, and sandstone beds are present at several intervals and are well exposed.

OLIGOCENE SECTION

Oligocene rocks crop out across part of the south and across most of the north coast of Puerto Rico. The Oligocene section in Puerto Rico has been well studied along the south coast (Frost et al., 1983; Moussa and Seiglie, 1970) and in the northwest corner of the island (Seiglie and Moussa, 1984). Oligocene outcrops of the east-central coast have not been evaluated in a detailed manner. This examination of Oligocene rocks is intended to complement studies of Oligocene strata in the Toa Baja borehole.

Some possible complications exist as to terminology of units above the San Sebastían Formation and below the Aguada Limestone (Fig. 2). In the northwest part of the island, the San Sebastían Formation is overlain by the Lares Limestone and the Cibao Formation. Moving eastward, the Lares disappears. As pointed out by Monroe (1973a), the Lares Limestone intertongues with the Mucarabones Sand in the Corozal area. As mapped by Nelson (1967), the Lares Limestone becomes less and less prominent toward the northeastern portion of the Corozal quadrangle where the Lares grades into the Mucarabones and is not present in outcrop in the Vega Alta quadrangle (Monroe, 1963).

The basal Cibao as defined by Montgomery et al. (1991) in the Toa Baja borehole remains problematic. As described by Seiglie and Moussa (1984), the Lares consists of deeper water deposits in the Dupont No. 5 well located near Manati 25 km west of Toa Baja. Seiglie and Moussa (1984) interpreted the fauna as accumulating in an outer neritic paleoenvironment. There appears to be no outer neritic or any deeper water facies above the San Sebastián in the borehole. The part of the section that is Mucarabones in outcrop does not appear to be represented in the well. Therefore, for lack of definitive characteristics immediately above the San Sebastián that compare favorably with the Mucarabones or with the Lares, that part of the borehole section should retain the name Cibao.

West of Corozal, the Lares Limestone rather than the Cibao Formation is the prominent upper Oligocene and lowest Miocene unit. The contact between the two units was placed at a sharp contact between the generally pure Lares Limestone, which contains abundant fossils of organic reef origin (Monroe, 1973a), and the Cibao beds, which contain more terrigenous sand, silt, and clay. This enrichment and interbedding of terrigenous material occurs in the Toa Alta cantera section in which, although the contact is not exposed, the Cibao is mapped above the Mucarabones (Monroe, 1963). In this study I have followed the geologic map of Monroe (1963) in assuming the Cibao interfingers with and directly overlays the Mucarabones. I have also incorporated the lithologic descriptions of Monroe (1973a) in defining the first appearance of the Cibao.

The Oligocene section of the NCTB rests on a regional unconformity and is well exposed in the hills surrounding Toa Alta. The Aguada and Cibao Formations and parts of the underlying Mucarabones Sand were measured in the Toa Alta area south of Toa Baja. In the Bayamón quadrangle the San Sebastián Formation rests on the Río Piedras Siltstone. Overlying the San Sebastián is the Mucarabones Sand, which is beneath and interfingers with the Cibao Formation. The Río Indio Limestone Member at the base of the Cibao Formation was measured in the Bayamón quadrangle 1.5 km southeast of the Toa Alta town square. The overlying Quebrada Arenas Member was measured in the Vega Alta quadrangle 2 km southwest of Toa Alta. The upper member of the Cibao was measured in the Vega Alta quadrangle at the Madelaine Urbanization 4 km east of Toa Alta. The uppermost Cibao and the overlying Aguada Limestone were measured at Río Lajas 1.5 km northwest of Toa Alta.

Mucarabones Sand

The Mucarabones Sand, composed mostly of locally glauconitic quartz arenite and calcareous sandstone, is particularly well exposed east and southeast of Toa Alta. The upper 22 m of section was measured (Fig. 6). Farther east near the town of Piña (P.R. m grid: 59,200; 174,060) a clear contact of the Mucarabones atop the San Sebastián is present, but little variation between the units is apparent aside from a slight color change. As is common with much of the San Sebastián and Mucarabones, no fossils were discovered in the area of well-exposed contact.

Age. The age of the Mucarabones is not well defined. Nelson (1966) reported *Lepidocyclina undosa*. Larger foraminifers in the grainstone stringers near the top of the unit are essentially limited to *Miogypsina panamensis* or *Miogypsinoides thalmanni*. The presence of these species suggests a range of upper Oligocene through lowest Miocene.

Depositional environment. Cross-beds and parallel-laminated beds are common in the upper part of the Mucarabones. Typical thin sections of the upper part of the Mucarabones in the study area contain coarse sand constituted mostly of quartz, larger foraminifers, and fragments of articulated coralline algae and echinoids. Much of the sand is winnowed, sorted, and abraded.

Although poorly exposed, San Sebastián/Mucarabones contacts in the area are typically gradational, indicating little or no change in paleoenvironments at the base of the Mucarabones. The underlying San Sebastián Formation was deposited in nonmarine, marginal marine, and restricted lagoonal environments. The upper part of the Mucarabones is markedly different, being clearly deposited in a high-energy, marine environment probably on a shallow clastic-dominated shelf. Mixed terrigenous (quartz) and shelly marine (larger foraminifers, algae, echinoids) sands were probably deposited on a shoreface in water depths of less than 5 m.

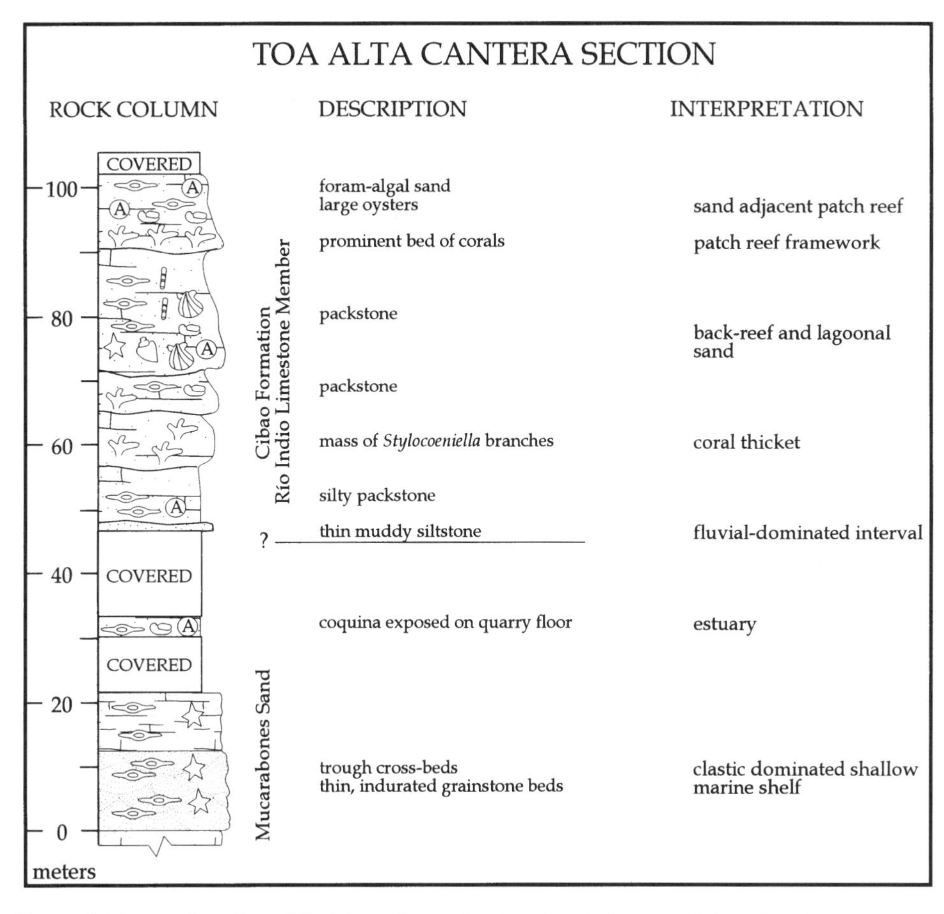

Figure 6. Measured section of the Mucarabones Sand and overlying basal Río Indio Limestone Member of the Cibao Formation at the Toa Alta cantera, P.R. m grid: 60,180; 172,450 (Monroe, 1973b). Explanation as for Figure 3.

Cibao Formation

The Cibao is highly fossiliferous with few beds composed predominantly of one fossil type such as corals, algae, or oysters. Most beds are composed of poorly sorted but clearly transported fossils, some concentrated as coquinas. At the Toa Alta cantera west of Toa Alta, the Mucarabones Sand is overlain by the Río Indio Limestone Member at the base of the Cibao Formation (Fig. 6). The interformational contact is not exposed. Oysters, larger foraminifers, and articulated red algae predominate near the base of the unit. Higher in the section prominent beds of corals, articulated coralline algae, and oysters are present. Eighty meters of the Río Indio were measured along the quarry floor and along a road bulldozed up the quarry wall.

The Quebrada Arenas Member of the Cibao measured near Toa Alta at the Barrio Contorno is approximately 50 m thick, although only the basal 35 m could be measured below heavy vegetation at the tops of precipitous cliffs (Fig. 7). The member contains abundant, well-preserved echinoids, pelecypods, and oysters protruding from chalky matrix.

The upper member of the Cibao was measured both in the Madelaine Urbanization east of Toa Alta (Fig. 8) and in the Río Lajas neighborhood of Toa Alta (Fig. 9). The Toa Alta section contains the uppermost part of the upper member as well as the overlying Aguada. The Madelaine section exposes approximately 70 m of the upper member, which was not measured at Río Lajas because of poor exposure.

Age. Planktic foraminifers were recovered from cuttings of the Oligocene interval drilled in the Toa Baja well. The most important specimens include *Globigerina gortanii* (upper lower Oligocene) near the base of the San Sebastián and *Globorotalia opima opima* (lower upper Oligocene) recovered at the base and in the middle of the Cibao Formation (Montgomery et al., 1991).

Depositional environment. Overlying the Mucarabones Sand, the Cibao records deepening marine waters and the onset of patch reef development, the first major phase of carbonate production above the Eocene-Oligocene unconformity. Beds of muddy, nonfossiliferous siltstone of probable fluvial origin interfinger with the Río Indio near the base of the unit, marking continued periodic but lessening terrigenous influx. Corals are widespread but not persistent being preserved in thin layers rather than in thick masses. Many coral heads are overturned and broken having been rolled during intermittent reef destruction. Beds of reworked fossils are interspersed between coral, algal, and oys-

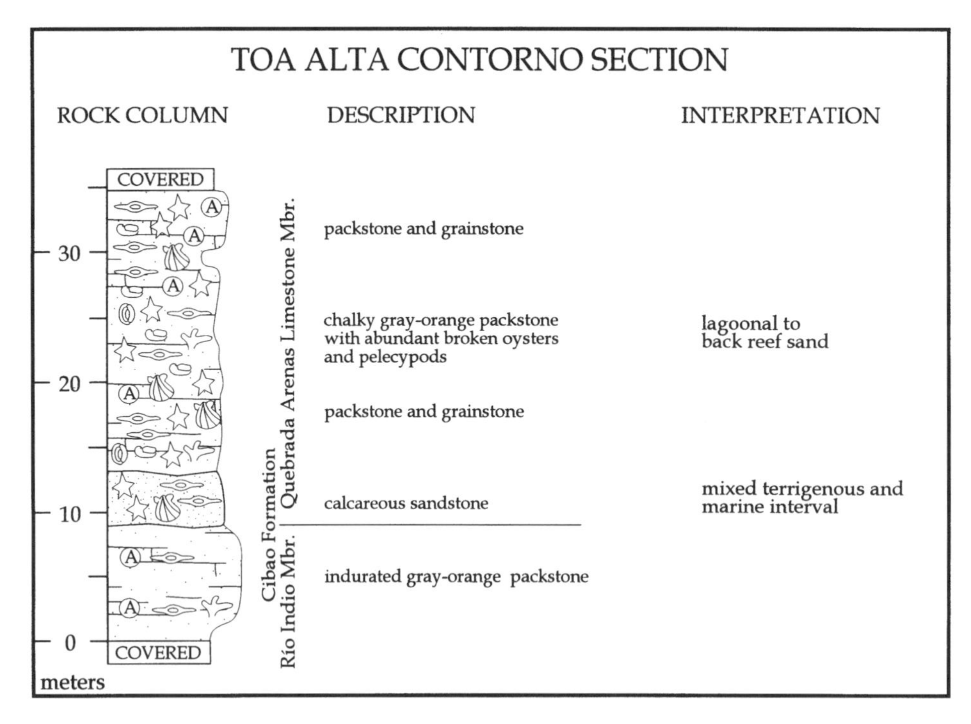

Figure 7. Measured section of the Quebrada Arenas Member of the Cibao measured near Toa Alta at the Barrio Contorno, P.R. m grid: 60,230; 170,670 (Monroe, 1963). Explanation as for Figure 3.

ter concentrations. The Río Indio Member continues extremely fossiliferous to the top of the section.

Based on fossils and terrigenous content, the overlying Quebrada Arenas Limestone Member is marine at the base (rich with echinoids, larger foraminifers, and pelecypods), mixed terrigenous and marine just above the base, and back reef sand at the top of the section. The back reef sand is rich with shells of shallow water organisms that have been well-winnowed.

The upper member of the Cibao Formation is chalky to sandy containing *Kuphus* tubes, various pelecypods, echinoids, encrusting and articulated coralline algae, and larger foraminifers. Few corals were observed. All of the upper member was deposited in back reef environments as sandy shoals and banks. Terrigenous input was variable, sometimes contributing great quantities of sand and mud. Wave energy was also variable, winnowing and reworking the shelly sands at several intervals.

Reef development in the Toa Alta area is limited to coral thicket and patch reef formation followed by destruction. The coral thicket intermediate in the Toa Alta cantera section was destroyed by wave action rolling coral heads about. Highly fossiliferous back reef sands predominate above the coral bed. The patch reef at the top of the cantera section was not persistent, as a return to restricted hyposaline waters produced oyster banks above the corals. River input was probably shifting through the area reflected by fluctuating terrigenous mud content, as well as switching of marine and hyposaline faunas. A few small channels and numerous scoured and sorted intervals attest to periodic currents refreshing what must have been a wide shelf with overall sluggish circulation.

COMPARISON OF OUTCROP SECTIONS WITH TOA BAJA WELL

The Toa Baja well penetrated strata that are broadly similar to Middle Eocene and younger measured sections with respect to lithologic assemblage and facies. Complications in comparing Upper Oligocene strata and in naming the units drilled in the borehole are significant. Outcrop sections at Hill Mansions, Corozal, and Río Cibuco are older than strata penetrated in the well.

The 2,119 m of Eocene rocks penetrated in the borehole below the major unconformity correlate well with well-exposed rocks at the Santa Rosa quarry (Fig. 2). Both contain extensive, turbiditic intervals composed of fine-grained volcaniclastic sandstone, siltstone, and shale. The shale appears to have a significant component of altered volcanic glass similar to that reported in the borehole (Smith et al., 1991). Numerous thin graded beds in outcrop are similar to those in borehole core 1 (648 to 656 m). The major difference between outcrop samples and borehole cuttings is faunal content. Much richer and better preserved planktic foraminiferal faunas are present in the outcrop section. The borehole fauna is too poor to allow direct correlation with outcrop for purposes of paleoslope determination.

Biostratigraphic control of the thick, shallow water, Oligocene carbonate sequence in the Toa Baja well was provided by

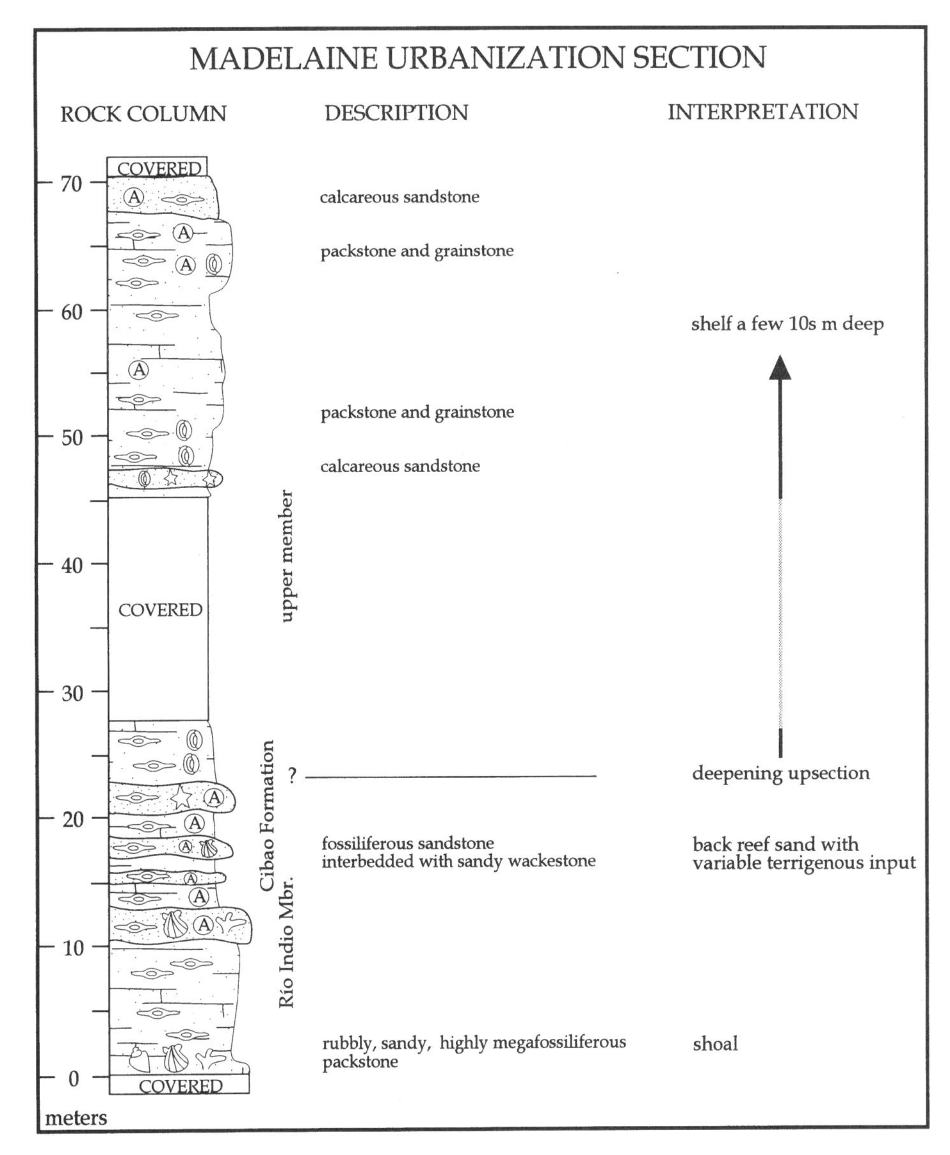

Figure 8. Measured section of the upper member of the Cibao at the Madelaine Urbanization east of Toa Alta, P.R. m grid: 62,450; 175,900 (Monroe, 1973b). Explanation as for Figure 3.

the presence of extremely few planktic foraminifers. Planktic foraminifers were not present in more than 200 washed samples and thin sections from Oligocene outcrop measured sections. The outcrop sections are farther to the south and thus were farther onshore during the Oligocene and would be expected to contain fewer or no planktic foraminifers.

Because these foraminifers from the borehole were found within a limestone sequence and not in the terrigenous sediments of the San Sebastían Formation, that unit was assumed to be the base of the Cibao Formation in the Toa Baja well (Montgomery et al., 1991). But is this the Cibao? To the west, Seiglie and Moussa (1984) place the Lares in the upper half of the Oligocene. Monroe (1973a) reported the lower two thirds of the Cibao is present only in the eastern part of the NCTB. Resting on the San Sebastían the Cibao would, thus, encompass most of the stratigraphic range of the Lares, "Montebello," and Cibao units of Seiglie and Moussa (1984). I see very little lithologic difference between much of the lower Cibao in the Toa Alta area and the Lares to the west, aside from greater admixture of terrigenous material in the east.

The boundary between the Lares Limestone and the overlying Cibao Formation is not clearly constrained, especially near Toa Alta. Seiglie and Moussa (1984, p. 91) pick the base of the Cibao based on "the accumulation of oysters and coastal lagoonal deposits interbedded with terrestrial sediments." Such appearances are present in several horizons throughout the entire extended Cibao section mapped by Monroe (1963), compromising the use of this marker in the Toa Alta area. Additional faunal data provided by Seiglie and Moussa (1984), the disappearance of *Lepidocyclina undosa*, and the appearance of *Miosorites americanus* are problematic in the borehole. First is the complication of transferring

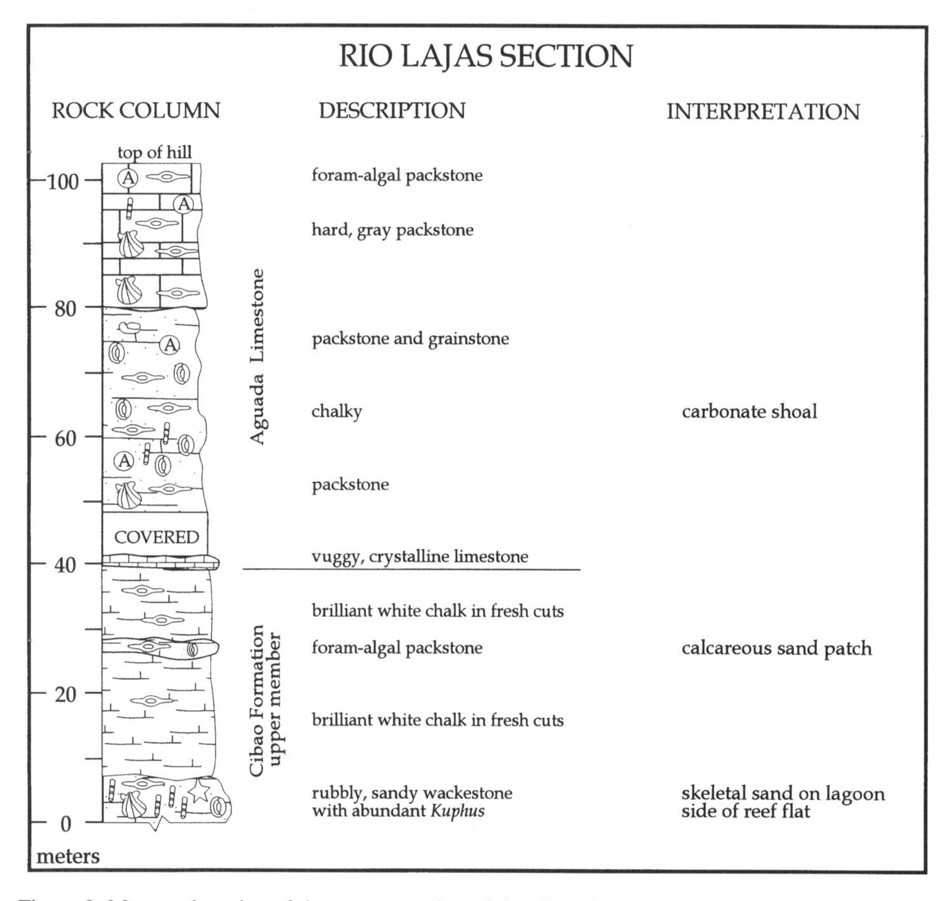

Figure 9. Measured section of the upper member of the Cibao in the Río Lajas neighborhood of Toa Alta, P.R. m grid: 62,400; 170,150 (Monroe, 1963). Explanation as for Figure 3.

biostratigraphic picks to different areas. Second, a pick based on larger foraminifers is inconsistent with the presence of planktic foraminifers in the borehole. *M. americanus* was positively identified and *L. undosa* was questionably identified at the base of the Cibao (Montgomery et al., 1991). This larger foraminifer transition is a late early Miocene event according to Seiglie and Moussa (1984). Inconsistent with this pick, the planktic foraminifer *Globorotalia opima opima* (late middle Oligocene) is present at the same interval. Thus, biostratigraphic data are insufficient to pick the base of the Cibao in the borehole.

Therefore, considering the above complications, I have elected to recognize the Cibao much as Monroe (1963, 1984) proposed, not to recognize the Lares or the shallow water Mucarabones, and to extend the base of the Cibao to rest directly on the San Sebastían. As the Mucarabones and Lares do not crop out in the Toa Alta Quadrangle and no further well data are available, the proper name of the unit resting atop the San Sebastían remains problematic.

Aside from rare planktic foraminifers from the borehole, the well and outcrop sections are essentially identical in overall carbonate allochem and terrigenous content. Limited patch reef and coral thicket development followed by periodic destruction observed in outcrop appear as pulses of coral fragments in a "bandygram" constructed from allochem percentages from well cuttings (Montgomery et al., 1991). Paleoenvironmental determinations based on microfacies analysis from the Toa Baja well were confirmed in outcrop. Therefore, no significant paleoenvironmental differences are noted between the well and outcrop areas.

SEDIMENTATION AND TECTONICS IN THE NORTH COAST TERTIARY BASIN

The geometry and polarity of the NCTB is relatively well established. Present depositional slope as well as seismic profile interpretation (Larue et al., this volume) supports a downlap-to-the-north model. The NCTB, at least as far north as the Toa Baja well, was dominantly filled with volcaniclastic sediments apparently derived from the uplifted margin of a nearby and dying volcanic arc. Uplifts exist on the east and west and north.

Tectonic rotation complicates paleogeographic reconstruction. As a microplate including the island of Puerto Rico and assumedly its associated basins have rotated as a ball bearing in a left-lateral transpressional regime, correction for post-Eocene counterclockwise rotation must be made. Counterclockwise rotations have been detected in each investigation conducted in Puerto Rico. Calculations of the magnitude of rotation vary from

24° ± 5.8° with respect to North America between 11 and 4.5 Ma (Reid et al., 1991) to 83° post-Eocene (Elston and Krushensky, 1983). A value of 45° post-Eocene rotation was calculated by Van Fossen et al. (1989) from the southwestern part of the island. No rotation corrections have been determined for the NCTB area. I have somewhat arbitrarily applied the Van Fossen et al. (1989) figure simply because it is of the correct time frame. Although counterclockwise rotations are common in Puerto Rico, it remains quite possible that the southwestern block (Bermeja) had a different rotational history. Excepting the Bermeja block, the entire island is rotated as a block in a counterclockwise fashion in this model rather than attempting to resolve each rotated block.

Paleocurrent directions derived from ripple laminations indicate a dominant paleocurrent from the north. Corrected for 45° counterclockwise rotation, the Río Piedras sediments at Hill Mansions were derived dominantly from the northeast, with secondary scatter from the north and east (Fig. 10). Imbricated pebbles also suggest a source from the northeast. Channel axes and grooves are oriented north-south, which corrects to northeast-southwest.

Paleocurrents in the Río Piedras from Santa Rosa quarry are less reliable. Rocks in this area are more highly deformed than at Hill Mansions, and evidence of paleocurrents is more subtle. Coarse volcaniclastic sandstone is spheroidally weathered and complexly fractured, thus complicating its paleocurrent utility. However, ripple lamination in fine-grained sandstone in a graded bed sequence produced rotated current directions mostly to the southeast and south (Fig. 10).

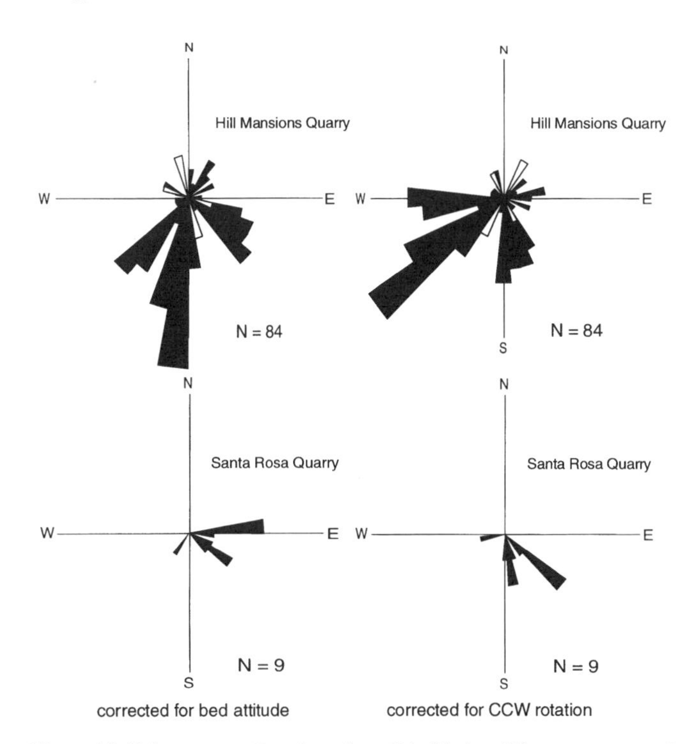

Figure 10. Paleocurrent directions from Río Piedras Siltstone measured at Hill Mansions. Unidirectional indicators are black. Bidirectional indicators are white. Rose diagrams on the left are corrected for bed attitude. Diagrams on the right are additionally corrected for 45° post-Eocene counterclockwise (CCW) rotation.

Corozal Limestone breccia is thicker and coarser to the northwest, whereas the intermediate outcrops along the northwest-southeast outcrop trend are thinner and clasts are smaller. Toward the southeast end of the trend at the Corozal southeast cantera composite section, grain size is the smallest with a sharply reduced volume of breccia with limestone composed more of sand-sized limestone fragments. Also present at this southeast section is the *Globigerina* ooze, which is of deep water origin. Interbedded with the ooze are beds of displaced shallow marine fossils. The Corozal thus fines and apparently exhibits deeper paleowater depths to the southeast along the northwest-southeast trend. Corrected for ~45° counterclockwise rotation, a Paleocene-Eocene source from the north seems to be indicated.

The source for the Corozal Limestone breccia remains problematic. None of the other stratigraphic units in the area is lithologic and faunal equivalents of the Corozal breccia. Dark clasts admixed with limestone breccia are exotic in appearance. Clasts in the Corozal Limestone are of sedimentary, volcanic, plutonic, and metamorphic origin. Clasts of sedimentary and plutonic origin are rare. Sedimentary fragments are chert and contain rare, poorly preserved, and unidentifiable radiolarians. Plutonic fragments were identified on the basis of small microcline grains.

Much more common through the Corozal Limestone are clasts of volcanic and metamorphic origin. Volcanic fragments are frequently silicified, altered to epidote, or contain prominent quartz veins. Isolated grains of high temperature quartz are of volcanic origin. Other volcanic clasts include basaltic rock fragments with chlorite amygdules. Much of the alteration of volcanic clasts appears to be of a hydrothermal nature.

Amphibolite rock fragments present in the Corozal are clearly extrinsic. Clasts contain clinopyroxene with hornblende reaction rims. No other amphibolites have been detected in sediments of the NCTB. The Corozal exotics are thus unique to the basin. The source for the amphibolite clasts in the Corozal cannot be the Bermeja Complex currently attached to the far southwestern corner of the island. During the Paleogene, the Bermeja Complex was located on the opposite side of, and perhaps some distance away from, the Cerrillos volcanic belt.

PALEOCENE-EOCENE PALEOGEOGRAPHIC RECONSTRUCTION

Paleocene-Eocene paleogeographic reconstructions of the northeastern Caribbean plate margin by various authors vary significantly in the relative positions of Hispaniola and Puerto Rico. Two basic schemes have been proposed. An Eocene paleogeographic reconstruction of Pindell and Barrett (1991) for the northern Caribbean aligns oceanic island arc components of Cuba, Hispaniola, Puerto Rico, and the Virgin Islands along a northwest-southeast trend. Puerto Rico was tightly sandwiched between Hispaniola and the Virgin Islands at this time. An alternate view (Larue et al., 1991) positions Eocene Puerto Rico

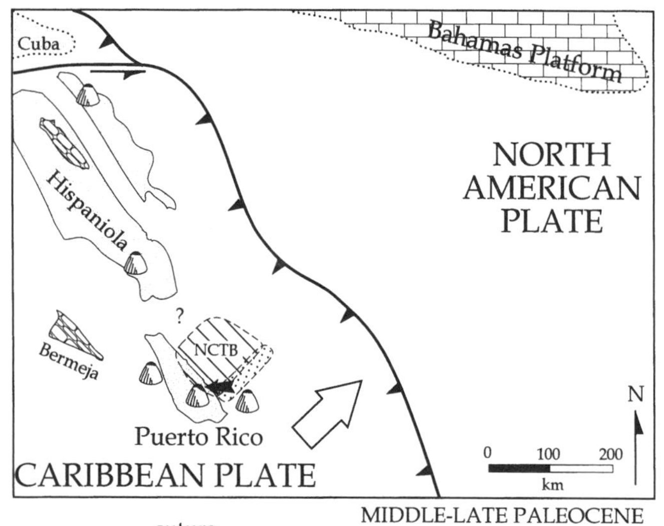

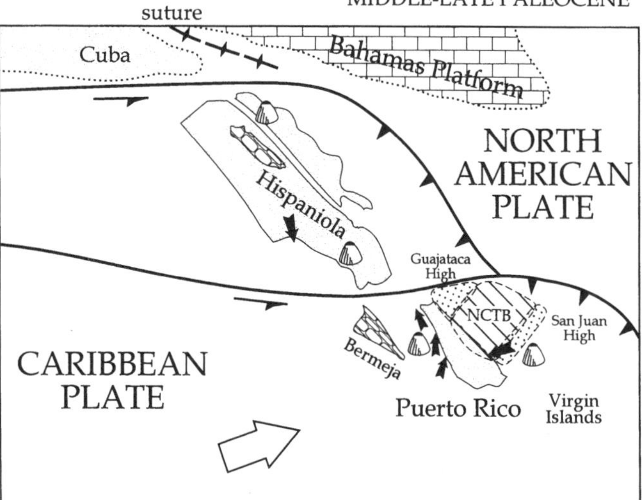

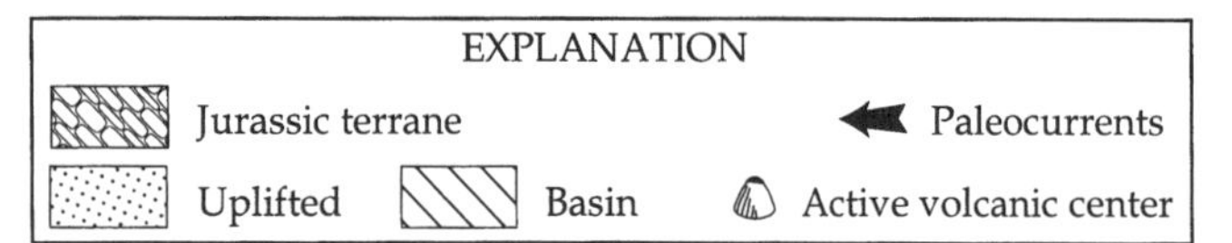

Figure 11. Tectonic model of the Puerto Rico region of the Caribbean plate during the Paleocene-Eocene interval. Tectonic reconstruction is a synthesis of Pindell and Barrett (1990), Larue et al. (1991), Smith et al. (1991), and Larue et al. (this volume). Rotations are based on data of Vincenz and Dasgupta (1978), Van Fossen and Channell (1988), Reid et al. (1991). Paleocurrents are from Dolan et al. (1991), and this chapter.

essentially in its current orientation with respect to Hispaniola. The model presented herein (Fig. 11) incorporates elements of both schemes, but it is hoped that it better explains the data presented in this chapter.

Diachronous Paleocene-Eocene collision of the Antillean arc with the Bahamas platform progressed from initial collision in Cuba followed sequentially by younger events of lessened effect in Hispaniola, Puerto Rico, and the Virgin Islands. Paleogene transpression rotated elements of the North American–Caribbean plate boundary region as ball bearings with Puerto Rico moving eastward and away from Hispaniola. Puerto Rico rotated counterclockwise within this boundary zone between the North American and Caribbean plates. Volcanism was mostly a Cretaceous and earliest Paleogene phenomenon in Puerto Rico.

Primary volcanic strata in the Río Piedras Siltstone are evidence of explosive volcanism continuing during the earliest Paleogene. Smith et al. (1991) reported glass shards and pumice fragments concurrent with deposition of the Eocene volcaniclastic sandstone from the Toa Baja well. Primary volcanic material was the product of active subaerial or shallow marine volcanoes located adjacent to a deep intra-arc basin. Petrology and geochemistry point to a convergent plate margin setting (Smith et al., 1991). Presumably the volcanoes formed in response to the American plate being subducted under the Caribbean plate.

The source for the NCTB volcanic strata is also problematic. The Cerrillos belt of Puerto Rico produced volcanic strata within the same time frame, but such a source is not consistent with paleocurrents determined in this study or from those measured within the Cerrillos by Dolan et al. (1991). The paleogeographic alignment proposed by Pindell and Barrett (1991) would perhaps allow Hispaniola to be a source for some of the basin fill, especially along the western margin of the NCTB. Bowin (1975) reviewed the stratigraphy of many lower Paleogene stratigraphic units that include all of the lithologic components of the NCTB. Unusual and distinctive facies similar to the Corozal Limestone breccia are present in Hispaniola. The Los Caguellas Limestone breccia contains minor volcanic fragments as does the Corozal. But because breccias are not readily transported significance distances, the Los Caguellas should be eliminated from consideration as a source.

Paleocurrents in the lower to upper Eocene Peralta Group near the southern margin of Hispaniola (Dolan et al., 1991) indicate a northern source. Although the southeast paleoslope would perhaps qualify Hispaniola as a source, the lack of volcanics and volcaniclastic sediments disqualify the region. In addition, Río Piedras sediments were derived from the east, opposite the proposed position of Hispaniola. Hispaniola would require a source from the northwest. The uplift on the eastern margin of the NCTB is a better option for volcaniclastic rocks. Volcanoes not currently exposed would logically be located off to the east, parallel to the axis of the subduction zone. Airborne volcanic material would be transported mostly to the west by prevailing winds much as ash is in the Lesser Antilles today.

Beginning in the middle Oligocene, fluvial and shallow water carbonate deposition predominated. Terrigenous sediments deposited on the broad Oligocene shelf were clearly delivered from uplifted areas on the south.

CONCLUSIONS

1. The Paleogene section of the NCTB is divisible into two distinct stratigraphies, the Paleocene-Eocene section and the Oligocene and younger section. Paleocene-Eocene strata are largely

composed of volcaniclastic sedimentary rocks with minor primary volcanic rocks and limestone. The Oligocene section is perhaps non marine to clearly marginal marine at the base, changing upsection into shoreface and ultimately thick shallow marine carbonates. Structural differences between the two rock packages are marked by strong contrast in bed attitudes above and below the separating unconformity and by deformation of the older section.

2. The NCTB began filling with clastic sediments during the late early Paleocene or earlier in the Corozal area and during the late Paleocene farther east in the San Juan area. Deposition occurred in deep water on volcanic arc basement. The contact with shallow marine arc basement volcanics is clearly unconformable. Sedimentary rocks of the Río Piedras Siltstone were derived from a northeastern source delivered into the eastern margin of the early Paleogene NCTB. The sediment source was probably uplifted arc basement and volcanoes to the northeast.

3. Refined biostratigraphy of the basal clastic interval based on planktic foraminifers indicates the Corozal Formation ranges from late early to early late Paleocene in age. The overlying Ortiz Formation spans latest Paleocene to earliest Eocene in age. The Río Piedras Siltstone ranges in age from middle Paleocene to middle Eocene.

4. Orogenesis in the Puerto Rico area during the late Eocene uplifted and planed the NCTB stratigraphic section. Volcanism completely ceased by this time. As currently understood, the collision event yielded a regional unconformity that spans the upper middle Eocene (above the Río Piedras Siltstone) through lower Oligocene (below the San Sebastián Formation). With reference to the 1983 DNAG time scale, this gap represents approximately 10 m.y.

5. Oligocene sedimentation reflects deepening marine invasion of a broad, north-facing shelf. A thick carbonate section accumulated in lagoonal settings. Rivers sporadically delivered terrigenous sediments from the south.

6. Stratigraphic and sedimentologic data and interpretations of this study closely mirror observations produced by the Toa Baja drilling project. Additional information provided by this study that could not be determined in the Toa Baja investigation includes the nature of contact between volcanic arc basement and sedimentary strata, the presence of Paleocene primary volcanics and exotic rock fragments, sediment source directions, and details of early Paleogene biostratigraphy.

ACKNOWLEDGMENTS

Support for this research was provided by a grant to the University of Puerto Rico Geology Department by the Puerto Rico Electric Power Authority. Additional fieldwork was funded through National Science Foundation EPSCoR and MRCE grants to the University of Puerto Rico. Thanks to Alan Smith and Hans Schellekens for detailed petrology analysis of volcanic, volcaniclastic, and metamorphic components of thin sections. Dave Larue provided stimulating discussions in the field and helpful review. Other constructive reviews were provided by Luis Gonzalez and Ted Robinson. Jeanne Holloway reviewed identifications of foraminifers. Ivette Muñoz was an able field assistant. This chapter is Contribution 767 of the University of Texas at Dallas.

REFERENCES CITED

Boersma, A., 1978, Foraminifera, *in* Haq, B. U., and Boersma, A., eds., Introduction to marine micropaleontology: New York, Elsevier Science, p. 1–77.

Bowin, C., 1975, The geology of Hispaniola, *in* Nairn, A. E. M., and Stehli, F. G., eds., The ocean basins and margins, vol. 3: New York, Plenum, p. 501–552.

Cox, D. P., Martin, R. F., M'Gonigle, J. W., McIntyre, D. M., and Rogers, C. L., 1977, Potassium-argon geochronology of some metamorphic, igneous, and hydrothermal events in Puerto Rico and the Virgin Islands: U.S. Geological Survey Journal of Research, v. 5, p. 689–703.

Dolan, J., Mann, P., de Zoeten, R., Heubeck, C., Shiroma, J., and Monechi, S., 1991, Sedimentologic, stratigraphic, and tectonic synthesis of Eocene-Miocene sedimentary basins, Hispaniola and Puerto Rico, *in* Mann, P., Draper, G., and Lewis, J. F., eds., Geologic and tectonic development of the North America–Caribbean plate boundary in Hispaniola: Geological Society of America Special Paper 262, p. 217–263.

Ekdale, A. A., and Mason, T. R., 1988, Characteristic trace-fossil associations in oxygen-poor sedimentary environments: Geology, v. 16, p. 720–723.

Elston, D., and Krushensky, R., 1983, Puerto Rico: a translated terrane exotic to the Caribbean: 10th Caribbean Geological Conference, Cartagena, Columbia, (abstr.), p. 33–34.

Frost, S. H., Harbour, J. L., Beach, D. K., Realini, M. J., and Harris, P. M., 1983, Oligocene reef tract development in southwestern Puerto Rico: Miami, Florida, Comparative Laboratory Division of Marine Geology and Geophysics, Rosenstiel School of Marine and Atmospheric Sciences, University of Miami, 144 p.

Kaye, C. A., 1956, The lower Tertiary of Puerto Rico: American Association of Petroleum Geologists Bulletin, v. 40, p. 108–121.

Larue, D. K., 1991, The Toa Baja drilling project, Puerto Rico: scientific drilling into a non-volcanic island arc massif: Geophysical Research Letters, v. 18, p. 489–492.

Larue, D. K., Joyce, J., and Ryan, H. F., 1991, Neotectonics of the Puerto Rico trench: extensional tectonism and forearc subsidence, *in* Larue, D. K., and Draper, G., eds., Transactions, 12th Caribbean Geological Conference, St. Croix, U.S. Virgin Islands, Miami Geological Society, p. 231–247.

Monroe, W. H., 1963, Geology of the Vega Alta quadrangle, Puerto Rico: U.S. Geological Survey Geologic Quadrangle Map GQ–191, scale 1:20,000.

Monroe, W. H., 1973a, Stratigraphy and petroleum possibilities of middle Tertiary rocks in Puerto Rico: American Association of Petroleum Geologists Bulletin, v. 57, p. 1086–1099.

Monroe, W. H., 1973b, Geologic map of the Bayamón quadrangle, Puerto Rico: U.S. Geological Survey Map I–751.

Montgomery, H., E. Robinson, J. Saunders, and V. Van den Bold, 1991, Paleontology of the Toa Baja Well, Puerto Rico: Geophysical Research Letters, v. 18, p. 509–512.

Montgomery, H., Pessagno, E. A., Jr., and Pindell, J. L., 1994, A 195 Ma terrane in a 165 Ma sea: Pacific origin of the Caribbean Plate. GSA Today, v. 2, p. 1–6.

Moussa, M. T., and Seiglie, G. A., 1970, Revision of mid-Tertiary stratigraphy of southwestern Puerto Rico: American Association of Petroleum Geologists Bulletin, v. 54, p. 1887–1893.

Nelson, A. E., 1966, Cretaceous and Tertiary rocks in the Corozal quadrangle, northern Puerto Rico: U.S. Geological Survey Bulletin, 1244–C, p. 1–20.

Nelson, A. E., 1967, Geologic map of the Corozal quadrangle Puerto Rico: U.S. Geological Survey, Miscellaneous Geologic Investigations, Map I-473.

Pease, Jr., M. H., 1968, Cretaceous and Lower Tertiary stratigraphy of the Naranjito and Aguas Buenas quadrangles and adjacent areas Puerto Rico: U.S.

Geological Survey Bulletin, v. 1253, 57 p.
Pindell, J. L., and Barrett, S. F., 1990, Geologic evolution of the Caribbean Region: a plate-tectonic perspective, *in* Dengo, G. and Case, J. E., eds., The Caribbean region: Boulder, Colorado, Geological Society of America, The Geology of North America, v. H, p. 405–432.
Reid, J. A., Plumley, P. W., and Schellekens, J. H., 1991, Paleomagnetic evidence for Late Miocene counterclockwise rotation of North Coast carbonate sequence, Puerto Rico: Geophysical Research Letters, v. 18, p. 565–568.
Sartorio, D., and Venturini, S., 1988, Southern Tethys biofacies: Milan, Amilcare Pizzi S.p.A., Publishers, 235 p.
Seiglie, G. A., and Moussa, M. T., 1984, Late Oligocene–Pliocene transgressive-regressive cycles of sedimentation in northwestern Puerto Rico, *in* Schlee, J. S., ed., Interregional unconformities and hydrocarbon accumulation: American Association of Petroleum Geologists Memoir 36, p. 89–95.
Seilacher, A., 1967, Bathymetry of trace fossils: Marine Geology, v. 5, p. 413–428.
Smith, A. L., Severin, K., and Larue, D. K., 1991, Stratigraphy, geochemistry, and mineralogy of Eocene rocks from the Toa Baja drillhole: Geophysical Research Letters, v. 18, p. 521–524.
Toumarkine M., and Luterbacher, H., 1985, Paleocene and Eocene planktic foraminifers, *in* Plankton stratigraphy, Bolli, H. M., et al., eds., Cambridge, Cambridge University Press, p. 87–154.
van Andel, Tj. H., Heath, G. R., and Moore, T. C., Jr., 1975, Cenozoic history and paleoceanography of the central equatorial Pacific Ocean: Geological Society of America Memoir 143, 134 p.
Van Fossen, M. C., and Channell, J. E. T., 1988, Paleomagnetism of Late Cretaceous and Eocene limestones and chalks from Haiti: tectonic interpretations: tectonics, v. 7, p. 601–612.
Van Fossen, M. C., Channell, J. E. T., and Schellekens, J. H., 1989, Paleomagnetic evidence for Tertiary anticlockwise rotation in southwest Puerto Rico: Geophysical Research Letters, v. 16, p. 819–822.
Vincenz, S. A., and Dasgupta, S. N., 1978, Paleomagnetic study of some Cretaceous and Tertiary rocks in Hispaniola: Pure and Applied Geophysics, v. 116, p. 1200–1210.

Manuscript Accepted by the Society June 20, 1997

Printed in U.S.A.

Geological Society of America
Special Paper 322
1998

Seismic reflection profiles of the Puerto Rico Trench: Shortening between the North American and Caribbean plates

D. K. Larue
Chevron Petroleum Technology Co., P.O. Box 446, La Habra, California 90633-0446
H. F. Ryan
U.S. Geological Survey, 345 Middlefield Road, Menlo Park, California 94025

ABSTRACT

The Puerto Rico Trench is located at the northern edge of the Caribbean–North America plate boundary zone and has been interpreted variously as a zone of translation, transpression, transtension, and extension. To help resolve the nature of motion in this portion of the plate boundary zone, six multichannel seismic reflection profiles across the Puerto Rico Trench were studied. Analysis of the seismic reflection profiles indicates that the trench is a broad, flat-floored valley that is underlain by up to 2 sec (on the order of 2 to 3 km) of sediment. Deformation within the Puerto Rico Trench is clearly contractional, but heterogeneous along its strike. Although trench sediments are actively deforming, no significant accretionary prism is present. Evidence of left-lateral strike-slip faulting is manifest only through sidescan sonar studies.

Contractional features noted in the Puerto Rico Trench are at odds with models of Caribbean plate motion that predict oblique divergence (transtension) in the plate boundary zone. Most extensional features observed in the Puerto Rico area, including the Virgin Islands basin and 19° North latitude fault, were formed during rotation of the Puerto Rico–Virgin Islands terrane. We propose that the flat floor of the central and western Puerto Rico Trench owes its origin to extensional tectonism during rotation of the Puerto Rico–Virgin Islands terrane. That is, during rotation of the Puerto Rico–Virgin Islands terrane, the Puerto Rico Trench was a zone of extension and possibly de-subduction of oceanic crust. Following cessation of terrane rotation, deformation in the Puerto Rico Trench has been contractional.

INTRODUCTION

The Puerto Rico Trench is the deepest known bathymetric feature in the Atlantic Ocean and is characterized by a broad, flat floor about 10 to 20 km in width (Figs. 1, and 2). No significant accretionary prism is present within or adjacent to the trench, and a south-dipping slab can be imaged by locating positions of seismic events (Schell and Tarr, 1978; Molnar and Sykes, 1969). The south-dipping seismic zone extends from the general region of the trench to depths in excess of 150 km, although it is not clear whether oceanic lithosphere is continuous and connected from beneath the trench to the seismic zone (Schell and Tarr, 1978) or is detached (Speed and Larue, 1991). Focal mechanisms associated with the south-dipping seismic zone indicate slab underthrusting to the southwest, oblique to the trend of the Puerto Rico Trench (Molnar and Sykes, 1969; Harvard focal-mechanism data, unpublished: see Speed and Larue, 1991, for review). The Puerto Rico Trench is located along the northern edge of the 250-km-wide North America–Caribbean plate boundary zone (Fig. 1), which consists of several terranes (Speed and Larue, 1991). One of these, the Puerto Rico–Virgin Islands terrane, is an oceanic island arc massif approximately 25-km thick that evolved into a carbonate

Larue, D. K., and Ryan, H. F., 1998, Seismic reflection profiles of the Puerto Rico Trench: Shortening between the North American and Caribbean plates, *in* Lidiak, E. G., and Larue, D. K., eds., Tectonics and Geochemistry of the Northeastern Caribbean: Boulder, Colorado, Geological Society of America Special Paper 322.

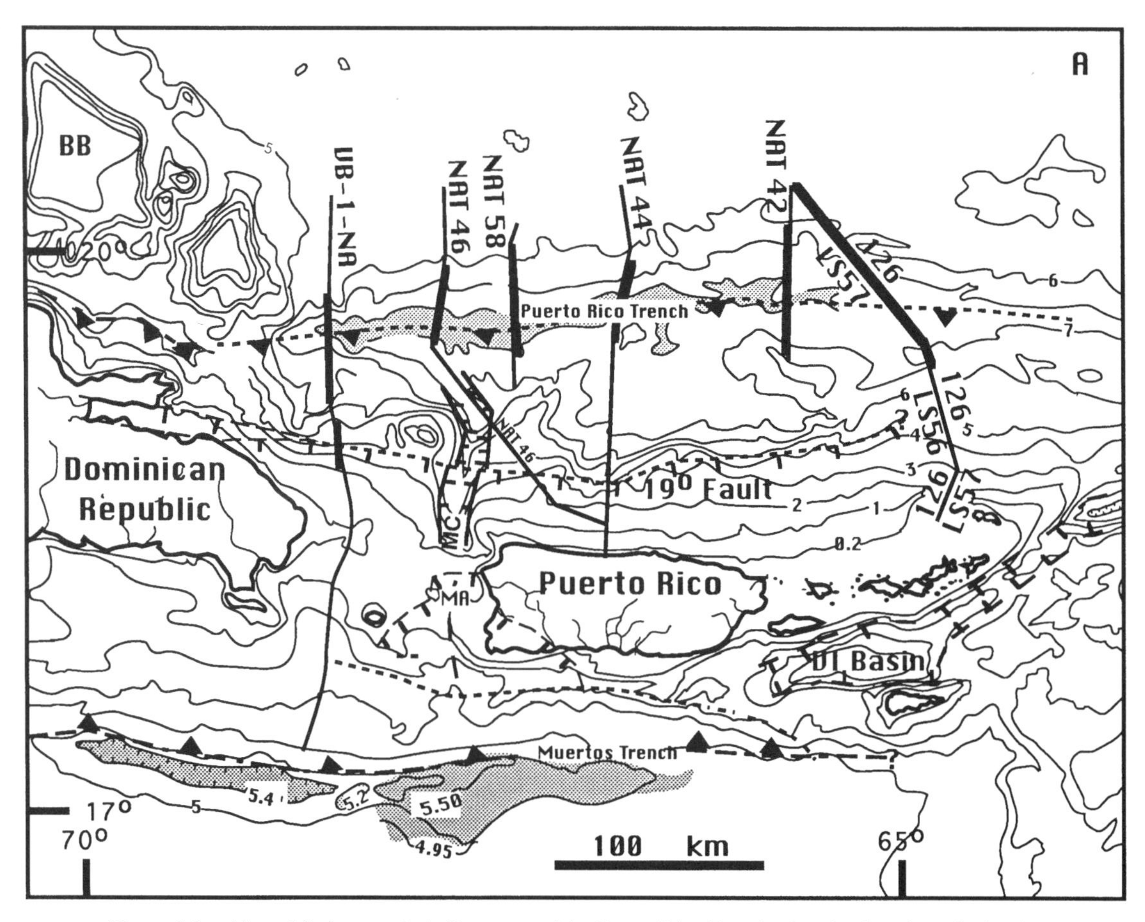

Figure 1 (on this and facing page). A, Base map of the Puerto Rico Trench, showing location of seismic reflection profiles described in text. BB, Bahamas Bank; MC, Mona Canyon; MA, Mona extensional allochthon (Larue and Ryan, 1991). Contour interval is km for bathymetry. Thrust faults shown with barbs on upper block, normal faults shown with hatchures indicating dip direction. Map is generalized. B, Tectonic terranes of the northeast Caribbean. Separating the North Slope and Puerto Rico–Virgin Islands Terrane is the 19° North Latitude fault, which extends laterally to Hispaniola to become two prominent faults. The Hispaniola terrane is separated from the Puerto Rico–Virgin Islands Terrane by the Mona Canyon (MC) and a diffuse zone of extensional tectonism, characterizing the Mona extensional allochthon. The Muertos terrane contains deformed strata associated with the Muertos accretionary complex.

bank after an Eocene orogenic event (Bowin, 1972; Case, 1975; Cox et al., 1977; Kesler and Sutter, 1979; Lewis and Draper, 1990; Larue, 1994). The northern boundary of the Puerto Rico–Virgin Islands terrane is the east-west–trending 19° North Latitude fault (abbreviated 19° fault; Figs. 1 through 3), which dips south and is apparently characterized by normal motion (Larue et al., 1991; Larue and Ryan, 1991; Speed and Larue, 1991). The 19° fault can be traced using bathymetric maps to the west to the Samana Bay, where it bifurcates into the northern Septentrional and Southern Samana Bay faults (Mann and Burke, 1984). The Cibao Valley is present west of Samana Bay, and represents its subaerial continuation. North of the 19° fault is the North Slope terrane, where dredge hauls have recovered and submersible studies have noted arc-related metamorphic rocks and limestones (Schneidermann et al., 1972; Weaver et al., 1975; Perfit et al., 1980; Heezen et al., 1985; Le Pichon et al., 1985). Figure 3 is a seismic reflection profile across the 19° fault (from Larue and Ryan, 1991) that shows the arc complex of the Puerto Rico–Virgin Islands terrane in normal fault contact with the underlying metamorphic rocks of the North Slope terrane. Larue and Ryan (1991) inferred that the North Slope terrane rocks were being exhumed by motion on the 19° fault. The northern boundary of the North Slope terrane is the Puerto Rico Trench. Normal motion on the 19° fault is inferred to diminish toward the east until it reaches zero northeast of the east coast of Puerto Rico (Speed and Larue, 1991). Sediment-filled basins south of the Puerto Rico Trench overlap the North Slope terrane. Dredging north of the Puerto Rico Trench has recovered blocks indicative of an oceanic-crustal origin, including chert, basalt, serpentinite, and gabbro (Perfit et al., 1980; Fox and Heezen, 1975). Atlantic Ocean crust north of the Puerto Rico Trench is Cretaceous in age and approximately 4 to 5 km thick (Officer et al., 1959).

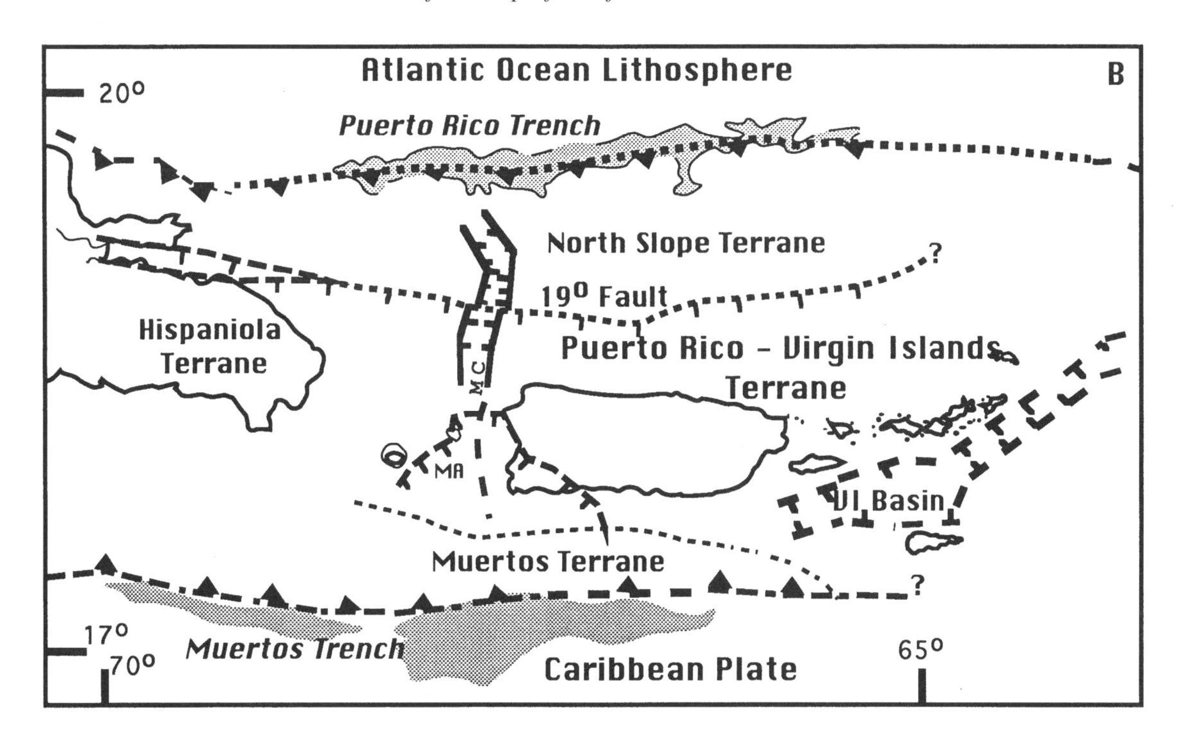

The Muertos terrane was accreted to the Puerto Rico–Virgin Islands terrane in the Eocene (Ladd and Watkins, 1978; Ladd et al., 1977, 1981). The Muertos Trench is a zone of active northward underthrusting and is characterized by a few earthquakes as deep as 55 km (Byrne et al., 1985). An extensive accretionary complex is present along the Muertos Trench (Ladd and Watkins, 1978; Ladd et al., 1977, 1981). Thrust displacement associated with Muertos Trench subduction apparently diminishes toward the east and becomes zero south of the island of St. Croix (Fig. 2) (Masson and Scanlon, 1991).

On the western margin of the Puerto Rico–Virgin Islands terrane is the Hispaniola terrane (Fig. 1). The boundary between the two terranes is the Mona Canyon and Mona extensional allochthon. The Mona Canyon is a graben system associated with east-west extension (Gardner et al., 1980), whereas the Mona allochthon is an extensional complex several kilometers thick with a headwall near the crest of the island arc massif, sliding toward the south into the Muertos terrane (Larue and Ryan, 1991). The nature of movement between the Puerto Rico–Virgin Islands terrane and Hispaniola terrane is poorly understood, and generally thought to be more complicated than simple extension. Key observations are the continuation of the 19° fault across the Puerto Rico–Virgin Islands and Hispaniola terrane boundaries, and apparently modest offset of the Mona Canyon by the 19° fault.

To the southeast of the Puerto Rico–Virgin Islands terrane is the Lesser Antilles arc complex. The Lesser Antilles arc terrane is separated from the Puerto Rico–Virgin Islands terrane by a zone of extension, which includes the Virgin Islands basin (Figs. 1 and 2).

There is considerable controversy about the sense of motion in and evolution of the Puerto Rico Trench. Regional plate motion studies propose that the Caribbean–North American plate boundary zone near the Puerto Rico Trench exhibits left-lateral strike-slip motion with a slight component of transtension (Jordan, 1975; Minster and Jordan, 1978; DeMets et al., 1991; Calais and Mercier de Lepinay, 1993). Based on plate motion studies, the overall linear character of the Puerto Rico Trench has been interpreted as a left-lateral strike-slip zone (Mann et al., 1984). Sykes et al. (1982), and McCann and Sykes (1984) argued that the Puerto Rico Trench is a zone of oblique convergence; they interpreted a number of contractional features in the trench on single channel seismic reflection data. DeMets (1993) and Deng and Sykes (1995) also presented evidence for contraction in the region of the Puerto Rico Trench. Masson and Scanlon (1991) relied on single-channel seismic reflection data in combination with GLORIA sidescan data (EEZ Scan Staff, 1987) to interpret extensional, contractional, and strike-slip features in the trench. Contractional features were located mostly in the eastern part of the trench (east of 65.5°), whereas increasing evidence of strike-slip and extensional tectonism was found in the west (EEZ Scan Staff, 1987). The east-to-west transition from contraction to strike-slip and extension was interpreted by Masson and Scanlon (1991) to be related to the counterclockwise rotation of Puerto Rico. Our seismic reflection studies do not support the interpretations presented by Masson and Scanlon (1991), and we present evidence for contraction along the entire length of the trench studied. Counterclockwise rotation was later documented by studying magnetic declination changes in Tertiary limestones on Puerto Rico (Reid et al., 1991). Reid et al. (1991) noted that all east-west motion could be accounted for by rotation, and that strike-slip fault zones need not be important. Speed (1989) argued that most features in the northeast Caribbean indicated extension. Speed and Larue (1991) noted that regional evidence

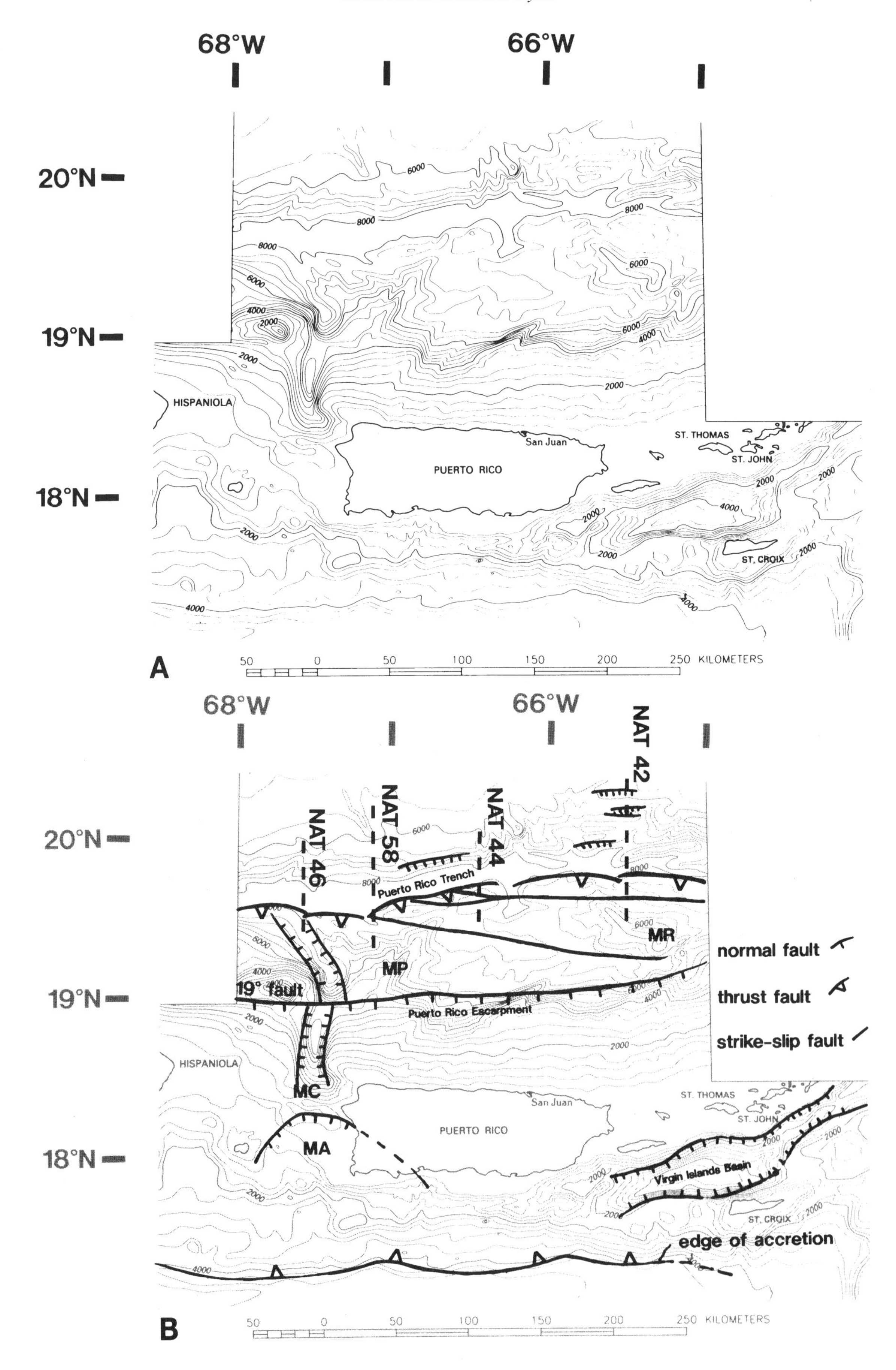
68°W
66°W
20°N
19°N
18°N
6000
8000
4000
2000
HISPANIOLA
San Juan
PUERTO RICO
ST. THOMAS
ST. JOHN
ST. CROIX
A
50 0 50 100 150 200 250 KILOMETERS
NAT 46
NAT 58
NAT 44
NAT 42
Puerto Rico Trench
MP
MR
19° fault
Puerto Rico Escarpment
MC
MA
Virgin Islands Basin
edge of accretion
normal fault
thrust fault
strike-slip fault
B

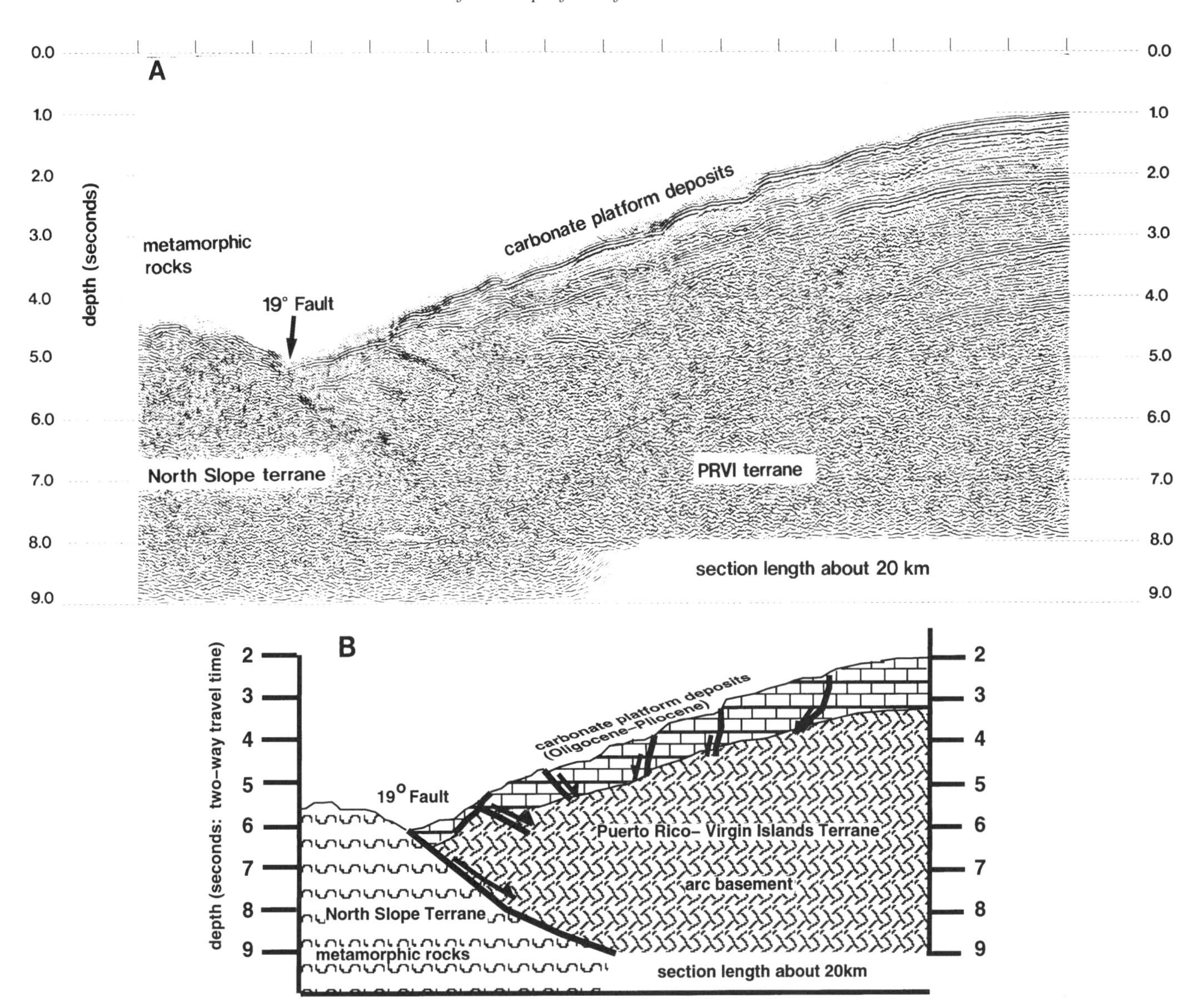

Figure 3. A, Multichannel seismic reflection profile VB 1 NA across the 19° North Latitude fault (see Fig. 1 for location). Surficial geology based on dredging and area submersible studies (see text for discussion). Profile shows arc complex with Tertiary carbonate platform drape in normal fault contact with underlying metamorphic complex, indicating that the metamorphic complex was unroofed or exhumed by motion on the normal fault. B, Interpretation of A, showing juxtaposition of arc basement above metamorphic rocks of the North Slope terrane along the 19° fault. Note the presence of additional normal faults in the sedimentary cover of the Puerto Rico–Virgin Islands terrane.

Figure 2. A, The Puerto Rico Trench and vicinity (map from EEZ Scan Staff, 1987; Masson and Scanlon, 1991). Bathymetry in meters. B, The Puerto Rico Trench and vicinity showing interpreted geology (map from EEZ Scan Staff, 1987; Masson and Scanlon, 1991). Lineations shown are interpreted from GLORIA sidescan mosaics by EEZ Scan Staff, 1987; Masson and Scanlon, 1991 and modified here. MC, Mona Canyon graben system; MP, Mona Promontory; MR, Main Ridge, MA, Mona allochthon.

from Caribbean–North American plate motion indicates that the plate boundary zone should be in transtension, and suggested a number of extensional fault systems in the trench area. By integrating previous studies with preliminary analysis of unmigrated multichannel seismic reflection data, Larue et al. (1991) argued for convergence, strike-slip faulting, and extension in different areas of the trench. The present study reevaluates a key tenet of the Larue et al. (1991) study, specifically the relationship between rotation of the Puerto Rico–Virgin Islands terrane documented by Reid et al. (1991) and tectonism.

OBJECTIVES OF THE PRESENT STUDY

Larue et al. (1991) originally published unmigrated seismic reflection profiles in a regional study of the Puerto Rico Trench and the shelf and slope north of the island of Puerto Rico. The seismic reflection data were subsequently reprocessed at the U.S. Geological Survey by one of us (HFR), so that we could evaluate in greater detail the deformation in the trench region. We present migrated and interpreted multichannel seismic reflection profiles across the Puerto Rico Trench (Fig. 1). These migrated seismic reflection profiles provide a new opportunity to investigate in detail structures present in the Puerto Rico Trench. Most data were migrated using industry standard techniques: a finite difference time migration, filtered and scaled using an automatic gain control. Line VB 1 NA was migrated using a frequency-domain migration, filtered, and scaled using an automatic gain. Line LS 126 57 was reprocessed but not migrated.

BATHYMETRIC EXPRESSION OF THE TRENCH

The most detailed recent study of the Puerto Rico Trench was by the U.S. Geological Survey (EEZ Scan Staff, 1987; Masson and Scanlon, 1991), and we show their map (Fig. 2) with minor modification such that we can incorporate the results of the present investigation. Note, however, that the present study area is slightly larger than its predecessor (cf. Figs. 1 and 2).

The Puerto Rico Trench is bathymetrically irregular, more V-shaped in profile to the east (east of latitude 65.5°W) (Fig. 2) where the trench floor lacks sediment and more flat-floored to the west where trench sediment is thicker (Fig. 2). The seafloor to the north of the trench has been broken by a number of normal faults, some of which are shown in Figure 2. South of the trench, a series of terraces or perched basins flank the steep, fault-controlled Puerto Rico Escarpment. The escarpment, forming the inner wall of the trench, is the topographic manifestation of the 19° fault (Larue et al., 1991; Speed and Larue, 1991). Two large promontories, the Main Ridge and the Mona Promontory (Fig. 2), are located along the inner wall of the trench. Based on dredge haul studies, these promontories into the trench are probably metamorphic massifs. The Mona Canyon, adjacent to the Mona Promontory, is a graben extending perpendicular to the trench axis that separates the Puerto Rico and North Slope terranes from the terranes of Hispaniola.

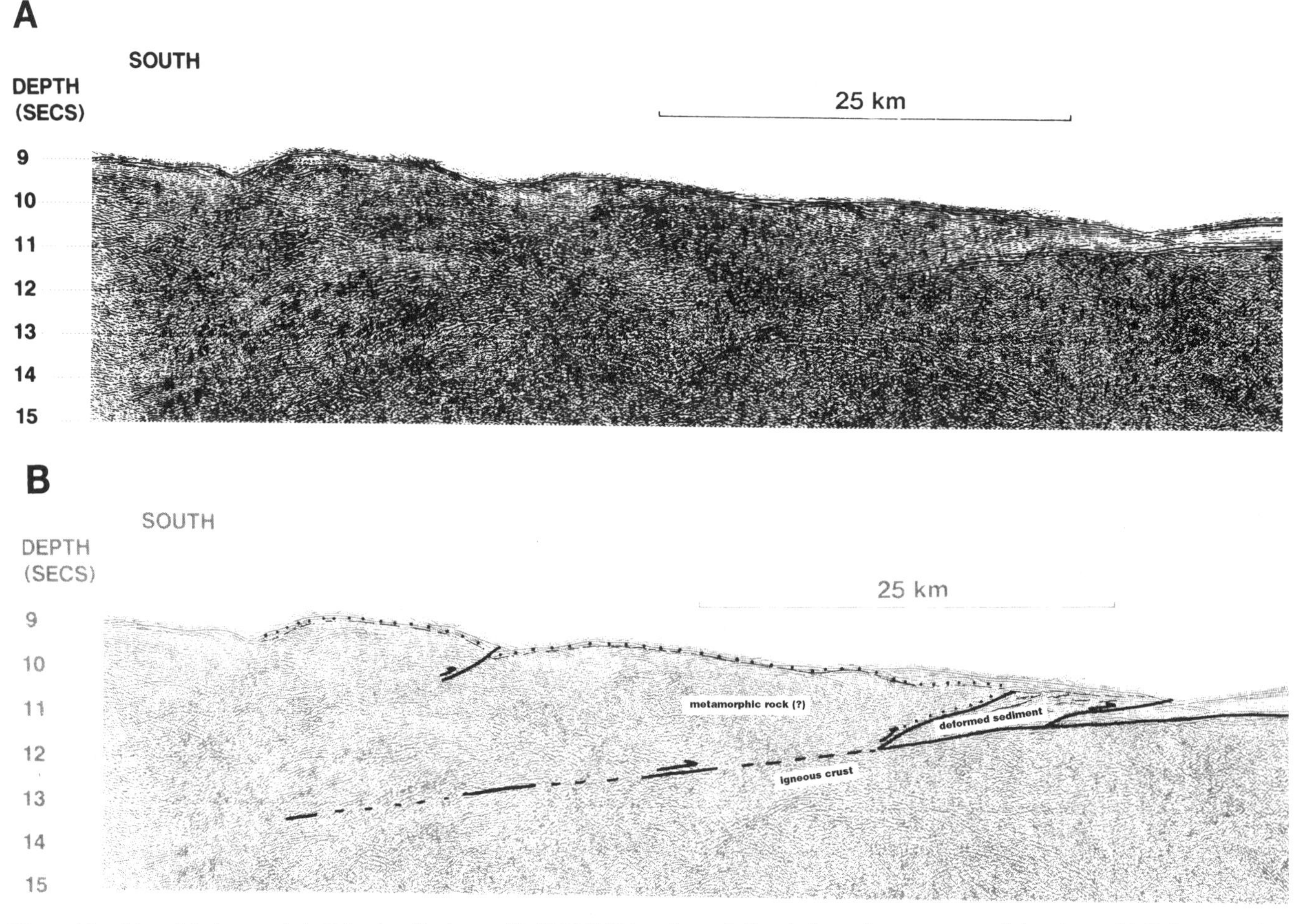

Figure 4 (on this and facing page). A, Seismic reflection profile 126 LS 57 (unmigrated). Depth shown in two-way travel time (seconds). B, Interpretation.

Sidescan sonar images collected by the U.S. Geological Survey (EEZ Scan Staff, 1987) were used to map seafloor lineament patterns in the Puerto Rico Trench (Fig. 2). The lineaments shown are similar to those described by the EEZ Scan Staff (1987) and Masson and Scanlon (1991); some of these lineations may represent seafloor traces of strike-slip faults (Masson and Scanlon, 1991). Note that two prominent sets of lineations are observed in the trench area, and that they converge with the deformation front toward the west.

SEISMIC REFLECTION PROFILES AND DEFORMATION IN THE TRENCH AREA

Eastern part of the trench

In the eastern region of the trench studied here, contractional structures are present and the trench area is narrow. LS 126 57 is the easternmost seismic reflection profile (Figs. 1 and 4). The irregular bathymetry of the oceanic crust north of the trench is the result of normal faulting (Fig. 4B). The trench itself is narrow, relatively poorly defined based on topography, and lacks significant sediment fill. A zone of south-tilted seafloor lies due north of the trench. The region south of the trench is probably composed of accreted sedimentary rock (Fig. 4B), evidenced by irregular southward-dipping reflecting horizons. A package of weakly deformed sedimentary rocks in clear angular discordance with underlying stratigraphy marks the deformation front south of the trench. A thin but prominent packet of two to four south-dipping reflectors interpreted as the top of underthrust oceanic crust can be traced more than 50 km arcward of the trench. Assuming that the packet is indeed the top of underthrust oceanic crust, the two to four reflectors indicate the boundary may be a layered zone or that the signal has been complicated by acoustic ringing. Reflectors above the oceanic crust are truncated along that surface, which indicates they are in fault contact with underlying rocks. If this interpretation is correct, this implies at least 50 km of underthrusting beneath the trench at this location.

Farther west, seismic reflection profile NAT 42 crosses the Puerto Rico Trench, and extends south across the northern part of the Main Ridge (Figs. 1 and 5). North of the trench, the oceanic crust is topographically irregular. Deformed sediment south of the trench axis is interpreted based on the presence of inclined dis-

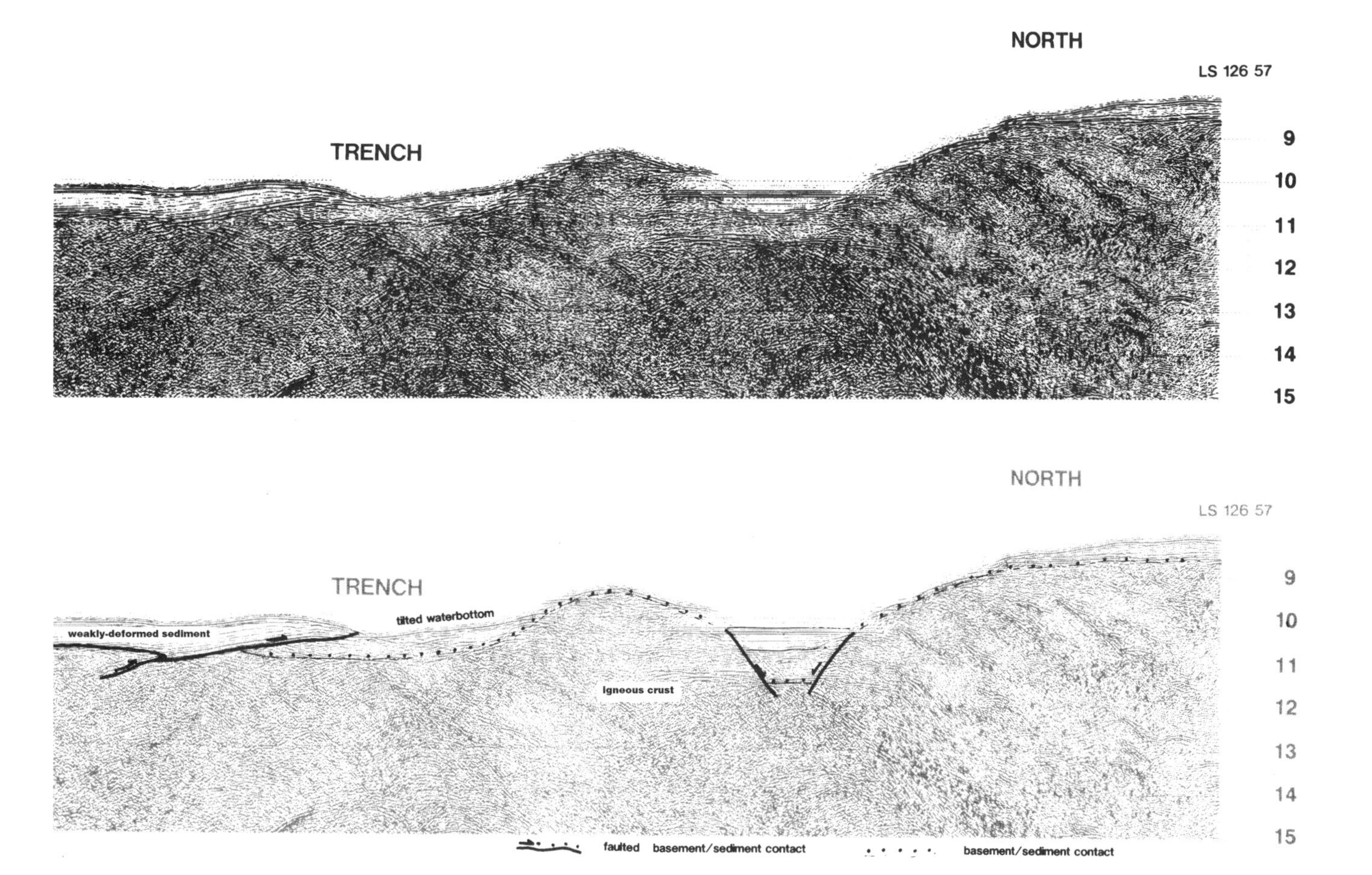

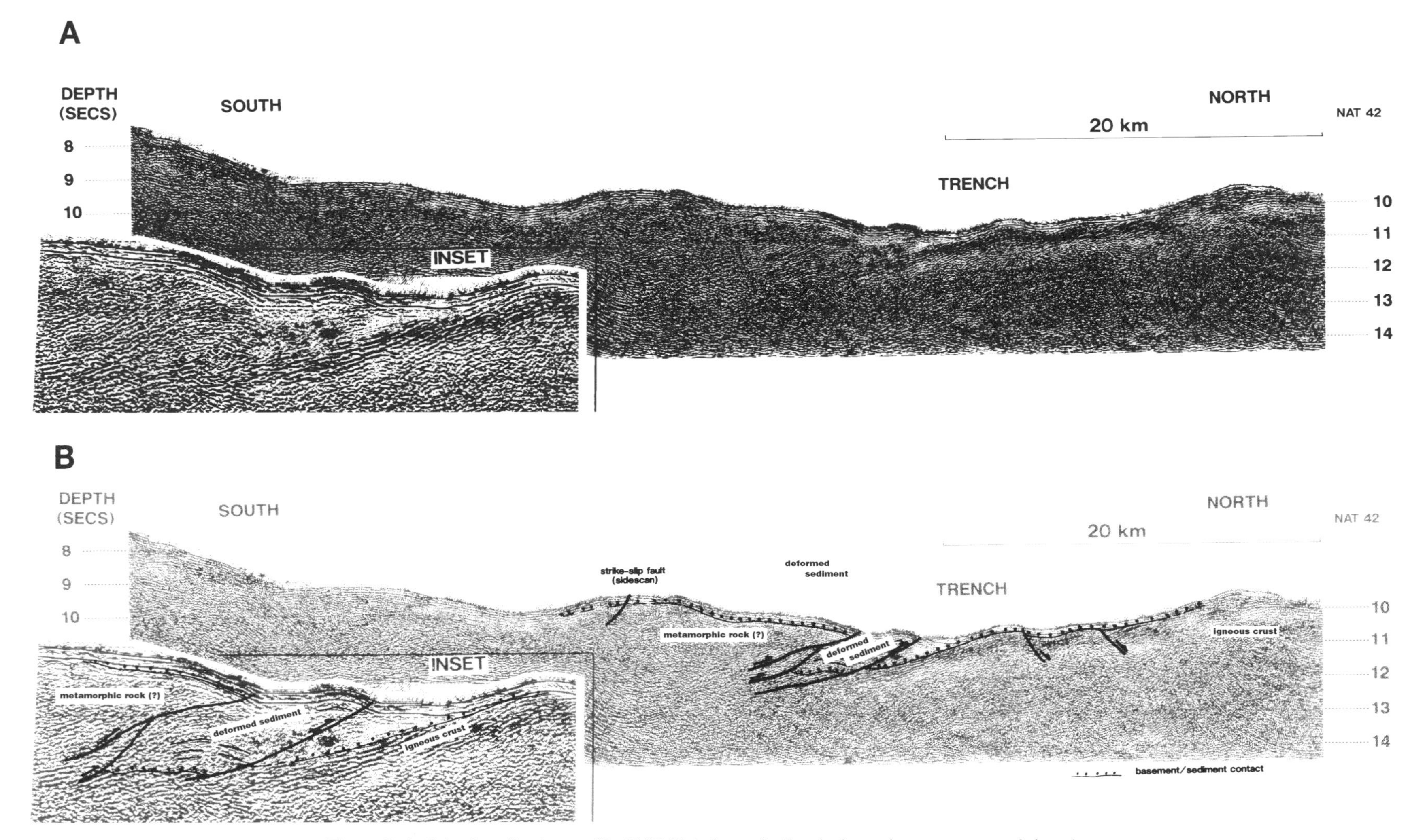

Figure 5. A, Seismic reflection profile NAT 42 (migrated). Depth shown in two-way travel time (seconds). B, Interpretation.

continuous reflectors. The extent of the deformed sediment is poorly understood. Farther south of the trench, a broad ridge, the northern edge of the Main Ridge, is imaged (see Figs. 1 and 2). Its lithology and internal architecture are poorly understood, but may be underlain by the metamorphic complex of the North Slope terrane based on dredge haul samples recovered to the west of the area (Perfit et al., 1980; Larue et al., 1991). An earlier hypothesis that the Main Ridge was the surficial manifestation of a subducting oceanic fracture zone (McCann and Sykes, 1984) was shown to be unsupported by available data (Larue et al., 1991). The topographic high on the south wall approximately 30 km from the southern edge of the section corresponds to a lineament defined using GLORIA sidescan studies (Fig. 2) (Masson and Scanlon, 1991); it has been interpreted as a left-lateral strike-slip fault trace. A zone of diffuse reflectors observed immediately south of the trench dips to the south for about 10 km. These reflectors are interpreted to be the acoustic boundary between Atlantic oceanic crust and the rocks underlying the south wall of the trench. The origin of the reflectors may be the acoustic impedance contrast between igneous oceanic crust and the overlying sediment column, because the reflectors appear to be continuous with oceanic crust north of the trench. High migration velocities suggest that the south wall of the trench is probably underlain mostly by dense rock and that accreted sediment is minimal.

Central and western part of the trench

In the central and western part of the trench studied herein, contractional features are observed throughout, but deformation style is dominated by fault wedges, and sidescan sonar studies indicate the presence of left-lateral strike-slip faults in the vicinity of the deformation front. Moreover, the trench floor is flat, and the trench fill is thick in comparison to the eastern part of the trench. Clear evidence of syn-sedimentary faulting can be documented.

In seismic reflection profile NAT 44, oceanic crust to the north of the trench is seismically opaque and has been deformed by normal faults (Fig. 6; note reversal of orientation of the line with north on left). Sediment overlying the oceanic crust is largely undeformed, although it is locally tilted and onlaps unlayered rocks believed to represent igneous rock. Evidence for south-directed normal faulting within the trench wedge is documented by deeper strata dipping north and flattening upward. Seismic reflection profile NAT 44 shows an active thrust fault in the Puerto Rico Trench with a minimum northward displacement of about 10 to 15 km. The trace of the fault is imaged discontinuously along the down-dip direction. Little deformation is observed in the trench strata, except a broad syncline. Weak discontinuous reflectors that may represent metamorphic rocks of the North Slope terrane are observed in the hanging wall of the thrust fault that demarks the southern edge of the trench. There is little evidence for the faults mapped by sidescan sonar in this area (Fig. 2). The paucity of strata south of the trench suggests that the area has remained topographically higher than the trench area and is largely an area of nondeposition and/or erosion.

Seismic reflection profile NAT 58 crosses the trench farther to the west near the convergence of a lineation defined using sidescan with the deformation front area (Figs. 1, 2, and 7). The north wall of the trench is bathymetrically relatively smooth (Fig. 7). Two prominent thin reflecting packets containing about three to five events are observed beneath the north wall, one south dipping, the other nearly horizontal. These two reflecting packets define a single curved fault surface in the Atlantic oceanic crust, representing an inactive listric normal fault (Fig. 7B).

The trench in profile NAT 58 is underlain by about 2 sec (on the order of 2 to 3 km) of layered strata, which appear to onlap the north and south walls of the trench. A fault wedge consisting of metamorphic rocks of the North Slope terrane is interpreted to penetrate and deform the trench fill. Faulting apparently accompanied deposition of sediments, as shown by stratal relationship to deformation fabrics in the trench wedge section. A south-dipping packet of reflecting surfaces underlies the fault complex at depth; this packet of reflectors can be traced approximately 15 km to the south, is composed of about four irregular and discontinuous reflectors and may represent the top of oceanic crust.

South of the trench are two terraces, which lead to the south wall of the trench. Slopes of the terraces are interpreted as products of motion on faults, including reverse based on seismic reflection character, and strike-slip, based on GLORIA studies (Fig. 2; see also EEZ Scan Staff, 1987). The higher terrace is underlain by a unit exhibiting inclined reflectors, or clinoforms. The clinoforms probably represent sediments deposited against an uplifted block along the terrace boundary, and provide evidence for the presence of bottom currents in the trench because the apparent direction of clinoform progradation is to the south, up local slope. Another thrust fault is inferred on the extreme southern edge of the profile, where a prominent change is topography is underlain by inclined reflectors.

The trench fill in seismic reflection profile NAT 46 is a triangular wedge of layered material almost 2 sec (on the order of 2 to 3 km) thick (Fig. 8). Layering in the trench wedge is mostly flat to gently undulating. Atlantic oceanic crust to the north of the trench is acoustically opaque as imaged using seismic reflection, and a clear onlap relation exists between trench sediments and the oceanic crust. The south side of the trench represents the mouth of the Mona Canyon (Fig. 2) and is imaged poorly. Seafloor south of the trench is bathymetrically irregular. The contact between the region south of the trench and the trench wedge is a steeply inclined deformation front. The origin of this deformation front is uncertain, but because individual reflectors can be traced to the south into the deformation front, an origin similar to the fault wedges described above may be likely. A poorly imaged reflector corresponding to the top of Atlantic oceanic crust can be imaged beneath the trench wedge and to the south of the trench. A few, poorly imaged reflectors are present beneath the lower trench slope, and probably represent deformed trench materials.

Seismic reflection profile VB1-NA2 is the western most crossing of the Puerto Rico Trench reported in this chapter (Fig. 9). North of the trench floor is Atlantic oceanic crust, which is

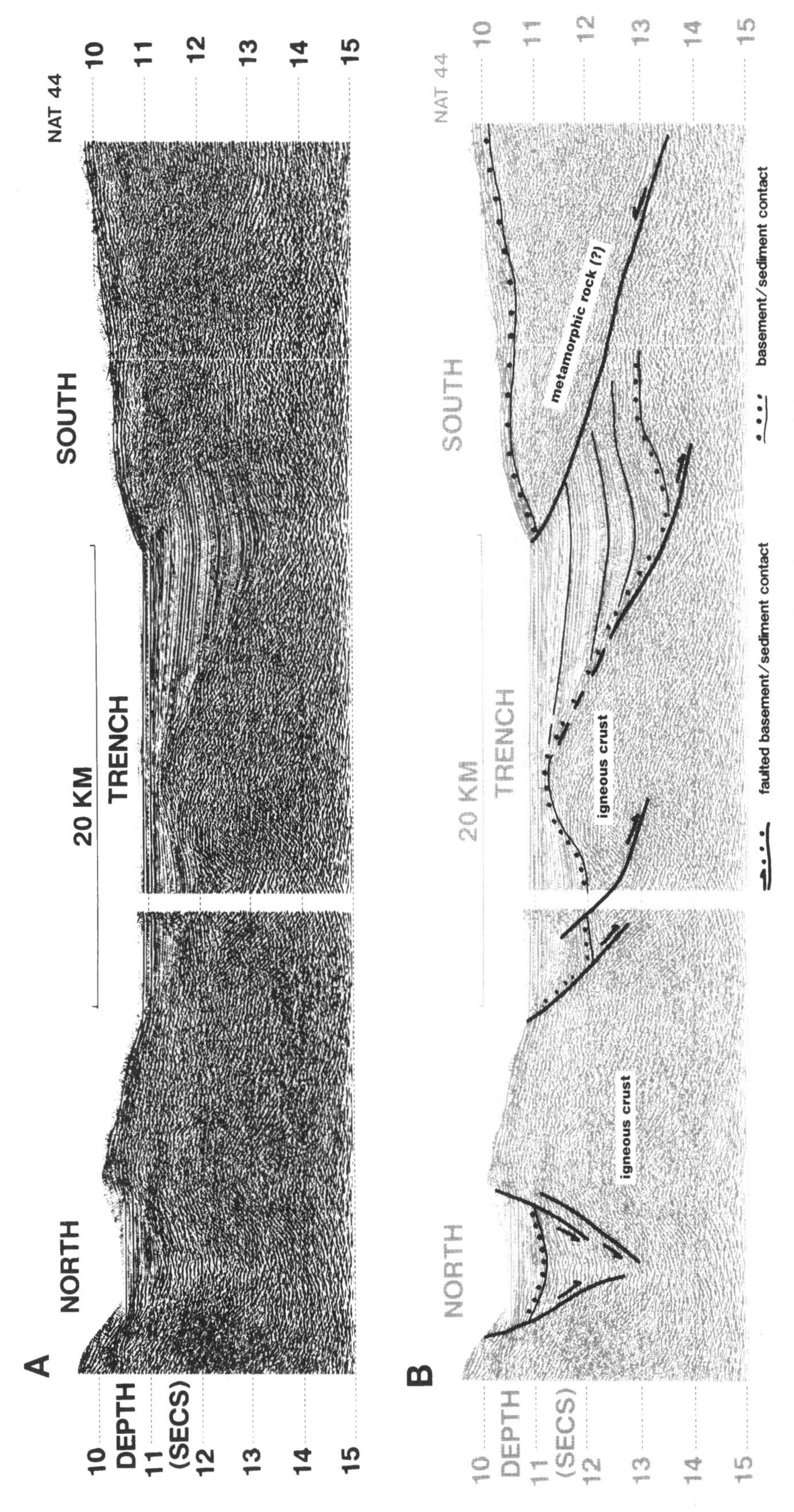

Figure 6. A, Seismic reflection profile NAT 44 (migrated). Depth shown in two-way travel time (seconds). B, Interpretation.

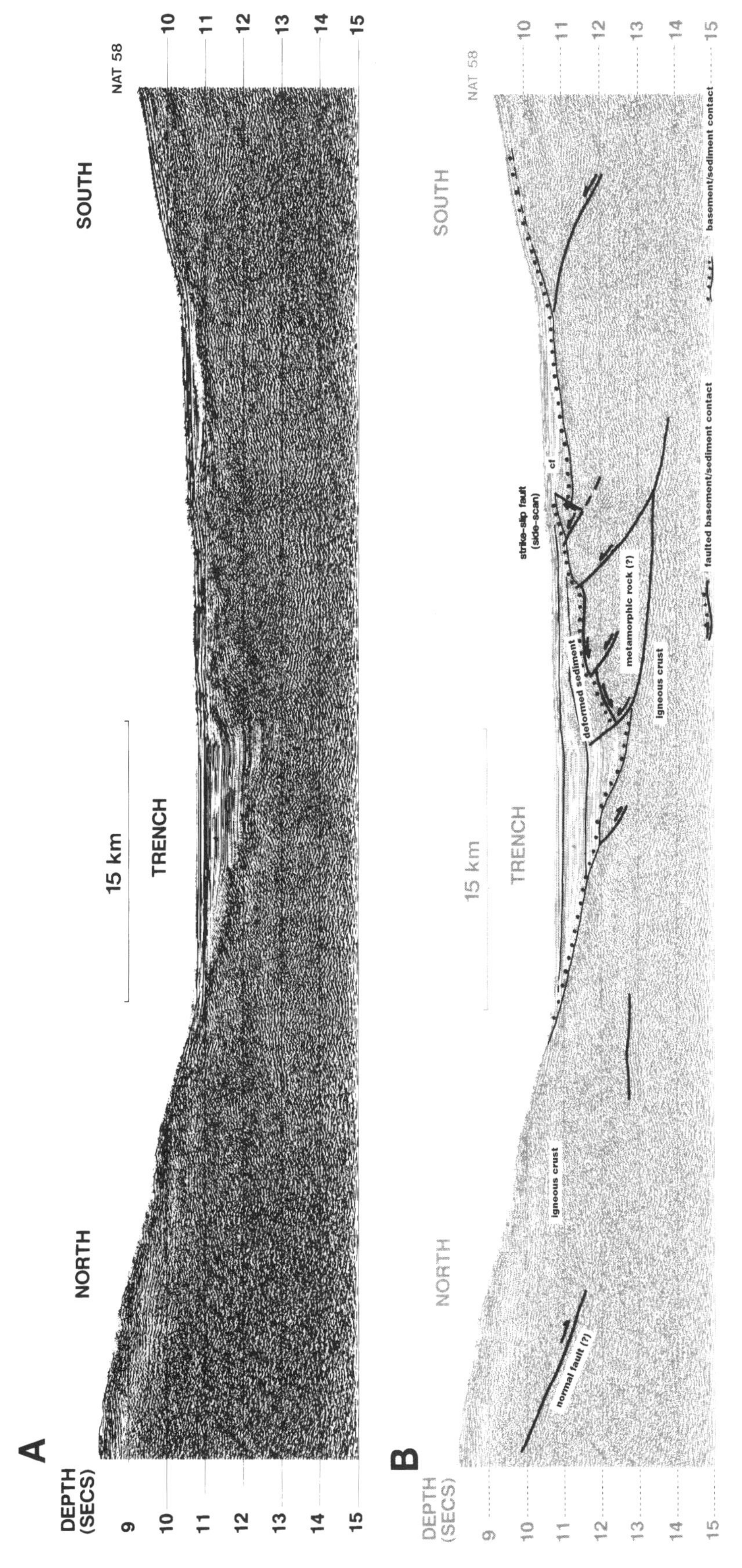

Figure 7. A, Seismic reflection profile NAT 58 (migrated). Depth shown in two-way travel time (seconds). B, Interpretation.

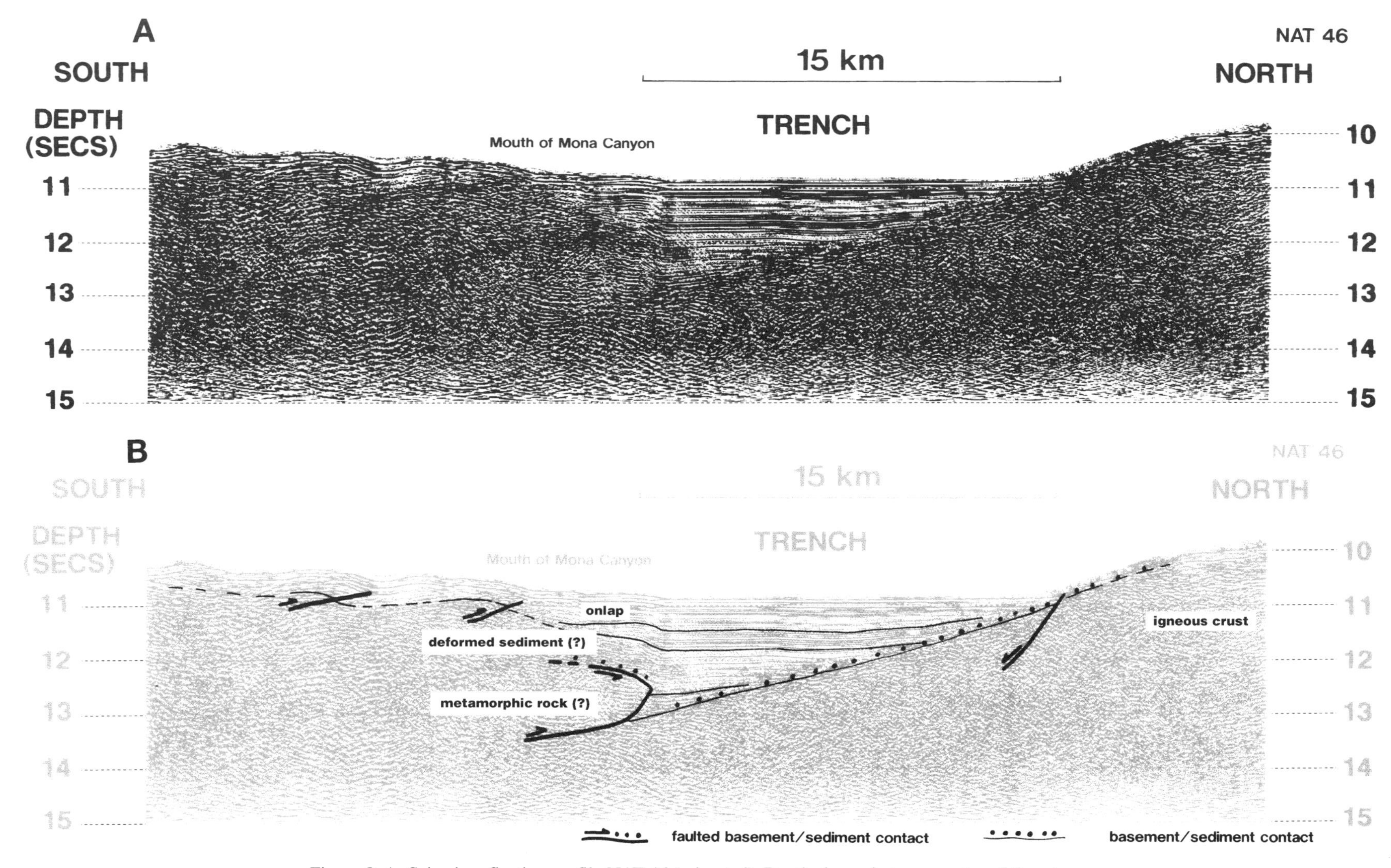

Figure 8. A, Seismic reflection profile NAT 46 (migrated). Depth shown in two-way travel time (seconds). B, Interpretation.

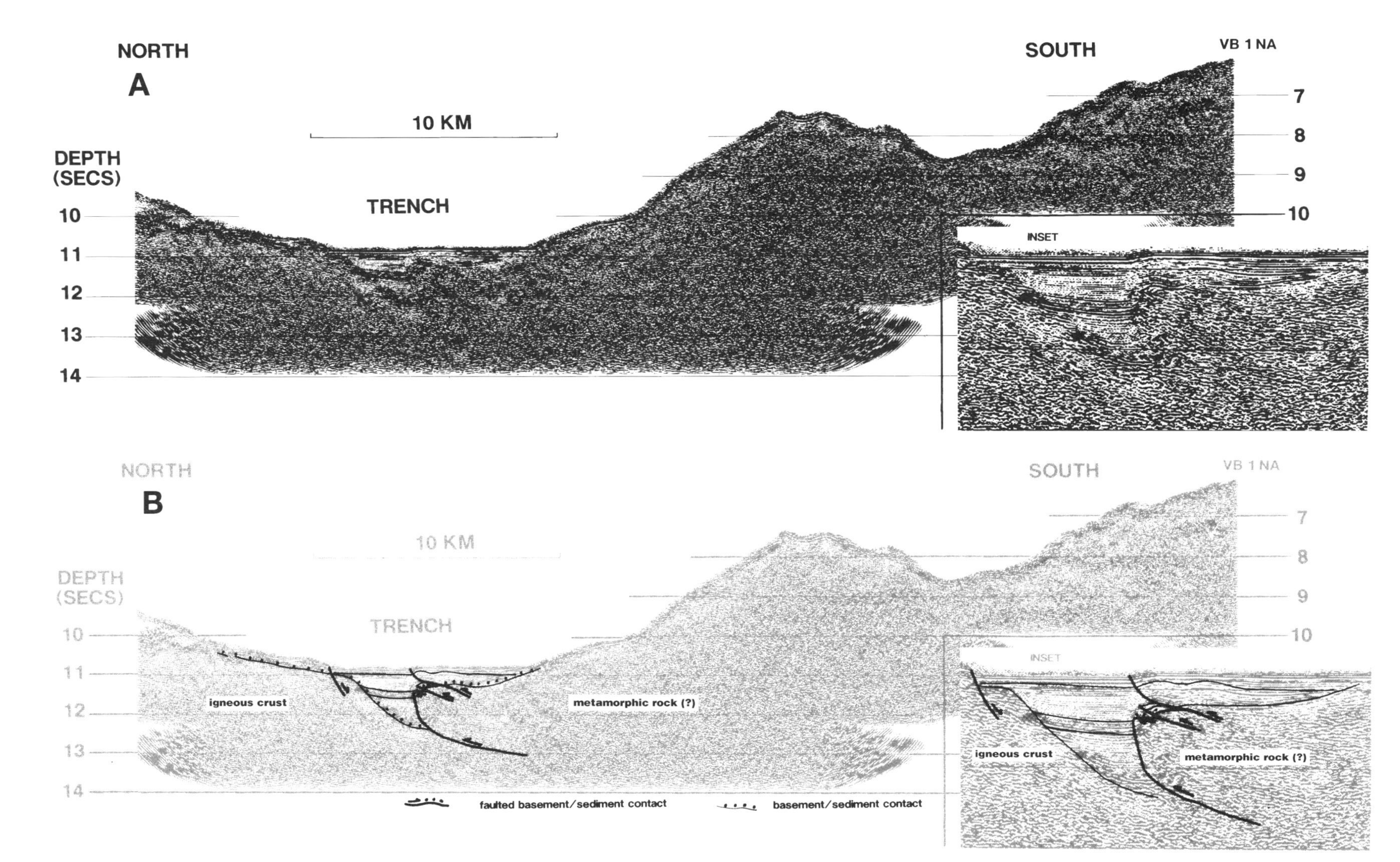

Figure 9. A, Seismic reflection profile VB 1 NA (migrated). Depth shown in two-way travel time (seconds). B, Interpretation.

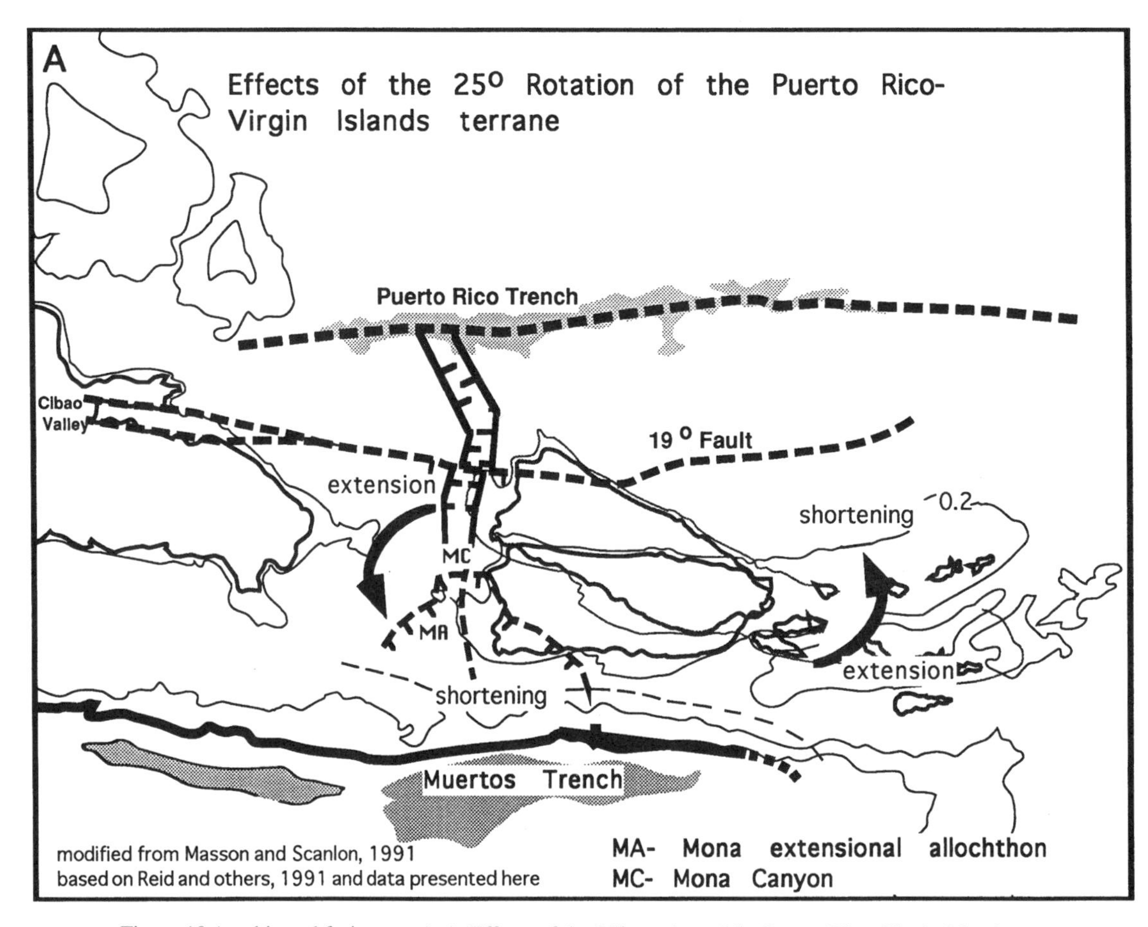

Figure 10 (on this and facing page). A, Effects of the 25° rotation of the Puerto Rico–Virgin Islands terrane. See text. B, The dominant extensional features in the Puerto Rico Trench, the 19° North Latitude fault, and the Virgin Islands basin can best be explained by rotation of the Puerto Rico–Virgin Islands terrane. See text for discussion.

internally massive. The trench floor can be subdivided into a lower floor and an upper terrace. The upper terrace was formed during penetration of the trench fill by the fault wedge. Beneath the lower trench floor is a triangular wedge of strata about 1-sec (on the order of 1 km) thick, two-way travel time. The triangular wedge onlaps Atlantic crust to the north and is penetrated on the south by the fault wedge mentioned above. A weak reflector underlies the trench wedge and can be traced with difficulty about 10 km to the south. Again, it is difficult to assess the relative importance of strike-slip versus contractional deformation, other than to note shortening seems to be documented. The upper terrace onlaps the south wall of the trench, which is internally massive in this profile. The south wall is underlain by metamorphic rocks, as indicated by dredge hauls and submersible studies (Perfit et al., 1980; Larue et al., 1991).

DISCUSSION AND CONCLUSIONS

Interpretations of the seismic reflection profiles in the study area suggest that the Puerto Rico Trench is characterized by heterogeneous contractional deformation from north of the Virgin Islands to north of the Mona Canyon (that is, its entire length in the study area), and that lineations interpreted as possible strike-slip faults converge with the deformation front to the west, but extend to the east. Evidence for contraction is the presence of what appears to be an underriding slab in several of the profiles (126 LS 57, NAT 42, NAT 44, NAT 58, NAT 46, and VB1-NA2) and evidence of thrust faulting in the trench (NAT 44, NAT 46, NAT 58, and VB1-NA2). Heterogeneous deformation is demonstrated by the variable nature of the shortening in the trench and the variability of structural styles.

The minimum amount of inferred shortening in the trench is on the order of 10 km in seismic reflection profiles NAT 42, NAT 44, NAT 58, and VB1-NA2, and 50 km for 126 LS 57. Our inability to quantify more accurately the amount of shortening along the trace of the trench is probably due to the lack of sensitivity of the seismic data and lack of appropriate markers. Similarly, attempts to quantify the amount of transcurrent motion are stymied by lack of markers such as offset submarine channels in the available sidescan data.

Another important feature is that the trace of the deformation front in the trench and the trace of inferred strike-slip faults

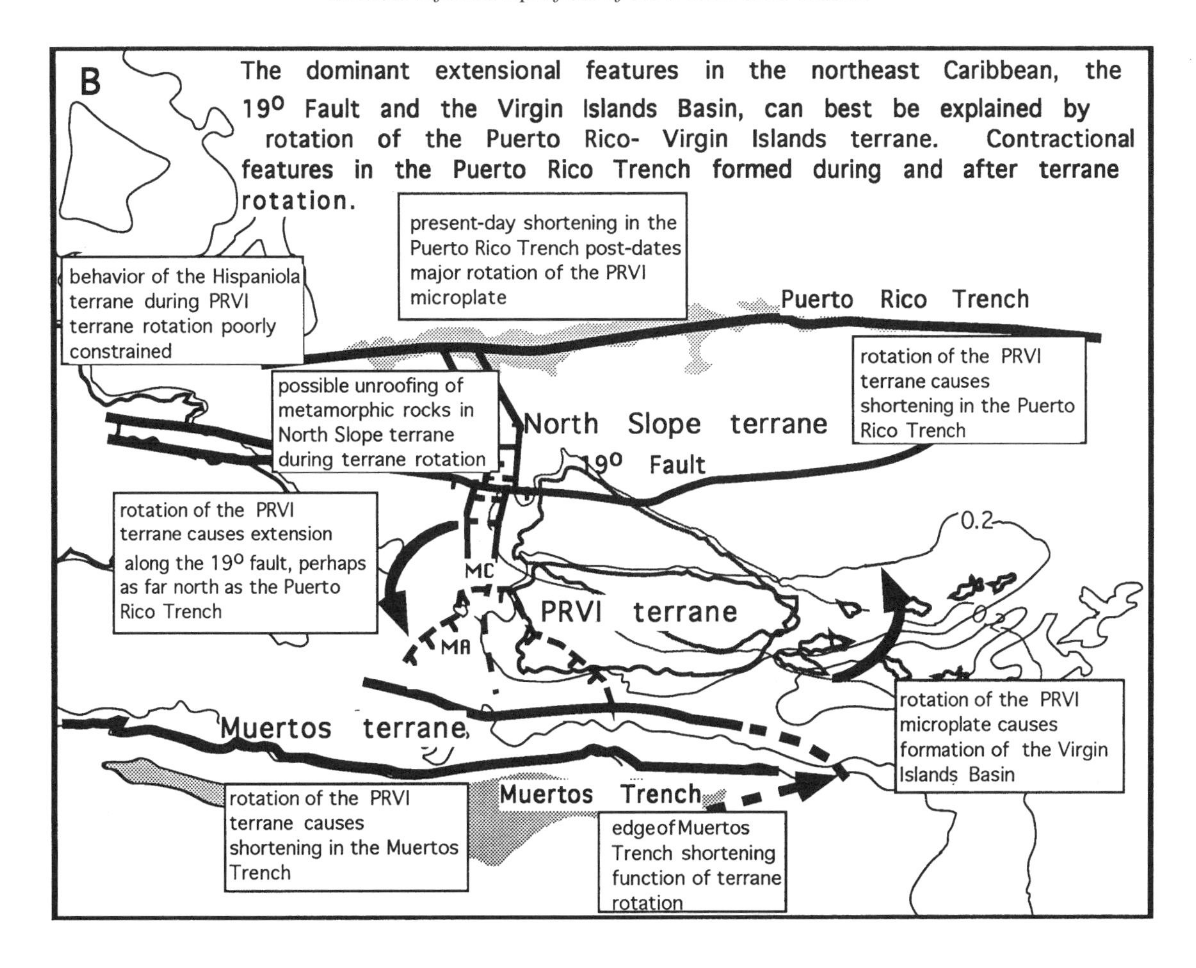

converge to the west (Fig. 2). An interpretation that explains this convergence of faults is that strike-slip faulting is progressively partitioned to the east. In the western part of the study area, the strike-slip faults are in close proximity to the deformation front of the trench. Toward the east, the strike-slip faults are present tens of kilometers south of the deformation front of the trench, and deformation in the trench is more clearly contractional.

Although the trench wedge is up to 2 sec (on the order of 2 to 3 km) in thickness, only minor quantities of accreted sedimentary rock were inferred on the reflection profiles. Migration velocities were high south of the trench, supporting the interpretation that the south wall of the trench is mostly indurated rocks, such as the Cretaceous through Miocene volcanic, metamorphic, and carbonate rocks that have been dredged from the south wall of the trench at shallower depths on exposed scarps.

Deformation model

Deformation in the Puerto Rico Trench specifically, and northeast Caribbean in general, is a result of two deformation regimes: regional plate motion and local plate boundary zone effects. By subtracting the local plate boundary zone effects, the regional plate motions in the northeast Caribbean can be ascertained. The key local plate boundary effects are thought to be associated with the Miocene-Pliocene rotation of the Puerto Rico-Virgin Islands terrane, documented by Reid et al. (1991).

Figure 10 is a deformation model, modified from that proposed by Masson and Scanlon (1991), and Larue et al. (1991). In Figure 10A, B, the effects of the 25° rotation of the Puerto Rico–Virgin Islands terrane are summarized. Terrane rotation will result in the formation of extensional features such as the Virgin Islands Basin in the southeast and the 19° fault in the northwest. Extension in the northwest could have reached all the way to the Puerto Rico Trench, such that during terrane rotation, the central and western trench (west of 65.5°W) may have been a zone of extension (Speed and Larue, 1991). It is believed that extension in the Puerto Rico Trench lead to the broad, flat trench floor west of 65.5°W. Such extension in the Puerto Rico Trench region may have contributed to the exhumation of the North Slope terrane metamorphic rocks (Fig. 3) and perhaps seafloor north of the trench (that is, oceanic crust may have been de-subducted). This is why Puerto Rico–Virgin Island terrane rocks cross the 19° fault in Figure 10: motion on the fault associated with rotation of the Puerto Rico–Virgin Island terrane lead to exhumation of the North Slope terrane. Extension along the 19° fault and the area north of there resulted in the northward tilt of the Tertiary carbonate platform of Puerto Rico (Fig. 3). The inferred eastern edge of extension associated with the 19° fault lies northeast of the east coast of Puerto Rico (marked by a question mark in Fig. 1).

Shortening was greatest in the northeast and southwest regions of the rotating Puerto Rico–Virgin Islands terrane. This observation explains the possible increase in fault displacement toward the east observed in Puerto Rico Trench seismic reflection profiles described here. In the southwest, terrane rotation caused shortening in the Muertos Trench. Aside from the local extensional effects of rotation of the Puerto Rico–Virgin Islands terrane, deformation in the Puerto Rico Trench is contractional, and is active today, as indicated by faults cutting the most recent sediment. This contraction is thought to be driven by regional plate motions.

Terrane rotation can account for most of the extension observed in the study area and its localized spatial distribution. Although extensional faults may be marginally active today, it is likely that most of the rotation of the Puerto Rico–Virgin Islands terrane, hence extension, ceased in the Pliocene (Reid et al., 1991). The Mona extensional allochthon and the Mona Canyon graben are not clearly related to rotation of the Puerto Rico–Virgin Islands terrane. The Mona Canyon graben formed during extension between the Hispaniola and Puerto Rico–Virgin Islands terranes, and the history of extension is not well understood. The Mona extensional allochthon may have formed during late Miocene uplift of Puerto Rico. The Mona extensional allochthon is clearly active today (Larue and Ryan, 1991). The entire length of the trench studied herein is undergoing shortening at present. There may be a decrease in fault displacement toward the west, but overall shortening is indicated.

In the model shown in Figure 10, the Hispaniola terrane is not considered in the rotation of the Puerto Rico–Virgin Islands terrane. The behavior of the Hispaniola terrane during the rotation of the Puerto Rico–Virgin Islands terrane is poorly constrained but has significant implications for northeast Caribbean plate motions. The Cibao Valley and Samana Bay in Hispaniola (see Fig. 1) are bound by the two fault systems representing the westward continuation of the 19° Fault. The central Cibao Valley experienced contraction perhaps in the Pliocene (Edgar, 1991), but Samana Bay is actively undergoing extensional or transtensional deformation (Edgar, 1991; Draper et al., 1994). Note that the crossing of the 19° fault in line VB-1-NA (Fig. 3) is located in the Hispaniola terrane. Normal motion on the 19° fault is therefore inferred from northeast of Puerto Rico west to the Samana Bay, and as discussed previously, this normal motion is interpreted to have accompanied rotation of the Puerto Rico–Virgin Islands terrane. Extensional deformation in the Mona Passage, including east-west extension associated with the Mona Canyon and north-south extension associated with the Mona extensional allochthon, obscures the nature of the boundary between the two terranes. Whether the Hispaniola terrane was actively involved in rotation with the Puerto Rico–Virgin Islands terrane, or whether a series of north-south–oriented strike-slip faults divide the Hispaniola and Puerto Rico–Virgin Islands terrane into smaller rotating blocks are problems that need to be addressed in future studies.

Significance of contraction in the trench

Previous studies have shown that in the vicinity of Puerto Rico, motion between the Caribbean and North American plate is predominantly transcurrent (Jordan, 1975; DeMets et al., 1991; DeMets, 1993; Deng and Sykes, 1995). We have shown that there is evidence of shortening along the entire Puerto Rico Trench, from north of the Virgin Islands to north of the Mona Canyon. Therefore, the model of Masson and Scanlon (1991), which predicts extension north of the Mona Passage, is incorrect. Strongly oblique shortening across the Puerto Rico Trench is compatible with the plate motion studies of Sykes et al. (1982), DeMets (1993), and Deng and Sykes (1995): however, those models that predict extension in the southeastern Caribbean are probably incorrect (e.g., Sykes et al., 1982; Deng and Sykes, 1995) based on clear evidence of latest Miocene to Recent deformation in northern Venezuela and Trinidad (e.g., Wielchowsky et al., 1991). We have also disproved Speed's (1989) interpretation of predominantly extensional tectonism in the trench region. The model of Speed and Larue (1991), which predicts mostly extensional tectonism in the Puerto Rico Trench, requires revision; extension was associated with terrane rotation, and subsequent to cessation of rotation, tectonism has been characterized by shortening. The following models of plate motion in the northern Caribbean plate boundary zone in the vicinity of Puerto Rico do apply.

1. If the Caribbean plate is rigid internally, then plate models that predict extension in the vicinity of the Puerto Rico Trench are in error. Extensional features are associated with terrane rotation, not regional tectonism. The Minster and Jordan (1978) model of relative plate motion predicts oblique extension ("transtension") between the rigid Caribbean and North American plates, which is clearly not applicable to the seismic reflection data discussed herein. However, if the Caribbean plate is not internally rigid (e.g., if slip or other deformation is occurring within the plate), then the Minster and Jordan (1976) model could be correct; that is, extension in the plate boundary zone is taken up elsewhere within the Caribbean plate (for example, the Beata Ridge), leaving the Puerto Rico Trench mildly contractional.

2. Rotation of the Puerto Rico–northern Virgin Islands terrane occurred from the Late Miocene to the Pliocene (Reid et al., 1991), with a vertical rotation axis northeast of Puerto Rico (Reid et al., 1991; Speed and Larue, 1991). This rotation lead to extension in the Virgin Islands Basin and along the 19° fault, and northward flexure of the carbonate platform on Puerto Rico into the listric 19° fault and regions north. Previous workers misinterpreted the effects of terrane rotation for indicators of regional extensional tectonic deformation. As indicated previously, rotation of the Hispaniola terrane from the late Miocene to the Pliocene is not tested, so the behavior of the terrane boundary between the Hispaniola and Puerto Rico–Virgin Islands terrane is poorly understood. Clearly, some rotation of the Hispaniola terrane is interpreted to have occurred based on normal movement of the 19° North Latitude fault (see Fig. 3). Therefore, the north-south lineament associated with the Mona Canyon and the west-

ern shelf edge of the island of Puerto Rico need not have been a zone of major displacement during the late Miocene to the Pliocene. This would, however, imply some significant rotation of the Hispaniola terrane, or portions of the Hispaniola terrane, which has yet to be documented.

A minimum of about 10 km of shortening is necessary to produce the features observed in the trench except in the eastern part of the trench where 50 km of shortening are necessary. Caribbean–North American plate motions are estimated to be about 2 cm/yr (Rosencrantz and Mann, 1991; Calais and Mercier de Lepinay, 1993). Using the 10-km minimum shortening value, if convergence were orthogonal, this could imply deformation started as recently as 0.5 Ma, assuming all plate boundary zone deformation is focused in the Puerto Rico Trench. Because plate motion is oblique with respect to the Puerto Rico Trench, slower convergence rates, hence older deformation are indicated.

ACKNOWLEDGMENTS

This chapter represents work initiated at the University of Puerto Rico Department of Geology by the senior author (DKL). We thank members of the Department of Geology for their continued support. We also thank the Texas Institute of Geophysics, especially Eric Rosencrantz, for allowing us access to these seismic data, including paper copies and magnetic tapes, and allowing us to publish the data. The U.S. Geological Survey, Menlo Park, provided computer time. Portions of this work were supported by National Science Foundation Grants RII–88–02961 and RII–85–13533, and grants from the Puerto Rico Electric Power Authority. Reviews by Scott Wilkerson, Tom Hague, Leon Aden, Troy Holcombe, Jim Pindell, Hans Avé Lallemant, Ed Lidiak, and others are appreciated.

REFERENCES CITED

Bowin, C., 1972, Puerto Rico Trench negative gravity anomaly belt: Geological Society of America Memoir 132, p. 339–350.

Byrne, D. B., Suarez, G., and McCann, W. R., 1985, Muertos Trough subduction-microplate tectonics in the northern Caribbean: Nature, v. 317, p. 420–421.

Calais, E., and Mercier de Lepinay, B., 1993, Semiquantitative modeling of strain and kinematics along the Caribbean/North America strike-slip plate boundary zone: Journal of Geophysical Research, v. 98, p. 8293–8308.

Case, J. E., 1975, Geophysical studies in the Caribbean Sea, *in* Nairn, A. E. M., and Stehli, F. G., eds., The ocean basins and margins; v. 3, The Gulf of Mexico and the Caribbean: New York, Plenum Press, p. 107–180.

Cox, D. F., Marvin, F. R., M'Gonigle, J. W., McIntyre, D. H., and Rogers, C., 1977, Potassium-argon geochronology of some metamorphic, igneous and hydrothermal events in Puerto Rico and the Virgin Islands: U.S. Geological Survey Journal of Research, v. 5, p. 689–703.

DeMets, C., 1993, Earthquake slip vectors and estimates of present-day plate motions: Journal of Geophysical Research, v. 98, p. 6703–6714.

DeMets, C., Gordon, R., Argus, D., and Stein, S., 1991, Current plate motions: Geophysical Journal International, v. 101, p. 425–478.

Deng, J., and Sykes, L. R., 1995, Determination of Euler pole for contemporary relative motion of Caribbean and North American plates using slip vectors of interplate earthquakes: Tectonics, v. 14, p. 39–53.

Draper, G., Mann, P., and Lewis, J., 1994, Hispaniola, *in* Donovan, S. K., and Jackson, T. A., eds., Caribbean geology: an introduction: Kingston, Jamaica, University of West Indies Publisher's Association, p. 129–150.

Edgar, N. T., 1991, Structure and geologic development of the Cibao Valley, northern Hispaniola, *in* Mann, P., Draper, G., and Lewis, J., eds., Tectonic development of the North America–Caribbean plate boundary zone in Hispaniola: Geological Society of America Special Paper 262, p. 281–299.

EEZ SCAN 85 Scientific Staff 1987, Atlas of the U.S. Exclusive Economic Zone, eastern Caribbean: U.S. Geological Survey Miscellaneous Investigation Series Map I–1864B, 58 p.

Fox, P. J., and Heezen, B. C., 1975, Geology of the Caribbean crust, *in* Nairn, A. E. M., and Stehli, F. G., eds., The ocean basins and margins, v. 3, The Caribbean and the Gulf of Mexico: New York, Plenum Press, p. 421–466.

Gardner, W. D., Glover, L. K., and Hollister, C. D., 1980, Canyons off northwest Puerto Rico: studies of their origin and maintenance with the nuclear research submarine NR-1: Marine Geology, v. 37, p. 41–70.

Heezen, B. C., Nesteroff, W. D., Rawson, M., and Freeman-Lynde, R. P., 1985, Visual evidence for subduction in the western Puerto Rico Trench, *in* Mascle, A., ed., Caribbean Geodynamics Symposium, Paris, March 5–8, 1985: Paris, France, Editions Technip, p. 287–304.

Jordan, T. H., 1975, The present day motions of the Caribbean plate: Journal of Geophysical Research, v. 80, p. 4433–4440.

Kesler, S. E., and Sutter, J. F., 1979, Compositional evolution of intrusive rocks in the eastern Greater Antilles island arc: Geology, v. 7, p. 197–200.

Ladd, J. W., and Watkins, J. S., 1978, Active margin structures within the north slope of the Muertos Trench: Geologie en Mijnbouw, v. 57, p. 255–260.

Ladd, J. W., Worzel, J. L., and Watkins, J. S., 1977, Multifold seismic reflection records from the northern Venezuela basin and the north slope of Muertos Trench, *in* Talwani, M., and Pitman, W.C., eds., Island arcs, deep-sea trenches and back-arc basins: Washington D.C., American Geophysical Union, p. 41–56.

Ladd, J. W., Shih, T., and Tsai, C. J., 1981, Cenozoic tectonics of central Hispaniola and adjacent Caribbean Sea: American Association of Petroleum Geologists Bulletin, v. 65, p. 466–489.

Larue, D. K., 1994, Puerto Rico and the Virgin Islands, *in* Donovan, S. K., and Jackson, T. A., eds., Caribbean geology: an introduction, Kingston, Jamaica, University of West Indies Publisher's Association, p. 151–166.

Larue, D. K., and Ryan, H. F., 1991, Extensional tectonism in the Mona Passage, Puerto Rico and Hispaniola: a preliminary study, *in* Larue, D. K., and Draper, G., eds., Transactions, 12th Caribbean Conference in St. Croix: Coral Gables, Florida, Miami Geological Society, p. 223–230.

Larue, D. K., Joyce, J., and Ryan, H. F., 1991, Neotectonics of the Puerto Rico Trench: extensional tectonism and forearc subsidence, *in* Larue, D. K., and Draper, G., eds., Transactions, 12th Caribbean Conference, St. Croix: Coral Gables, Florida, Miami Geological Society, p. 231–247.

Le Pichon, X., Iiyama, J., Bourgois, Mercier de Lepinay, B., Tournon, J., Muller, C., Butterlin, J., and Glacon, G., 1985, First results of the test dives of the French submersible Nautile in the Puerto Rico Trench (Greater Antilles): Acadamie de Sciences Paris transactions, 301, Serie II, no. 10, p. 743–749.

Lewis, J. F., and Draper, G., 1990, Geology and tectonic evolution of the northern Caribbean margin, *in* Dengo, G., and Case, J. E., eds., The Caribbean region: Boulder, Colorado, Geological Society of America, The Geology of North America, vol. H, p. 77–140.

Mann, P., and Burke, K., 1984, Neotectonics of the Caribbean: Review of Geophysics and Space Physics, v. 22, p. 309–362.

Mann, P., Burke, K., and Matumoto, T., 1984, Neotectonics of Hispaniola: plate motion, sedimentation and seismicity at a restraining bend: Earth and Planetary Science Letters, v. 70, p. 311–324.

Masson, D. G., and Scanlon, K. M., 1991, The neotectonic setting of Puerto Rico: Geological Society of America Bulletin, v. 103, p. 144–154.

McCann, W. R., and Sykes, L. R., 1984, Subduction of aseismic ridges beneath the Caribbean plate: implications for the tectonics and seismic potential of the north eastern Caribbean: Journal of Geophysical Research, v. 89, p. 4493–4519.

Minster, J. B., and Jordan, T. H., 1978, Present-day plate motions: Journal of Geo-

physical Research, v. 83, p. 5331–5354.
Molnar, P., and Sykes, L. R., 1969, Tectonics of the Caribbean and Middle America regions from focal mechanisms and seismicity: Geological Society of America Bulletin, v. 59, p. 801–854.
Officer, C. G., Ewing, J. K., Hennion, J. F., Harkrider, D. G., and Miller, D. E., 1959, Geophysical investigations in the eastern Caribbean: summary of 1955 and 1956 cruises, *in* Ahrens, L. H., Press, F., Rankama, K., and Runcorn, S. K., eds., Physics and chemistry of the earth: London, Pergamon Press, v. 3, p. 17–109.
Perfit, M. R., Heezen, B. C., Rawson, M., and Donnelly, T. W., 1980, Chemistry, origin, and tectonic significance of metamorphic rocks from the Puerto Rico Trench: Marine Geology, v. 34, p. 125–156.
Reid, J., Plumley, P., and Schellekens, J., 1991, Paleomagnetic evidence for late Miocene counterclockwise rotation of north coast carbonate sequence, Puerto Rico: Geophysical Research Letters, v. 18, p. 565–568.
Rosencrantz, E., and Mann, P., 1991, SeaMarc II mapping of transform faults in the Cayman Trough, Caribbean Sea: Geology, v. 19, p. 690–693.
Schell, B. A., and Tarr, A. C., 1978, Plate tectonics of the northeastern Caribbean Sea region: Geologie en Mijnbouw, v. 57, p. 319–324.
Schneidermann, N., Beckmann, J. C., and Heezen, B. C., 1972, Shallow water carbonates from the Puerto Rico Trench region, *in* Petzall, C., ed., 6th Caribbean Geological Conference, Isla de Margarita, Venezuela, 1971, Transactions: Caracas, Venezuela, Chromotip, p. 423–425.
Speed, R. C., 1989, Tectonic evolution of St. Croix: implications for tectonics of the northeastern Caribbean, *in* Hubbard, D. K., ed., Terrestrial and marine geology of St. Croix, U.S. Virgin Islands; Special Publication Number 8: Teague Bay, St. Croix, West Indies Laboratory, p. 9–22.
Speed, R. C., and Larue, D. K., 1991, Extension and transtension in the plate boundary zone of the northeastern Caribbean: Geophysical Research Letters, v. 18, p. 573–576.
Sykes, L. R., McCann, W. R., and Kafka, A. L., 1982, Motion of the Caribbean plate during last 7 million years and implications for earlier Cenozoic movements: Journal of Geophysical Research, v. 87, p. 10656–10676.
Weaver, J., Smith, A., and Seiglie, G., 1975, Geology and tectonics of the Mona Passage: Eos (Transactions, American Geophysical Union), v. 56, p. 451.
Wielchowsky, C. C., Rahmanian, V. D., and Hardenbol, J., 1991, A preliminary tectonostratigraphic framework for onshore Trinidad, *in* Gillezeau, K. A. ed., Transactions, 2nd Geological Conference of the Geological Society of Trinidad and Tobago: Port-of-Spain, Trinidad, April 3–8, 1990, p. 41.

Manuscript Accepted by the Society June 20, 1997

Printed in U.S.A.

Index

[Italic page numbers indicate major references]

D

E

F

G

H

I

J

K

L

M

N

O

P

Printed in U.S.A.